The Butterflies
of
Yorkshire

Edited by Howard M Frost

**Butterfly
Conservation**

ISBN 0-9548249-0-3

British Library-in-Publication Data: A catalogue record for this book is available from the British Library.

Butterfly Conservation Yorkshire
Butterfly Conservation, Manor Yard, East Lulworth, Wareham, Dorset BH20 5QP
Tel: 0870. 774 4309
Email: info@butterfly-conservation.org

Butterfly Conservation is a registered charity and non-profit-making company, limited by guarantee.
Registered Charity No 254937
Registered in England No 2206468

Front cover photo: Upper Ribblesdale. Denis & Mary Sykes.
Front cover design: Nick Lawman & Amanda Bradbury.

Production facilitated by East Riding Print and Design,
Beverley, East Yorkshire.

The Co-ordinators of map referenced records:
(who have vetted and computerised 169,000+ items of data for our maps and phenograms)

1995: Derek Parkinson, Susan Stead

1996-2003:
County Recorders: Butterfly Conservation – Howard M Frost
Yorkshire Naturalists' Union – Philip Q Winter

VC61: Sean Clough, Howard M Frost
VC62: Dave O'Brien, Peter Waterton
VC63: Roy Bedford
VC64: David Blakeley, Susan Stead, Terry Whitaker
VC65: Derek Parkinson

Adjacent County Co-ordinators:
(who have allowed us to draw upon their data and reports)
Cheshire: Barry Shaw **Cumbria:** Steve Hewitt **Derbyshire:** Ken Orpe **Greater Manchester:** Peter Hardy
Lancashire, Manchester & Merseyside: Laura Sivell
Lincolnshire: Allan Binding, Mark Tyszka **Nottinghamshire:** Michael Walker
Northumberland & Durham: Mike Hunter, Roger Norman, Ian Waller.

Designed and typeset by: Howard M Frost
With a great deal of assistance from: Amanda Bradbury and Richard Smith of East Riding Print & Design.

The Butterflies of Yorkshire

Edited by: Howard M Frost

Maps: Jim Asher. **Artwork:** Nick Lawman

The Writers:
Mike Barnham, Harry E Beaumont, Roy Bedford, David S Blakeley, Sean A Clough, Peter A Crowther, James Dickinson, Sam Ellis, Bill Ely, Marie-Christine Frost, Howard M Frost, Geoffrey Fryer, Adrian F Johnson, John P Killingbeck, Jeff Lunn, Derek Parkinson, Robert Parks, Ted Rimington, Peter C Robinson, Arnold Robson, Bill Smyllie, Peter Waterton, David W Wise, Stuart D Wise, Terry Whitaker

The Reviewers:
Jenn & Ian Atkin, Mike Barnham, Nigel Bourn, Nick Bowles, Sam Ellis, Richard Fox, Marie-Christine Frost, Tim Frost, Rebecca Frost, Geoffrey Fryer, Martin Greenland, Edie Jolley, Paul Kirkland, Steve Kirtley, Nick Lawman, Jeff Lunn, Ted Rimington, Barry Spence, Dave Wainwright, Philip Q Winter

The Species Co-ordinators 1996-2003:
(whose analytical work has provided the backbone of new information in this book)

Mike Barnham, Roy Bedford, David Blakeley, Dave Booth, Sean Clough, Peter A Crowther, Marie-Christine Frost, Howard M Frost, Martin Greenland, Adrian Johnson, Dave Howson, John Killingbeck, Steve Kirtley, Dave O'Brien, Derek Parkinson, Robert Parks, Craig Ralston, Peter Robinson, Arnold Robson, Bill Smyllie, Peter Waterton, Terry Whitaker

Butterfly Conservation Yorkshire

ENGLISH
NATURE

Forestry Commission
England

SWALE & URE
WASHLANDS PROJECT

YORKSHIRE DALES
National Park Authority

Yorkshire Naturalists' Union

YORKSHIRE
WILDLIFE
T R U S T

EAST YORKSHIRE
REGION

The
Sponsors

Without the generosity of the sponsors listed below, this book would have been impossible to produce. Butterfly Conservation Yorkshire gratefully acknowledges the support of:

Mike Barnham, Roy & Margaret Bedford, Pat & Jim Bone, Harry & Pauline Bursell, George Carmichael, Bill & Marjorie Curtis, Mark Earnshaw, Andrew Freebrey, Howard & Marie-Christine Frost, Tim Frost, Rebecca Frost, Geoffrey Fryer, Martin Greenland, Greg Herbert, Brian Hewitt, Anthony H Hindley, Humber Growers Ltd/Van Heyningen Bros Ltd, Mike Hunter & Denise McGowan, Barbara & Derek Jewell, Adrian Johnson, Lawrie King, Stephen Kirtley, Phil Lazenby, Alan Lowe, Barry Nattress, MJ & K Speck, Stephen Martin, C Ian Massey, Alexander Murray, DD Murray, Derek Parkinson, Arnold Robson, Rosie, R&R Studio Ltd Hull, Jason Sargerson, Knora & Stephen Schonut, Jim Smith, Bill Smyllie, Mr & Mrs Christopher Stamp, Susan Stead, John Walford, Richard Walton, Terence M Whitaker, Roy & Liz Wilson, David & Stuart Wise, David Woodmansey, Ken Woolley, www.yorkshiremoths.org.uk ,Yorkshire Conservation (Peter Wright), plus an anonymous gift from Leeds.

Butterfly Conservation Branches

Butterfly Conservation Herts & Middlesex Branch
Butterfly Conservation NW (Cumbria) Branch
Butterfly Conservation North Wales Branch
Cornwall Butterfly Conservation
Surrey & SW London BC Branch

Yorkshire Natural History Societies and Nature Reserves

Army Training Estate North, Wathgill
Beverley Naturalists' Society
Cleveland Naturalists' Field Club
Craven Naturalists & Scientific Association
East Yorkshire Bat Group
East Yorkshire Birdwatchers
Foxglove Covert Local Nature Reserve, Catterick Garrison
Harrogate & District Naturalists' Society
High Batts Nature Reserve
Hull Natural History Society
Leeds Urban Wildlife Group
Lower Ure Conservation Trust
Sorby Natural History Society
Upper Wharfedale Field Society
Wharfedale Naturalists' Society
Whitby Naturalists' Club
Wolds & Riverbank Countryside Society
Yoredale Natural History Society

CONTENTS

FOREWORD

I welcome this book as a landmark in the long history of butterfly recording in Yorkshire. It provides an insight into the status of all our current species, and highlights some of the factors which have influenced their expansions and contractions over the last two centuries. Most of all, it attempts to put county distribution into a wider regional, national and international context.

It is a privilege to have participated in such a detailed investigation into the distribution and movements of all the species we see in our gardens and countryside. I cannot praise too highly the tremendous efforts of those who have dedicated their time in recording and reporting their local butterfly populations over the last ten years. Also the expertise of those who have collated, studied, illustrated and presented the information, and brought it together into one book, the like of which we have never previously seen in Yorkshire.

Climate change is now widely recognised, and our native butterflies are already adjusting their habits and territories accordingly. Some species have become scarce, whilst others have expanded their ranges quite dramatically.

As a national organisation, Butterfly Conservation will make every effort to preserve and enhance the habitats needed by our butterflies and moths, both nationally and locally. However, before it can act, it needs to know what is happening on the ground. This book provides an attractively presented turn of century summary of the situation we have now, but we must continue to monitor future changes. We hope that what you read here will not simply inform, but also encourage you to help us with our ongoing survey work.

Roy Bedford,
Walton, Wakefield, 2005.
Butterfly Conservation
Yorkshire Branch Chairman
1996-2004

The *Butterflies of Yorkshire*

Introduction

Howard M Frost

This book has been written as a statement of what we know about Yorkshire butterflies at the beginning of the 21st century, using the traditional pre-1974 boundaries as the definition of our recording area. It is the first book of its kind in relation to Yorkshire, its various predecessors having covered the whole of the Lepidoptera (ie butterflies and moths), leaving only minimal space to devote to butterflies. Everyone involved in writing and illustrating the book is a volunteer.

We have endeavoured to produce a work that is readable, attractive, and scientifically valuable, the kind of information source we (the writers and illustrators) would have loved to discover already existed when the fascination of butterflies first beckoned. In particular, we have tried to put things into context. There seems little point in producing a book, which sees the county as a kind of fortress with a fence round it! To this end we are immensely grateful to fellow recorders in neighbouring counties who have been so helpful in sharing their ideas and their data. We are also grateful to recorders throughout the country without whose voluntary efforts we would not have the detailed national maps available to us today. In this respect, special thanks must go to Butterfly Conservation's national recorder, Jim Asher who created maps to our specifications and who worked so hard to perfect them in a way acceptable to our printers.

ORIGINS: The Yorkshire Butterfly Book project grew out of the national Millennium Atlas Survey (1995/1999). The idea was first mooted in 1994 during a casual conversation between the Editor (then a birdwatcher on the sidelines of butterfly recording) and Philip Winter (YNU Macrolepidoptera Recorder). At the time there appeared to be fewer than 40 naturalists involved in butterfly recording within the county, and for many of those it was not a primary interest. The publishing of Ted Rimington's *Butterflies of the Doncaster District* in 1992 was a particularly strong influence. This excellent Sorby Natural History Society booklet was our initial model for a county book, particularly in its approach to unearthing historical records. The first challenge was to build a stronger recording network to ensure that Yorkshire was covered with a respectable number of dots in the proposed national Atlas publication. During 1995, Butterfly Conservation Yorkshire Branch approached the Yorkshire Naturalists' Union Lepidoptera Group regarding working together more closely, and by 1996 we had set up a joint recording system based on a Co-ordinator for each of Yorkshire's five Vice-Counties (VCs).

Modern recording is map-referenced to the grid system on Ordnance Survey maps, whilst the 'Watsonian' 'Vice-County' system was devised by HC Watson as long ago as 1859 for the purposes of botanical recording. He divided the whole country into 112 numbered, and roughly equal, parcels, based mainly on existing county boundaries, together with natural features such as rivers and watersheds. The system became widely used, and many old records (for all branches of natural history, not just plants) are referenced to VCs. In Yorkshire, Watson mainly followed the old Riding boundaries to create five VCs, numbered 61 to 65. Some observers have questioned the validity of continuing to use such a dated system when we actually record on the OS grid. However, Vice-Counties not only provide suitably equal areas, but also preserve a valuable awareness of these old boundaries, enabling greater understanding of past recording. In our book we have also used them to indicate in which part of the county the places mentioned are to be found.

From 1996 onward, annual Yorkshire Lepidoptera Reports were produced, using an edition of BC Yorkshire's *Argus* membership magazine to save on funds. Species Co-ordinators were sought from both participating organisations, and they played an important part in processing records and writing up reports. In addition, most of the original Species Co-ordinators have contributed to this book. The Annual Reports were particularly effective in encouraging increased recording, with participation rising annually to as many as an estimated 400 people in some years. This gave VC Co-ordinators a challenging task, but one made possible through the growing availability of computers and Jim Asher's *Levana* recording software. Without such tools, it is doubtful if our Yorkshire book would have been contemplated!

By 1998, the hope of producing a book had crystallised into a determination, and a small independent steering committee representing BC and YNU was set up to see it through (Howard Frost, Nick

Nick Lawman who has been responsible for all our butterfly paintings.

Lawman & Philip Winter). As the one member of that committee recently retired (and apparently with lots of time to spare!) I found myself leading the project and becoming its Editor. I little realised how it would come to take over my life for the next six years and end up being a full-time job! It has nonetheless, been a fascinating experience. We have taken a team approach and tried to involve everyone with an expertise in the county's butterflies, hence the large number of names on the title page. The writers have allowed their texts to be modified by other members of the team, and the Editor has endeavoured to overlay a unity of style, using the best ideas put forward by everyone else. In addition, he has expanded many of the historical reviews, a task in which he has been valuably aided by Geoffrey Fryer and Ted Rimington.

We are particularly grateful to our many sponsors without whom this book would have been impossible to produce. They have enabled us to develop it in our own way and in our own style, and with more pages than we ever thought possible. Sponsorship has also enabled us to use a large number of illustrations and we are particularly fortunate in having an artist of Nick Lawman's calibre amongst our voluntary contributors. His labour of love has taken more than three years to complete. Our choice of photographs from over 600 submitted has been based on interest and relevance rather than quality. When a butterfly does something interesting in front of you, there are usually only seconds to point and shoot. The result can be disappointingly blurred, or wrongly exposed, yet still full of interest. Most of us are only amateur photographers with snapshot cameras. We hope you will find many of our pictures unusual, and an encouragement to look much more closely at what butterflies are doing, rather than simply be mesmerised by their undeniably attractive colours!

STATISTICAL 'WOW' FACTOR: Yorkshire is big! Dauntingly big when you set out to map butterfly distribution on a tetrad (2x2km square) basis. The county (traditional and current) measures around 150km (93mls) N to S, and 170km (105mls) E to W. This embraces all or part of around 200x10km squares, the number varying slightly according to the scale of maps used, and an interpretation of where exactly the traditional boundary ran. Older maps showing that boundary are drawn on a grid based on imperial measurements, whereas modern maps use a metric grid, which can make comparisons confusing! Traditional Yorkshire covers most of 100km square SE and parts of NY, NZ, OV, SD and TA.

There are minor (though largely irrelevant) inaccuracies on the computerised maps we use, as well as in the various attempts by BC and YNU to produce working 10km maps for recording purposes. The large scale OS Explorer Series of maps has revealed three overlooked coastal squares with sometimes substantial corners of beach and cliff-top which don't figure in our database map (ie TA42, TA25 and OV00). Hundred km square OV is mainly over the N Sea, except for a tiny corner of land just to the south of Ravenscar. We still await the first-ever butterfly record from this 100km square. A challenge to someone out there!

Our Survey period has covered 9yrs (1995/2003), an odd number perhaps. However, the National Atlas Survey didn't gather real momentum in Yorkshire until 1997 and we originally intended five years of maximum recording from that point (1997/2001). As the book has taken longer to finalise than originally envisaged, we added in 2002 and 2003 as well.

Over the 9 years an estimated 1000+ observers have made 64,548 visits and produced an amazing 169,537 records. (Many visitors to nature reserves hand in records, which are collated by wardens and passed to us without recorder names, hence our need to estimate the number of observers.) Observers have visited 196x10km squares, and recorded in 3319 tetrads out of 4120 tetrads in the county, a coverage of around 80%. However, that doesn't mean to say that all these tetrads have been covered thoroughly. Even better distribution patterns could have been achieved if every tetrad had been visited two or three times a year over several years. But that would have needed even more people taking part! There is still a great deal to discover about Yorkshire's butterflies. We hope that this book will serve both as a baseline study and as a challenge to future recorders to do even better! That said, we hope that all the participants in the current survey will feel satisfied that together, they have achieved a greater and more detailed coverage than anything which has gone before.

THANKS!! So many people have helped our project in so many different ways that it would be impossible to say a personal thank-you to everyone. The writing team deserve special thanks not simply for all the research they have put into their write-ups but also for the way they have put up with an Editor who is always wanting more, and usually at the very last minute! Those involved in reviewing have done a marvellous job in raising our standards all round. Our many photographers too have been extremely generous in their offerings, some even taking pictures to order. They have entrusted prize possessions to the cause, sometimes for very long periods of time. Thanks!!

We are also grateful to English Nature (Jeff Lunn in Wakefield and Simon Christian in York), not only for financial support, but also for help in checking parts of the text. A book like this needs to draw considerably upon past publications and sources of records. We particularly appreciate the help and permissions enabling us to draw upon published and unpublished resources from: Butterfly Conservation, the Centre for Ecology & Hydrology (Jon Cooper, Paul Harding, Mark Hill), Forest Enterprise, N York Moors Forest District (Charles Critchley, Brian Walker), N York Moors Forest District Recording Group (Peter Robinson and his team), Scarborough Field Naturalists' Society (Brian Cockerill, Ian Massey, Jax Westmoreland, & Philip Winter), the Sorby Natural History Society (Sheffield) (Austin Brackenbury), Spurn Bird Observatory (Barry Spence), the Yorkshire Dales National Park (Ian Court), the Yorkshire Naturalists' Union (John Newbould), the Yorkshire Wildlife Trust, and Michael Barnham & Graham Foggitt, authors of the privately published *Butterflies in the Harrogate District*. We have also received much valued help from: Butterfly Conservation national staff (Nigel Bourn, Richard Fox, Carmel Mallinson & Sandra Muldoon), Doncaster Museum (Colin Howes), Hull University Archives (Helen Roberts), New Walk Museum, Leicester (Jan Dawson), Nostell Priory (Edward Potten & Gareth Williams), and the Tolson Memorial Museum, Huddersfield (Chris Yeates). The help of many others is acknowledged in the text, with the names of photographers included at the side of their photographs. We are particularly grateful to French lepidopterist Tristan Lafranchis for permission to use two of his photographs. To everyone else who has had a part in this production, however small, your help has been very much appreciated.

My own participation might not have come about had it not been for an enthusiasm for natural history, generated in the 1950s by Derek Price, Biology Master at Scarborough High School for Boys, through participation in the school Natural History Society. Members were encouraged to join Scarborough Field Naturalists Society at a time when Geoffrey Watson and Michael Clegg were promoting a buzz of activity amongst several dozen older teenagers, with badger watching, transect studies and lab work in Wood End Museum. The generous time they gave to encouraging youngsters left a lasting impression!

Most of all, our debt of gratitude is to those 1000+ individuals who have done the recording. 64,548 visits must add up to a lot of walking! We have highlighted many of your records (and your names) in the text, but the real value of your contribution has been in the noting down of everyday observations, enabling us to create the most detailed distribution maps and flight period graphs (or phenograms) yet produced for Yorkshire. In this respect every record has been important. Thanks!

Howard M Frost
Withernsea, 2005.

Limestone pavement: Whernside viewed from Southerscales (VC64).

The Shape of Yorkshire

Howard M Frost

This chapter should be read in conjunction with the diagrammatic view of Yorkshire. It shows in simplified form the layout of the county's main landforms as mentioned in various parts of the book. The descriptions run from the west (on the left of the diagram) to the east.

1. THE PENNINES: These present their steepest face to the west and dip more gently to the east. The highest parts lie towards the north in the Dales National Park with peaks like Ingleborough and Pen-y-Ghent rising to about 700m (2,300ft). The Pennines form a region of high moors, deep valleys and spectacular scenery. There are limestone grasslands in the north where the Northern Brown Argus is an important species. Bilberry is a common plant throughout the area and in many parts supports large populations of Green Hairstreak. Patches of forest are found to quite high levels (eg The Stang, close to the northern border where the hardy one-generation form of the Green-veined White can be found). Small Pearl-bordered Fritillaries inhabit the valley 'mosses' like Austwick Moss, and Swarth Moor. Dark Green Fritillaries are also found in this area. The region is often cloudy, with high rainfall and wintry extremes. Rainfall is highest towards the western edges and decreases sharply towards the eastern edges. Although not an ideal climate for butterflies, most of our commoner species can be found along the valley bottoms.

2. PENNINES – THE EASTERN FOOTHILLS: This is an area of low hills dissected by river valleys running eastward. The county's urban heartland stretches from Sheffield in the south to Leeds in the north and extends westward up the river valleys. Formerly based on the woollen industry, coal mining and iron and steel production, the region is now much greener and cleaner than in the past with a wider range of industries. Although home to a large population, it is also an area full of parks and woodlands, with many local nature reserves. Many of the spoil heaps of mining days have been turned into country parks, whilst canal banks, disused railway tracks and old industrial sites have become butterfly havens. Most of our regular butterfly residents can be found in these areas, as well as Dingy Skippers and even Graylings, in forgotten industrial corners. Green Hairstreaks occur on hillsides within the urban fringes. The southern edges of this region are often the warmest parts of the county in early spring, producing some of our earliest butterfly records.

3. The MAGNESIAN LIMESTONE BELT: This is a long narrow strip of low limestone hills, running right through the county from north to south (and beyond in both directions). It is followed by the route of the A1, the main road from London to Scotland. Chalk and limestone areas provide a home for a range of plants, which attract butterflies such as Dingy Skipper and Marbled White. Unfortunately, most of the natural pastures formerly found along the belt have been destroyed by industrial developments and modern approaches to farming, but there remain many

View west from Wolds escarpment over Vale of York (VC61).

Yorkshire

Diagrammatic view. Not to scale.

Based on an original drawing by David Booth.

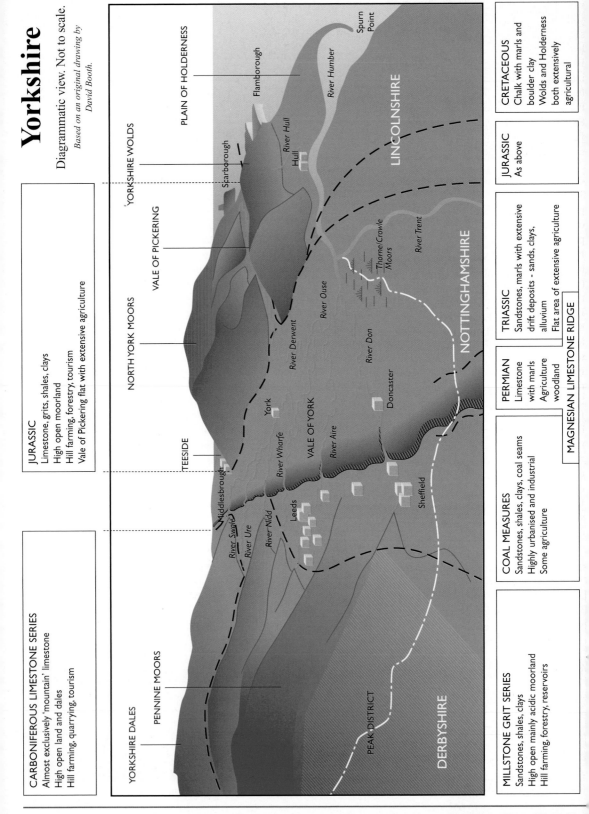

CARBONIFEROUS LIMESTONE SERIES
Almost exclusively 'mountain' limestone
High open land and dales
Hill farming, quarrying, tourism

JURASSIC
Limestone, grits, shales, clays
High open moorland
Hill farming, forestry, tourism
Vale of Pickering flat with extensive agriculture

CRETACEOUS
Chalk with marls and boulder clay
Wolds and Holderness both extensively agricultural

JURASSIC
As above

TRIASSIC
Sandstones, marls with extensive drift deposits - sands, clays, alluvium
Flat area of extensive agriculture

PERMIAN
Limestone with marls
Agriculture woodland

COAL MEASURES
Sandstones, shales, clays, coal seams
Highly urbanised and industrial
Some agriculture

MILLSTONE GRIT SERIES
Sandstones, shales, clays
High open mainly acidic moorland
Hill farming, forestry, reservoirs

MAGNESIAN LIMESTONE RIDGE

YORKSHIRE DALES

PENNINE MOORS

PEAK DISTRICT

DERBYSHIRE

NOTTINGHAMSHIRE

LINCOLNSHIRE

TEESIDE

Middlesbrough

River Swale

River Ure

River Nidd

River Wharfe

Leeds

York

River Aire

VALE OF YORK

River Derwent

River Ouse

River Don

Doncaster

Sheffield

River Trent

Thorne/Crowle Moors

NORTH YORK MOORS

VALE OF PICKERING

YORKSHIRE WOLDS

PLAIN OF HOLDERNESS

Scarborough

Flamborough

River Hull

Hull

River Humber

Spurn Point

attractive corners, not least, on brownfield sites and in quarried areas. In the 1800s you could find Marbled Whites in the southern part of the belt, although these had disappeared by the 20th century. However, in recent times private re-introductions have successfully returned the Marbled White to the area. Many of the special butterflies, like Grizzled Skipper, Small Blue and various fritillaries, formerly found here, have long since disappeared.

Howardian Hills (VC62), a region of forests, moors and smaller fields.

4. The VALES of YORK and TRENT: The county's central area is a huge river plain, part of a system draining around one sixth of England. A line of roughly parallel rivers flow eastward out of the Pennines and join either the Ouse (running south) in the north, or the Trent (running north) in the south. These in turn meet near Goole, forming the Humberhead Levels, before flowing into the River Humber itself. The Humber is a long estuary, starting near Goole and stretching some 40 miles to the N Sea. It is about half a mile wide near Goole, reaching to almost 9 miles in width near Spurn Head. Much of the estuary bank from Goole to Spurn is prime butterfly habitat with salt marshes attracting migrants. The Humberhead levels were formerly a huge marshland, of which today, the National Nature Reserve covering Crowle, Goole, Thorne and Hatfield Moors, is but a remnant (albeit a substantial remnant!). This marshland once extended back along the Derwent, Ouse and Trent Valleys. Today the Humberhead Levels are Yorkshire's only

lowland site for the Large Heath. The Vale of York is a fertile area of large farms and narrow roads, with river crossings often few and far between. This is not an easy place to explore on the way to somewhere else, as you often have to go long distances to get to the riverbanks, which are usually good butterfly habitats, with Wall and Brimstone often quite common. This is an under-recorded region except for a handful of hotspot sites like Bishop Wood (near Selby), Skipwith and Allerthorpe Commons, and Wheldrake Ings. The verges of minor roads are also good places to seek out the commoner species, with Gatekeeper and Speckled Wood an increasingly common feature of country lanes.

5. The MOORS and WOLDS: As you move further east, you encounter the N York Moors in the north and the Yorkshire Wolds to the south. These are separated by the Howardian Hills (a region of Outstanding Natural Beauty) in the west; and the Vale of Pickering, a former glacial outflow lake towards the east. The N York Moors, (much of it covered by the N York Moors National Park) is our richest butterfly area with limestone outcrops along its southern edge providing habitat for the Duke of Burgundy and the Pearl-bordered Fritillary, as well as Small Pearl-bordered and Dark Green Fritillaries. It is a region of high moorlands, large forests and dramatic scenery. Green Hairstreaks, Dingy Skippers and Large Heaths are found in various parts of the moors, with Newton Dale (also written Newtondale) one of the most interesting areas to visit. The highest parts (just over 400m) are in the north where the Cleveland Hills present a dramatic escarpment overlooking the River Tees and Middlesbrough. Some industrial sites along the Tees support the Grayling whilst the sand-dune habitats around the mouth of the Tees at South Gare and Coatham Sands are good places to spot migrant butterflies. The north-east coastal area between Whitby and Middlesbrough, once home to the Grizzled Skipper, is one of our least well-recorded regions and deserves further exploration. The Howardian Hills are well wooded with many attractive walks, yet extremely under-recorded for butterflies. The Gatekeeper and Holly Blue have reached this far north, and Brimstones and Commas are not uncommon. The Vale of Pickering is equally under-recorded. Yet take the minor roads and you discover this extremely flat area is full of local character and hidden corners, with one site producing large numbers of Small Copper.

The chalk Wolds are marked by escarpments to the north and west (200m+), and a gentler slope towards the east. The chalk becomes

Roseberry Topping (320m) at N end of N York Moors (VC62), overlooking Middlesbrough.

Sunk Island, Holderness, reclaimed from the Humber: a region of whole kilometre squares with hardly a hint of butterfly habitat.

dramatically apparent in the white cliffs of Flamborough, Bempton and Speeton where the cliff tops are a good place to spot incoming migrant butterflies, occasionally as rare as the Camberwell Beauty. The Wolds are a region of intensive agriculture with large fields and an emphasis on cereals. The higher hills to the north are dissected by steep valleys, suitable only for grazing, or for planting trees. Grazed areas provide habitat for

Marbled White, Brown Argus and occasionally for Grayling, as well as large numbers of Small Heath and other grassland species. In the south of the Wolds, the Hudson Way 'leisure route' follows the former Beverley to Market Weighton railway line and provides a good cross-section of chalkland habitats with Marbled White and Dingy Skipper not uncommon.

6. The HOLDERNESS BOULDER CLAYS: To the east of the Wolds lies the valley of the River Hull and an area of undulating glacial deposits made up of sands, gravel and boulder clay stretching from Flamborough to Spurn and inland to Hull, Beverley and Driffield. This is an area of prairie farming, often with huge hedge-less fields and very little butterfly habitat, although the Hull/Patrington and Hull/Hornsea disused railway routes, the fringes of Hornsea Mere and the gravel pit region around Brandesburton are notable exceptions. The boulder clay coast from Bridlington southward is steadily eroding away whilst at the south-eastern extreme Yorkshire points a sandy finger southward in the shape of Spurn Head, a National Nature Reserve, extending 4 miles into the Humber estuary. This is a key observation point for migrants and an arrival point for newcomers from the south, with colonies of Essex Skipper, Green Hairstreak, Brown Argus, and Speckled Wood surviving amongst the sheltered sand dunes. The influence of warm autumn seas, less cloud and lower rainfall than elsewhere, often encourages butterflies to continue flying at Spurn well into November.

Bempton chalk cliffs: a seabird paradise with lots of butterflies on the cliff tops as well.

Upper Ribblesdale VC64

Swallowtail woodcut from Morris (1853).

Butterfly Naturalists

A Brief History 1500 - 2000

Marie-Christine Frost

1. THE WIDER CONTEXT

Summary: The earliest recorded interest in British butterflies dates to the later 1500s. The 1600s became an age of discovery, distinguishing species and developing the idea of collecting, whilst the 1700s saw the naming and classifying of species, with Ray and Linnaeus being key figures in this process. The 1800s saw the popularisation of the subject with collecting becoming a fashionable hobby. In the first half of the 20th century, two world wars resulted in butterfly recording becoming a minority interest at a time when changes to forestry and farming and the spread of industry were destroying the value of many habitats. The second half of the century saw a huge growth of interest in natural history and conservation, and the launch of the national conservation charity Butterfly Conservation in 1968.

In this chapter we offer a brief resume of the background to some of the key figures mentioned in the text, especially in the historical reviews of each species. We look at national figures in the first section and local people in the second. Inevitably, space dictates a very limited choice. Anyone interested in more detail and a greater range of people of national importance is recommended to read *The Aurelian Legacy* by Michael A Salmon (Harley Books 2000), which has been used as a source for some of the facts below.

Early days: The naming of our butterflies (in English) has been a hit and miss process with the origins of some names lost in the mists of time and others invented and re-invented according the whims of individual authors. There are recognisable pictures of butterflies on Egyptian tomb paintings from 3,500 years ago, and in 14th century illuminated manuscripts. Our earlier ancestors must have been familiar with some of the commoner species and had names for them. Indeed, there are suggestions (not accepted by everyone) that the word 'butterfly' was originally derived from 'butter-coloured fly', a reference to the Brimstone. The first-ever British book on insects (which included a number of butterflies) was produced by a medical doctor, Thomas Mouffet (Moffet or Muffet) (1553-1604), and written in Latin with the title *Insectorum Theatrum* (*The Theatre of Insects*). It was an illustrated book about insects rather than a book which gave them names. Mouffet was also interested in spiders and his daughter Patience is thought to have been the original Little Miss Muffet of nursery rhyme fame. He was the first person to refer in writing to hairy caterpillars as 'woolly bears'. Mouffet's volume was not published until 1634, well after his death, and an English translation appeared in 1658 as an appendix to Edward Topsell's *History of Four-footed Beasts and Serpents.* It remained the main work on insects until a blacksmith's son, John Ray (1627-1705) wrote his *Historia Insectorum*, also published posthumously, in 1710. Ray was a pioneer in the classification of insects later developed by Linnaeus.

James Petiver (1663-1718) ran a pharmacy and museum in London and was the first to give names to butterflies. He published a series of papers and pamphlets between 1695 and 1717 covering 49 species in all. He also preserved butterflies by pressing them between slivers of mica, a few of which still exist! He corresponded with other entomologists of his day including Eleanor Glanville (née Goodricke) (c1654-1709) who was born in Yorkshire but mainly lived elsewhere. She was first to capture a species of fritillary, which was later named after her as the Glanville Fritillary. She supplied Petiver and others with specimens, and one she gave him still exists in the Natural History Museum (London).

Benjamin Wilkes (fl1690-1749) was a professional painter who began to specialise in butterfly and moth illustrations around 1738. His book, *The

English Moths and Butterflies (1749) was actually written by Henry Baker (a well-known biologist) but from notes provided by Wilkes. As the 1700s progressed the first Lepidoptera societies began to appear in London, the earliest being the **Society of the Aurelians,** which grew out of London coffee-house get-togethers in the 1720s.

Carl Linnaeus (1707-1778) was born in Sweden, the son of a Lutheran pastor. His father encouraged an interest in plants from an early age, although expecting his son to become a clergyman, not a botanist! In fact Linnaeus became a medical doctor, a career in which plants were an important element. He began to outline a systematic approach to classifying and naming plants whilst still at university in the late 1720s, and eventually named over 9,000 species. He devised a system of two Latin names (the binomial system), a broad generic name coming first, and a species name second. During his lifetime he tried to classify the entire animal kingdom and gave names to a wide range of creatures. He remained a very religious person and saw his work of naming God's creatures as a continuation of that of Adam in the Garden of Eden. The 10th edition of his *Systema Naturae* published in 1758 is internationally accepted as the starting point for zoological nomenclature, and many species listed then still carry the name he gave them, although generic names have constantly evolved in tandem with our growing understanding of insect structures and relationships. Linnaeus is sometimes credited with inventing the field trip (although in England, the Society of Apothecaries founded in 1620 already ran them to search for medicinal plants). His were so successful that they sometimes numbered several hundred participants!

Linnaeus had more than a passing relationship with Britain. A Scottish doctor, Isaac Lawson contributed to funding the publication of the *System Naturae*. George Clifford, an English director of the Dutch East India Company living in the Netherlands, became his patron, enabling him to visit London in 1736 and meet people like Sir Hans Sloane, president of the Royal Society. After Linnaeus died his wife sold his huge collection of specimens and books to an Englishman, James Edward Smith (who was later knighted). Smith chartered a ship to carry the 26 large crates to England and there is a story, supported by cartoons of the time, but probably apocryphal, that the Swedish government, realising its loss, sent a warship in hot pursuit of Smith's boat, but to no avail. The collection led to the founding of the Linnean Society of London in 1788, now the oldest surviving scientific society devoted to natural history, with James Smith its first president. The Linnaeus collection is housed in an atmospherically controlled strong room at the Society's headquarters in Piccadilly.

Moses Harris (1730-1788), whose book, *The Aurelian*, was published in 1766, was Secretary to a second London based Aurelian Society, whilst Hull-born Adrian Hardy Haworth (1767-1833), author of *Lepidoptera Britannica* (published in 4 vols 1803-1828), moved to London in 1792 and founded a short-lived third Aurelian Society. Haworth trained to be a solicitor, but inheriting the family estate when still quite young gave him independent means, enabling him to live in Chelsea and pursue his interests in natural history. He was a keen botanist and became an authority on bulbs and mesembryanthemums. His *Lepidoptera Britannica* was the first comprehensive volume of its kind. It was based on the system of classification developed by Linnaeus and introduced many species not previously described. Haworth died of cholera in one of the epidemics of the time.

Danish born Johann Christian Fabricius (1745-1808), whose abbreviated name, 'Fab.' appears after many species names, was a pupil of Linnaeus who carried on his master's work. As a young man he lived in England for a number of years and later made regular visits to London to examine the collections held by members of the various Aurelian Societies. William Spence (1783-1859) was another Hull man who made an impression on the national scene in co-authoring an important book, *Introduction to Entomology*, with William Kirby, which was published in a number of volumes between 1815 and 1826.

The 19th century: Butterfly books in the 1700s largely catered for wealthy lepidopterists and a great deal of interest in the subject came from ladies in society. The books were mainly about the developing knowledge of butterfly and moth life histories. In the 1800s, education began to wider opportunities for learning to read. Improved production methods introduced cheaper printing, and the advent of the bicycle and the coming of the railways, enabled people to reach areas formerly inaccessible. Previously, the centre of entomological development had been in London but now it began to disperse to all parts of the country. Natural history societies were founded in many towns and cities, and magazines began to appear, the first being **The Entomological Magazine** (1833-1838), soon followed by **The Entomologist** (1840-1842, 1864-1973, 1988-) and a number of others. By the middle of the century butterfly collecting was becoming a fashionable hobby and the field trip enabled like-minded people from all walks of life to visit interesting sites and observe and collect together. Unfortunately, the amount of collecting also made those concerned jealous of their own favourite areas. As a result, many records and reports given to societies and published in 'lists' and annual reports only gave the home town of the observer or the most generalised indication of where a rarer species had been found. Passionate collectors would pay high prices for rare specimens and a support trade developed to supply all their needs. Unfortunately, this also led to forgery and fraudulence, with specimens imported from Europe being passed off as locally caught in Britain. Today this can still cast doubt on the information held on data labels attached to interesting specimens from old collections.

Information about the distribution of species began to appear, and amongst the growing numbers of accessible 19th century books was the *'Natural History of British Butterflies'* by the Rev James Duncan (1804-1861), a slim but useful volume first published in 1835 as part of a series called *The Naturalists' Library* edited by Sir William Jardine. This includes some of the earliest references to distribution in Yorkshire and many of the historical review sections of our species accounts include quotes from an 1844 edition of the same work.

From a Yorkshire viewpoint one of the most important sources of early records comes from one of the century's main national publications, *A History of British Butterflies* (1853) by the Rev Francis Orpen Morris (1810-1893). Morris was born in Co Cork and ordained in 1834. His first post was in Dewsbury (VC63).

The Rev Francis Orpen Morris.

He then moved to Doncaster (VC63) in 1835 where he remained until 1837 before moving to Northamptonshire. He returned to Yorkshire in 1844, becoming vicar of Nafferton (just to the NE of Driffield, VC61). Ten years later he moved to the west side of the Wolds at Nunburnholme (between Market Weighton and Pocklington VC61). Morris was a prolific writer who also wrote an important series on British moths (4 vols 1872) and two titles on British birds. His butterfly book ran to 10 editions, being a standard work for over 50yrs. All the butterflies were illustrated in colour and printed by Benjamin Fawcett of Driffield. Although a book about **British** butterflies Morris's distribution summaries invariably begin with his known Yorkshire sites, greatly adding to our knowledge of county distribution prior to 1850. His style is somewhat flowery, and as befits a country parson he slips in little sermons at intervals through the text, but this in no way detracts from the value of this fascinating work.

A little later in the century Edward Newman (1801-1876) wrote two *Illustrated Natural Histories*, one for British Moths (1869) and one for British Butterflies (1871). At varying times he edited **The Entomological Magazine**, **The Zoologist** and **The Entomologist** as well as being natural history editor of **The Field**. In such positions he had contacts all over the country including Yorkshire. Therefore, his books are another useful source of past county records. He was a skilled naturalist and his *History of British Ferns* is considered a botanical classic. He also had a notable sense of humour and was a good cricketer.

The life of Richard South (1846-1932) straddles the 19th and 20th centuries and he is widely known for his contributions to the *Wayside and Woodland* natural history series published by Frederick Warne. South wrote *The Butterflies of the British Isles* (1906) and the two-volume *Moths of the British Isles* (1907-1908) and these have been reprinted and revised many times, remaining available well into the second half of the 20th century.

Frederick William Frohawk (1861-1946), whose sight was restricted to one eye, is one of the most celebrated lepidopterists of all time. A natural history writer and artist, he was the first to systematically study and illustrate the development of each British butterfly species from egg to adult. He used captive breeding to observe minutely every activity of each species, a project which took 24yrs (1890-1913) to complete. Much of today's knowledge of butterfly lives owes its origins to his meticulous efforts. His *Natural History of British Butterflies* (1924) is now a collector's item. He also wrote *The Complete Book of British Butterflies* (1934) and *Varieties of British Butterflies* (1938).

The 20th century: The first half of the 20th century was fairly quiet on the butterfly front. Many potential lepidopterists of note must have been lost during two world wars. Studies still continued via many natural history societies, but largely as a minority interest. Edmund Brisco Ford (1901-1988), a Professor of Ecological Genetics, wrote one of the most important books of the century: *Butterflies*, which was first published in the Collins *New Naturalist* series in 1945 and reprinted as a Penguin paperback in 1975. It marked a change of approach to butterfly recording, from collecting sets of species and their variants, to trying to understand how genetics caused the variations and how butterflies had adapted to changing conditions over the centuries. Ford also included a selection of rudimentary but nonetheless highly important dot distribution maps, presaging the change of emphasis to the detailed map-based recording work of the second half of the 20th century. John Heath (1922-1987) who worked with the Nature Conservancy Council and later at the Biological Records Centre (founded in 1964) organised the Lepidoptera Recording Scheme (1967-1981), which led to the publication of the *Atlas of Butterflies in Britain and Ireland* (Heath *et al* 1984) and the first published set of 10km square butterfly distribution maps. This encouraged many counties and regions to develop their own local atlases. Parallel to these developments there was a huge growth in nature reserves and conservation initiatives both nationally and locally. Butterfly Conservation (originally the British Butterfly Conservation Society) was founded in 1968 by Thomas Frankland and Julian Gibbs and its first president was artist and ornithologist Peter Scott. The new society built up slowly but steadily to become a major force by the 1990s, championing the ecological requirements of butterflies and moths. The need for regular assessments of the state of our butterflies nationally, now became apparent, and during the early 1990s plans were laid to collect data for a new national atlas. The **Butterflies for the New Millennium** project (BNM) was officially launched in 1995 and ran for a five-year period, culminating in the splendid 436 page *Millennium Atlas of Butterflies in Britain and Ireland* by Jim Asher (Butterfly Conservation's national Recorder), Martin Warren, Richard Fox, Paul Harding, Gail Jeffcoate and Stephen Jeffcoate. The success of this project was linked to the fact that ownership of computers mushroomed in the last decade of the 20th century and Jim Asher's *Levana* recording software provided a simple and straightforward method of entering data into the national recording system, as well as allowing participants to produce their own dot-distribution maps. A national butterfly recording system has evolved out of the BNM project and in the future it is hoped to produce national atlas updates every five years. A national moth-recording project is also being developed.

2. THE YORKSHIRE SCENE

How far back can we trace the earliest records of butterflies or moths in Yorkshire? The awakening interest in the subject outlined in the first part of this account was largely centred on London. We have yet to find any Yorkshire references pertaining to the 16th or 17th centuries although there could well be indirect references hidden away in the paintings of stately homes or the illuminations attached to old books. The first hints that Yorkshire folk were looking at and recognising named species comes in the 18th century. Geoffrey Fryer (2000) has written a fascinating account of the lepidoptera paintings of James Bolton (1735?-1799) of Halifax (VC63). James and his brother Thomas (1722?-1778) were both naturalists, the latter having a collection of 400 butterflies, and one or other of the brothers is known to have sent moth specimens to Moses Harris as models for illustrations in *The Aurelian*. James Bolton's *Harmonia Ruralis; or An Essay towards a Natural History of British Songbirds* was published in two volumes in 1794 and 1796. Some of the plates in the second volume include peripheral butterflies, which Bolton felt the need to justify in the following terms: *'Flies* [ie butterflies] *being the food of birds, may undoubtedly on that account be introduced with propriety.'* The species illustrated are: Clouded Yellow, Brimstone, Black-veined White, Small White, Orange Tip, Red Admiral, Small Tortoiseshell, Peacock, and a Garden Tiger Moth. No provenance is given, but it would seem possible, if not likely, that all could have been local species, although the Black-veined White might raise some eyebrows! (See p250 for further details.) Geoffrey Fryer also includes other Bolton paintings dated between 1782 and 1795, which add Small Copper, Camberwell Beauty, and Large Tortoiseshell to the list of species with which he was obviously familiar.

Geoffrey Fryer (pers comm.) has drawn our attention to one of the earliest Yorkshire butterfly references yet discovered which was ascribed to James Bolton, who referred to the Painted Lady as being plentiful around Halifax in 1780. This was cited in Crosland (1910) who did not say where Bolton made the statement. Geoffrey Fryer has tried, so far in vain, to locate the exact source, but there seems little doubt that Bolton must have left a record of this somewhere.

During the 18th century, society ladies often took an interest in developing painting skills and it became fashionable to paint butterflies and moths, especially in the later part of the century. Salmon (2000) notes that 25% of the sales of Adrian Haworth's *Lepidoptera Britannica* (1803/1828) were to women. An exhibition at Nostell Priory (nr Wakefield VC63) in 2004 revealed what could be interpreted as a contender for Yorkshire's

A page from Mary Strickland's book.

Holly Blue painting by Sabine Winn dated 1780.

reported in some detail in the press. It included references to the local presence of butterfly species not reported elsewhere. Rimington's earliest sources often provide Yorkshire's earliest known records of particular species, eg from later annotations in a book published in 1832 and from an anonymous Wath-on-Dearne list found in a village magazine dated 1832. Dr Edwin Lankester also included a summary of local butterfly species in *An Account of Askern* published in 1842.

As the 19th century progressed, so interest in natural history and butterfly collecting mushroomed. The first Yorkshire natural history society to be founded appears to have been the **Huddersfield Naturalists' Society** in 1847. By 1861 a federation of four West Riding societies had emerged, known as the West Riding Consolidated Naturalists' Society, and by 1877 this had widened its membership and become the **Yorkshire Naturalists' Union (YNU)**. Its membership journal, *The Naturalist*, was founded within the West Riding Consolidated Naturalists and has appeared continuously since 1875, being a monthly magazine until 1942 and a quarterly thereafter. (Six other *Naturalist* magazines published at intervals between 1833 and 1873 are sometimes mentioned as predecessors to the YNU *Naturalist* but the first four of these were independent and mainly national journals, although often with Yorkshire editors and sometimes printed in Yorkshire. Two magazines published 1864/1867 and 1872/1873 had some connection to the West Riding Consolidated Naturalists' Society.) The *Naturalist* is now a rich source of Lepidoptera records and entomological comment, although in its earlier editions often with more about the moths than the butterflies. The YNU Entomological Section (which still functions) was founded in Dec 1876 and marked a coming of age in the history of butterfly and moth studies in the county.

It is recorded that by 1901, 70 different societies were or had been members of the YNU since its foundation in 1877, which gives some measure of the huge growth of interest in the natural world around this time. Amongst the many names which came to the fore, Joseph William Dunning (1833-1897) was considered important enough to be included in the 101 lepidopterists whose lives are featured in Salmon (2000). Born in Leeds and educated at Storthes Hall, (nr Huddersfield VC63), he became a barrister, practising at Lincoln's Inn. He also became Secretary to the Entomological Society of London in 1862, editing its publications and facilitating its incorporation into the Royal Entomological Society. He made his first mark on the entomological world in 1845, when, as an 11yr old schoolboy he re-discovered the presence of the rare Spotted Sulphur moth *Emmelia trabealis* in Suffolk, a species now thought to be extinct in the British Isles. His headmaster at Storthes Hall was Peter Inchbald (1816-1896), himself an enthusiastic entomologist originally from Doncaster, who, with Thomas Wilkinson, helped to produce an important summary of Scarborough area Lepidoptera for Theakston's *Guide to Scarborough* (1868 and subsequent editions). No doubt Inchbald had some considerable influence on the young Joseph who recorded Lepidoptera around Storthes Hall in 1846 and 1847 and whose manuscript lists have recently been discovered, providing us with more of Yorkshire's earliest records, and the earliest known to have survived from the Huddersfield area. Fryer & Lucas (2001) point to considerable activity in the Huddersfield area where Charles P Hobkirk produced one of the county's earliest regional 'lists' in, *Huddersfield: its History and Natural History*

earliest dated butterfly record, in the form of a painting of a Holly Blue by Sabine Winn labelled June 12th 1780. The painting looks as though it was based on observations of a live specimen. The same exhibition also included a leather bound book of paintings called *Specimens of British Lepidoptera drawn from Nature between 1804 and 1816* by Mary Strickland. Mary lived at Boynton Hall (just W of Bridlington VC61) She illustrates the stages, (often all stages from egg to adult) of over 50 moth species, and in many cases she includes details of the dates and places where her specimens were found. These reveal her as a genuine enthusiast who found eggs and larvae, then bred them on so as to paint from life in the most stunning detail and almost photographic quality.

Ted Rimington (1992) gives details of the lives of a number of early enthusiasts from the Doncaster (VC63) area. Hugh Reid (1783-1863) ran a taxidermy and natural history business in Doncaster between c1812 and 1853 and probably supplied Morris with some of his information. Unfortunately, like so many of our earliest recorders he left no written notes regarding the butterfly sites he must have known so well. John Riley Hawley (1815-1883) was another well-known Doncaster naturalist and a lecture he gave to the local Philosophical Society in 1866 was

(1859, reprinted 1868), followed by S L Mosley's *A Catalogue of the Lepidoptera found in the Huddersfield district* (1883), published in the *Transactions of the Huddersfield Naturalists' Society.*

The Scarborough area was also actively covered in the mid-19th century with Thomas Wilkinson (d1876), a butler, becoming nationally known for his work in investigating the life histories of some of the smaller moths. The name of James Henry Rowntree (1850-1937), son of William Rowntree who founded a drapery business in Scarborough's main street also crops up in national butterfly comment (eg in Newman 1871). He was active in the YNU Entomological Section, being its President in 1894, and wrote articles for the *Naturalist*. **Scarborough Field Naturalists' Society** was founded in 1889 and he was its first Entomological Recorder from 1889 to 1892.

As the 19th century progressed, assessments of local and regional lepidoptera distribution began to appear, through the publication of 'Catalogues' and 'Lists' (containing brief comments about each species). George Taylor Porritt (1848-1927) became Yorkshire's point of contact for amassing suitable material and a *List of Yorkshire Lepidoptera* was published serially in the *Transactions of the Yorkshire Naturalists' Union* between 1883 and 1886 and is now often referred to as 'Porritt's List'. A Supplement was published in 1904 and a further update

George B Walsh

was included in the 1907 edition of *A History of Yorkshire* (Victoria County History series). As Porritt's Lists included moths as well as butterflies, the comments on butterfly distribution are frustratingly minimal. Few exact sites are mentioned and the presence of a species is often given as the observer's hometown, meaning it was seen within a day trip of that place! Nonetheless, these publications represent the first-ever attempt at assessing county distribution, and as such they are vitally important.

As we move into the 20th century, interest in butterflies and moths appears to wane although there were still individual enthusiasts whose names stand out. Thomas Ashton Lofthouse (d1944) from Linthorpe, Middlesbrough contributed many butterfly and moth reports to the *Naturalist* and to the *Proceedings of the Cleveland Naturalists' Club*. Regular annual reports on the Lepidoptera began to appear in the *Naturalist* in 1909 although butterfly information was often minimal and sometimes rather vague. For the first half of the century, recording work ticked over, but was no doubt greatly affected by the general struggle for survival during two world wars and the loss of so many potential enthusiasts. Arthur Smith (1887-1957) from Heworth, York collected for over 50yrs and his collection was acquired by Leicester Museum in 1962. A Headmaster of Scarborough High School for Boys, Alfred Samuel Tetley (1868-1916) wrote a valuable article on *Lepidoptera round about Scarborough* published in *Entomologist's Record* (1915). George Beckwith Walsh (1880-1957) a chemistry and biology teacher at the same school (from 1919 to 1943) was a very active entomologist in the YNU and in the Scarborough Field Naturalists' Society. He is known to have written over 50 articles as well as contributed to and jointly edited the two volumes of the *Natural History of the Scarborough District* (1953/1956), the latter volume with an important Lepidoptera chapter. One of his most important contributions was an article on the status of butterflies in the Scarborough area published in *The Entomologist's Monthly Magazine* in 1952.

George Hyde FRES (1902-1986) was born in Doncaster and became a mechanical engineer at the Doncaster Railway Plant. He 'retired' in 1950 to develop a new career as a full-time writer, becoming well known nationally for his general interest nature books, many written with children in mind. He collaborated with L Hugh Newman to produce *Looking at Butterflies*, published by Collins in 1959. Hyde was a skilled photographer and one of the pioneers in using colour in insect photography. He also bred butterflies and built up a fine collection, now in Doncaster Museum. Frank Hewson (YNU Lepidoptera Recorder 1955-1962) developed a huge card index of past records and references from the *Naturalist* and elsewhere, which prompted the need to produce the first fresh assessment of the state

Courtesy: Scarborough Field Naturalists' Society

Alfred S Tetley

of our Lepidoptera since Porritt. The work was undertaken by Maurice Jackson, Cecil Haxby and Eric Richards under the editorship of C Ian Rutherford. The result was published serially in the *Naturalist* between 1967 and 1970 and later combined into a slim booklet. As it included all the Macrolepidoptera, butterflies were again given minimal space but with some valuable comments regarding a handful of rarer butterfly species.

From the 1960s onward biological records centres began to collate reports in the south of the county around Sheffield and Rotherham leading to a growth of information which could be turned into local assessments and reports. In 1981 Sorby Natural History Society (Sheffield) and the Sheffield Museums jointly published the first regional assessment in the county which used dot distribution maps (Stephen P Garland 1981). It marked an important new trend followed soon after by *Butterflies in the Harrogate District* by Mike Barnham and Graham Foggitt (1987), and *Butterflies of the Doncaster District* by Ted Rimington (1992).

By the 1980s the need for a more detailed county update was becoming apparent and in October 1985 Joyce Payne called a meeting of like-minded enthusiasts who formed the Lepidoptera Study Group, an independent group working closely with the YNU. They produced *Butterflies and Moths of Yorkshire: Distribution and Conservation* edited by Stephen Sutton and Harry Beaumont, aided by Helen Smith as a full-time assistant, and published by the YNU. It was a landmark publication running to 380 pages and providing a great deal more information about our butterflies and moths than anything which had appeared previously.

In 1981 a new group was set up in Yorkshire, a branch of the steadily expanding national conservation charity Butterfly Conservation, which became known as **Butterfly Conservation Yorkshire**, or BC Yorkshire. Beverley naturalist Tom Upton was its founder and early inspiration. At the outset the group was small, with a membership of just 18, rising to around 50 over the next ten years. Then in the 1990s butterfly numbers began to increase noticeably and new species like Holly Blue and Speckled Wood appeared as from nowhere. More and more people wanted to know what was happening and why. In 1995 BC Yorkshire turned its regular newsletter into a magazine about Yorkshire butterflies and moths, called *Argus*, (initially edited by Howard M Frost and Nick Lawman, and later carried forward by Howard alone). In the same year the national organisation launched its Millennium Atlas Survey intent on producing the most comprehensive national survey of butterfly distribution ever undertaken.

In 1996, in response to the need to submit a larger volume of records to the national survey, BC Yorkshire, the YNU Lepidoptera Recorders and the former Lepidoptera Study Group (now the YNU Lepidoptera Group) came together to promote a jointly administered, but independent butterfly recording scheme, known as **Butterfly*NET* Yorkshire**, with a Co-ordinator in each of Yorkshire's five vice-counties. A 60-page Annual Lepidoptera Report was produced for 1996 (as an edition of *Argus* magazine in co-operation with Harry Beaumont, YNU Microlepidoptera Recorder, and Philip Winter, YNU Macrolepidoptera Recorder). Further Reports have followed in every year since. BC Yorkshire worked with the YNU Lepidoptera Group to help produce an update to Sutton & Beaumont (1989): *Butterflies and Moths of Yorkshire: A Millennium Review* edited by Harry E Beaumont and published in 2002 by the YNU. BC Yorkshire membership soared to around the 500 mark by 2003 and the numbers of butterfly records submitted rose in tandem, from a few hundred in 1995, to a record 35,000 in 2003. Processing and making sense of such huge a volume of records was only made possible by the computer and by the participation of a team of Species Co-ordinators who have subsequently helped to produce *The Butterflies of Yorkshire*. The ability to turn map-referenced records into detailed dot-distribution maps at the press of a button, marked a great leap forward in the ongoing story of recording the butterflies of Yorkshire. The appointment of a Butterfly Conservation N of England Officer (Sam Ellis), in 2001, also marked a new phase in the study and conservation of our most threatened species.

This chapter has been prepared with assistance from: Jan Dawson (Curator Biological Collections, Leicester Museum), Howard M Frost, Geoffrey Fryer, Colin Howes, C Ian Massey, Anne Winter, the staff at Nostell Priory (Edward Potten and Gareth Williams) and with special thanks to Lord St Oswald of Nostell Priory and Richard Marriott of Boynton Hall for permission to examine and photograph the paintings of Sabine Winn and Mary Strickland.

References: Bayford (1940), Emmet (1991), Fryer (2000), Heath *et al* (1984), Jenkins (1978), Law (2001), Paragon Review 5 (1996) (Hull University Archives), Rimington (1992), Salmon (2000), Sutton & Beaumont (1989), Walsh & Rimington (1953, 1956), Whalley (1980), Williams (1961).

Small Tortoiseshell.

The Biological Records Centres
in South Yorkshire

Bill Ely

Biological recording has been a continuing activity for naturalists in South Yorkshire and one not supplanted by the development of Biological Recording Centres within local authorities. BRCs were inaugurated within local museums as an integral part of the work of their natural history curators – local people expect their museum staff to be knowledgeable about and interested in local wildlife and to inform them through museum displays. Collecting information is a necessary precursor to all of these.

Doncaster Museum & Art Gallery was the first to collect information on local wildlife to augment the collection of specimens, starting in the early 1960's, followed by Sheffield City Museum in the mid-1960's. Rotherham Museum's involvement began when the first natural history curator was appointed in 1975. Each BRC is funded by the taxpayers of one local authority, and their activities are limited to the boundaries of those local authorities. Cross-boundary co-operation has tended to be managed through local societies such as the Sorby Natural History Society, which has had a long-running programme of publishing distribution maps to serve 'the Sheffield area'. In this way the volunteer and professional are mutually supportive with a reasonably clear demarcation of their roles and responsibilities. In practice, most enquirers want to know about defined areas of land and these usually fall into the area of a single BRC. Cross-boundary requests are rare.

Although the collection of wildlife records began as an 'academic' activity, it soon found a practical use in site protection and, later, in active conservation through site management. The existence of wildlife records allowed planners, conservationists, concerned residents and developers to make a more objective assessment of the value of a particular site, rather than relying on a purely subjective one. Over the decades this approach has been formalised and local authorities are now required by law to make sure that they have access to adequate environmental information (including wildlife) when making planning decisions. Barnsley Metropolitan Borough Council (MBC) does not have natural history as part of its museum services so the Barnsley planning service decided to establish one of its own in order to provide access to the available information.

The use of records in relation to site management, is also a standard practice today. It is no longer acceptable to manage an important site without taking account of the interests of its non-human users. Butterflies are a significant amenity and, no matter how common a particular species may be, it deserves to be encouraged because of the pleasure it gives to so many people. Management for butterflies is, therefore, a sensible policy on any site where people have access. The other aspect of site management relates to rare or threatened butterflies in need of positive management. Their ecological requirements should be high on the list of management priorities for any site lucky enough to have them.

BRCs use as wide a range of taxa as they can when providing information to users and aim to cover their 'patch' as widely as possible. In practice, BRC staff are fully committed to entering data, managing the databanks and providing services, so they rely on volunteers to provide the bulk of the records. This means that the more popular groups such as flowering plants, birds, amphibians and, of course, butterflies, are much better recorded than lower profile groups such as beetles, bugs and fungi. In the Rotherham BRC butterflies account for 10% of the invertebrate records, which is a significant proportion when you consider how few species are involved. Doncaster BRC's butterfly records are not yet computerised so comparable figures are not available, but the Lepidoptera account for 41% of the enquiries and reports produced on invertebrates.

Once again, there is a clear separation of the roles and responsibilities of volunteer and professional recorders. Society members take on the roles of butterfly or bird recorder for the benefit of their society and its members. They are under no obligation to provide information to anyone else, although they may wish to do so and may wish to charge a reasonable rate for their time. BRCs, on the other hand, are there to provide services to anyone who asks for them. A local society which feels that it ought to contribute to the conservation cause, but whose recorders are not able or willing to spend time answering requests from planners or developers, can discharge its responsibilities by lodging copies of its records with its local BRC. This does not prevent that society from providing information if it chooses to do so, and it does not affect its ability to comment on planning applications or management plans.

A BRC aims to combine records from all available groups to provide a statement of wildlife interest on each site. This aim, of course, depends on those records being added to the computerised databank so that they can be included. Once entered, the records can be accessed very quickly. Unfortunately, none of the BRCs in South Yorkshire has sufficient staff to enter backlogs of records and they all depend on local naturalists for voluntary help with this.

Biological recording bridges the gap between local government and individual naturalists – it can only operate as a partnership in which both sides feel that they are gaining (or contributing) in a satisfactory manner. As such, its position in a local authority is unusual and may not be well understood by senior managers. They may have different priorities and see the BRC as a peripheral activity. The fortunes of South Yorkshire's BRCs were affected by changing priorities during the 1990's. When the management of Sheffield City Museum was handed over to a trust, that trust decided not to continue with the Museum's biological recording activities. The BRC was transferred to the Sheffield City Ecology Unit, but the staff were not. The Sheffield Ecologist has gained a large volume of extra work but no additional staff to carry it out. Rotherham BRC transferred from Rotherham Museum to the Countryside Service on the decision of a senior officer. Doncaster Museum continues to operate a BRC service but with a reduction in the natural history staff and a re-allocation of priorities. Barnsley's BRC has found that local naturalists are not particularly willing to provide information directly to a planning service, so its data holdings have suffered.

In order to make its data holdings more accessible to the public, Rotherham BRC is developing an internet site within the Rotherham MBC website. The initial release will concentrate on lists of plants and animals recorded from council owned sites which are accessible to the public.

Mating pair of High Brown Fritillaries. Gait Barrows Lancashire 1991. See p277.

Forest District Recording

View NW over Newton Dale to Cropton Forest.

Peter C Robinson

NOTE:

In spring 1992, John Mackenzie, the then North York Moors Forest District Manager for the Forestry Commission, approached Butterfly Conservation Yorkshire with a request for help in monitoring butterfly populations within the District. BC Committee member, Arnold Robson, took on the role of contacting volunteers, which led to the setting up of a voluntary 'Forest Recording Group'. Peter Robinson was appointed leader of the Group, a post he held from 1993 to 2003. A number of transects were set up and an annual report was produced to summarise each year's results.

The North York Moors Forest District is divided into five Strategic Zones with most of the butterfly recording discussed here, being carried out within the North Riding Forest Park Zone, consisting of the forest blocks of Harwood Dale, Broxa, Wykeham, Sneaton, Langdale, Dalby, Goathland, Wheeldale and Cropton. The area is a high moorland plateau, dissected by steep-sided glacial outwash channels, formed by the overspilling of a series of ancient glacial lakes. The Jurassic rocks of the area give rise to a complex series of soils and natural vegetation types.

The planting of large blocks of conifers in the 1950s eventually shaded out many butterfly habitats and probably contributed to the loss of species like the Grizzled Skipper and Grayling. The Duke of Burgundy struggled to survive, and other species like the Small Pearl-bordered and Dark Green Fritillaries were seen less and less. Fortunately, attitudes have changed, and today the Forest Estate places amenity and wildlife conservation high on its list of priorities. To this end, the forest is being landscaped to fit in with the topography. Conifers and broadleaved species are being planted in relation to soil and microclimate to produce a mosaic of habitats designed to promote maximum biodiversity within the woodland. The forest cycle, from ground preparation to planting and eventual reaping, is being carried out in such a way that, as operations proceed, wildlife can find new homes nearby. Many exciting projects are also on the way, or in the pipeline, including the widening of rides, the re-instating of former moorland and moorland bogs, and the clearance of trees in favour of grassland.

The Forestry Commission is very sensitive to the importance of butterflies as good indicators of biodiversity, as well as the necessity for providing and maintaining habitats for rare or endangered species. The Forest Recording Group was created to support this policy. Transect monitoring was set up on three sites (Dalby, Pexton and Ellerburn) in 1993 and later extended to others. In 1996 a general recording project was developed, embracing the whole North Riding Forest Park and the Western Moors. The aim was to learn more about the distribution of butterfly populations within these Forest Zones, and to identify butterfly 'hotspots', as well as sites associated with nationally threatened species.

Since 1993, 29 butterfly species have been recorded in the Forest District, making it one of the most important regions for butterflies in the North of England. Forest management is giving attention to the maintenance of populations of Common Blue, Brown (or Northern Brown?) Argus, Dingy Skipper, Duke of Burgundy and Small Heath within areas of herb rich calcareous grassland; Small Pearl-bordered Fritillaries in alkaline wet flushes and marshes; Large Heath in areas of blanket bog, Dark Green Fritillaries, Green Hairstreak and Small Copper along forest rides and in areas of limestone scrub; Holly Blue and Purple Hairstreak in ancient and broad-leaved woodland, as well as many other species of resident and migrant butterflies including populations of Brimstone and Marbled White.

The Forest District is also represented on the North York Moors Butterfly and Moth Action Group, which ensures that all the bodies concerned with conservation within this area are working together.

Levisham Moor VC62 March 2004

200 Years of Weather

Roy Bedford

Butterflies are amongst the most weather-dependent insects in Yorkshire, and the position of the county, centred roughly to the north and south of Lat. 54°N (almost in line with Moscow and Lake Baikal in Russia, and Edmonton in Canada), puts it far enough to the north to produce a climatic cut-off effect on the distribution of a number of species. Over the years, the most northerly frontal zone in the distribution of species such as Brimstone, Peacock, Comma, Holly Blue, Gatekeeper and Ringlet, has moved north and south within the county (and sometimes beyond its northern or southern borders) in reaction to the prevailing weather conditions.

Butterflies variously pass winter as eggs, larvae, pupae or hibernating adult butterflies. All stages can be affected by the severity of the season, and from spring onward, through summer and autumn, cold-blooded butterflies generally need strong sunshine in which to bask and warm up their systems sufficiently to galvanise activity. Cool cloudy conditions, such as those which frequently afflict the higher regions of the county, or east coast sea fogs, which sometimes roll in as far as the Yorkshire Wolds or the North Yorkshire Moors, can have an adverse effect on many of our county's species. There is also an important correlation between European weather conditions and butterfly movements. These affect the degree of immigration in species like the Red Admiral, Painted Lady and Clouded Yellow as well as many migrant moths and other insects, which head our

way when southerly winds and summer warmth create the right conditions. Other conditions in the countries of origin such as land use or habitat quality, will also have a bearing on the size of such migrations.

Yorkshire is a very large county, with the high Pennines tending to block and slow the progress of rain-bearing low pressure systems from the west, whilst the North Yorkshire Moors and Yorkshire Wolds often protect the central Vale of York from the worst of the cold winds blowing in across the North Sea. As a result, this area tends to be drier and sunnier than elsewhere, though also prone to frosts and fogs in winter. In the far south-east lies the low undulating boulder clay region of Holderness, protected from the west by the Yorkshire Wolds and with its temperatures ameliorated by proximity to the North Sea. It is often the mildest and driest area of the county, producing some of the earliest and latest butterfly sightings in the region. Comparing regional weather reports within the county reveals that temperatures in coastal areas like Scarborough (VC62) are also less extreme than in inland areas such as Leeds (VC63/64), where summer temperatures may be several degrees higher. Rainfall is much greater in Sedburgh or Giggleswick (VC65) in the north of the county than in Doncaster (VC63) in the south. There are also many local variations such as between city centres and rural locations, sheltered valleys and open windswept areas around hilltops. Height above mean sea level is critical in this context and even on summer's warmest days convection cloud can build up above the hills and fells, reducing butterfly activity to a minimum.

The main aim of this chapter is to summarise two centuries of weather in the county and to highlight some of the features, which may have contributed to the past ups and downs of butterfly distribution. As the presence of many species within the county depends on what is happening in the whole country, especially in the south of England, the comments and tables are based on Central England Temperature (CET) statistics (derived from an average of all major recording stations and therefore less liable to regional aberrations or errors) with local information from many sources added in, to highlight the Yorkshire situation. The CET statistics are also a very reliable source of information stretching back through three centuries, compared to around 50 years only for most city records. By contrast, detailed butterfly recording in the county has only evolved over the last two or three decades.

Whilst the Central England Temperatures provide a useful guideline to past weather, readers should be aware that such averages and generalisations can easily hide short bursts of weather which might have had marked effects on butterfly migration or survival. For example, March 1947 began with blizzards and freezing conditions but ended with a mini heat-wave. Yet the mean temperature for the month was close to average, even though the real weather at the start of the month was pretty disastrous for butterflies. By the same token, not all noted 'Clouded Yellow Years' register as being in 'warm' summers. The conditions which may promote an arrival from the continent, may be quite short-lived, as in the cold summer of 1922, when southerly winds in a warm May encouraged the Clouded Yellows northward.

A VOLCANIC EFFECT
Yorkshire butterfly populations affected by volcanoes?

Many of our Yorkshire butterfly populations were decimated during the 19th century, especially in the latter two decades. Growth of industry brought serious smoke pollution to the West Riding, bad enough to weaken sunshine and produce potentially lethal fall-out onto many butterfly habitats. According to Brimblecombe (2002) shepherds in upland areas described the sooty coating, which accumulated on sheep, as 'moorgrime'! Habitats were also lost to mining, population expansion, drainage projects and the steady spread of railways. In addition, butterflies were hit by clusters of notably cold winters and poor summers in the early, middle and later years of the 19th century.

Intriguingly, the periods of bad weather correlate pretty well with major volcanic eruptions of a sort known to produce global cooling. It looks as though Yorkshire butterflies were particularly affected, as many species which were lost, were already on the northern edges of their ranges. For this reason, they were more susceptible to the effects of cooling weather, particularly where experienced in conjunction with some of the other problems noted above.

Volcanic eruptions are a fairly constant factor in the state of the world's weather. At any moment in time there may be hundreds of separate eruptions going on in volcanic hot-spots around the world. Most of these are little publicised and have only very marginal effects on the weather. However, in each century a handful produce massive upward explosions, which throw huge amounts of dust and gas 20/25kms into the stratosphere. A veil of particles and sulphuric acid droplets can spread around the globe reflecting sunlight and reducing average temperatures by up to two or even three degrees C over the following few years. If such an eruption corresponds with years that would have been cold anyway, the effects may be dramatic. In warmer periods, the cooling may be less noticeable. Summers tend to be affected even more than winters, as there is more sunlight available to be reflected.

THE 19th CENTURY
Three exceptionally cold periods.

For most of the 19th century, hot and cold seasons were distributed erratically through the years, but with some notable exceptions. A marked cold period occurred between 1810 and 1817 with very few hot days recorded. 1814 had a particularly sustained winter lasting almost three months. Volcanic evidence in Greenland ice cores indicates a major eruption from an unknown source in 1810, and at least 3 others up to 1817. Of these Tambora (East Indies), in 1815, produced the most powerful eruption in recorded history. Together, these volcanoes created a dust veil over 4 times that of Krakatoa detailed later and may have lowered world temperatures by as much as 3°C (Kious & Tilling 1996). This influenced the weather over the next two years and was responsible for the very cold summer of 1816 in both Europe and N America, remembered as 'the year without a summer'! This led to the first Irish Potato Famine and widespread crop failures around the northern hemisphere.

Butterfly populations must have been badly affected by these conditions and would have taken some years to recover. Morris (1853) draws attention to what was probably the first notable butterfly year of the 19th century. In writing about the Meadow Brown he says: *'I well remember the extraordinary numbers which appeared in the unusually hot and dry summer of the year 1826'.*

A further cold period occurred in 1860/61, and was referred to in newspaper editorials of the time as a benchmark in meteorological events. A disastrous succession of five cold seasons culminated in a winter so cold that water mains froze in the streets. Temperatures of -9°F (ie 41 degrees F of frost!) were recorded in Darlington on Christmas Day, and farmers were unable to find their stocks of turnips under the snow.

An editorial in the *Leeds Mercury* of 27/12/1860 noted: *'Winter has set in with a severity of cold almost, if not altogether, unequalled during the present century. We doubt whether the thermometer in England has ever, even in the recollection of old men, reached so low a point as it reached on Christmas Day morning. In most places it hovered within a few degrees of 0°F, or 32 degrees below freezing point, and was below zero in one place. After the cold weather of the summer – a summer in which the thermometer has been several degrees below its usual average – and a summer too in which sunshine seemed rather a happy exception than the rule...'* It would seem likely that the cold spring and summer were the features which most affected our butterflies.

Robson (1902), referring to the distribution of the Wall in Durham and Northumberland, notes: *'The years 1861-2-3 were particularly disastrous seasons for Lepidoptera, and though this species appeared to survive in a few places for some years longer, I fear it has now totally disappeared.'* In other parts of the same work he blames the loss or near loss of Orange-tip, Holly Blue, Comma, Peacock, Large Tortoiseshell, Silver-washed Fritillary, Marsh Fritillary, Speckled Wood and Ringlet on the weather of this period. He even notes that the Red Admiral virtually disappeared: *'Then somewhere in the sixties* [ie the 1860s] *when so many other Butterflies left us, it disappeared from both counties. Now* [ie in the 1890s] *after more than 20yrs absence, it has again become a more familiar object…'*

The cause of this cold spell is not easy to explain, as several meteorological factors may have been involved, but it is known that major volcanic eruptions occurred in N America: Mt St Helens in 1857 and Mauna Loa, in Hawaii (1859). By contrast 1868 produced an exceptional heat wave with a record maximum temperature of 36.6°C (98°F) confirmed at Tunbridge Wells. This was a year noted nationally for spectacular butterfly immigration, when even the Queen of Spain Fritillary reached Yorkshire!

The most marked cold period of the century began with the bad winter of 1881 when 39 degrees F of frost were reported in Thirsk (VC62), and Yorkshire disappeared under 18inches of snow. Hundreds died in snowdrifts in southern England, especially on the Isle of Wight! In 1883 a lively correspondence in the *Naturalist* found entomologists blaming birdwatchers for a dramatic drop in insect numbers, especially moths and butterflies! They argued that recent bird protection laws had increased the numbers of birds to the detriment of the insects they fed upon! However, in the Dec 1883 edition Alfred

Newton pointed out that a more likely reason was *'the excessive severity of several winters in succession and still more, the inclemency of two springs'* which had also taken their toll on the birds.

On Aug 27th 1883 Krakatoa erupted, and over the next few years reduced world temperatures by an estimated 1.2°C. The resulting veil of dust took some months to reach the northern hemisphere but then the years 1885 to 1892 were disastrously cold for butterflies. In 1885, London had snow in September, the earliest ever recorded in the capital. In 1886 a row of cottages near Richmond (VC65) were completely buried under 36ft drifts, and the 11-week winter ended with a mid-May snowstorm, when thousands of freshly arrived summer birds died in the extreme cold. In 1888, winter carried on into summer, and Scotland and Wales recorded hill snow on 10th July!

In 1891, Devon and Cornwall disappeared under 20ft snowdrifts in March, with over 200 deaths. The Paddington express train to Plymouth left on a Monday and was still snowed up at Brent (Wembley) the following Wednesday! In the same year, 15cm (6 inches) of snow fell in Norfolk in mid-May. 1893 was warm and probably marked the first year back to normal, although the winter of 1895 was extremely cold. In February 1895 the River Wharfe froze in the Wetherby/Tadcaster area and both football and cricket matches were played on the ice, whilst in the Lake District around 20,000 people were estimated to be skating on Lake Windermere at peak times. 200 Rosedale (VC62) miners were cut off by 40ft snowdrifts and survived by burning furniture to keep warm.

The cumulative effect of so many cold seasons decimated butterfly populations in many parts of Britain. When you add to this, the diminution of sunlight resulting from the growth of smoke pollution across the industrial north, it is no wonder that Yorkshire's butterflies took such a hard knock. Our investigations into the historical distribution of each species, (revealed in the following chapters), suggest that virtually all our residents suffered in some degree during the latter years of the 19th century, and around this time we permanently lost Silver-spotted Skipper, Wood White, Silver-studded Blue, Small Blue, High Brown Fritillary, Silver-washed Fritillary, Marsh Fritillary, and close to Yorkshire's southern border, the Mazarine Blue in Lincolnshire. In addition, many other more common species like Holly Blue, Peacock, Comma, Speckled Wood, Marbled White, Gatekeeper and Ringlet also either disappeared or became very scarce. Walsh (1952) notes: *'It is a well-known fact that a recession in the numbers of many British butterflies took place at the end of the nineteenth century and the beginning of the twentieth. About 1915, however, the graph of frequency of a very few species began to take an upward turn…'*

Although the volcanic dust had probably largely cleared by 1893 and butterfly populations began a slow recovery, it was 1917 before Peacocks started to reappear in the south of the county!

20th CENTURY

At first sight the 20th century appears to show a similarly erratic spread of hot and cold summers to that of the 19th century. However, careful perusal of the statistics shows that most of the colder summers were clustered within the early decades, whilst the hottest were grouped in the last quarter of the century.

Between 1900 and 1912 there were three very cold summers and two moderately poor ones. These occurred soon enough after the Krakatoa years to have a suspected effect in further accelerating the decline of many of our then resident butterflies, such as fritillaries, Comma and Holly Blue. Indeed, the Comma is thought to have retracted to its historical stronghold around Hereford and Worcester, although some sources consider it may have held on in some isolated pockets further north.

One indicator of a good summer is the appearance of migrants such as the Clouded Yellow and the Painted Lady. When a spring or summer high pressure becomes established over England or the continent, it often draws hot air from central France, which arrives on gentle S to SE winds. The same winds encourage immigrant butterflies to head north and cross the Channel. Similar conditions in 1922, 1933, 1941, 1947, 1949, 1983 and 1996 brought about 'Clouded Yellow Years'. 1996 will also be long remembered as one of the best-ever Painted Lady years. It should be noted that such years don't simply depend on the right winds developing in a summer warm spell. It requires a combination of favourable weather and habitat conditions in the countries and regions of origin, perhaps over a year or more before the migration gets underway.

After the disastrous winters of the late 1800s, there were very few really cold ones until 1940, when glazed frost brought southern counties to a standstill and sheep died in their hundreds, encased in ice. The Second World War period also brought some reasonably good summers and the more common species in particular, fared well, especially Large and Small Whites, the caterpillars of which were able to fatten up on the increased abundance of brassicas being grown in parks and gardens as part of the war effort.

The winter of 1947 brought deep snow and some of the worst floods to be experienced in Yorkshire in modern times.

The 1950s were not noted for sustained good weather and some of the coolest, cloudy, wet summers were recorded in this period, with the notable exception of 1959. Butterfly recorders had a disappointing time and several species, including the whites, suffered a marked decline.

The winter of 1963 was in some ways worse than 1947, with temperatures down to -19°C in parts of Yorkshire. It was the century's coldest winter throughout Europe. In March 1963 the volcano Mt Agung erupted violently, on the East Indies island of Bali. This has been reported as the biggest eruption of the 20th century, the ensuing dust veil being estimated as having about 80% of that produced by Krakatoa. Worldwide temperatures dropped by about one third of a degree C. (Calder 1974). However, the effect in Yorkshire seems to have been quite marginal, although the years 1964 to 1966 were definitely on the cool side and not particularly good for butterflies.

In 1975, the weather changed dramatically, with the most intense heat wave in living memory up to that time. 1976 was similar, establishing many national and regional records. Almost immediately, butterfly populations began to increase. January 1987 was notable for one of the coldest periods on record with hard frosts persisting all day. Peacocks and Small Tortoiseshells suffered and Small Coppers and Commas (which had only recently been re-appearing after many years) almost disappeared. But as it turned out, this was to be the last severe winter weather of the century. From 1988 onward, winds were predominantly S to SW, and mild, with no more damaging frosts and very little snow. Mt Pinatubo (Philippines) produced a major eruption in 1991 causing a temporary global temperature drop of up to 0.5°C, but did little to alter the steady trend towards rising temperatures seen in Britain over the last 25 yrs of the 20th century. A record high of 37.1°C (98.8°F) was reported from Cheltenham in 1990, followed by 1995 and 1999 becoming the two hottest years out of the hundred.

THE LAST DECADE
A time of increasing warmth

Since 1990 Commas and Holly Blues have once again become common Yorkshire butterflies and many of the more mobile species such as Small Skipper, Brimstone, Speckled Wood, Gatekeeper and Ringlet, have pushed their northern distribution edge even further north. Orange-tips and Peacocks have been seen at higher levels than ever before and new species like Essex Skipper and even White Admiral have been recorded in the county for the very first time.

However, the story was not all to the benefit of our butterflies. Drought became a media highlight in the early 1990s with some Yorkshire reservoirs drying up completely. In many areas, grassland sites became parched and brown, even in early summer, and a number of species suffered when their nectar and caterpillar plants shrivelled. There were variations from site to site, with Small Skipper, Green-veined White, Common Blue and Ringlet amongst the worst affected. The rains returned with a vengeance in 1998 bringing the start of an exceptionally wet spell which lasted until 2003 became the driest year for 250yrs. Floods affected many parts of Britain in this period, with Malton (VC62) and Stamford Bridge (VC61) being badly affected in 1999, and the Vale of York experiencing one of its worst-ever floods in 2000. Filey and Scarborough hit the national headlines with summer floods in August 2000. But at least, those butterfly species affected by drought and not washed away, soon recovered!

The last decade of the 20th century was full of surprises. There was little doubt that Red Admirals were now successfully wintering in Yorkshire, albeit in small numbers. Rather more unexpectedly, Clouded Yellows and Painted Ladies were shown to be surviving winter in parts of southern England. Hibernating species were increasingly seen emerging on warm sunny days in January and February when temperatures sometimes reached as high as 16°/17°C even as far north as Yorkshire. By the end of the 20th century, spring was arriving some three weeks earlier than at the beginning, and the Yorkshire butterfly season was lengthening steadily, with earlier starts and later finishes for many species.

The most significant change has been in the persistent rise in temperatures, to such an extent that the latest decade has been the hottest since records began in the 1600s. In global terms, the ten warmest years have all occurred since 1991. In Europe, 2003 was the hottest of all time, and the second warmest in Britain. In the SE of England we saw the temperature exceed 100°F (37.8°C) for the first time since records began in the 1600s. 2003 was also the sunniest year on record, a fact appreciated by most of our butterflies, as well as the observers who went out to count them!

It is now widely accepted that the Earth's climate is undergoing a dramatic change, although it is only in recent years that scientists have finally agreed a cause and even now, not all of them hold the same opinion. However, there has been enough international agreement to convince national governments that atmospheric pollution has accelerated climate change beyond anything seen in the recent history of our planet. 'Global Warming' has become the buzz phrase of the last decade of the 20th century.

A product of global warming appears to be the increased variability and unpredictability of our weather. We all remember the floods of 2000, a year in which it never seemed to stop raining. Parts of Sussex received almost 5ft of rain in the year! At the same time, many Yorkshire towns and cities were also inundated by floods. Only 3 years later trees were dying through lack of water in the driest 12 months for 250yrs!

It is a fascinating time to be observing our Yorkshire butterflies and seeing how they cope with such rapid change. We have not had a taste of severe winter since the cold spell of January 1987. However, there could yet be more reversals. Scientists have recently discerned a world-wide weather cycle based on water movements within the Pacific Ocean, which suggests we may already have embarked on a 20yr cool period. No-one dares to predict how far this may or may not be cancelled out by global warming, but there is no guarantee that we won't have any more severe winters. Another major volcanic eruption could easily bring a further run of cold years, which might, at least temporarily, turn back the clock on recent temperature rises. Such is the delicate balance between the workings of our planet, the weather and butterfly survival!

KEY TO CHART OVERLEAF:

The seasons are defined as by the Met Office:

Winter	= Dec 1st - Feb 28th/29th.
Spring	= Mar 1st - May 31st
Summer	= June 1st - Aug 31st
Autumn	= Sept 1st - Nov 30th

The seasonal assessments are based on Central England Temperature Statistics modified by local information derived from the many sources listed below. Local information has been cross-referenced, checked and corrected wherever possible. Grades are based on seasons containing one or more 30-day periods of extreme temperatures compared to the long-term average.

Mild, Warm, Cool:	one period (±2°C)
Warm winters:	two periods (+2°C)
Hot, Cold:	two periods (±2°C)
vHot, vCold, vWarm:	period of sustained extremes (±3°C)
Mixed:	Periods of hot and cold, warm or cool.
O:	Average, containing no significant variations.

The chart should be seen as a generalisation, even for Yorkshire where weather can vary considerably from one part to another at any one time. In the context column, butterfly comments are for national highlights except where specified.

References: Brimblecombe (2000), Burroughs *et al* (1996), Eden (1995), Eden (2003), Foggitt & Markham (1993), Frost & Winter (1999), Holford (1977), Hudson & Rust (2003), Kious & Tilling (1996), Ludlum (2001), Newson (2002), Newton (1883), Viner & Jones (2000), plus local and national newspaper archives and the *Journal of Meteorology*.

Weather 1800 - 1849

Year	Winter	Spring	Summer	Autumn	O = **Average**. * = **major eruption**. CY=Clouded Yellow.
1800	Cool	O	Warm	O	Union of GB & Ireland.
1801	O	O	Warm	O	Trevithick's steam carriage.
1802	Cool	O	Mixed	O	First practical steam ship launched.
1803	O	O	Warm	Cool	Haworth's *Lepidoptera Britannica*. Napoleonic Wars start.
1804	O	Warm	Warm	O	CY Yr. Spain declares war on GB. Napoleon Emperor.
1805	O	O	O	Mixed	Battle of Trafalgar.
1806	O	O	O	Warm	Napoleon blockades Britain.
1807	Mild	Cool	Warm	Mixed	Slave Trade abolished.
1808	Cool	Mixed	Warm	Cool	CY Yr. Fabricius (1745-1808) dies. Peninsula War begins.
1809	O	Mixed	O	O	Battle of Corunna.
1810	O	Cool	O	O	*Major eruption. Source unknown. No sunspot activity.
1811	Cool	Warm	O	Hot	CY Yr. Luddite Riots.
1812	O	Cold	Cold	O	*Soufrieres, St Vincent. Napoleon retreats from Moscow.
1813	Cool	O	O	Cold	Wellington beats French at Vitoria
1814	vCOLD	Mixed	Cool	Cool	*Mayon, Philippines. **Frost Fairs on Thames.**
1815	Cool	Hot	O	Cool	*Tambora (Indonesia)-one of biggest ever. Battle of Waterloo.
1816	O	Cool	vCOLD	Cold	**The year without a summer. Food shortages.**
1817	O	Cool	Cold	Mixed	Irish Potato Famine.
1818	O	O	Hot	Hot	CY Yr. Cholera pandemic 1817-1822.
1819	O	O	Warm	Cool	**Camberwell Beauty Yr.** Peterloo Massacre.
1820	Cold	O	O	Cool	George III dies. George IV King. Eruption Mt Rainier USA.
1821	O	Mixed	Cool	Hot	**Pale CY Yr.** Snow in May. Death of Napoleon Bonaparte.
1822	Mild	Hot	Warm	Warm	CY Yr. First photo image: Niépce.
1823	Cold	Cool	Cold	O	**A year of extreme cold.**
1824	O	O	O	O	Storm surge disaster in Baltic. Byron dies.
1825	O	O	O	Warm	Stockton-Darlington railway opens.
1826	Cool	O	vHOT	Warm	**Memorable butterfly year. One of best ever for CY.**
1827	Cool	O	O	Warm	Beethoven dies.
1828	Mild	O	O	O	**Pale CY Yr.** Cholera pandemic 1826-34.
1829	Mixed	Mixed	O	Cold	Stephenson's *Rocket*. 1st Oxford & Cambridge boat race.
1830	Cold	Warm	Cold	Cool	George IV dies. William IV King.
1831	Cool	O	Warm	Warm	CY Yr. Darwin's *Beagle* voyage begins.
1832	O	O	O	O	**Wath-on-Dearne butterfly list published.**
1833	Cool	Warm	O	O	First Factory Act.
1834	Warm	Warm	O	O	Tolpuddle Martyrs.
1835	O	O	Warm	O	*Coseguina, Nicaragua CY & PCY Yr. Duncan's *British Butterflies*
1836	O	O	O	Cool	October snow in East Anglia.
1837	O	Cold	Warm	O	William IV dies. Victoria crowned Queen.
1838	Cold	Cool	O	O	National Gallery opened.
1839	O	Cool	O	O	Chartist riots in Birmingham & Newport
1840	O	Warm	Cool	Cold	Launch of penny post.
1841	Cold	Hot	Cold	O	Britain annexes New Zealand.
1842	Cool	O	Hot	Cool	**Good CY Yr in Yorks.** *An Account of Askern* - E Lankester.
1843	Mild	O	Cool	Cool	Irish Potato Famine: 1842-1848.
1844	Mixed	Warm	Cool	O	Glaciers advance: 1835-1850.
1845	Cold	Cold	Cold	Cool	**Mt Hekla (Iceland) erupts.** Potato blight & famine.
1846	Mild	O	Warm	Warm	**Camberwell Beauty Yr.** Joseph Dunning at Storthes Hall.
1847	Cool	Cool	Warm	Mixed	**Huddersfield Naturalists' Soc formed.** 1st NHS in Yorks.
1848	Cool	Warm	Cool	O	**George Porritt born. Heavy Feb snow:cold early spring.**
1849	O	Cool	O	O	Chopin dies.

Year	Winter	Spring	Summer	Autumn	O = Average. * = Major eruption. CY = Clouded Yellow.
1850	Cool	O	O	Cool	Taiping Rebellion in China.
1851	O	O	O	Cool	Great Exhibition
1852	O	O	Warm	Mixed	CY Yr. Wells Fargo founded in US.
1853	Mixed	Cool	O	O	*A History of British Butterflies* F O Morris
1854	Cool	O	O	O	Met Office created.
1855	vCOLD	Cold	O	O	End of Crimean War.
1856	O	Cool	Warm	O	Livingstone explores Africa.
1857	O	O	Hot	Hot	Indian Mutiny.
1858	Mild	O	Warm	Mixed	CY Yr.
1859	O	Warm	Warm	O	*Mauna Loa Hawaii. CY Yr Hobkirk's List published.
1860	Cold	Cool	vCOLD	Cool	**Yorkshire Cleopatra! One of coldest periods recorded.**
1861	vCOLD	O	O	Mixed	**At or below freezing in Yorks 15/12/1860 to 16/01/1861**
1862	O	O	Cold	Cool	Cotton famine in Lancashire.
1863	Mild	O	O	Cool	Battle of Gettysburg. London Underground opened.
1864	O	O	Cool	O	CY Yr. **Notably snowy year.** Red Cross founded.
1865	O	Mixed	Warm	Warm	CY Yr. President Lincoln assassinated.
1866	O	O	Warm	O	Mendel theories proposed. *Yorkshire Post* launched.
1867	Mixed	Cool	O	O	**January blizzards.** Dominion of Canada created.
1868	O	Warm	v HOT	O	**Superb immigrant yr. Q of Spain, American PL in Yorks**
1869	Warm	Mixed	O	O	**Notable Christmas snow.** Suez Canal opened.
1870	O	O	Warm	O	Charles Dickens dies.
1871	Cold	Warm	Mixed	Cool	Newman's *British Butterflies* published.
1872	Mild	Cool	O	O	**Pale CY & Camberwell Beauty Yr.**
1873	O	O	O	Cool	Livingstone dies.
1874	O	Warm	O	O	**Last Yorks Silver-spotted Skipper.** Disraeli PM.
1875	Mixed	O	O	Warm	CY Yr. YNU *Naturalist* first published.
1876	O	Cool	O	Warm	CY Yr. Bell invents telephone. Heavy April snow.
1877	O	Cool	O	Cool	**Spectacular CY Yr.** YNU founded.
1878	O	O	O	Cool	Electric light invented.
1879	Cold	Cold	vCOLD	Cool	Cold summer led to farming depression. Tay Bridge disaster.
1880	Cold	O	O	Mixed	1st Boer War.
1881	vCOLD	O	Cool	Mixed	**5 weeks of severe winter starting around 21/12/1880.**
1882	O	Warm	O	O	**Queen of Spain immigration.**
1883	O	Cool	O	O	*Krakatoa erupts. Porritt's 'List' published (1883-1886).
1884	Mild	O	Warm	Warm	Rover Safety bicycle: 1st modern style bike.
1885	O	Cool	Cool	Cool	Sept snow in London. 1st Karl Benz cars Germany.
1886	Cold	O	O	Warm	**3 month winter & May snowstorm kills migrant birds.**
1887	Cool	vCOLD	O	Cold	**Record low temperatures with snow in March.**
1888	O	Cold	vCOLD	Mixed	**July hill snow in Wales and Scotland.** 1st Kodak camera.
1889	O	Warm	O	O	CY Yr. Paris: Eiffel Tower finished.
1890	O	O	vCOLD	Warm	CY Yr. **July hill snow. Forth Bridge opened.**
1891	Cold	Cold	Cool	O	**Mid-May snowstorm & frosts after warm spell.**
1892	O	Cool	Cool	Cool	CY Yr. Basketball invented.
1893	Cool	Hot	vHOT	O	**73 day drought.**
1894	O	Mixed	Cool	Mixed	Manchester Ship Canal & Blackpool Tower opened.
1895	vCOLD	O	O	Mixed	CY Yr. **Record low temperatures.** Radio demonstrated.
1896	O	O	Warm	Cold	Bikes with pneumatic tyres become the norm.
1897	O	O	O	O	Q Victoria Diamond Jubilee.
1898	Mild	O	O	Hot	Gladstone dies. Radium discovered.
1899	Mild	O	vHOT	Warm	Start of 2nd Boer War.

Weather 1900 - 1949

Year	Winter	Spring	Summer	Autumn	O = Average. * = Major eruption. CY = Clouded Yellow.
1900	O	O	Warm	O	CY Yr + 2200 Pale CY nationally! Floods in Ilkley.
1901	Mild	O	Warm	O	Queen Victoria dies. First radio signals.
1902	Cool	Cool	O	O	* Mt Pelée (Martinique) eruption. Edward VII King.
1903	Mild	Cool	vCOLD	O	Wright brothers 1st flight.
1904	O	O	O	O	Porritt's update 'List'.
1905	O	O	O	Cool	Norway separates from Sweden.
1906	O	O	O	O	Record Sept heatwave.
1907	O	O	vCOLD	O	Porritt's Vic Co History 'List'.
1908	O	Cool	O	Warm	Last Yorks Small Blue? Comet hits Tunguska, Siberia.
1909	O	O	vCOLD	Cool	1st flight across English Channel.
1910	O	O	Cool	Cool	Edward VII dies.
1911	Mild	Warm	vHOT	O	Doncaster Cleopatra? George V King. Record temp. 98°F.
1912	O	O	Cool	Cold	*Katmai (Alaska) erupts. *Titanic* disaster.
1913	Mild	O	O	Warm	CY Yr. Panama Canal opens.
1914	Mild	Warm	O	O	Start of FIRST WORLD WAR. Scarborough and Whitby shelled.
1915	O	O	O	Cool	Sinking of *Lusitania*.
1916	Mild	Cool	Cool	O	Battle of Somme.
1917	Cold	Mixed	O	Mixed	Cold winter. Russian Revolution. USA joins war.
1918	O	Mixed	O	Cool	End of FIRST WORLD WAR.
1919	Mild	Warm	Cool	Cold	*Mauna Loa (Hawaii) erupts. Alcock&Brown fly Atlantic.
1920	O	O	vCOLD	O	*Katmai (Alaska) erupts. Radio broadcasting begins.
1921	Mild	Warm	Warm	Warm	*Katmai (Alaska) erupts.
1922	Mild	Mixed	vCOLD	Cool	CY Yr. Porritt's Hull area 'List'. BBC broadcasts begin.
1923	O	Cool	Mixed	Cool	France invades Germany. Tokyo destroyed in earthquake.
1924	O	O	Cool	O	Lenin dies.
1925	vWARM	O	O	Cold	Hitler's *Mein Kampf* published.
1926	Mild	O	O	Cool	General Strike in Britain. 1st TV demo by Baird.
1927	O	Warm	Cool	O	Last Yorks Scotch Argus? 1st movies & sound.
1928	O	O	Cool	O	CY Yr. Penicillin discovered. 1st Mickey Mouse film.
1929	Cold	O	O	Warm	Cold winter. Wall Street Crash.
1930	O	O	O	O	Floods in Whitby. Amy Johnson flies to Australia.
1931	O	O	O	Mixed	*Katmai (Alaska) erupts.
1932	Mild	O	Warm	O	*Mt Pelée (Martinique) erupts.
1933	O	Warm	vHOT	Warm	CY & Monarch year. Hitler becomes German Chancellor.
1934	Cool	O	Warm	Warm	Discovery of nuclear fission.
1935	vWARM	O	O	O	Hitler becomes German Dictator.
1936	O	Cool	O	O	George V dies. Edward VIII abdicates. Spanish Civil War.
1937	O	O	Warm	O	George VI crowned King.
1938	O	Warm	O	Warm	Nylon discovered.
1939	O	O	O	Mixed	Start of WORLD WAR TWO.
1940	vCOLD	Warm	Warm	O	Dunkirk Evacuation. Sheffield and Middlesbrough bombed.
1941	Cold	Cold	O	Warm	CY Yr. Pearl Harbour. 1st computer, ZuseZ3 Germany.
1942	Cold	O	O	O	Battle of El Alamein. Bombing of York & Hull.
1943	vWARM	Warm	O	O	Dambusters. 1st British computer: Colossus.
1944	O	Warm	Warm	O	D-Day Invasion.
1945	Mixed	Hot	O	Warm	PCY Yr. Hull bombed again. End of WORLD WAR TWO.
1946	O	Warm	O	Warm	Bread rationing. 1st US computer: ENIAC
1947	vCOLD	Warm	vHOT	Warm	Spectacular CY, PCY ,PL and C Beauty Yr. Severe winter.
1948	O	Warm	O	O	PCY Yr. Railways nationalised.
1949	O	Warm	vHOT	Hot	CY & PCY Yr. NATO formed.

The Butterflies of Yorkshire

Year	Winter	Spring	Summer	Autumn	O = Average. * = Major eruption. CY = Clouded Yellow.
1950	O	Warm	Warm	O	CY Yr. Korean War begins.
1951	Cool	O	O	Warm	Festival of Britain.
1952	O	Hot	O	Cold	Great London Smog. Lynmouth Flood. George VI dies.
1953	O	Warm	O	Warm	Great North Sea Flood. Elizabeth II Queen.
1954	Mild	O	vCOLD	Warm	1st 4-minute mile. 1st live TV weather forecasts.
1955	Mixed	Cold	vHOT	O	CY Yr. London becomes smokeless.
1956	Cool	O	vCOLD	O	*Nat Hist Scarboro' Dist Vol 2* published with Butterfly List.
1957	O	Warm	O	O	EEC set up. Myxomatosis widespread. Sputnik 1 launched.
1958	O	O	O	Warm	Munich air disaster. Clean Air Act passed. 1st stereo records.
1959	O	vHOT	vHOT	Hot	The 'Long Hot Summer'. M1 opens.
1960	O	Warm	Warm	O	Fylingdales early warning station planned.
1961	Mild	Hot	O	Warm	Gagarin makes first space flight.
1962	O	Cool	Cool	O	Cuban missile crisis. 1st TV link to USA via *Telstar*.
1963	vCOLD	O	O	Hot	*Mt Agung, Indonesia. **Record winter.** Fylingdales operational.
1964	O	Warm	O	O	Start of Vietnam War.
1965	O	O	Cool	O	Churchill dies. Crisis in Rhodesia.
1966	O	O	O	O	England Cup Winners. First heart transplant.
1967	O	O	O	O	*The Lepidoptera of Yorkshire* YNU 1967/70. BBC2 in colour.
1968	O	O	O	Warm	**Butterfly Conservation (BC) founded.**
1969	Cool	Cool	O	Warm	CY Yr. (last until 1983!). 1st man on the moon.
1970	O	Mixed	Warm	Warm	**Hekla (Iceland) erupts.** Start of oil drilling in N Sea.
1971	O	O	Cool	Warm	Decimal Day in UK.
1972	Mild	O	Cool	Cool	Queen's Silver Wedding. 1st pocket calculators.
1973	O	O	O	O	Icelandic Cod Wars start.
1974	O	O	O	Cool	Miners strike. Flixborough chemical works explodes.
1975	vWARM	O	vHOT	O	First floppy disks, first home video recorders.
1976	O	O	vHOT	O	C Beauty Yr. Concorde & 1st BR high speed trains in service.
1977	Cool	O	Cool	Warm	Queen Elizabeth Jubilee. Elvis Presley dies.
1978	O	Cool	O	Hot	First 'Test Tube' baby.
1979	vCOLD	O	O	Warm	Mrs Thatcher PM. Fastnet gale disaster.
1980	O	O	O	Warm	* Mt St Helens, USA. Humber Bridge built. 1st Walkmans.
1981	O	Warm	O	Hot	**BC Yorkshire founded. Garland (1981) Sheffield Butterflies.**
1982	Cool	O	Warm	Warm	* El Chichon, Mexico. Falklands War. 1st CDs.
1983	Mixed	O	vHOT	O	CY Yr. IBM launches personal computer.
1984	O	O	Warm	Hot	First national butterfly atlas (Heath *et al*1984). York Minster fire.
1985	Cool	O	Cool	Mixed	Bradford City fire disaster. Gorbachev USSR leader. End Cold War.
1986	vCOLD	Cool	Cool	Mixed	Chernobyl explosion. Halley's Comet. Ozone layer hole.
1987	Cool	Warm	Cool	O	Harrogate Butterflies (Barnham & Foggitt). **Great Oct Storm**
1988	O	O	O	O	Seals die in N Sea of canine distemper.
1989	Warm	Mixed	Warm	Hot	*Butterflies & Moths of Yorkshire* Sutton & Beaumont, YNU.
1990	Warm	Hot	vHOT	Warm	Yorks Holly Blue arrival. **Record: 37.1°C.** Germany re-unified.
1991	Cool	Warm	Mixed	Warm	*Mt Hudson Chile & Pinatubo Philippines. Drought in England.
1992	O	Hot	Warm	Cool	CY Yr. '*Sheffield*' & '*Doncaster*' b-fly booklets Sorby NHS.
1993	O	Warm	O	O	USA: storm of the century. Mississippi Flood.
1994	O	Warm	Warm	Warm	1st Yorks White Admiral. Channel Tunnel opened.
1995	Mild	O	vHOT	Hot	C Beauty Yr. Start of 5yr National Millennium Atlas Survey.
1996	O	Cool	O	Warm	P.Lady Year of the century. CY Yr. 1st Yorks Essex Skipper.
1997	Mild	Warm	Warm	Warm	Death of Princess Diana. Big floods in Poland. Tony Blair PM.
1998	Mild	Hot	O	O	CY Yr. **Record rainfall in Britain.** Birth of Euro currency.
1999	Mild	Warm	Warm	Warm	Monarch Yr. Up to record 15.7°C recorded in parts of UK on 06/01.

Mike Barnham

White Admiral: New Forest 1988

Ever Changing
Butterfly
Distribution

What are the causes?

Geoffrey Fryer

Butterfly populations are seldom static over even short periods of time. Numbers fluctuate from year to year, and individual species sometimes change their range within only a few years. Were this not so, the survey with which this book is concerned would, if efficiently carried out, render any future survey superfluous. Even within the relatively short period within which reliable information has been available – less than 200 years in the case of most species – there have been changes in the distribution of a considerable proportion of the butterflies of the county. Carefully documented, these changes tell us *what* happened. What is even more interesting, but often more difficult to ascertain, is *why* the changes took place. The well-being of a butterfly population depends on many factors that either influence it directly, or indirectly via its environment, and these interact in a complicated manner. They include climate, topography, the nature of the vegetation, the distribution and abundance of food plants, and the incidence of predators and parasites. Moreover, throughout the area covered, butterflies are subject, in some degree, to the influence of human activities, and this has been so throughout the period for which information exists.

A classical example of change is Yorkshire's loss of the Swallowtail, which was found near Beverley as recently as the end of the 18th, and apparently survived even into the 19th century. Rimington (1987) (see p240)

finds little reason to doubt Haworth's (1803) reports of the species being there in about 1778 and 1796, and the claim that in 1803 it *'breeds near Beverley yet'*. In Rimington's view these insects represented *'the last dwindling remnants of a population once common throughout the extensive marshlands of Yorkshire and Lincolnshire'*. While other factors may have been involved, the main cause of the disappearance was almost certainly the draining of the once extensive wetlands of this part of Yorkshire.

Another case is that of the Scotch Argus which apparently disappeared from its Yorkshire stronghold near Grassington (VC64) in the 1920s, but may have persisted there until the 1950s. It was also recorded at Buckden, Whernside and Arncliffe, all VC64, (plentifully at the last site in 1892). Long known from Grassington, it was described by Porritt (1883) as being *'as abundant as ever'* in 1882, and was subsequently seen there in other years (abundantly in 1884, 1902 and 1923) (Shaw 1978). What may have been the last sighting of the indigenous Grassington population was in 1955 when Reid (1955) saw two individuals, though it has been suggested that these may have been re-introductions. Unfortunately any subsequent history of this population was rendered meaningless by an introduction in 1976, from which insects seen in the 1980s may have been derived. The last sighting here seems to have been in 1984, and the Scotch Argus now appears to be extinct in Yorkshire. The reasons for this disappearance remain unclear. The planting of conifers in Grass Wood, which may have shaded out its preferred habitats at Grassington, could have been a contributory factor here, but there is no explanation of its disappearance from the other three sites.

A different kind of change may yet be provided by the White Admiral, of which one (the first ever in the county) was seen in Yorkshire in 1994 (Frost 1995). This had evidently crossed the Humber from North Lincolnshire where there are now several known sites. An explanation of the long continued range expansion of this species was sought by Pollard (1979). If the White Admiral establishes itself in Yorkshire this will offer the opportunity not only to follow its progress but to test the validity of aspects of the explanation of its spread already put forward.

Changes in range not only provide puzzles for solution but sometimes reveal other biological problems. For example the Green Hairstreak has increased in abundance and greatly expanded its range in upland areas of Yorkshire during the second half of the 20th century. It was unknown in the Pennines around Huddersfield (VC63) until one was seen there in the early 1950s. Since then it has spread over an ever widening area of upland terrain (Fryer and Lucas 2001) and there has been a similar increase and expansion elsewhere in the uplands, as around Sheffield (VC63) to the south (Garland 1981, Whiteley 1992), and Harrogate (VC64) to the north (Barnham and Foggitt 1987, Barnham et al.1993), and also in the north east. This upsurge has not been accompanied by similar expansion in the lowlands where the Green Hairstreak is uncommon and where there have indeed been losses. This remarkable change in the fortunes of populations in different habitats confirms and extends the observations of Jackson (1980) that it previously occurred in several lowland areas of Yorkshire but by 1980 seemed to be confined to hilly regions. Disappearance from the lowlands has not been complete: there is for example a small but persistent population at Spurn (VC61) which appears to have spread northwards from the Lincolnshire coast, but there have been losses from central Yorkshire, as there have in lowland Lincolnshire and Nottinghamshire (see Asher et al. 2001), and these stand in striking contrast to the dramatic increase in upland areas. To provide an explanation of these facts is an exciting challenge. Comparisons, ecological and molecular, between upland and lowland populations may prove enlightening. Whatever the approach, investigation may reveal that an apparently simple change in range by a butterfly may in fact pose a subtle and complex scientific problem. Is it possible that there are two genetically distinct forms of the Green Hairstreak in Britain, each of which has its own ecological preferences?

Habitat modification, and sometimes destruction, have clearly been involved in some changes in distribution. Almost always their effects have been deleterious and have led to reductions in range or, in some areas, to the extermination of various species. Changes in agricultural practices often had adverse effects and are too well known to merit repetition, as are losses of, and changes in, woodland habitats. Occasionally one species may have benefited at the expense of another, as when woodland was converted to grass, but the general trend has been adverse.

Another factor has been the inexorable increase in the human population. Vast areas of land have been taken over for housing and for buildings related to industry and commerce, and much land has been lost to a network of roads. Such developments not only destroy but fragment habitats, which makes dispersal difficult, though some, such as railways and motorways, sometimes provide not only habitats on embankments and verges, but also corridors for dispersal. Moreover some butterflies are resilient and have availed themselves of the opportunities provided by gardens, waste ground, and other modified habitats.

More insidious than the obvious physical destruction of the environment has been pollution of the atmosphere of densely populated areas with smoke, and by such gases as sulphur dioxide and oxides of nitrogen that give rise to both wet and dry acidic precipitation. Their effects extend beyond the confines of such areas. Although the matter has received scant attention from lepidopterists in Britain, some observations made in Yorkshire in the 19th century hint strongly that atmospheric pollution may have had highly deleterious effects on butterflies, especially when added to the effects of weather. In a paper published in a local journal in 1883 Seth Lister Mosley recorded that, probably between about 1865 and 1870, several species that had formerly been common in the Huddersfield area disappeared. What was particularly significant was that these included such common species as the Meadow Brown and Small Heath. Others that disappeared were the Dingy Skipper, Holly Blue, Speckled Wood, Wall and Ringlet, as did two species, the Wood White and Pearl-bordered Fritillary that were already very rare in the area. The Comma had probably done so before these extinctions took place. Moreover, the Orange Tip and Common Blue, became so rare that Mosley thought that they too had disappeared but they actually persisted in small numbers in a few places. Others, such as the Small Copper, Small Tortoiseshell and Peacock suffered reductions in numbers, as did the Red Admiral, a species whose continued survival in Britain depends on immigrants and whose decline therefore poses peculiar problems. Several moths, some of them formerly abundant, also suffered extinction at about the same time.

A noteworthy feature of these extinctions was their local nature. Some of the species concerned persisted, and flourished, especially in areas to the east and south-east, just outside the Huddersfield area. Later consideration of likely causes points very strongly to the effects of atmospheric pollution, and more particularly to the adverse effects of smoke and soot (Fryer and Lucas 2001), perhaps made worse by five consecutive seasons of cold weather in the 1860s (see p22). The extinctions occurred at a time when smoke pollution, to which the textile industry was a major contributor, had reached high levels – the area not only produced much smoke but was the recipient of more from South-east Lancashire – but when SO_2 levels were lower than they were later to achieve. Smoke and soot disperse for shorter distances than do acid-producing gases and more readily explain the localised nature of the extinctions. Enormous amounts of soot were deposited in industrial areas of Yorkshire at this time, a process that continued well into the 20th century. The accompanying photograph conveys a dramatic impression of conditions in parts of Leeds in the early 20th century. Here well over 500 tons of soot per square mile fell on the industrial parts of the city each year from the smoke-laden atmosphere. Similar conditions prevailed in Huddersfield, Halifax, Bradford (all VC63) and elsewhere. The tar content of soot caused it to adhere to plants, to their detriment, and indirectly to that of the larvae of butterflies that fed on them. Soot also contains toxins and may sometimes have been a physical irritant, especially to

View of Leeds, overlooking Kirkstall Road; 1911 or earlier. (From Cohen and Ruston 1912). An example of what the Yorkshire poet Ammon Wrigley (1861-1946) described as the dawn-strangling '*ropes of smoke far flung from black chimneys in coils of death*'.

small larvae with soft cuticles. Good evidence that Lepidoptera are affected by, and react to, smoke and soot is indicated by the fact that more than 40 species of moths in the Huddersfield area produced melanic forms at around this time.

Smoke reduces sunshine levels, as the accompanying photograph makes plain, and most butterflies are sunshine-dependent. Cohen and Ruston (1912, 1925) calculated that, in 1897, at least 160 tons of soot were discharged each day into the air above the 16 square miles covered by the city of Leeds, (VC 63/64), which dramatically reduced the amount of light and sunshine reaching the ground. Most of this suspended soot (smoke) was blown elsewhere, and conditions improved downwind, light intensity and the amount of sunshine rising sharply with increasing distance from the smoke source. The metabolism of butterfly larvae benefits from warming of the ground by the sun, and larvae of some species bask in sunshine. Adults often fly and feed only when the sun is out, and use of the wings as solar panels is common. Reduction of sunshine by smoke clearly had adverse effects. It is significant that of the moths that suffered extinction at that time a disproportionately large contingent were day-flying species.

Surprisingly little attention has been paid to the effects of atmospheric pollution on butterflies in Britain. In the mid-19th century, when heavy loads of smoke and soot in northern towns were all too obvious, and elicited frequent comment and concern, it was already apparent that vegetation was adversely affected by such conditions (see references in Seaward 1975, Fryer and Lucas 2001). More specifically, Nowell (1866) attributed the loss of a considerable number of species of mosses near Todmorden to '*the super-abundance of factory smoke*', and Moss (1901) gave the same explanation for the disappearance of various flowering plants near Halifax where heavy smoke pollution had prevailed for more than half a century. In this context the views of Herbert Spencer (1884 - 1949) of Elland, (NW of Huddersfield VC63), an outstanding lepidopterist and an all-round naturalist, deserve mention. As Collinson (1969) records with reference to Lepidoptera he was wont to remark '*As the chimneys went up the species went down*'.

Levels of smoke and soot production gradually fell during the 20th century. Towards the end of the 19th century high levels of black smoke emissions from mill chimneys had been restricted to five minutes per hour (a regulation often flouted) and Clean Air Acts of 1956 and 1968 led to great improvements in air quality. In any case changes in technology – the replacement of steam engines by electric motors, and a change from coal to other fuels – and later the decline of the textile industry, inevitably reduced smoke and soot levels. As pollution levels gradually fell, several species of butterflies recolonised the Huddersfield area. This happened while levels of SO_2 were still rising, suggesting that smoke and soot were the agents particularly responsible for the earlier declines. Smoke reduction led to an increase in the amount of sunshine received and to higher temperatures at ground level during sunny periods. The amount of soot deposited per unit area also gradually, and eventually dramatically, fell.

The Butterflies of Yorkshire

Although change and destruction of their habitats has been said to be the main cause of changes in the distribution and abundance of British Butterflies (Heath *et al*.1984), this does not explain what happened in the Huddersfield area. Here, not only did the virtually simultaneous extinctions of several species take place too rapidly to be explained by such change, but the suggestion is contradicted by subsequent events. Recolonisation by species that had become extinct, recovery of others that had become rare, and colonisation by species never previously known in the area, took place in spite of the fact that, as measured by the loss of plant species, habitats had deteriorated, were reduced in area, and had become more fragmented. Reduced plant diversity was itself largely the result of earlier atmospheric pollution. New arrivals that established themselves in the second half of the 20th century were the Large and Small Skippers, the Green, Purple, and White-letter Hairstreaks (there is a single (lowland) record of the Green Hairstreak from sometime before 1884), and the Gatekeeper.

Towards the end of the 20th century the effects of global warming appear to have been implicated in a northward shift in the ranges of several species in Britain, and in Europe 63% of 35 non-migratory butterflies for which adequate information is available, extended their range northwards by between 35 and 240 km. during the 20th century (Parmesan *et al*.1999). The northward expansion into, and beyond, Yorkshire by the Comma is probably, one example, and the expansion of the Speckled Wood was probably facilitated by the warming climate though, as Jackson's (1980) comments make clear, a direct correlation is probably too simplistic as an explanation. Few of the 20th century expansions into the Huddersfield area were simple northward extensions of range, but a warming climate may well have reduced environmental stress and thereby facilitated the process. Moreover, the Meadow Brown and Small Heath recolonised the area before global warming began.

The many changes that have taken place in the Huddersfield area in a short period of time provide a dramatic example of the dynamic nature of butterfly faunas as a whole and of the populations of individual species. Excluding irregular migrants, a single vagrant Monarch, and the Small Pearl-bordered Fritillary of which there is just one record, but including the Red Admiral which, although a migrant, is consistently represented, 22 species were present in about 1840-1850. Following the extinctions in the second half of the century the number had fallen to 11 by 1900 and of these the Silver–washed Fritillary and Large Tortoiseshell were very rare. Then, over the next hundred years several additional species established themselves, doing so at an increasing tempo as the century progressed, and by the year 2000 no fewer than 23 species were present. Thus, over a period of about 150 years the number of species present was first halved, then more than doubled. The amazing dynamism of these changes is strikingly demonstrated by the careful observations of D.S. and V.A. Ives and S. Graham in two gardens at Almondbury on the fringes of Huddersfield (VC63). Here, in the last few years of the 20th century they recorded 17 species (plus the migrant Painted Lady). This is more than half as many again as were known in an area of more than 300 square miles in 1900. The magnitude of these changes is perhaps greater than that recorded in any other local butterfly fauna in Britain.

Two views of Huddersfield in 2004 with Castle Hill on the right and a much greener landscape than in past times.

Lawrie King

Dingy Skipper

Butterflies and Brownfield Sites

The value of wastelands

Jeff Lunn

The term 'brownfield' is applied here to land which has been used at some time in its history, for industrial, commercial or business use, including residential or leisure activities, and which is now abandoned and unmanaged. As such it is distinctive from land used for agricultural, forestry and water interests (which makes up the bulk of our countryside), and land in urban areas, which is actively occupied, by housing, factories, offices, roads and so on.

Taking the long history of human occupation in the county, and the myriad of uses that land has been put to through recent centuries since the industrial revolution, there is a huge range of sites that could be described as 'brownfield'. On the one hand, old quarries (such as stone quarries in the Pennines, chalk or limestone quarries of the Wolds, Dales and Magnesian Limestone ridge, and alum quarries on the North Yorkshire coast), long abandoned and left to nature, can have a well-developed wildlife interest. Some are now nature reserves and Sites of Special Scientific Interest. On the other hand, the massive legacy of colliery spoilheaps in the Yorkshire Coalfield, which might appear to be amongst the most inhospitable places for wildlife to flourish, can more understandably be termed 'brownfield'. In between are the places of temporary clearance and re-use – the dismantled old factories, housing clearances, old railway tracks and so on which are often referred to as wasteland even though they may be wildlife havens.

Manvers Tip, S Yorkshire, an old colliery spoil heap (1993).

What all these areas have in common is that, once they have ceased to be used and are abandoned, nature then takes its course and the process of natural colonisation and re-establishment takes place. For sites like stone and lime quarries, nature has had a healing hand for centuries, and the vegetation which has had a chance to establish, can mirror the sort of plant cover once more widespread on natural sites in the vicinity. In contrast, the new and often large urban and industrial sites, have had much less time for colonisation and can consist of large tracts of bare or sparsely vegetated ground. Today's sources of colonising material will also be very different from previous centuries, especially where much of the surrounding natural landscape has already been transformed.

Despite their different origins, all 'brownfield' sites have characteristics which are attractive to wildlife colonisers. They have varied topography, often with a myriad of slopes and hollows, plus areas of shade and full sun, patches of bare ground, and pools, which may be shallow, deep, temporary or more permanent. There may be warm, south-facing slopes, with the presence of scrub as a shelter, and a varied vegetation structure containing

oth tall and short plants, interspersed
with bare ground. The vegetation can
consist of a great variety of larval
foodplants and nectar sources for
butterflies and other insects. Moreover,
they are relatively free from intervention
by human management – no fertilisers,
pesticides, or grazing stock; and all are
subject to the serendipity of chance
colonisation and the establishment of flora
and fauna.

The vegetation of older 'brownfield' sites
is often well established. Pennine quarries
may be cloaked with typical moorland
plants such as Heather *Calluna vulgaris*,
Bilberry *Vaccinium myrtillus*, Bracken
Pteridium aquilinum and Wavy Hair-grass
Deschampsia flexuosa. Limestone
quarries boast swards of Sheep's Fescue
Festuca ovina, Tor-grass *Brachypodium
pinnatum*, Upright Brome *Bromopsis
recta* and a wealth of flowers such as
Bird's-foot Trefoil *Lotus corniculatus*,
Harebell *Campanula glomerata*, Great
Knapweed *Centaurea scabiosa* and Salad
Burnet *Poterium sanguisorba*.

Urban and industrial sites also support a
wide range of vegetation. On expanses of
bare ground or rubble, tufts of colonising
grasses, especially Yorkshire Fog *Holcus
lanatus* and Creeping Bent *Agrostis
stolonifera* are the most ubiquitous
colonisers, but there is often a bewildering
wealth of flowering plants, almost always
at very low density which colonise
amongst the grasses. On old colliery and
industrial sites in the West Riding,
legumes such as Bird's-foot Trefoil, White
and Red Clovers *Trifolium repens* and *T.
pratense* and Lesser Trefoil *T. medium* can
be abundant. Perhaps more surprisingly is
the range of diminutive annuals and
ephemerals growing in sparse swards, the
most frequent being Thyme-leaved
Sandwort *Arenaria serpyllifolia*, but often
accompanied by species more typically
associated with coastal or inland sand
dunes and thin, parched soils. This
includes Annual Pearlwort *Sagina apetala
apetala*, Sand Spurrey *Spergularia rubra*,
Common Storksbill *Erodium cicutarium*,
Changing Forget-me-not *Myosotis
discolor*, Kidney Vetch *Anthyllis*

Grimethorpe Colliery Tip (1998) showing pioneer plants, with developing grassland and scrub.

vulneraria and Rest-harrow *Ononis repens*. The early phases of colonisation provide ideal butterfly habitats with rich nectar sources, and a microtopography and vegetation structure which complement patches of warm, bare ground.

As plant colonisation proceeds, many types of habitat can develop which generally reflect typical plant communities found elsewhere. Besides various types of grassland, fragments of heathland, swamp, open water, scrub and woodland communities can be found. On maturing, older sites, rich and complex mosaics of various habitats can provide a variety of niches. Even on sites which have been subject to modern restoration and landscaping, the resulting planted grasslands and young plantations are often left rough and unmanaged, providing niches in which butterflies can become established. For the lepidopterist, these are the most spectacular areas to visit, where rough maturing grasslands, dominated by meadow grasses and studded with plants such as Knapweed *Centaurea nigra*, Ragwort *Senecio jacobaea* and thistles *Cirsium* spp, can support huge numbers of the commoner butterflies.

On old colliery sites, the most frequently encountered species (in descending order) found in a study of the Yorkshire coalfield were Meadow Brown, Common Blue, Small Skipper, Small Heath, Peacock, Gatekeeper, Dingy Skipper, Small Tortoiseshell, Small Copper, Wall, Painted lady, Orange Tip, Large Skipper, Small White, Red Admiral, and Ringlet (Lunn, 2000). The populations of some species can be dramatic e.g. 379 Common Blues, 150 Gatekeepers and 134 Meadow Browns counted at Walton Nature Park, (formerly Walton Colliery) in 1997 (Frost & Winter, 1997).

One of the most significant and regularly encountered scarcer butterflies found on such sites is the Dingy Skipper, which requires Bird's-foot Trefoil as its foodplant, and frequent areas of sunny but sheltered bare ground, both of which are commonly found in wasteland areas. Since many 'brownfield' locations are unmanaged, this also means that the absence of grazing will produce more of the longest shoots of the large Bird's-foot plants preferred by the females for ovipositing (Asher *et al*, 2001), perhaps giving a clue as to why 'brownfield' sites are so attractive to this species. Despite the Dingy Skipper's sedentary nature, the presence of old railway routes, built for the transport of coal and other materials, has often aided a wider dispersal.

Two other uncommon Yorkshire species are notable for their liking of wasteland. The Grayling has recently been discovered at a number of 'brownfield' locations in the Middlesborough and Wakefield areas, possibly using railway land as a conduit for dispersal. The Brown Argus, which is colonising from the south, has also been recorded from 'brownfield' sites such as re-vegetating gravel workings where Common Storksbill, (a characteristic component of the 'Coversand Heath' vegetation, formerly found in southern Yorkshire and the Isle of Axholme), is the likely foodplant.

The value of 'brownfield' sites to the county's butterfly populations must be very significant. The abundance and distribution of quarries, old railway lines and industrial wasteland spans the whole region and cuts across all geological strata and altitudinal and climatic gradients. The main value of these sites may be as centres of production, especially for the commoner species such as Meadow Brown, Common Blue, Gatekeeper and

Small Skipper, which can then disperse outwards to colonise new areas. They are also important for maintaining populations of those species which require, or are greatly aided by, the varied microstructure of habitats, foodplants and physical features (such as bare ground) for their survival coupled with a virtual absence of intervention such as grazing, habitat management, pesticide and herbicide usage. Not only are they good places for the commoner species, but others such as skippers, Wall, Small Copper, Small Heath and Gatekeeper clearly find such sites to their liking. It is not surprising that they are often also good places for supporting large numbers of migrants and wanderers such as Red Admiral, Peacock, Painted Lady and, in good years, Clouded Yellow, as well as the rarer species detailed above.

'Brownfield' sites are by their very nature ephemeral, and subject to pressures for re-use and development. Since the demise of the coal mining industry, many large sites have been subjected to restoration, where the main aim has been to hide the previous industrial land-use by a standard, unimaginative and quick 'greening-over' project, usually with no consideration for any intrinsic or potential wildlife interest. The fine grained variation of topography, habitats and physical features – so important for a wealth of wildlife – is usually obliterated. The outlook for wildlife on many sites, particularly with potential for development in and around the towns and cities, is consequently poor. However, hopefully there will always be a 'stock' of other sites around. For butterflies, the continued difficulty of managing sites after restoration is a benefit, and it will be interesting to chart the development of the new rough grassland and young plantations.

An important human link is that many 'brownfield' sites are close to settlements, and are well used by people for casual recreation. Butterflies are a hugely attractive and exciting component of the enjoyment of such local amenities, and can and should be a first introduction to the natural world, helping to engender sympathy for the care and conservation of the local environment. We should treasure our wastelands!

Military brownfield site, Cowden (VC61)

After vehicles had churned up this area it sprouted masses of bird's-foot trefoil followed by a large colony of Common Blues.

Male Small Skipper

Butterflies and Plants

Aspects of Dynamic Change

David S Blakeley

NOTE

Butterflies need plants. Most of them lay their eggs on plants, often on a particular species or group of species. We refer to such a plant as the **hostplant** or larval **foodplant**. So when we refer to a butterfly foodplant (or just a 'foodplant') we mean the plant eaten by the larvae (or caterpillars), not the adult butterfly. The food of many adult butterflies is plant nectar, so we often refer to **butterfly nectar plants** (or just 'nectar plants') to indicate those species favoured by a particular butterfly. Butterflies may spend winter as eggs, larvae, pupae or adults, according to the species. In most cases they are dependent on having the right kind of plants situated close by (or for an adult, within flying distance) to enable them to hide away safely in winter. Butterflies are also grouped into **habitat generalists** (or **wider countryside species**) and **habitat specialists**. The former are generally mobile species which occur widely across the countryside and in urban areas, whilst the **habitat specialists** are relatively sedentary and largely confined to localised patches of suitable habitat.

We can hardly help noticing that the number of butterfly species we see around us has been changing a great deal in recent times. Less obvious is the fact that the plants on which they depend have also been changing. This is not a new process, but one dating back to Neolithic times and the first clearances for settlements. By 1086, only 15% of the original 'wildwood' cover originally found in Great Britain still remained (Robertson *et al* 1995), and today, only 2% is covered by natural woodland, plus a further 6% by planted coniferous or mixed woodlands. Many of the rarer butterflies we now treasure would have benefited from those early clearings, which would have increased the availability of larval foodplants like violets *Viola* spp. Most butterflies are lovers of grasslands (not just meadows or pastures but wherever grassy areas can develop), whilst a few live mainly in the canopy of woodlands. Some are generalists, able to use their favoured larval foodplants in a wide range of situations. Others are specialists, often dependent on a single hostplant species and with very specific needs.

In the more recent past, up to the latter part of the 19th century, many woodlands were coppiced to provide a regular and sustainable supply of timber. The work of coppicing opened up temporary clearings, which suited many butterflies and provided the ideal conditions for many of our fritillaries: sun, shelter, foodplants and nectar plants. As one coppiced area grew up and became unsuitable, so another would be created nearby, usually near enough for butterflies with limited mobility to locate it easily. After the 1st World War many old woodlands were felled and replaced with conifers. Initially, many woodland butterflies thrived in the cleared areas, but slowly shade began to increase and eventually many species of plants and butterflies simply disappeared, unable to tolerate the excessive shade. Today, our remnant population of two or three linked colonies of Pearl-bordered Fritillaries on the N York Moors is all that is left of a once much more widespread species. Woodlands have become so fragmented that such butterflies are unable to cover the distances needed to find another suitable area even if one exists. Fortunately, attitudes to woodland management are changing and the Forestry Commission is currently involved in many positive projects to remove conifers and open up woodlands once again.

Today's plant distributions result from a complex inter-relationship between man and nature. Morris (1853) highlights one of the county's more dramatic changes: *'The whole of the Yorkshire Wolds, now all enclosed, were sixty years ago, open downs with heath and gorse scattered*

Modern prairie landscape in the northern Wolds (2004) where once there was nothing but natural grassland.

here and there: it is but very little that is left. Then you could ride over the Wolds, so I'm told, from Driffield to Malton, twenty miles, without meeting a hedge or a gate – all was turf – fine old downs: now 'quantum mutatis' it is one of the principal corn-growing districts of England'. The traditional types of pastoral farming have, over hundreds of years, helped to shape the flora present in grassland, but such habitats are now in steep decline with most pastures having been ploughed out or re-sown with low diversity, high yield grass mixtures. Fortunately, there are still corners of the Wolds where you can glimpse the natural grasslands of the past, especially around Millington and Thixendale. Here too countryside stewardship agreements are encouraging the clearance of scrub and the maintenance of these pastures for their plants and insects.

Drainage has also played an important part in changing many habitats, few more marked perhaps than the reclamation of the Holderness marshes in the valley of the River Hull where the Swallowtail and Large Heath were found in the late 1700s. Thomas Stainforth (1919), writing about Cottingham (once at the edge of these marshes) in relation to the area being a favourite butterfly haunt visited by Thomas Stather (who died in 1878), notes: 'The Cottingham locality consisted of marsh, called Stainton Bogs, situated near the railway. Only a small area of this now exists, devoid of any special interest and serving as a convenient tipping place for garden refuse, but in the middle of the century past the Marsh Ringlet [ie the Large Heath] was common there. Near the marshes grew a wood of Scotch Pines…An odd gaunt pine or two still survive on the boundaries of allotments, draining and deforestation having done their work as in many other parts of Yorkshire…'

Within Yorkshire there is little or no truly 'wild' and untouched habitat remaining. Large areas of the Dales and N York Moors have been 'improved', with the removal of heather and scrub and the planting of grassland. Drainage has completely altered the Vales of York and Pickering and even sites like Skipwith and Strensall Commons, which appear to be untouched, have at some stage been used for human activity. Likewise, the peatlands of the Humberhead Levels (Thorne, Crowle, Goole and Hatfield), one of the most sensitive habitats in the county, have been considerably degraded to satisfy growing demands for peat. Large-scale peat removal has inevitably had a serious effect on species diversity and led to the apparent loss of the Large Heath butterfly on Hatfield Moors. Fortunately, this story is now being reversed as you can read in the Large Heath species chapter. Nor is human impact necessarily always a bad thing. Abandoned quarries and spoil heaps left over from mining can be amongst the most important habitats for plants and butterflies, providing areas which nature can reclaim, using colonising plants like Bird's-foot Trefoil Lotus corniculatus (amongst many others). This in turn supports species such as the Dingy Skipper.

It is often forgotten that within every landscape the composition of plant species is dynamic. It is constantly changing and moving towards a climax which is usually a forest, except where this is prevented by the harsher climate induced by height or higher latitudes, or where 'management' or man's 'interference' (such as controlled grazing or annual ploughing and planting) intervenes. Grazing by rabbits can also have an important effect. In addition, coastal and river margins tend to be dominated by plants adapted to disturbance, since these habitats are more liable to change. Any area of grassland left to its own devices will eventually revert to scrub, isolated trees will appear, and eventually the whole area will become woodland. Within these broad changes are many others, less obvious, as plants battle with one another for dominance. Butterflies may often need to adapt to habitats which are not exactly the same from one year to another.

A good example of dynamic change is often found along disused railway lines. Many of these were abandoned in the 1960s (following the 1963 Beeching Report) and had verges which were open and grassed. They were ideal butterfly habitats, providing linking routes which species could colonise and potentially use as habitat corridors. But in the 40+ years since, they have developed through increasing stages of scrubbiness until now they are primarily woodland patches, which shade out grassland growth, and restrict the easy movement of butterflies along their lengths. As a result, a rich butterfly fauna has often become severely depleted, leaving the tracks in need of considerable management if this situation is to be reversed. Unfortunately, the cutting down of shrubs and trees is often misunderstood by the public, even though this may be the best approach to increasing the biodiversity of disused railway tracks.

GENERALISTS AND SPECIALISTS

Of the 36 species currently breeding annually (or almost annually) in Yorkshire, 22 are usually considered habitat generalists (or wider countryside species), 11 are specialists with specific needs which limit their distribution, and 3 are migrants (and also generalists). On the whole, the resident generalists occupy a similar range to that mapped for their hostplants, but the same is not true for the specialists, the ranges of which may have become isolated by the increased fragmentation of their habitats. They may also require a specific set of features within their habitat, such as a warm south-facing slope, a particular mixture of plant heights or the right kind of leaf litter to provide cover for their larvae, all of which may restrict the use of their full hostplant range.

Some species considered habitat generalists nationally are more suitably classed as specialists in Yorkshire, conceivably as a result of their being on, or close to, the edge of their ranges. The Marbled White is a case in point. In Yorkshire we think of it as largely restricted to chalk or limestone habitats, whilst in southern England it is found across many habitats. The Brown Argus is also a generalist in S England being able to utilise wild geranium species as well as Rock-rose *Helianthemum numularium*, but until recently in Yorkshire was restricted to Rock-rose in chalk and limestone areas, much the same as its near relative the Northern Brown Argus. However, Brown Argus colonisers have been moving in from the south, introducing their generalist approach to life, which may eventually influence our more sedentary populations.

In considering butterfly hostplants it is necessary to be cautious. Lists in butterfly books (our own included!) are often compiled from many sources and may include continental plant species not used by the butterfly in the British Isles. There is, in fact, still a lot to find out about this subject, and an investigation into the foodplants used by Yorkshire butterflies would be of considerable interest. Breeders of butterflies can often rear a species on plants the butterfly itself would never choose to use in the wild, and sometimes such plants are included in published hostplant lists. Isolated populations of butterflies tend to adapt to a specific plant, or range of plants, which is a subset of those used by the same species in less isolated environments. This may even involve ignoring normally acceptable plants. Experiments have shown that where larvae have been taken from an area traditionally using one suite of hostplants, and transferred to an area using another, they have not developed as well (Singer 1989).

Butterflies seem to be equally choosy about nectar plants, with the result that some plant species recommended as attracting butterflies to gardens may be completely ignored, perhaps because the attraction is more regionally localised than the compiler of the list realised. Garden plants that attract one year may fail to do so the following year. Perhaps the quality of nectar produced varies more than we can judge.

CLIMATE CHANGE

Global warming is already giving us rising temperatures, which should be good for butterflies. However, the effects could be much more profound, as plants are also subject to the same environmental controls. Evidence in the *Atlas of British Flora* (Perring & Walters 1990) suggests that northern (Arctic/Boreal) species are retreating northward whilst those associated with Mediterranean distributions are increasing their ranges. This could well help to encourage generalist butterfly species to spread further northward, but it might spell disaster for habitat specialists like the Large Heath and the Northern Brown Argus which in Yorkshire are on the southern edge of their ranges. The generalist butterflies currently widely distributed in the county could find themselves benefiting or being disadvantaged, according to the way their hostplants respond to climate change. The recent widespread crash in Wall populations across S England, at a time when the species has been expanding in Yorkshire, may be a case in point.

There could also be problems with commonly used nectar plants, some of which (eg thistles *Cirsium* spp) are already showing signs of flowering increasingly out of phase with the flight periods of some of the butterflies which favour them. Long hot summers leave grasslands parched and dry, with little nectar for adults and no suitable foliage for larvae. There are likely to be more subtle effects as well, resulting from changes in the composition of plant species within specific habitats. Habitat specialists may not be able to adapt quickly enough to such changes.

Warm spells in winter (such as we had in 1998 when a total of 66 butterflies were recorded across the county on 14/02) may increasingly affect the timing of adult emergence, leading to problems if there are no nectar plants available to support these early appearances. In addition there appears to be a trend towards an increase in the length of butterfly flight seasons, with adults on the wing both earlier and later in the season. It is likely that plants are already following similar trends, growing, flowering and setting seed earlier than before, and running the risk of being out of phase with butterflies which depend upon them. This could be of critical importance to species which overwinter as larvae. A decline in plant quality in late summer when larvae are building up stores for winter could result in increased larval mortality, or weaken the subsequent adults.

In altering the plant composition on any given site, climate change may favour strong-growing species with no particular value to butterflies, especially in the increasingly wet weather we have been experiencing recently. Such species may even take over from important hostplant species resulting in the degradation of some habitats. In turn this might reduce the diversity of butterfly species present. Butterflies are much more careful about how they select a breeding site than might appear. One important key to their choice is the need to maintain adequate body temperatures (thermoregulation), so butterflies search for sheltered, sunny sites where the plant composition is just right. In spring adults prefer to thermoregulate close to the ground, protected from cool temperatures by the vegetation. Later in

Yorkshire Species: Generalist **Specialist** *Italics = migrant & generalist*	No. of Yorks. Tetrads 1995/ 2003	% of total 3319 recorded tetrads
Small Tortoiseshell	2131	64.2
Green-veined White	2109	63.5
Small White	2061	62.1
Peacock	1922	57.9
Large White	1899	57.2
Meadow Brown	1760	53.0
Red Admiral	1508	45.4
Orange-tip	1386	41.8
Painted Lady	1348	40.6
Ringlet	1128	34.0
Small Skipper	1098	33.1
Wall Brown	1084	32.7
Comma	1061	32.0
Small Copper	890	26.8
Gatekeeper	843	25.4
Common Blue	770	23.2
Small Heath	753	22.7
Holly Blue	724	21.8
Large Skipper	682	20.5
Brimstone	525	15.8
Speckled Wood	451	13.6
Green Hairstreak	284	8.6
Purple Hairstreak	281	8.5
White-letter Hairstreak	248	7.5
Marbled White	161	4.9
Clouded Yellow	156	4.7
Dingy Skipper	102	3.1
Brown Argus	75	2.3
Small Pearl-bordered Fritillary	53	1.6
Dark Green Fritillary	50	1.5
Northern Brown Argus	42	1.3
Large Heath	20	0.6
Duke of Burgundy	13	0.4
Grayling	9	0.3
Essex Skipper	5	0.2
Pearl-bordered Fritillary	4	0.1

he season they switch to the top of the vegetation and in some cases actively seek cooler situations to avoid overheating (Shreeve 1992). Females usually select egg-laying sites with great care to provide feeding and overwintering opportunities for their offspring. Butterfly conservation work is not just a case of encouraging the spread of a particular foodplant, but requires the creation of a whole mosaic of suitable habitat.

AGRICULTURE AND PLANTS

Agriculture forms a dominant feature in the Yorkshire landscape, and since the late 1940s there has been a significant intensification in the way farmland has been managed, partly in response to government policy, but also due to improved technology. This has led to many larger and more specialised farms. Inevitably intensification has had serious effects on farmland biodiversity, with the loss of up to 50% of hedgerows and a significant decline in unimproved grassland meadows compared to 1935. Between 1945 and 1999, the number of farms decreased by 35% and in 1999, 6% of farms covered more than 200 hectares (500 acres) (Robinson & Sutherland 2002). One consequence has been the increase in the size of fields and the attendant loss of hedgerows.

Hedgerows which remain are invariably heavily managed to maintain a 'tidy landscape'. There has also been a significant trend towards smaller headlands within arable fields, further reducing the potential habitat available to those plants and butterflies normally associated with farmland landscapes. Headlands, ditch banks and track verges can also provide important butterfly egg-laying and nectaring sites, as well as corridors to other habitats. However, the outlook for headlands appears to be changing with new ways of subsidising farming to encourage their spread. Sensitive restoration and management, with the sowing of seed mixes designed to attract butterflies and other insects, could provide an important means of reversing some aspects of the fragmentation of the countryside. However, experiments in the Flamborough area have shown that this form of conservation is not as simple as it sounds, due to the highly fertile nature of our fields producing too lush a growth of wild plants sown (pers comm. Howard Frost). Many butterflies seek out the finer grasses and more lowly nectar plants which may not grow readily in such a competitive situation. The timing and degree of mowing such sites may be extremely important, with a need to remove the cut material to progressively reduce fertility.

Additional references: Porter *et al* (1992), Preston *et al* (2002), Shreeve (1986).

Butterflies are especially attracted to wild corners with thistles. Here you can compare Comma (above) with Small Tortoiseshell.

Controlled grazing is good for plants and
butterflies. Kiplingcotes YWT NR.

Action to Conserve

Sam Ellis

Butterfly Conservation's North East England Regional Action Plan

Butterfly Conservation has highlighted the main conservation priorities for butterfly species and habitats in Yorkshire, through the development of a Regional Action Plan (RAP) for North East England (1st edition 1999, 2nd edition 2000), encompassing Vice-Counties 61-68 (East Yorkshire, North Yorkshire, South Yorkshire, West Yorkshire, North-west Yorkshire, Cleveland, County Durham, Tyne and Wear and Northumberland). The RAP was produced as part of the **Action for Butterflies Project**, which aims to place all the work of Butterfly Conservation within both a national and regional framework.

The first stage of the plan was to identify those butterflies most at risk, as well as key areas and sites in the region supporting populations of those threatened species. Nationally, Butterfly Conservation had already graded species as low, medium or high priority depending upon the degree of threat. Using the *Butterflies for the New Millenium* database, the priority of each species was raised at the regional level, if one or more of the following four criteria were met:

1. The estimated rate of decline was greater than 32% loss of 10 km² over the last 25 years.

2. The species occupied less than 0.6% of the tetrads in the region.

3. The region held greater than 20% of the total number of British records for a species.

4. The species had a restricted geographical distribution within the region.

Six species were identified as high priority and under the greatest threat (criteria used to change regional status from national priority in brackets): **Grizzled Skipper** (1, 2 - probably extinct), **Northern Brown Argus**, **Duke of Burgundy** (1, 2), **Small Pearl-bordered Fritillary** (2), **Pearl-bordered fritillary** (1, 2) and **Grayling** (1, 2). A further six species were classified as medium priority: **Dingy Skipper** (4), **Green Hairstreak** (4), **Purple Hairstreak** (4), **White-letter Hairstreak**, **Dark Green Fritillary** (4) and **Large Heath**. It should also be noted that the RAP does include moths, with twelve species identified as high priority: Chalk Carpet, Argent and Sable, Scarce Pug, Dark Bordered Beauty, Narrow-bordered Bee Hawk-moth, Scarce Vapourer, Lunar Yellow Underwing, Northern Dart, Square-spotted Clay, Bordered Gothic, Sword Grass and Least Minor.

Six key areas were identified in the region, with three in Yorkshire. By far the most important is the **North York Moors**, supporting nine priority species, including all the region's Duke of Burgundy and Pearl-bordered Fritillary colonies, as well as significant number of Small Pearl-bordered and Dark Green Fritillary sites. A diverse range of butterfly habitats are found on the Moors including, heathland, wet acid grassland and valley mires in the uplands, and a mosaic of limestone grassland, bracken, scrub and woodland on the southern and western edges. The other two key areas are the **Yorkshire Dales** (Wensleydale, Wharfedale and the Craven Limestones) and the **Yorkshire Wolds**. A further seventeen smaller sites were also identified as supporting populations of key species including Spurn Point, Thorne and Hatfield Moors, Hugset Woods, Skipwith Common, Allerthorpe Common, Strensall Common and Clapham-Austwick Mosses in Yorkshire.

The second stage of the plan was to devise a set of actions and targets to safeguard all colonies of high and medium priority species through appropriate management and also to identify and implement further survey, monitoring and research as required. Actions and targets for high priority species have been planned for the five years from 1999, and those for medium priority butterflies over the ten years from that year.

The Butterflies of Yorkshire

Each priority butterfly (and moth) has a separate species plan. The summary below represents the types of actions proposed, although obviously not all are appropriate to each species:

1. Protect all surviving populations of high and medium priority species - through site designation as SSSIs or County Wildlife Sites as appropriate.

2. Undertake survey work to determine the current status of all high and medium priority species in areas where this is unknown or doubtful.

3. Continue to monitor all current butterfly transects providing a high or medium priority species is present.

4. Establish transects or undertake timed counts on at least two key sites for each high and medium priority species.

5. Implement or encourage implementation of appropriate management regimes which maintain or enhance breeding areas of high and medium priority species - through SSSI management agreements (e.g. Wildlife Enhancement Scheme) or other agri-environment schemes (e.g. Countryside Stewardship) on non-SSSI land. The plan includes a separate section on habitat management. Nine habitat types are recognised as of particular concern for butterflies: magnesian limestone (County Durham), chalk grassland (Yorkshire Wolds), oolitic limestone grassland (North York Moors), carboniferous limestone grassland (Yorkshire Dales), woodlands, heathland, bracken/violet-rich grassland, mires and sand dunes. General management guidelines are provided for each of these, including the main provisions of existing agri-environment schemes designed specifically to conserve them.

6. Undertake or encourage ecological research, through universities and colleges, which may assist the long-term conservation of high and medium priority species.

7. Seek opportunities to restore suitable habitat in the former range of high priority species to encourage recolonisation from occupied sites.

8. Consider strategic introductions to suitable habitat in the former range of high priority species if natural recolonisation is unlikely - programmes should take account of Butterfly Conservation's Code of Practice on Lepidoptera Restoration.

Writing a Regional Action Plan is, of course, the easy part. The real challenge is to implement the actions. Butterfly Conservation members will be able to undertake some of the survey and monitoring work, but as a relatively small organisation, with few nature reserves, the majority of land management actions will require the co-operation of other individuals and organisations. A common theme throughout the RAP is therefore liaison with all the possible partners who might contribute to the implementation of the actions. Butterfly Conservation aims to provide feedback on survey work, monitoring, research and land management to these partners, and to build on existing relationships in the region. The RAP is already providing the framework to prioritise the conservation actions of Butterfly Conservation and its partners, and it is hoped this will continue for many years to come.

Methods Used For Assigning Regional Priorities

Criteria 1. Rates of decline estimates

Table 1 lists the butterfly species showing increases and declines in the region when 10 km² records from 1970-1982 (taken from Heath, Pollard and Thomas 1984) are compared with 10 km² records for 1995 to 1998. Estimated declines are calculated for a 25-year period and where they exceed 32% at the 10km² level, the national priority is increased. Species whose regional priorities have been increased as a result of applying this criterion are highlighted in magenta. Where a species has increased its range it is indicated by (+). The recent records for the Grizzled Skipper are unconfirmed.
See Table 1.

Criteria 2. Rarity Estimates.

The rarity of the species within the region was assessed by calculating the number of tetrads occupied as a proportion of the total number within the region. If less than 0.6% of the tetrads in the region are occupied by a species then its priority is increased above its national rating. Species showing a change in priority as a result of this criterion are shown in magenta.
See Table 2.

Total number of regional tetrads is 6125 including those on the borders of the region. There are records for 2306 of these tetrads (38%). Where a species occupies <1% of region's tetrads, the loss of a few colonies may result in a change in their priority. The recent records for the Grizzled Skipper are unconfirmed.

Criteria 3. Proportion of Total National Resource.

Where a region holds more than 20% of the total number of British records for a particular species its priority should be increased above the national rating. No species in the N of England region meet this criterion.

Table 1. Estimated rates of increase and decline for butterflies in the North East England region 1973-1998 approx.

Species	10 km² records (1970-82)	10 km² records (1995-1998)	25 yr. decline/ increase estimate
Small Skipper	80	143	(+) 123%
Large Skipper	128	139	(+) 13%
Dingy Skipper	39	38	(-) 4%
Grizzled Skipper	5	2?	(-) 94%
Clouded Yellow	3	25	(+) 1146%
Brimstone	38	58	(+) 82%
Large White	230	201	(-) 20%
Small White	227	216	(-) 8%
Green-veined White	241	222	(-) 12%
Orange Tip	172	193	(+) 19%
Green Hairstreak	36	47	(+) 48%
Purple Hairstreak	2	24	(+) 1719%
White-letter Hairstreak	21	34	(+) 97%
Small Copper	172	171	(-) 1%
Brown Argus	2	5	(+) 234%
Northern Brown Argus	9	18	(+) 156%
Common Blue	175	174	(-) 1%
Holly Blue	8	93	(+) 1660%
Duke of Burgundy	5	3	(-) 63%
Red Admiral	153	209	(+) 57%
Painted Lady	111	168	(+) 80%
Small Tortoiseshell	236	237	(+) 1%
Peacock	145	217	(+) 78%
Comma	8	148	(+) 2734%
Small Pearl-bordered Fritillary	9	17	(+) 139%
Pearl-bordered Fritillary	4	2	(-) 78%
Dark Green Fritillary	14	22	(+) 89%
Speckled Wood	7	29	(+) 491%
Wall	133	132	(-) 1%
Marbled White	6	36	(+) 781%
Grayling	7	4	(-) 67%
Gatekeeper	25	79	(+) 338%
Meadow Brown	214	204	(-) 7%
Ringlet	73	141	(+) 146%
Small Heath	179	166	(-) 11%
Large Heath	16	26	(+) 98%

Table 2. Rarity estimates for butterflies in the North East England region: 1995-1998 statistics.

Species	Total no. tetrad records in region	Regional Rarity (%)	Rarity (% of recorded tetrads)	Occupies <0.6% of area
Small Skipper	567	9.3	24.6	
Large Skipper	411	6.7	17.8	
Dingy Skipper	88	1.4	3.8	
Grizzled Skipper	2?	0.1?	0.1?	YES
Clouded Yellow	39	0.64	1.7	
Brimstone	130	2.1	5.6	
Large White	922	15.1	40.0	
Small White	934	15.2	40.5	
GV White	1133	18.5	49.1	
Orange Tip	776	12.7	33.7	
Green Hairstreak	80	1.3	3.5	
Purple Hairstreak	42	0.7	1.8	
White-letter Hairstreak	56	0.9	2.4	
Small Copper	511	8.3	22.2	
Brown Argus	11	0.2	0.5	
NB Argus	48	0.8	2.1	
Common Blue	584	9.5	25.3	
Holly Blue	286	4.7	12.4	
Duke of Burgundy	7	0.1	0.3	YES
Red Admiral	672	11.0	29.1	
Painted Lady	423	6.9	20.5	
Small Tortoiseshell	1244	20.3	53.9	
Peacock	1005	16.4	43.6	
Comma	426	7.0	18.5	
Small Pearl-bordered Fritillary	38	0.6	1.6	YES
Pearl-bordered Fritillary	4	0.1	0.2	YES
Dark Green Fritillary	40	0.7	1.7	
Speckled Wood	61	1.0	2.6	
Wall	436	7.1	18.9	
Marbled White	87	1.4	3.8	
Grayling	8	0.1	0.4	YES
Gatekeeper	264	4.3	11.4	
Meadow Brown	1050	17.1	45.5	
Ringlet	472	7.7	20.5	
Small Heath	537	8.8	23.3	
Large Heath	107	1.7	4.6	

Painted Lady

Butterfly Migration in Yorkshire

Some Mysteries to Solve

Howard M Frost

Many years ago, I was staying at Spurn Bird Observatory during August and logging birds heading south, from the vantage point of the 'Narrow Neck', about half way along the peninsula. Suddenly, I became aware that a stream of insects had begun to move south, on the east (or seaward) side of the line of dunes that make up Spurn. There were bees, hoverflies, dragonflies and every now and then, one or more butterflies: quite a few Red Admirals and Small Tortoiseshells, the occasional Peacock and Painted Lady, and even a single Brimstone. What really amazed me was the way that all these insects were moving in a narrow space below the dunes and about 2m above the beach. It was as though there was an invisible pipeline along which they were all passing.

In more recent times I have become aware that migrations like these are a regular feature at Spurn, usually occurring in late August and early September when light south-westerly winds are blowing on warm, sunny days. This tends to restrict movements to between about 10.30hrs and 14.00hrs, but they can go on for longer or shorter times according to the weather conditions. It is thought that bird movements, which follow the line of the peninsula, often result from a funnelling effect, caused by the shape of the coastline and the northern bank of the Humber Estuary. The theory implies that birds follow visual cues and try to avoid having to travel over water. Does this apply to insects as well? If so where and why do they start coming together into such an obvious migratory flow? The fact that Spurn National Nature Reserve covers parts of 14x1km squares does not make this easy to study!

Observations at Spurn indicate that butterflies typically pass by at a rate of 50/60 per hour. In 1997, between 21/08 and 09/09 a huge migration of Small Tortoiseshells occurred along the east coast with between 2,000 and 5,000 being seen each day. My wife and I did a 1¹/₂ hr count at the Spurn Narrow Neck on 28/08 and discovered to our surprise that Small Tortoiseshells were actually moving northward **and** southward at the same time, something we had never observed before. Even stranger, was the way the two streams of movement were virtually on the same track, flying along the same invisible pipeline. As a result, from time to time two individuals would actually meet head on, with dramatic results! The two would spiral upward out of the shelter of the dunes and into the rather brisk SW wind, only to get blown eastward and out to sea! In the 1¹/₂ hr period we noted

113 fly south, 238 north, and 24 disappeared out to sea. It is not easy to see butterflies against seawater, but I managed to follow one through binoculars to a point a few hundred metres out and was amazed to see it drop down, close to the water, and begin tacking back at an angle of about 45° to the shore. Then I walked northward fast enough to keep up with it and see it return to the beach about 500m from the point at which it was blown away. So at least one saved itself from a long journey or a watery grave. I wonder how the others fared?

Observers at Spurn have sometimes questioned whether these movements are a part of bigger migrations, or just local movements along the 4mls of the peninsula. So on the occasion detailed above we also travelled the extra two miles to the tip of the peninsula to see what was happening there. We were able to confirm that Small Tortoiseshells were indeed moving in both directions across the five miles of open water to and from Tetney Haven on the Lincolnshire side of the Estuary. Interestingly, we also discovered that those coming northward with the wind behind them were coming in low over the water, whilst those heading south, into the wind, flew low over the wide beach marking the tip of Spurn, but rose high in the air as soon as they found themselves over water (so high that they quickly disappeared even to the binocular view). A *New Scientist* news report (02/11/1996 p18) drew attention to an American study by Robert Srygley and colleagues of the University of Washington, which noticed that butterflies migrating short distances across water (up to 1.5km in the study) flew in straight lines. They argued that this indicated they were not navigating by fixing on a single visual landmark ahead, otherwise, when they were affected by crosswinds, they would fly in a curved path. Instead, it was suggested they might be using two landmarks, and navigating to minimise the apparent motion between them. Alternatively, they might use the apparent motion of the surface water as a guide. Long distance migrants might also navigate by using the earth's magnetic

View of estuary from tip of Spurn, with Grimsby and Cleethorpes just visible on the other side.

field. All these possibilities seem to suggest that butterflies are capable of higher levels of processing information than previously realised.

On occasion, Holly Blues have been seen flying in from the Humber Estuary, or the sea, near the tip of Spurn, and this, added to a scatter of reports along Yorkshire's east coast of Holly Blues coming in from the sea, raises further questions about what exactly is happening here. The Holly Blue is not normally thought of as a migrant, although it does periodically expand northward when populations in the south do well. However, before 1990, the Holly Blue had been largely absent from the eastern half of Yorkshire since 1971 or earlier. Then on a single day in 1991, 300 or more suddenly appeared at Spurn, and since then further smaller, but significant arrivals have taken place, with some observers having seen them flying in from the S or SE and coming up the beach. The big question is where are they coming from? The most likely answer would be from Tetney, just across the Estuary. One could imagine some of these butterflies getting slightly blown off course, and like the Small Tortoiseshell described above, having to tack back again, with the result that they end up flying in from the east. It would also seem possible that they might collect together along the N Norfolk coast and head north-westward across the open sea. There are records of Holly Blues reaching some of the many oil and gas rigs in this part of the N Sea. Are rig records the result of British butterflies being blown offshore, or migrants investigating potential landfalls? Could they even be continental Holly Blues heading for Britain? As yet no-one appears to have reported Holly Blues massing at coastal sites to the south of us. So, many mysteries remain!

Green Hairstreaks are not normally thought of as migrants, yet they appear to have expanded northward along the Lincolnshire coast in recent years and have managed to fly that extra distance across the Humber Estuary to establish a small colony at Spurn, as indeed have Essex Skipper and Brown Argus. Purple and White-letter Hairstreaks also appear to have expanded: yet we rarely get a glimpse of any cross-country movements. But then, would we even recognise such a species out of context? When my wife and I encountered a small brown butterfly on Withernsea promenade one cloudy and blustery July day, we immediately thought, Ringlet. Had we not managed to make a lucky grab and catch it by hand, it would have disappeared through the railings and out to sea, and we would have been completely unaware that it was a White-letter Hairstreak, at least a dozen miles from the nearest known colony. (It now accounts for a dot on the national map not linked to any known colony site!)

There are days when migration is visible across the wider countryside. It is possible to see Peacocks and Small Tortoiseshells heading across country and all going in the same direction, roughly NW in spring and SE in late summer. A big arrival of Painted Ladies, as we had in 1996 can be quite dramatic. One report from a garden near York estimated some 14,000 Painted Ladies passed through in a single day, and in one long line! This figure may have been exaggerated, but it illustrates a similar phenomenon to that experienced at Spurn, although in this case it is not related to moving along a sheltered 'pipeline'. The ability of some species to fly considerable distances in long lines, more or less one behind the other is intriguing. How does it come about? I saw a smaller example during the same immigration where some 70 Painted Ladies arrived at Welwick Strays just up the river from Spurn. They arrived in ones and twos over about 40 minutes and were on a north-westerly track. Had they flown the N Sea on the same track, or had they come up the Lincolnshire coast to Tetney and headed across the Estuary in this direction, rather than fly across the shortest distance to Spurn first? If so, why? Could they be locked into a magnetic line of force? At other times butterflies migrate in broad fronts, or thinly spread in ones and twos over many square miles. What are the factors, which result in one kind of movement rather than another?

Of our regular long-distance migrants, there is evidence that Red Admirals and Clouded Yellows attempt to return to S Europe in the autumn, but the Painted Lady seems much less inclined to do so. Is it possible that we could be missing something here? As reported in the Peacock chapter, Brian Morland has noticed Peacocks migrating under cover of darkness. Quite a few observers who run moth traps have caught Red Admirals and other species from time to time. During the 1996 Painted Lady invasion, movements were reported as continuing until too dark to observe. Although we tend to think of butterflies as creatures of the daytime, it may be that in suitable conditions they not infrequently travel by night. Is it possible that Painted Ladies choose to return southward by night and high up, and are, therefore, overlooked? Unlikely, perhaps, but how would we know?

We urge future recorders to look out for and to take note of any butterfly movements they see, and to report them together with details of the weather and wind direction. In this way we might be able to build up a volume of information, that could help to throw light on some of the mysteries of butterfly migration, which take place around us.

Spurn provides an unusual setting for both resident and migrant butterfly species.

Nick Lawman

Wykeham Forest 1992

Variations
in the
Green Hairstreak
Could we be missing something?

David and Stuart Wise

The Green Hairstreak 'normally' has green underwings with a curving line of tiny white dots on the lower underwing and no dots on the upper underwings. There are also two varieties which are fairly common on some sites: *punctata* in which the dots become more like dashes or streaks and extend to the upper underwing; and *caecus* which is variably described as having one dot only or no dots at all. The version with no dots at all seems to be virtually non-existent and we have yet to find a specimen or see a photograph of a specimen than can certainly be put in this category. Close perusal of possible specimens invariably reveals a few pale scales, which are either a reduced dot, or one which has been partially worn away. A whole range of spot variation is found in between the *caecus* and *punctata* extremes.

We would like to encourage more observers to question the meaning of these variations. For a start, are we really dealing with one pure species, or might we actually have a mixture, or even more than one? Tolman & Lewington (Collins 1997) draw attention to an interesting fact which might just possibly be relevant. They infer that on the continent *punctata* tends to be found where the habitats of the Green Hairstreak *Callophrys rubi* and Chapman's Green Hairstreak *Callophrys avis* (thought to be restricted to southern Europe) overlap! (These are the only two European green hairstreaks.)

Interestingly, the seven species of Green Hairstreak in North America are also the subject of some controversy. Many American lepidopterists are not sure if they can be classified as separate species. In *The Audubon Society Field Guide to North American Butterflies*, Robert M Pyle (1981) notes, '*As a group, the green hairstreaks of the genus Callophrys are difficult to identify; even specialists differ on exactly which species should be recognised. Most of these species seem to intergrade with each other to some degree in one place or another.*' Just as in Europe, the variations are in the spotting. The situation regarding 'intergrades' seems to be similar to that now being researched in the Brown Argus group in Europe! It is also intriguing that some of the American Green Hairstreaks look so like our own. The British *caecus* form looks very much like the American Bramble Green Hairstreak *Callophrys dumetorum* and indeed some American lepidopterists regard our own species as a sub-species of the Bramble Green Hairstreak! The American Immaculate Green Hairstreak *Callophrys affinis* is also remarkably similar in looks to our own *punctata* variation.

The second question we would like to see addressed is why there seem to be so many variant Green Hairstreaks in the Pennine area near Bradford (VC63) and why *punctata* and *caecus* seem to be dominant in separate areas. Emmet & Heath (Harley Books 1989) suggest that spots on the underside wings are extended to the forewing in about 20% of any given population. However, our impression from searching the area to the south-west of Bradford, is that this can be as high as 60%. In June 2000 we visited the steep south-facing hillsides which run some 18 miles from the fairly high, bleak part of the Pennines near the M62 Yorkshire/Lancashire border, then along the valley of the River Ryburn, and across Caldervale, and Shibden Dale to Shibden Head and the outskirts of Bradford. We were unable to find one 'typical' specimen of Green Hairstreak. The dominant form was *caecus*, with *punctata* noted occasionally, but most of these had spots which were weakly formed and at times barely visible.

We find it intriguing that *punctata* tends to be the dominant variety to the north and north-west of the urban region of Bradford, especially around Otley Chevin, whilst to the south-west you tend to find *caecus* in the area described above. Is this a product of sheer chance or are there as yet unseen environmental factors at work? Could it be, for instance, that the prevailing westerly winds have played a major part in the distribution of the *caecus*

Green Hairstreak on emerging hawthorn: Gill Brow, west of the Chevin (Otley VC64), 23/05/2001.

Green Hairstreak nectaring on gorse which may also be used for egg laying. Gill Brow (Otley VC64), 21/05/2001.

Green Hairstreak on the fringes of Oats Royd NR, Ambler Thorn, Bradford (VC63). The industrial estates fringing Halifax are vaguely visible in the distance.

Well-marked Green Hairstreak *punctata* variation. The disguise is near perfect here, even down to matching the reddish brown fringe of the bilberry leaf.

variety? All the colonies so far discovered follow through on a SW/NE line from Oldham (Lancs), west of the Pennines, to Bradford, on the east, so the spread could have been wind assisted.

The third area in which we would like to see more study is in the green colouration of the underwings. This is a butterfly which invariably perches with wings closed and therefore presents itself as green. Once we expect the Green Hairstreak to be green we tend to become blind to any subtle differences in tint. We probably also dismiss any tint variations in our photographs as variation in the quality of the film or its processing. John Wacker of Cornwall wrote to us with his memories of large Green Hairstreak colonies on the North Downs near

Canterbury in the late 1930s. He recalled that there, they were often found on the edges of beech woods and *'they exactly matched the colour of fresh beech leaves'*. Early in 2000 we had a phone call from Susan Stead of Eldwick (Bingley) to say that she had discovered Green Hairstreaks in Deepcliffe Woods near Harden in the Bradford Metropolitan District and that they were a beautiful shade close to *'viridian green'*. Susan's observation puzzled us, but her colour sensitivity proved acute. Checking a colour chart, viridian, with its hint of blueness, initially seemed an inappropriate choice of colour, especially when compared to set specimens in museums and to book illustrations.

We checked through available guides discovering that Emmet & Heath (1989) described the colour as *'metallic green'*. Thomas & Lewington (1991) described it as having a *'velvety look'*. Sanders (1939) noted the colour to be *'a perfect camouflage when it is sitting still among leaves'*. However, at Otley Chevin on 28/05/2000, during the only brief period of sunshine for two weeks, we also came across examples which could be described as viridian, making them highly visible as they basked on the bilberry and young oaks. The near faultless cryptic colouration had for the moment been abandoned.

It seems likely that the success of the Green Hairstreak as a species has a great deal to do with its cryptic colouration. But we wonder if the bluish tinge of the viridian shade could be a signal of a mutual readiness to mate. The fact that the species is visible to us (and presumably to insectivorous birds) in this shade, could mean that they are also more visible to one another, perhaps at a considerable distance. R B Morris (1975) studied the iridescence qualities of Green Hairstreaks in the lab and showed that the green underside wings have a perforated lattice visible under the electron microscope. Theoretically this lets light through onto the underlying melanin layer, which absorbs or attenuates light of a blue or other colour cast, so that the overall green iridescence is maintained whatever the angle of the wing.

This is all well and good in the laboratory, but it doesn't account for the fact that on a sunny bank side covered in bilberry in late May, the wings of this butterfly can turn 'viridian'. Could the lab experiments have overlooked the possibility that in direct sunshine, the transparent wing membrane might be responsible for trapping and scattering the shorter blue waves of light which, when mixed with the green of the wing scales might produce the viridian effect? Is there a possibility that this colour change could be an essential part of the reproduction of the species because it is only at this moment that the butterflies can be sure they have correctly identified each other? Or is it just a chance reflection or refraction of light?

We are not trained scientists but rather enthusiasts with wide ranging interests, and our various ideas may well be questioned, but at the very least, we hope our thoughts will encourage others to look, to think and to wonder, not just about this species, but also about all the others. Once you have learned to identify them all, there is so much more to learn and to marvel at. Watch a Green Hairstreak fly low over the greenery and you might just pick up a hint of reddish brown. Apart from its heat absorbent capacity, the brown melanin pigment on the upperside wings appears to serve no purpose. But look again as the butterfly skims the bilberries and you will notice that the hint of reddish brown blends with the pale crimson bilberry flowers. Also at this time of the year between April and early June, the new shoots of leaves, particularly bilberry and oak (much favoured as a perch), have a typical reddish tinge from the absorption of soil nutrients prior to the full development of green pigment in the leaves. The Green Hairstreak is a master of disguise!

Additional references: Emmet & Heath (1989), Sanders (1939) Thomas & Lewington (1991), Wise & Wise, (2000), Wise & Wise (2001).

David and Stuart Wise

Gill Brow near Otley showing how close to the town the butterfly comes.

Grayling

Introductions
A Need to Stop and Think

What are we talking about? Introductions involve catching a butterfly species on one site and releasing it on another, where it has never been recorded before, but within its natural geographical range. Re-introductions are similar, but involve releasing the species on a site where it had previously existed but had become extinct. We refer to 'private', 'unofficial' or 'casual introductions', where this is done on the whim of an individual, and 'official introductions' where these are conducted by organisations in co-operation with all the relevant parties that might have an interest in such a project. We also speak of unauthorised introductions/re-introductions, particularly where these are undertaken without obtaining the permission of the owners of the donor and receptor sites.

Why do it? Over the last century we have lost many butterfly species, whilst others, once much more common, have become relatively rare. Everyone involved in releases would like to see the situation reversed. Unfortunately, the issues involved are often far more complicated than appear at first sight, and those involved in casual releases may actually be doing harm when they intend good. It is usually much more important to create suitable butterfly habitats, (ie places that butterflies can move into), rather than to interfere with nature by moving butterflies between sites.

Are releases legal? On the whole, yes, as long as the owners of donor and receptor sites have given permission (preferably in writing), and as long as the species concerned are not on the protected lists.

Which butterflies are protected? There are two groups. The following are fully protected: Swallowtail, Large Copper, Large Blue, High Brown Fritillary, Marsh Fritillary, and Heath Fritillary. It would be illegal to catch, sell or harm any of these species in any way. Any re-introduction projects involving these species would require special Government permission.

The following species are protected but only from being caught or sold (alive or dead) by way of trade, unless the seller has a specific licence: Chequered Skipper, Lulworth Skipper, Silver-spotted Skipper, Wood White, Brown Hairstreak, White-letter Hairstreak, Black Hairstreak, Small Blue, Silver-studded Blue, Northern Brown Argus, Chalk Hill Blue, Adonis Blue, Duke of Burgundy, Purple Emperor, Large Tortoiseshell, Pearl-bordered Fritillary, Glanville Fritillary and Small Mountain Ringlet.

Are there any other legal restrictions? Yes!! Introducing butterflies to, or removing them from nature reserves without the owner's permission is not only morally questionable, but often illegal. Many nature reserves and wildlife-rich areas are protected by SSSI (Site of Special Scientific Interest) status. This invariably means they are protected against introductions or removals of any kind. 'Damaging' SSSIs by any means is a serious matter and could attract fines up to £20,000. Other wildlife sites may also be protected by local bylaws.

So, is Butterfly Conservation against introductions? No! Far from it. But as a respected conservation organisation, it also encourages responsibility, openness and good practice in any release projects which take place. The key features of its policy are summarised in the separate panel.

Are there any other problems with casual introductions? Yes. It is possible to damage other species on a receptor site by unknowingly introducing parasites or diseases via the introduced specimens. It is also possible to upset the ecological balance on a site by releasing a large number of a new species. There is currently a growing interest in genetics and what they can tell us about particular populations. Making casual introductions, especially from bought-in captive stock, which might itself have been developed from mixed genetic backgrounds, may cause problems for future studies. The biggest problem of all is the confusion created by unreported introductions in respect of trying to monitor population changes. It can appear that a species is actually spreading by its own efforts when in fact it is retracting! Further problems are highlighted in the policy panel.

Is it true that past Yorkshire Recorders have been involved in releases? Yes that's right. But you should understand that when that was done, quite along time ago now, the whole ethos surrounding butterfly studies was different. Then, people collected specimens. Now people take photographs. Then, people caught specimens to examine them closely. Now, we can use close-up binoculars to watch a butterfly without disturbing it. Then, there was little conservation work going on, and little was known about a butterfly's ecological needs. Those early attempts at re-introduction were explorations into the practical possibilities. Out of those and similar beginnings around the country a greater knowledge has developed and with it many new and better approaches.

I'm a teacher and involve my pupils in breeding butterflies as part of their studies. We usually release our offspring every year. Is that wrong? Far from it! You are helping to interest future generations in the beauty and excitement of the butterfly world. You will be breeding common species, the release of which will have little impact on wild populations. However, it would be good training to get your pupils to report their releases to the local Vice-county or County Recorder (traceable via the Butterfly Conservation website).

What is the situation regarding the release of long-extinct or foreign butterflies? It would be illegal to introduce/re-introduce any species not currently on the British list. However, it might be possible to get a Government licence for a widely approved re-introduction project such as successfully organised for the Large Blue.

Do you know what species have been introduced in Yorkshire? In many cases yes, although only rarely as a result of open reporting. We are aware of about a dozen species for which introductions have been attempted, most of them casually. Where known, these have been reported in the species write-ups. We are particularly grateful to those who have openly reported their releases or who have privately informed the County or VC Co-ordinator of what they have done. We would still value further reports regarding those species and projects, about which we have few details.

RELEASE POLICY

From time to time butterfly release projects are considered by university research departments, wildlife groups, nature reserve owners and individuals. The notes below provide a framework around which a project should be planned. They are adapted from Butterfly Conservation's policy document on this issue. Fuller details are available from Butterfly Conservation headquarters.

1. Prepare a written plan of your proposed project.
2. Consult with Butterfly Conservation, and all relevant recording bodies, statutory agencies, local groups, wildlife trusts and landowners concerned. In Yorkshire this should include Butterfly Conservation's Yorkshire Branch, the Yorkshire Naturalists' Union Macrolepidoptera Recorder, the Yorkshire Wildlife Trust and English Nature.
3. Any proposed project should be part of a national or regional recovery strategy, linked to the national Species Action Plans (SAPs) or Regional Action Plans (RAPs).
4. It is essential to have permission and support from the landowners of donor and receptor sites.
5. Donor sites should be chosen so as to be the closest available geographically due to the advisability of using stock likely to be genetically similar to any former populations in the given latitude.
6. For re-introductions, extinction needs to be confirmed and natural re-establishment shown to be unlikely.
7. All legal requirements must be taken into consideration.
8. Where habitat modifications are required to provide the right conditions, care should be taken not to damage other important wildlife populations.
9. Evidence should be provided that the proposal will not harm the donor population. This might require prior study of the donor population over several years.
10. Habitat needs and reasons for previous extinction should be understood and the latter removed on the receptor site.
11. Care should be taken to ensure the receptor site is large enough to sustain a viable population (or population network if relevant).
12. A long-term management plan should be drawn up to ensure maintenance of suitable habitat.
13. The likely success of the project should be carefully evaluated.
14. The project should be fully monitored and documented with reports sent to all parties concerned and if possible published in relevant journals. It is important that we all learn from both the successes and the failures.

The Butterflies of Yorkshire is a reference book designed to be dipped into, whenever information about our butterflies is required. The notes below help to explain the layout. In the species chapters information blocks are colour-coded to assist in finding particular types of information. Note-form English has been used in some sections to save space.

Key to the Species Chapters

BRACKETS: Wherever possible, we have given literature references so that researchers can check on our original sources of information, and readers can discover the names of books which they might want to read or add to their libraries. Such references are given in the form: Porritt (1883) or (Porritt 1883) according to the context, being the author's name and year of publication. Look up the author's name in the bibliography at the back of the book to find the name and details of the publication. Square brackets in the form [GT Porritt] are used to indicate the originator of a particular butterfly record. They are also used to distinguish comments or information added in the middle of a quotation.

VICE-COUNTIES: Yorkshire is divided into 5 Vice-Counties (61 to 65) and these numbers are used throughout the book to indicate approximately where places can be found. We use the abbreviation VC to indicate Vice-County. See VC map below. Information about the history of VCs is given in the Introduction on p5. The VC system divides the whole country into roughly equal blocks of land as shown on the adjoining map.

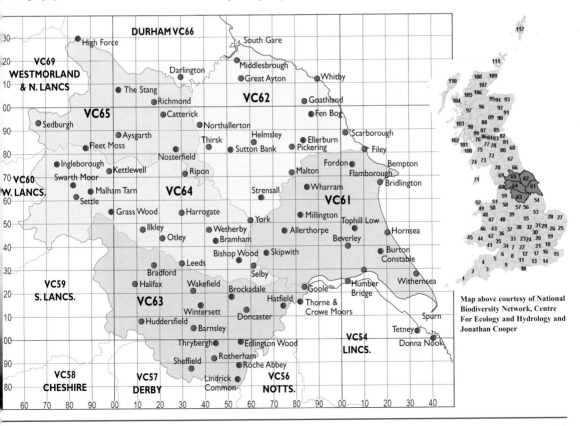

Map above courtesy of National Biodiversity Network, Centre For Ecology and Hydrology and Jonathan Cooper

GLOSSARY: Whilst we have tried to avoid using too many scientific words, we have also deliberately introduced a few which are in fairly common use. In particular, we have referred to larva and pupa rather than caterpillar and chrysalis. A short glossary is included on p307.

BUTTERFLY LIFE CYCLE:

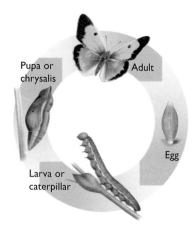

THE SPECIES CHAPTERS: Yorkshire currently has 35 regular butterfly species, made up of 32 residents and 3 immigrants. In addition there are another 26 species which are either very rare, or extinct (including a few which might be categorised as doubtful). In **Section 2** of the book we devote 5 pages to each of the regular species, using the headings detailed below. In **Section 3** we follow a similar layout for the rare and extinct species, but only cover the subject areas considered relevant.

1) HEADING:

1) The number, together with the English and Latin (scientific) names, and the order of species, follow Bradley (2000). (The Bradley number system also includes moths, hence the large numbers given to the butterflies.) This system has been adopted to keep our species accounts in line with Sutton & Beaumont (1989) and Beaumont (2002).

2) The coloured bar behind the heading is coded to indicate family groupings:

1526 SMALL SKIPPER *Thymelicus sylvestris* (Poda 1761)
Family: Hesperidae ('the Skippers').

Skippers: golden brown
Whites & Yellows: yellow
Hairstreaks, Blues & Argus: blue
Vanessids (eg Peacock): reddish brown
Fritillaries: mid-brown
Browns: dark brown
Monarch: purple

3) The English name is followed by the scientific (Latin) name, the first part (with capital) indicating genus, the second (with small letter) the species. The Latin is followed by the name of the person credited with giving the name and the year in which it was given. This is enclosed by round brackets when the species is no longer the same genus in which it was first placed, or square brackets when the name was originally published anonymously and authorship established at a later date.

4) The second line of the heading gives information in English and Latin about the family grouping of the species.

5) The site photo gives a typical Yorkshire habitat picture or a countryside scene in which the butterfly can be found. The paintings of each regular breeding species are the work of Nick Lawman.

2) CONSERVATION STATUS BOX: This information is drawn from Asher *et al* (2001), but adds in regional (N of England) and Yorkshire variations as listed in Ellis (2000a) and discussed annually at the N of England Regional Conservation Day (a conference attended by representatives of N of England Butterfly Conservation Branches). Other status indications are derived from: *The UK Biodiversity Action Plan*, UK Biodiversity Group (1998), *Assessing national conservation priorities: an improved red list of British butterflies,* Warren *et al* (1997), and the *European Red Data Book*, Swaay & Warren (1999).

3) WORLD STATUS BOX: These brief details are intended to put the Yorkshire presence of each species into a broader context. Information has been derived from: Asher *et al* (2001), Carter (1992), Kurdrna (2002), Lafranchis (2000), Pyle (1981), Roine (2000), Thomson (1980) and Tolman & Lewington (1997).

4) YORKSHIRE STATUS SECTION: The comments and statistics here are mainly based on our 1995/2003 Distribution Survey (involving over 1000 volunteers collecting and collating the data) and from our Annual Lepidoptera Reports (1996 to 2003) as published in *Argus* editions: 31, 33, 35, 37, 39, 41, 43, & 45. Vice-County (VC) numbers are given to most place names to assist readers in roughly locating their positions. (Some of these may seem rather obvious to local people, but are also designed to be helpful to those living further afield.) VC boundaries are shown on the accompanying map and on the tetrad distribution map for each species. A small amount of 2004 data has also been included in this section where it is particularly relevant.

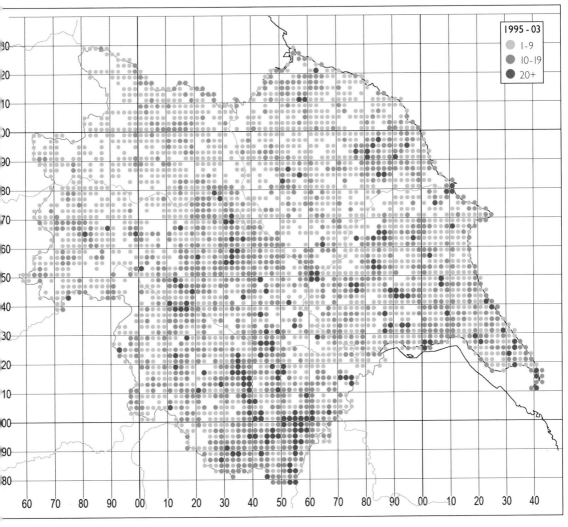

ALL RECORDS MAP: Number of species recorded in each tetrad.

5) DISTRIBUTION MAPS: Our distribution maps are based on the National Grid system found on Ordnance Survey (OS) maps. Britain is mapped in units of 100km squares, each square being distinguished by two numbers or two letters. Yorkshire is covered by parts of 8x100km squares and we use letters to distinguish each one. These (plus one near-neighbour SJ) are indicated, as reminders, in a small box to the right of each N of England map in each of the regular species chapters. Map reference numbers are repeated for each 100km square so it is essential to use their letter 'names' to distinguish one from another, Each 100km square is sub-divided into

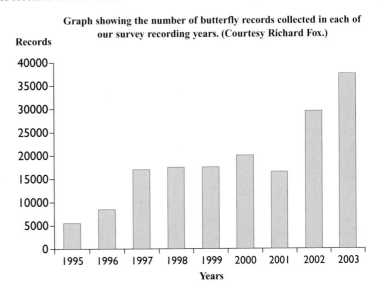

Graph showing the number of butterfly records collected in each of our survey recording years. (Courtesy Richard Fox.)

10km and 1km squares. Most butterfly records are now submitted with 6-figure spot references or 1km square references. Our main map, the 'tetrad' map uses one dot for records made within a 2x2km square (ie comprising 4x1km squares on the OS map). In butterfly recording, OS 1km square references are used in the form SE2345**k** (where 'k' = kilometre) and tetrad references distinguished by adding a 't' (for tetrad) in the form SE1244**t**. This is necessary because even numbered references like SE1244 could refer to 1km squares or tetrads.

Three maps have been produced to help put Yorkshire distribution into national and regional context. The British Isles map utilises records from Butterfly Conservation's national database (1995-1999) with Yorkshire records (1995-2003) distinguished in dull purple. The 10km N of England map uses coloured dots for Yorkshire records (1995-2003) and grey dots to signify records from neighbouring areas (1995-1999). The coloured dots are coded in relation to the number of records made, whilst the grey dots simply indicate a record made outside the county without any indication of numbers. For 10km squares through which the traditional Yorkshire boundary passes, records from neighbouring recording areas (1995-2003) have also been included on the tetrad maps. These recorders and areas are listed on the title page. Where relevant, place names are given 10km OS references as well as VC numbers, in the form VC63/SE58.

Yorkshire distribution (1995/2003) is based on 64,548 visits generating 169,537 records from 196x10km squares. Tetrad (2x2km square) maps are based on visits to 3319 tetrads out of 4120 in the county (ie a coverage of c80%). However, not all recorded tetrads have been covered in the same detail. For generalist species the 10km distribution map is thought to give a better idea of real distribution than the tetrad map, whilst the reverse is true for specialist species. The **all-records** map indicates our unrecorded and weakly recorded areas especially in higher areas like the northern Dales, and in the central parts of the Vales of York and Pickering.

In the text 'common' refers to numbers, ie. frequently encountered in suitable numbers for the species. 'Widespread' is used in a geographical context where recorded in many tetrads.

PHENOGRAMS: These graphs draw upon all 169,537 records made over 9yrs. They plot the northing of each record (ie the latitude) against its date, using the colour scale indicated on each diagram to emphasise the peaks in each flight season (the stronger colours showing bigger numbers). Bear in mind that the bottom of each diagram represents S Yorkshire and the top N Yorkshire. The latitude scale represents 100km steps. On many of these diagrams it is possible to see the strong colours bending towards the right as you go upwards (ie to the north), showing a later emergence and later peaks as you move from south to north. Butterfly phenograms for the whole country (1995-1999) can be found in Asher *et al* (2001).

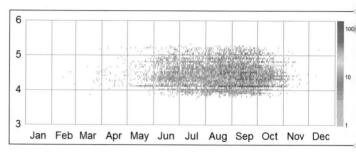

ID NOTES: These are intended to be used in conjunction with other ID books. The notes are mainly derived from the knowledge and experience of the writers, and try to fill in those bits of information not usually included in other sources. ID books are many and varied and it is useful to build up a library of several volumes so as to be able to draw upon the variety of approaches used. For beginners we would currently recommend Lewington (2003) illustrated with paintings, and Tomlinson & Still (2002) illustrated with photographs. Thomas & Lewington (1991) is more than just an ID book with fascinating write-ups of each species and still the favourite with many of our writers. If interest extends to European species, Tolman & Lewington (1997) with paintings and Lafranchis (2004) with photographs are amongst the best available.

We have given brief notes about aberrations, as we feel this is an interesting area of butterfly study, especially as many varieties result from hotter weather conditions, leading to more being seen in recent years. Unfortunately, as yet, there is no single book covering the many hundreds of variations which have been observed. In addition, the giving of names to varieties has been somewhat subject to the whims of individuals, leading to a certain amount of overlap. A great deal of information about naming appears to be hidden away in the entomological magazines which carried the original descriptions. In attempting to name some of the varieties in photographs we have received, we have used Russwurm (1978) and Harmer (1999) both of which provide useful selections but are far from being comprehensive. Therefore our ability to name varieties has been largely restricted to the scope of these sources and it is possible that inaccuracies have crept in as a result. Howarth (1973) has provided the main source of information about the totals of described variations for each species.

LIFE STORY: This section as been compiled with the help of Asher *et al* (2001), Emmet & Heath (1989), Howarth (1973), Lafranchis (2000), Thomas & Lewington (1991), and many other sources as referenced in the text, together with each writer's own experience. References to 'foodplants' in butterflies mean the specific foodplants used by larvae. Where these are named as specific foodplants we have used capital letters for the plant and included its Latin name in italics. Elsewhere, plant names are usually indicated without capitals or Latin names to save space. Plant names follow Fitter (1987), except for one or two recent changes.

HISTORICAL REVIEW: The history of each butterfly's name has been mainly derived from: Emmet (1991), Emmet & Heath (1989), Garland (1981), Graves (1996), Pyle (1981) and Salmon (2000). Emmet (1991) also includes explanations of the Latin name derivations of all the moths and is recommended reading for anyone interested in this subject. The historical record of Yorkshire butterflies has been drawn from a large number of sources all carefully referenced. However, the inclusion of historical records does not mean we can vouch for their accuracy. It should be born in mind that 19th century published records often gave the observer's home town or the starting point of a day's journey rather than the site on which the observation took place. Therefore, although we have tried to map reference many of the historical records we have included, these should be seen as approximate rather than exact indications of distribution. We are particularly grateful to Philip Winter for allowing us to use the YNU Lepidoptera Card File which includes cross-references to many historical butterfly reports given in the YNU *Naturalist*.

THE RARER SPECIES SECTION: Some species have bracketed headings to indicate that we lack sufficient information to make definite decisions on the accuracy of the given report. In these cases we have simply tried to present the facts as known. Information boxes in this section are restricted to those considered relevant.

PHOTOGRAPHS: Photographs remain the copyright of the owners as named beside each picture. Any photos without a name have been taken by the Editor. Selection of pictures has been based on interest rather than quality, therefore, the varying range of sharpness should not be attributed to the printer. We have sometimes used extremely poor quality originals.

CABINET SPECIMENS: Where particularly relevant, we have used pictures of set specimens from historical collections. Although today, it is generally unnecessary and undesirable to catch and kill butterflies, this was formerly considered an essential part of lepidoptera studies. It should not be overlooked that old collections can still provide us with an extremely valuable research tool, and many of today's recorders became interested as a result of being encouraged to collect when they were young. They may have continued to add to such a collection during a lifetime of interest and still draw information from it. In addition those who go on to study moths often find it useful to make a reference collection to help separate species which are difficult to distinguish from one another. It is also customary to keep 'voucher specimens' of some moths to prove the identification of unusual species. Moths generally occur in very large numbers, therefore, taking a few specimens has no impact on populations. Vehicles have a much larger impact! However, butterflies need our protection, and today it is more appropriate to collect photographs or video footage of live specimens, allowing our 'captures' to live on.

CONSERVATION ISSUES: These sections summarise key conservation requirements for each species and point to sources of further information. We would encourage conservation managers a) to look at ways butterflies use sites under their care, and to develop management strategies that ensure the conditions required by each species are maintained, and b) to see their reserves as centres from which any radiating corridors such as tracks, hedgerows, shelterbelts, ditches, streams and headlands etc have a key importance as insect corridors. The possibilities of influencing management along such routes could be explored.

We need to value 'wasteland' sites as important butterfly reservoirs. The butterflies we see in our gardens and on many of our nature reserves may depend on such areas to help build up and maintain adequate populations.

Verges and banks of roads, tracks, railways, canals and rivers provide routes along which butterflies can fly in search of nectar plants and new breeding areas. Disused railway tracks are often home to around 20 species. Unfortunately, many of the tracks are becoming overgrown after some 40yrs of disuse and are rapidly developing into linear woodlands. Their continued value as butterfly havens will depend on periodic clearances of shrubs and trees in order to maintain sunny patches of grassland and wild flowers. Likewise in many woodlands there is scope a) for opening up over-shaded rides to let in sun and encourage wild flowers and b) for designing wider rides in new plantings.

Organisers of amenity projects, need to be wary of seeing every patch of 'overgrown' grassland as an ideal place to plant trees. Once the grassland is shaded out, the local grassland butterflies will disappear!

1526 SMALL SKIPPER *Thymelicus sylvestris* (Poda 1761)
Family: Hesperidae ('the Skippers').

Paul W Forster

South Gare (Middlesbrough VC62). Yorkshire's most NE point. View S to Corus Steelworks, Coatham Sands and N York Moors.

UK BAP status: *Not listed.*
BC Priorities: National: *Low.*
N of Eng : *Low.* Yorkshire: *Low.*
European status: *Not threatened.*

WORLD STATUS: Resident, 0-2600m. One brood (May/Sept). Range: NW Africa through Europe to N England, Denmark and Baltic States, and east to S Urals and Iran. Widespread and common in suitable habitats throughout range, expanding on northern edge. In England has a more northerly distribution east of Pennines than on west, as far north as Alnwick (Northumberland), but (except for odd sightings) only to Wensleydale and S Cumbria in west. 1980s/1990s English range expansion has extended northern limit by approx 100km (Asher *et al* 2001).

Small Skipper

YORKSHIRE STATUS 1995/2003:

Resident: 0-300m+, expanding range. Widespread but local, and common in suitable rough grassland habitats. As such habitats come and go according to changes in management and land use, presence in any given area may fluctuate. One brood (mid-Jun/mid-Sept, usually peaking mid-Jul/early Aug). Found throughout county, except higher Pennines, western half of VC65 and higher parts of N York Moors. In 1996 it was recorded in Pennine areas of VC64 at Hellifield, Langber Lane (N of Long Preston) and the Stephen Park area of Gisburn Forest (where it was found to be already well-established). It reached Austwick Moss in 1998 (presumably having moved up the Ribble Valley from the west), and Clapham Station/ Newby Moor area by 2000, a movement of approx 15km in 5yrs. Gaps down the centre of the county, revealed by the tetrad map, are an indication of under-recording rather than proven absence. The butterfly is widely overlooked on roadside verges. Assessment of its status is complicated by the fact that it is confused with Large Skipper and often not reported by observers due to lack of confidence in ID. Appears to be colonising Pennine Dales from both east and west (but see below). Generally found in small discrete colonies with counts typically in 10-20 range. Larger areas of suitable habitat (often on nature reserves) produce larger colonies with counts in the low hundreds eg: **VC61:** Fordon Dale (Wolds) 12/08/2000 **150** [Peter Gibson], Withernsea Station Meadow 17/07/1997 **282** [Howard Frost], Filey Pastures 09/07/2003 **375** [Filey Brigg Ornithological Group]; **VC62:** Strensall Common (YWT NR) 15/08/1998 **100+**, and 30/07/2000 **c150** [Pat & Jim Bone]; **VC63:** Potteric Carr (YWT NR) 18/07/2000 **136**, and 16/07/2001 **224** [Ken Woolley and Potteric Carr Recording Group], Denaby Ings (YWT NR) 21/07/1997 **100+** [John Law]; **VC64:** Plompton Rocks 03/08/1999 **c100** and Bramham Hall Farm 07/07/1998 **c100** [both Mike Barnham]; **VC65:** Richmond area 26/07/2002 **200** [Arnold Robson]. It is notable that in previous years regular counts in the Richmond area have been in the 8 to 30 range. Emmet & Heath (1989) suggest that colony sizes are often underestimated, because at any one time most males will be perching in the open whilst

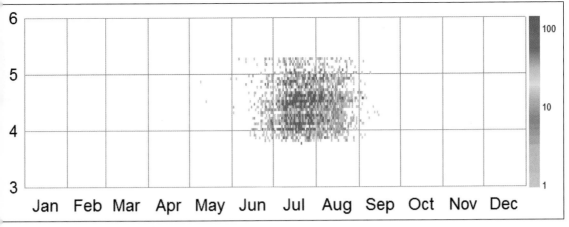

PHENOGRAM: Yorkshire 1995-2003. The main flight season is clearly in Jul and Aug, with population peaks notably later as you move north.

ID NOTES: Small, compact, **plain**, orange brown butterfly, with dumpy, moth-like body. Freshly emerged specimens shine golden in sunlight, but look very drab when worn. Male and female alike except for male's sex brand, a thin, black, slightly curving line on upper forewings. Often rests in characteristic 'skipper' fashion, with forewings held upwards in a V-shape, and hindwings horizontal. Swift, darting, moth-like flight can almost defeat the eye. Can be confused with Large Skipper and Essex Skipper (see p66), but note especially: size is **not** diagnostic. Large and Small Skippers completely overlap in size. Aberrations unusual with only 13 variations described, mainly affecting ground colour: eg silvery cream in ab *pallida* Tutt; yellowish white in ab *margarita* Frohawk, and chocolate brown in ab *brunnea* Verity. Melanism also occurs, both partial, as in ab *obscura* Tutt, and complete, as in ab *suffusa* Tutt. Porritt (1883) reported a *'bone-coloured variety'* seen occasionally in the Wakefield area (VC63) (probably ab *margarita*).

females are hidden. **Earliest record 1995/2003:** 01/06/2003 Kippax VC64 [Mary Palmer]. **Latest:** 13/09/1999 North Cave VC61 [Rosemary Roach].

Assumptions are sometimes made that after colonising the east of the county, the butterfly then spread westward, perhaps along the east/west valley systems associated with Pennine drainage. Whilst that cannot be ruled out, the mapping evidence collected over the last 40yrs also fits with a general northward movement on a diagonal SW to NE front. In the drier, hotter conditions of the east, populations build up faster so might be expected to move northward faster. Expansion in the cloudier, wetter, west is slower, but still develops steadily, given reasonable summer temperatures. It may well be that a broad northward movement is also combined with a fanning out from newly established colonies, especially along corridors like river valleys. Observations indicate Pennine valleys are being colonised from both the east and the west, but even there, we should be wary. Height is no barrier for this species, which is found up to 2600m on the continent. Observations in VC63 from Oxenhope and Ripponden (250m+/c750ft), and the Huddersfield area (300m+), eg c1025ft [J Dale] and c1100ft [BD Cain], suggest that the species could also be moving northward over the Pennine uplands, and dropping down into valleys at various points along.

Small Skipper: pale form with hint of straw colour, Muston (Filey VC62) 1991. Probably ab *intermedia* Frowhawk. A completely white form would be ab *pallida* Tutt.

CONSERVATION ISSUES: This skipper thrives in clumpy grassland areas often dismissed as 'wasteland'. It is possible that some of its recent success is linked to roadside verges being rarely cut except for the metre strip nearest the road, providing a huge area of potentially suitable habitat along which this species can expand. Although not yet investigated, the rebuilding of the A1 to motorway standards, with broad grassland verges, may be providing a major corridor northward. Many of the biggest colonies are found on nature reserves, so conservation managers need to be aware of the value of any rough grassland areas. Scrub control and very light grazing may be necessary to maintain such areas. Skippers tend to avoid machine cut or regularly grazed grasslands, as these will lack large enough grass tussocks. Overwintering larvae may be lost if grassland is heavily grazed or machine cut after egg laying. Maintenance might best be approached by tackling a small area each year or by very light grazing.

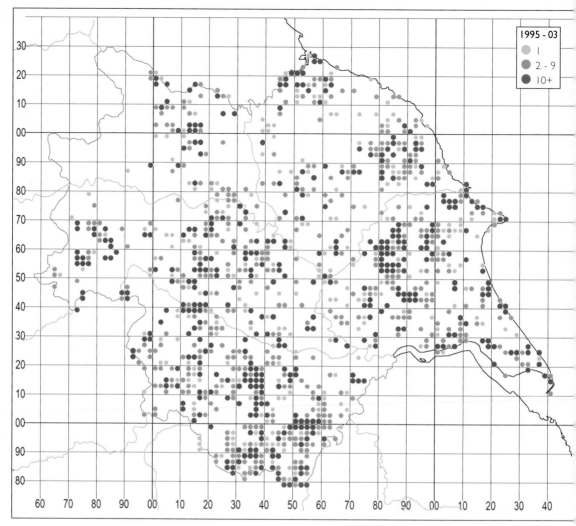

Small Skipper: Yorkshire Tetrad map 1995-2003

MAP NOTES 1995-2003: Noted in 1098/3319 recorded tetrads (ie 33.1%), and out of 4120 tetrads in Yorkshire. Ranked 11th most widespread out of 36 breeding species in county. It has expanded over recent years and although now quite widespread there is still an expansion front to the NW of the county where higher land appears to be an inhibiting factor, although with the species also spreading along Pennine valleys possibly from both east and west. The 10km map probably gives the best picture, with the patchier distribution of the tetrad map a likely result of under-recording in central areas, particularly along roadside verges.

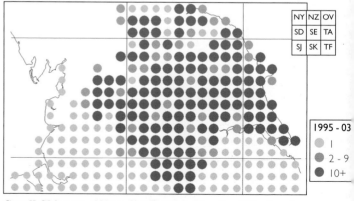

Small Skipper: 10km distribution North of England

 = 1 or more records out of county 1995-1999

LIFE STORY

HABITAT: The main larval foodplant is Yorkshire-fog *Holcus lanatus*, which is very common and grows on all soil types. Other common grasses are also used including: Timothy *Phleum pratense*, False Brome *Brachypodium sylvaticum*, Creeping Soft-grass *Holcus mollis,* Cock's-foot *Dactylis glomerata*, and Foxtail *Alopecurus pratensis*. The butterfly requires its foodplant growing in tall clumps so that any habitat where grasses are allowed to grow tall may be suitable. These include abandoned industrial sites, used and disused rail tracks and rail embankments, road verges, open woodland rides, abandoned meadows, and the edges of any site where grasses grow wild and undisturbed, even quite small areas being suitable. The butterfly is generally associated with open space habitats rather than enclosed areas or deep woodland. Although not a typical garden butterfly, occasional specimens on the move may drop into gardens to investigate, and may even nectar on Buddleia *Buddleia davidii*.

Lawrie King

Small Skipper in typical skipper pose.

Female Small Skippers fly unusually slowly when searching for suitable grasses on which to lay eggs. They then crawl backwards down the stem, keeping abdomens in contact with the surface, until meeting the opening of the furled leaf sheath. Inside this they deposit a row of up to 8 white, oval eggs. A single blade may sometimes hold several batches from different females, but apparently never more than 8 from any one individual. Eggs become creamy-yellow with age and hatch after 3 to 4 weeks. Each larva eats its eggshell, then spins a silken cocoon around itself and immediately hibernates inside the grass sheath until the following spring. By going straight into hibernation it can make the most of feeding up on fresh growth the following year. Larvae are green with 3 pale stripes and develop through 5 instars, until Jun or early Jul, when green pupae are formed at the base of a grass clump inside a protective tent made by binding leaves together with silk. They hatch after about 2 weeks. The exact starting date of the emergence is often difficult to determine due to confusion with the Large Skipper which is usually on the wing earlier, from late May onward. Over much of the county the peak is usually in mid-Jul, although wet weather in late Jun/early Jul may push this on to early Aug, as happened in 1998 and 2000. Emergence is also later in the north and west, and at elevation, eg on the Wolds. Occasional records for early Sept have been made in all our Survey years (1995/2003) except for 2001 and 2003, which benefited from warm Junes, very early emergence, and an early end to the flight period. Small Skippers utilise a wide range of nectar plants including species of scabious, knapweed, thistle, trefoil and vetch. Individual butterflies have been shown to choose a particular species in preference to others. This is usually the most abundant suitable plant in the colony area. If this plant's availability drops significantly, the butterfly will change its preference (Goulson et al 1997).

Disused rail tracks provide valuable Small Skipper habitats. This is Enthorpe Cutting (western edge of Wolds VC61), former Driffield – Market Weighton line.

HISTORICAL REVIEW:
Small Skipper *Hesperia linea* Fab. in
Porritt (1883);
Adopea flava in Tetley (1915)

First described by Petiver (1704), who thought male and female were different species, and called the former, **the streaked golden hog**, and the latter, **the spotless golden hog**. Harris successfully introduced the name **Small Skipper** in 1766, and so it has remained. In the Latin, *Hesperia* refers to the Hesperides, a group of nymphs who guarded the golden apples of Hera, whilst *sylvestris* (given by Austrian physics professor N. Poda von Neuhaus in 1761) implies (somewhat inaccurately!) 'linked to woodland'.

Just as today, this somewhat secretive butterfly appears to have been generally overlooked in the past, so that its historical distribution is far from clear. Morris (1853) provides the county's earliest known records: Sutton-on-Derwent (S of York VC61), Buttercrambe Moor (E of York VC62), and Sandall Beat (nr Doncaster VC63), the latter probably dating from his years as a curate in Doncaster 1835/37. Porritt (1883) described the species as *'fairly common'*, giving: **VC61:** Filey, **VC62:** Raskelf (N of York) and Scarborough, **VC63:** Sheffield and Wakefield, **VC64:** Askham Bog (nr York), Bishop Wood (nr Selby) and Bramham (nr Wetherby) and Thorner (NE of Leeds). Porritt (1904) adds Thorne (nr Doncaster VC63) for which site Rimington (1992) gives a number of other reports made between 1881 and 1908, all indicating that the Small Skipper was *'abundant'* or *'common'* in that area. Porritt (1907) changes his assessment to, *'Well distributed, and in some localities*

Small Skipper: Cowlam (Wolds VC61) 1982.

abundant'. Stainforth (1919) notes that Thomas Stather's specime (collected in the mid-19th century and lost in the bombing of Hull in 194 had been obtained in Riplingham and Brantingham on the southern edge the Wolds (VC61). Stainforth adds that (in 1919) the species was *'s common in the neighbourhood of Riplingham'*. Neither Boult (1899) Porritt (1922) mention Small Skipper in their Hull area lists. Walsh (195 notes that JH Rowntree had recorded the species as common in Scarborough District (probably 1860s/1870s). Tetley (1915) comment that it was *'locally abundant on the Wolds'*.

Robson (1902) had no 19th century records for Durham a Northumberland, suggesting that the northern edge of the Small Skippe national distribution must have been somewhere across N Yorkshi perhaps across the southern edge of the N York Moors between Raskelf a Scarborough. There were no 19th century records from VC65. The spec also seems to have been largely absent from the west of the county at t time. Garland (1981) says it appears to have been rare around Sheffield pr to 1900, although known further east at Maltby, and to the north at Royst Fryer & Lucas (2001) discovered it was not known to 19th century naturali in the Huddersfield/Halifax area and point to a comment by Newman (18 1871) that nationally the species had *'mysteriously disappeared from m places where it was formerly common'*. A further contraction appears to ha taken place in the first half of the 20th century, although with so (presumably small) colonies persisting in the eastern half of the county. was present around Sheffield in the 1930s though *'very local and scar* (Garland 1981). Fryer and Lucas (2001) found the first hints of a com expansion in VC63 in the 1940s, with Sheffield area records at Ewden, D and in the Limb Valley around 1948 (Garland 1981), a report from Ship Glen in 1949 [C Brown], plus a record at Cawthorne c1949 [JH Seag which was the first-ever Huddersfield area record. Rimington (19 suggests that the first-ever reported records for S Derbyshire (VC57) in 1950s, sightings in Barnsley and Bradford (VC63) around 1950, and report from Wentbridge (VC63) in 1955, were also indications of improving situation. The YNU 1967/70 Report summed up the status *'Apparently absent from large areas of the county, but occurring commo though locally in the eastern half (VC61)'* and at *'Strensall and adjac areas (VC62)'*. Walsh (1952) notes that the species was common in Scarborough area (VC62) in the 19th century, *'and still quite common rough grassland on the Moors and Wolds'*.

The population surge that we see continuing today began in the south of county around 1970. By the end of the 1970s counts on some Doncaster a sites (VC63) were beginning to rise above the 100 mark. Fresh arrivals the Huddersfield area started with 1983 reports from Bretton [DS& Ives], and Fryer & Lucas (2001) chart subsequent developments considerable detail. Surprisingly, the Small Skipper was first noted in Harrogate area (much further north and west than the sites in VC63) in mid-1960s, and by 1987 it was considered the third most common butter in terms of abundance (Barnham & Foggitt 1987). It is unclear as to whet this represented a northward jump or an expansion from the east. By 19 Sutton & Beaumont were able to record: '**VC61:** *spread over the whole since 1970;* **VC62:** *patchily recorded over the whole district;* **VC** *widespread in the eastern half of the VC;* **VC64:** *spreading up the Dales far west as Pateley Bridge;* **VC65:** *increase noted from 1981 onwa records as far west as Colsterdale* [N of Pateley Bridge] *and as far north the Tees'*. Between 1979 and 1985 the species surged further north i Durham and Northumberland where it has since become well establish Expansion in Yorkshire continued in the 1990s and is still continuing.

Sean A Clou

View north from Ravenscar to Robin Hood's Bay VC62.

UK BAP Status: *Not listed.*
BC Priorities: National: *Low.*
N of Eng Priority: *Low.* Yorkshire: *Low.*
European Status: *Not threatened.*

WORLD STATUS: Resident, 0-1800m. One brood (May/Aug) (possibly bivoltine in Spain). Range: from European Mediterranean coast (except most of S Spain, Portugal and Mediterranean islands) north across Europe to Scottish borders (but not Ireland), S Norway, S Finland, and eastward across Europe and temperate Asia to China and Japan. A notable expansion took place in Britain between the 1940s and 1980s, which filled in many gaps in a previously localised distribution. Common and widespread in suitable European habitats with some increase noted in Netherlands.

YORKSHIRE STATUS 1995/2003:

Resident: 1 brood (Jun/Aug with emergence occasionally starting in May in good years). Widespread but local, except in NW Dales area (VC65) where it is yet to be found. The butterfly also appears to be largely absent from the Vale of York (down the centre of the county) and in the Vale of Pickering (between the Wolds and the N York Moors). However, these are notably under-recorded areas and sampling suggests the species is being widely overlooked as a butterfly of roadside verges. As a result the 10km map probably gives a more realistic idea of general distribution than the tetrad map. That said, many observers have expressed a subjective view that the Large Skipper has declined since the late 1980s, in tandem with the general increase in Small Skipper colonies. Rimington (1992) puts forward some comparative site counts to justify the same argument. There is a suspicion that the species does very well whilst in expansion mode, but for unknown reasons may have difficulty in maintaining populations on particular sites for any length of time. Close to the northern edge of its range, the butterfly may suffer from some aspects of the weather, whilst the grassland sites it uses tend to evolve or be subject to management, and may lose their suitability. We have more to learn about the needs of the Large Skipper.

Lowland colonies tend to peak in June, whilst in higher areas the peak is often later, in Jul or even Aug. Weather can be a key factor here. A cold, wet period in Jun/Jul 2000 (particularly marked in the east of the county) led to very late peaks in higher areas eg **VC62:** 05/08/2000 Ellerburn Bank (N York Moors c150m) **20** [Martyn Brewer]; **VC61:** 12/08/2000 Fordon North Dale (N Wolds c100m) **c50** [Peter Gibson]. Typical colonies are small with only 5 or 6 adults visible at any one time (although there may be many more resting and unseen). Typical counts on larger colonies are: **VC61:** 17/06/2002 Skeffling YWT NR **27** [Howard Frost]; 15/06/2003 Highfield Dale (Wolds) **35** [Alan Lowe]. **VC62:** 25/06/1996 Newton Dale **40** [Louise Howard]; 24/07/1999 York Cemetery Nature Reserve **46** [Pat Bone]. **VC63:** 25/06/2000 Haw Park (nr Wakefield) **c50** [Wintersett Wildlife Group]; 20/06/2002 Carlton Marsh **55** [Ralph Hibbert & Chris Parkin). **VC64:** 02/07/1998 Heaton Shay **35** [Richard Trees]; 22/06/2002 Stainburn Forest **c200** [David Howson]. **VC65:** 27/07/2002 Nosterfield

Large Skipper

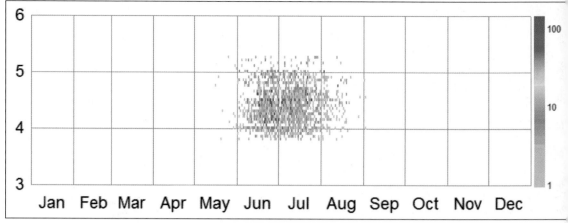

| | Jan | Feb | Mar | Apr | May | Jun | Jul | Aug | Sep | Oct | Nov | Dec |

ID NOTES: Small, compact, heavy-bodied, rich to dark brown butterfly. Both upper and undersides of wings show blotches or panes, usually orange brown on uppersides and dull yellow on undersides, but variable in brightness and becoming paler with wear. Undersides often suffused with olive green, more evident when fresh. Often rests in characteristic 'skipper fashion' with forewings held upwards in a V-shape and hindwings horizontal. Swift, darting flight can almost defeat the eye. Can be confused with Small Skipper and Essex Skipper. Size no guide as sizes overlap. **Hooked antennae are diagnostic** of Large Skipper, and combined with the pattern of panes, make this species readily identifiable. See p66 for further details in separating skippers. Males have a prominent black sex brand on each forewing, much larger and more clearly defined than that of Small Skipper. Variation is uncommon, with only 18 varieties described. These mainly cover alterations in ground colour eg to creamy white in ab *pallida* Mosley, and straw yellow in ab *intermedia* Frohawk. In ab *clara* Tutt, the panes are lighter and brighter against a darker than normal background.

PHENOGRAM: Yorkshire 1995-2003. Shows a single generation with most sightings in Jun/Jul (compared to Small Skipper's Jul/Aug). A pattern of rather isolated sightings can also be discerned (compare to the more solid colour blocks in Small Skipper).

NR 20 [Jill Warwick]; 02/08/1998 the former Richmond Racecourse 60 [Arnold Robson]. All other counts on this latter site have been in single figures. **Earliest record 1995/2003:** 15/05/2002 Ripon Parks (VC64) [Jill Warwick]; **latest:** 01/09/2001 Brampton Bierlow (VC63) [Dean Stables].

Large Skipper feeding on horse manure. Wombwell (VC63) 14/06/2004.

Gary Vause

Large Skipper: unusually strongly marked specimen. Skipwith Common 20/07/2003.

CONSERVATION ISSUES: The Large Skipper has survived 200+yrs as a Yorkshire butterfly in spite of considerable variations in the weather, and is probably more widespread now than at any time since the 19th century. However, its need for tall clumps of Cock's-foot grasses for egg laying, feeding and hibernation make it especially vulnerable to grass cutting and tidying operations eg along roadsides, tracks and forest rides. Wherever possible any necessary management should be carried out in rotation, leaving as much tall grass untouched as practical.

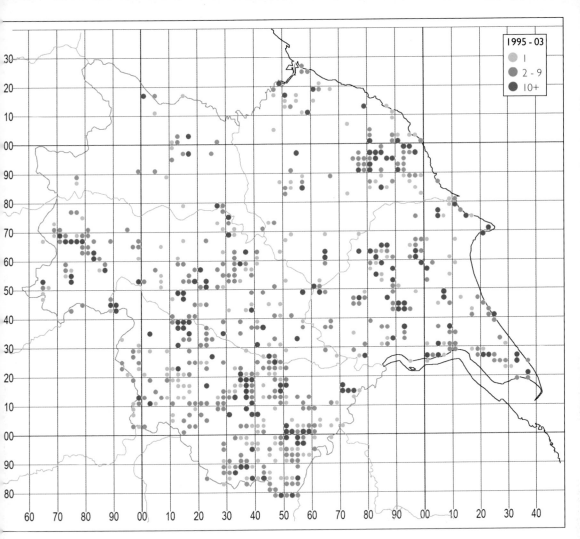

Large Skipper: Yorkshire Tetrad map 1995-2003

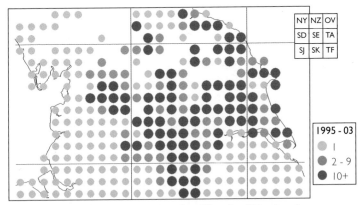

Large Skipper: 10km distribution North of England
● = 1 or more records out of county 1995-1999

LIFE STORY

HABITAT: Large Skippers exploit a variety of rough grassland habitats, such as edges of woodland rides, road verges, railway tracks (used and disused), urban brownfield sites, abandoned grasslands, wet heathland, the banks of rivers, streams and drains, and even parks and churchyards. The key is the presence of specific grass species growing tall and uncut, particularly Cock's-foot *Dactylis glomerata*, a common and widespread grass, found throughout the British Isles. Purple Moor-grass *Molinia caerulea* can support colonies on wet acidic soils (Thomas & Lewington 1991) whilst females have also been observed laying on False Brome *Brachypodium sylvaticum*, Torgrass *B. pinnatum* and Wood Small-reed *Calamagrostis epigejos* (Asher *et al* 2001). However, no studies of foodplant choice have been undertaken in Yorkshire. The butterfly shows a preference for the damper, more sheltered parts of any given site. A wide variety of nectar sources is used, with brambles and thistles especially favoured.

Round, domed, white eggs are laid singly on the undersides of grass blades, typically 20-40cm above the ground (Emmet & Heath 1989). The larva hatches after 12-18 days and eats its eggshell. At this stage it is creamy white with a dark head. It uses silk threads to bind a leaf into a tube where it can hide whilst not feeding. At first the leaf edges above the tube are eaten, after which it travels further to feed. To prevent the build up of faecal matter in the tube the larva has a comb-like appendage above the anus, which is capable of flicking a dropping up to 1m (c3ft) away! Around Sept, the 4th instar larva constructs a winter hideout (hibernaculum) by pulling several grass blades together with silken threads, and hibernates in the larval stage (now blue-green and grub-like with a cream-striped dark head). Feeding resumes in spring and in the 7th instar (or moult) the larva constructs another grass blade tent, and inside that, a loose silken cocoon in which it pupates. The pupa is black and covered in a white waxy powder. Adults emerge after about 3 weeks, with males usually first to appear. Males will either perch or patrol, depending on the time of day, with patrolling favoured in the morning and perching in the afternoon. It has been suggested that whilst patrolling, the males locate newly emerged females by scent (Emmet & Heath 1989). When in perching mode, they will launch from their vantage point (usually a grass blade), to chase off rival males and other insects from their territories, whilst awaiting the passing of a virgin female. Once mated, females mostly bask, with occasional sallies to feed or lay eggs.

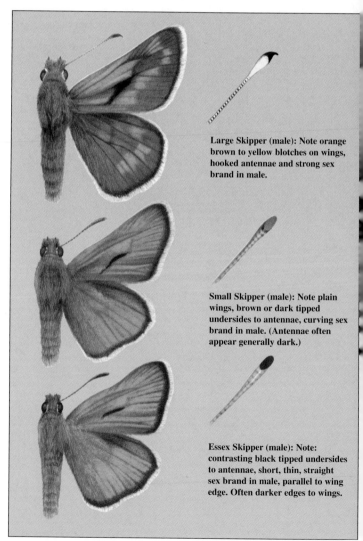

Large Skipper (male): Note orange brown to yellow blotches on wings, hooked antennae and strong sex brand in male.

Small Skipper (male): Note plain wings, brown or dark tipped undersides to antennae, curving sex brand in male. (Antennae often appear generally dark.)

Essex Skipper (male): Note: contrasting black tipped undersides to antennae, short, thin, straight sex brand in male, parallel to wing edge. Often darker edges to wings.

Large Skipper: mating pair. Cowden (VC61) June 2003.

HISTORICAL REVIEW:

Large Skipper
Formerly *Ochlodes venata* Bremer &
Grey 1852.
Hesperia sylvanus Fab in Porritt (1883)

First described by Petiver (1704) as two species, the male being the **Chequer-like Hog** and the female the **Chequered Hog**. In 1717 he renamed them the **streakt Cloudy Hog** and the **Cloudy Hog**. Harris (1776) introduced **Large Skipper**, which survived in spite of later efforts by Samouelle (1819) and Rennie (1832) to use a translation of the Latin name *sylvanus*, and call it the **Wood Skipper**. The current Latin name *Ochlodes* suggests 'turbulence', in a reference to the butterfly's flight, whilst *faunus* (given by Turati in 1905) means *faun*, or a *woodland deity* or *satyr*.

Over the last 2 centuries or more, the northern edge of the Large Skipper's range has been across southern Scotland (particularly SW Scotland) and has been largely static. Thomson (1980) highlights a probable record from the Isle of Bute dating back to c1769, and gives details of other Scottish records published in 1811, 1845, 1852 and 1896-1898. However, the extent and density of distribution across Northern England seems to have been much more variable over the same period. Robson (1902) commented, *'This Butterfly has very seldom been met with in our district* [ie Durham & Northumberland] *and so far has been confined to the County of Durham. Mr Sang took it at Darlington and records it as scarce and local'*. He goes on, *'It ought*

Large Skipper: male. Note thick sex brand and hooked antennae.

to occur in our counties, as it is a species of general distribution and common in most places, occurring at York, Scarborough and Richmond in Yorkshire, at many places in Lancashire, and in the south of Scotland'.

In Yorkshire the species appears to have been mainly present in the eastern half of the county during the 19th century and only spread into western areas in the second half of the 20th century. Large Skippers do not appear in the 1832 Wath-upon-Dearne (VC63) list or Lankester's 1842 Askern (VC63) list. Rimington (1992) suggests that this could have been an error or accidental omission. However, Morris (1853) also fails to mention any Doncaster area presence giving only Sutton-on Derwent (S of York VC61) for this species. Stainforth (1919) records that the Thomas Stather (b1812/d1878) collection (destroyed in WW2) had specimens from Riplingham (nr Hull VC61) and that the Large Skipper was still common in the same area in 1919. Boult (1899) includes 2 Hull area records: Sutton, July 1888 [CW Russell], and Victoria Ave, Hull 1889 [JW Boult]. Walsh (1952) notes that it was recorded as *'common at Scarborough'* (VC62) by JH Rowntree (b1850/d1937). Rimington (1992) includes Doncaster area (VC63) records from Maltby Wood (1858), Edlington Wood and Thorne Moors, both c1880. Between 1880 and 1896 Rimington notes only one record from Wadworth Wood in 1888. Then between 1896 and 1908 there is an increase in reports and comments, eg *'scores'* at Edlington Wood in 1898 [A Whitaker] and *'common'* at Thorne Moors between 1896 and 1908 [B Morley]. Could this be an indication of a recovery after the effects of the 1879/1895 cold years? Porritt (1883) makes no attempt at any assessment, but merely notes sites (with none from VC61!): **VC62:** Scarborough, **VC63:** Edlington Wood (Doncaster), Pontefract, Sheffield. Thorne Waste, Wakefield, **VC64:** Askham Bog (York), Bishop Wood (Selby), Bramham (Wetherby), Ledston (E of Leeds), **VC65:** Richmond [recorded by John Sang]. Brady (1884) noted the species *'rare and local'* in the Barnsley area, with records from Royston and Hemsworth.

Large Skippers continued to be recorded around Doncaster in the first half of the 20th century and no particular population changes were noticed. Further west, around Sheffield the species was initially rare, but by 1938 a presence had been noted on the Permian Limestone belt in that area and by 1945 a northward range extension was underway. By the 1960s the species had become locally common in the Sheffield area (Garland 1981). Fryer & Lucas (2001) describe how, in the early 1940s, the first hints of an expansion were noted around Barnsley. The Large Skipper was seen in Shipley in 1949, and by 1951 it was expanding into the Huddersfield area where it had never been previously recorded. Fryer & Lucas chart this spread in some detail indicating that by 1970 it was widely distributed and relatively common in the Huddersfield area. The YNU Report (1967/70) noted the species to be *'the commonest and most widely distributed of our Skippers. It occurs in varying numbers in almost all parts of the county'* including *'in some industrial areas where it was formerly absent'*. Dunn & Parrack (1986) observe that this butterfly also spread rapidly through County Durham from about 1950 onward and into Northumberland in the 1960s. It is unclear as to whether these various expansions were part of a single northward thrust from areas to the south of Yorkshire, or several expansions outwards from existing colonies in the east, or even a combination of the two. However, the phasing of dates from an arrival in Sheffield in the 1930s to reaching Northumberland in the 1970s fits well with a northward thrust theory. By 1989 Sutton & Beaumont were able to state that the species was now, *'Common generally, except on high land in all five vice-counties'*.

Sean A Clough

1532 DINGY SKIPPER *Erynnis tages (Linnaeus 1758)*
Family: Hesperidae ('the Skippers').

Wharram Quarry YWT NR (VC61) showing newly scraped area.

UK BAP Status: *Not listed.*
BC Priorities: National: *Low.*
N of Eng Priority: *Medium.*
European status: *Not threatened.*

WORLD STATUS: Resident, 0-2200m. 2 broods in S of range and 1 (or 1 plus partial 2nd in warmer summers) in N and higher areas (Mar/Sept). Range: from Mediterranean coast through Europe to C Norway (Lat 62°N) and eastward across C Asia to China. Declines noted in some European countries. Fairly widespread but localised in England and Wales, with colonies becoming more scattered N of a line from the Mersey to the Humber. British range extends to Cumbria and S Northumberland, with further isolated populations in SW and NE Scotland. The only skipper present in Ireland, with subspecies *baynesi* found in the Burren (Co Clare).

Dingy Skipper

YORKSHIRE STATUS 1995/2003:

Very localised, usually single brooded, resident: largely confined to chalk and limestone habitats, or artificial habitats, like railway sidings, which have chalk or limestone foundations. Very small 2nd brood suspected in some years, and almost certainly occurred in 2003. Usually flies early May/late Jun (sometimes Apr/early Jul). Site counts generally small, in the 1/10 range. Highest site counts: **VC61:** 14/05/2000 Wharram Quarry **186** [Howard Frost], **VC62:** 31/05/1997 Lownorth Camp **36** [Sean Clough & Louise Howard], **VC63:** 22/05/2002 Sprotborough **63** [Ralph Hibbert & Chris Parkin], 27/05/2003 Dodworth Colliery Spoil Heap **c100** [David & Stuart Wise]; **VC64:** 06/06/1997 Grantley **9** [Mike Barnham], 31/05/2003 Ellington Banks (nr Ripon) **34** [JD Postlethwaite]; **VC65:** 01/06/1999 Hunton (nr Bedale) **1** [Charles Chandler] and 20/05/1999 W Tanfield **11** (VC64/65 border) [Mike Barnham]. **Earliest (1995/2003):** 16/04/2003 Wharram Quarry YWT NR [Howard Frost]; **latest** (presumed 1st brood): 07/07/1996 Wharram Quarry and 07/07/1997 Hudson Way (both Wolds VC61) [Howard Frost *et al*]. In 2003 Yorkshire's first-ever reported 2nd brood sightings were noted at: Millington (VC61 Wolds) **2** seen on 26/07/2003 [P Townsend]; **1** seen between 06/08 and 10/08 Bardsey (N of Leeds VC64); and **2** seen on 16/08 at Ellington Banks (nr Ripon VC64) [JD Postlethwaite]. Sites in VC63/SK58 (Lindrick area) and VC63/SK59 (Maltby area) are thought to have been subject to unofficial introductions on a fairly large scale over the last 20yrs. No details of this project have been published, which complicates any status assessment.

However, it seems unlikely that local introduction projects could account for the large numbers now being discovered on many VC63 sites, especially as the butterfly was previously recorded in these areas in the 1940-1969 period. David and Stuart Wise, who have been highlighting the need to conserve and protect these colonies, note: '*It is probably fair to say that nearly all the former pits in South Yorkshire, even ones closed decades ago, contain Dingy Skipper colonies, some quite small, while others are very large indeed, with a hundred or so butterflies on the wing at any given time in the height of the flight season.*' (Wise & Wise 2003).

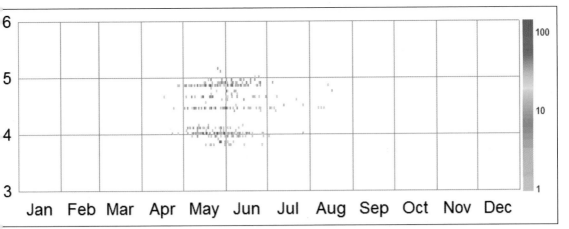

	Jan	Feb	Mar	Apr	May	Jun	Jul	Aug	Sep	Oct	Nov	Dec

ID NOTES: Small, inconspicuous, fast-flying, moth-like butterfly, easily overlooked. Sexes similar. Confusable with day-flying moths such as Mother Shipton *Callistege mi* and Burnet Companion *Euclidia glyphica* which may share same habitat, so note if antennae are clubbed (butterfly) or not (moth). Brownish, with variable pale markings, which become less distinct as the butterfly ages and loses scales. May show burnished lustre when fresh. 2nd brood specimens paler, with more chequered pattern and pale yellowish undersides. Major variations rare with only 21 described aberrations mainly concerned with ground colour or in the transverse bands on the upperside of the forewings. Where these are pronounced on a drab brown specimen the name ab *transversa* Tutt is given.

PHENOGRAM: Yorkshire 1995-2003. The localised nature of this species stands out in the widely separated higher numbers (in reds and browns). The hint of a small partial second generation can also be discerned.

David & Stuart Wise

Top of Dodworth Colliery spoil heap (VC63) (Holme Moss TV mast in background). Yellow patches mark colonising Bird's-foot Trefoil with flourishing Dingy Skipper colony.

Roosting Dingy Skipper. Note moth-like appearance.

CONSERVATION ISSUES: Rated *medium* priority by Butterfly Conservation due to an apparent 55% loss in Yorkshire over 25yrs, although only a 4% loss across the N of England (ie Yorkshire, Durham and Northumberland). Being a rather drab, moth-like butterfly, it is not readily recognised or valued by the public: a species with an image problem! On top of that, its main foodplant is mainly found in temporary situations and quick to lose out through scrubbing over, overgrazing, or shading out. Modern farming tends to clean up suitable grassland corners. Industrial habitats are subject to development, quarries filled in, disused railway tracks and sidings get overgrown. The butterfly appears to be fairly sedentary and probably needs a mosaic of linked habitats in which to thrive. Isolation may spell extinction. Warmer springs may lead to foodplant desiccation, especially in drier years. In S Yorkshire (VC63) colliery spoil heaps are often reclaimed and turned into country parks, destroying ideal habitat areas. Even where the foodplant has been deliberately planted it is rapidly superseded by ranker growth. Management needs to ensure the regular renewal of bare patches into which the Bird's-foot Trefoil can spread. Wise & Wise (2003) note that even ad hoc dirt track riding can contribute to this butterfly's bare ground needs! An outstanding example of positive management can be seen at Wharram Quarry YWT NR (VC61) where, during our 1995/2003 Survey, large areas of the quarry floor were scraped back to bare rock to rejuvenate plant succession. As a result, the growth of Bird's-foot Trefoil mushroomed and so did the Dingy Skipper population, from counts around 40 (thought quite high at the time) to counts as high as 186. The species needs more projects like this to build up populations.

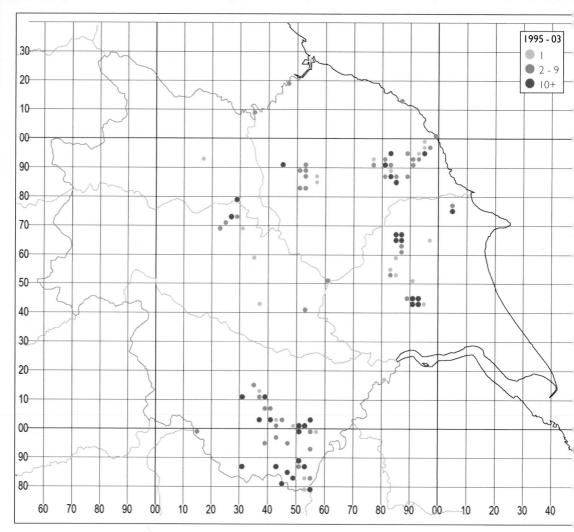

Dingy Skipper: Yorkshire Tetrad map 1995-2003

MAP COMMENTS 1995-2003: Noted in only **102/3319** recorded tetrads (ie 3.1%), and out of 4120 tetrads in Yorkshire. **Ranked 27th most widespread** out of 36 breeding species in county. Clearly a very localised species, the presence of which strongly associated with the Magnesian Limestone ridge, the Yorkshire Wolds chalk and the N York Moors limestone.

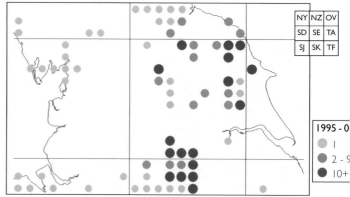

Dingy Skipper: 10km distribution North of England

● = 1 or more records out of county 1995-1999

HABITAT: In Britain, largely dependent on Bird's-foot Trefoil *Lotus corniculatus,* although it will also use Greater Bird's-foot Trefoil *L. uliginosus* and Horseshoe Vetch *Hippocrepis comosa.* Bird's-foot Trefoil is a colonising plant which thrives best in the neighbourhood of disturbed soils, conditions which are often provided on brownfield sites such as quarries (chalk, limestone, sand and gravel), coalmines with spoil heaps, and rail routes and sidings (used and disused). Chalk and limestone grasslands, coastal dunes and undercliffs, and woodland rides and edges can also provide suitable habitats. In Yorkshire, sites appear to be largely restricted to chalk and limestone areas associated with the Magnesian Limestone ridge, the Yorkshire Wolds and the N York Moors. Sites away from these areas often have a rail connection (past or present) where chalk or limestone foundations may have been used for sidings etc.

Dingy Skipper: mating pair.

Pale yellow eggs (changing to distinctive orange) laid singly on upperside of leaf or angle of leaf stalk, hatch after c2 weeks. Larvae are green with fine yellow bands, a lateral yellow stripe, and distinctive dark head. Leaves drawn together with silk to make a tent in which larva feeds. Successive tents are made as required until full grown around mid-Aug. Larva then spins a hibernaculum, and sleeps

inside it until the following spring when it pupates, still inside, and takes 4/5 weeks to develop. Based on the 1995/2003 Survey, typical emergence of butterflies in Yorkshire is in the first week of May in VCs 61 and 63, but a little later further north. April emergences occurred in 2002 (Sprotborough VC63, 22/04) and 2003 (16/04, details above). Emmett & Heath (1989) indicate that April emergences can lead to a partial 2nd brood in S of England (in late Jul/Aug). This did in fact happen on several Yorkshire sites in 2003 (see above).

VC63. Rother Valley landscaping with Dingy Skipper colony in middle distance. But for how long?

Roosting Dingy Skipper, Ellerburn (VC62).

VC63. Orgreave Colliery spoil heap in distance. Several Dingy Skipper colonies found in this landscape.

HISTORICAL REVIEW:
Dingy Skipper
Formerly: *Thanaos tages* (in Porritt 1883)

First mentioned by Merrett in 1666. Initially known as **Handley's brown Butterfly** (Petiver 1704), and later as **Handley's Brown Hog Butterfly**. Harris (1766) re-christened it **Dingey Skipper**, a name which has remained unchanged since, except for spelling. The current Latin family name *Erynnis* is derived from the Erynyes who pursued evil-doers, whilst *tages*, given by Linnaeus in 1758, comes from the Etruscan *Book of Tages*, Tages being the name of a wise boy.

The earliest known county record is found in the anonymous 1832 list for Wath-upon-Dearne (VC63/SE40) (Rimington 1992). The reported historical distribution appears to have been very similar to that of today, although actual sites within each area may well have changed. Indeed, it seems probable that over the 200+yrs period there has been a steady shift from permanent grassland sites to industrial habitats. 19th century railway building would have provided a great deal of new habitat, with bare verges, cuttings and embankments, ideal for the spread of a colonising plant like Bird's-foot Trefoil, and providing corridors to encourage the butterfly to move to new areas. Robson (1902), writing about the Durham and Northumberland region, referred to this connection, noting that the Dingy Skipper was found *'especially on railway embankments'*. It is quite possible that past distribution may also have been influenced by butterflies hitching lifts in railway goods wagons.

Dingy Skipper: Easily missed! Wharram Quarry YWT NR (VC61).

There are few early records from **VC61** as the Wolds were largely unrecorded. Morris (1853) notes Buttercrambe Moor (SE75) and Sutton-on-Derwent (SE74). Stainforth (1919) refers to a presence in the S Wolds, around Riplingham and Brantingham (SE92/93). Boult (1899) indicates that he recorded one on the Humber Bank near Hessle in 1884, adding that it was, *'formerly very common there but now extinct'*. For **VC62** Porritt (1883) noted Raskelf (N of York SE47) [George Tyers], and Scarborough [JH Rowntree]. Tetley (1915) commented that it was, *'generally distributed in the Scarborough area'*. Walsh (1952) noted that JH Rowntree (b1850/d1937) recorded it as *'common in the Scarborough District'* and that in 1952 it was *'still quite common on rough grassland in the Moors and Wolds'*. Walsh (1956) added that it was *widely distributed but local'* in the Scarborough area, including colonies at Langdale (SE99), Beast Cliff (nr Ravenscar TA09), and Pickering (SE78). Porritt (1904) included two additional sites: Levisham (SE89) where the YNU recorded it as *'common in 1895'*, and Strensall, nr York where it was also considered common.

For **VC63**, besides Wath-upon-Dearne, Rimington (1992) gives: Adwick (probably Adwick le Street SE50, but possibly Adwick upon Dearne SE40) recorded by JW Dunning in 1846; Maltby (SK59) (Batty 1858), and Roche Abbey (SK58) (Smith 1858). Rimington also mentions that GE Hyde recorded it as *'an occasional rarity'* on Bull Moor (SE60) between 1920/1960. Fryer & Lucas (2001) note Huddersfield (SE11) area reports including JW Dunning's 1847 sighting from Storthes. Hobkirk (1859, 1868) also listed this site together with Castle Hill and Lepton Great Wood (SE21). However, by 1883 Porritt had to report that although formerly common in the Huddersfield area it was now extinct, perhaps a victim of the smoke and pollution brought about by industrial growth. He still lists Barnsley (SE30), Pontefract (SE24), Sheffield (SK38) and Wakefield (SE32). Porritt (1907) summed up the turn of the century presence as, *'generally distributed in suitable localities but has disappeared from some parts of the south-west where it was formerly common'*.

In **VC64** Porritt (1883) notes Askham Bog (York SE54) where it was recorded by William Prest (b1824/d1884), Bishop Wood (Selby SE53) [George Tyers], and Pannal (nr Harrogate SE35) [JW Taylor]. A Harrogate Naturalists' Survey (1976/1985) located the butterfly in 21x1km squares around Harrogate (Barnham *et al* 1993). There appears to be only one **VC65** record from the 19th century, which comes from the Richmond area (NZ10), where it was recorded by John Sang (b1828/d1887). 20th century records from VC65 are also rare and the comment in Sutton & Beaumont (1989) appears a little misleading: *'Widespread but very local **in all five vice-counties**, and recorded right up to the northern boundaries of VC62 and VC65. Not reported from the west of VCs 63/65'*. The YNU 1967/70 Report was also rather generalised: *'Widely distributed **in most parts of the county**, but becoming scarcer and more local near industrial areas'*. However, records on the national database up to 1982 and published in Heath *et al* (1984) show Yorkshire distribution largely confined to 100km square SE, with no records from the westernmost row of 10km squares. That placed much of Yorkshire's distribution (just as today), in association with the Wolds, the N York Moors and the Magnesian Limestone ridge (with most of the VC65 records coming from the SE corner, on or close to that same ridge). The Millennium Atlas (Asher *et al* 2001, covering the 1995/1999 Survey) indicates an apparent Dingy Skipper loss of 34x10km squares out of 61x10km squares recorded in the county in 1970/82, a 55% loss compared to a national decline of around 40%. However, it is still possible that some of this loss in Yorkshire is due to under-recording. The Dingy Skipper is very easy to overlook, and its liking for little visited railway and industrial habitats, only adds to this possibility.

Howard M Frost

St Hilda's Abbey, Whitby (VC62). Clouded Yellows can turn up anywhere. The writer spotted one in the grounds here whilst leading a school visit.

UK BAP Status: *Not assessed.*
BC Priorities: National: *Not assessed.*
N of England: *Not assessed.* Yorkshire: *Not assessed.*
European Status: *Not assessed.*

Clouded Yellow: helice variety. Flamborough 2004.

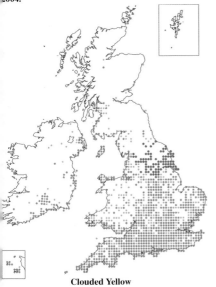

Clouded Yellow

CURRENT YORKSHIRE STATUS:

An irregular immigrant from S Europe, the arrival of which is controlled by factors outside Yorkshire. Can turn up anywhere in the county, but more frequently on the southern half of east coast (VC61) or in S Yorkshire (VC63). Although not recorded every year, most years see one or two reports. 1995/2003 produced 3 moderately good years: **1996**: 100+ sightings totalling 200+ butterflies: first arrival 07/06 Spurn VC61 [Barry Spence], highest count **11** on 20/08 at Aldbrough (VC61) [Adrian Johnson], last record 15/09 at Spurn; **1998**: 60 sightings totalling 70+ butterflies across 21x10km squares with earliest record at Long Nab (VC62) 01/06 [Scarborough Field Naturalists' Society], highest count **5** on 07/09 at Fairburn Ings (VC64) [Steve Wadsworth], and last sighting at N Duffield Carrs (VC61) 12/10 [Craig Ralston]; **2000**: 196 reports recording 582 butterflies in 54x10km squares, mainly in the south of VC61. Earliest at Filey VC61 on 09/06 [Filey Brigg Ornithological Group], highest count **152** Brough area VC61 [Birdline], and last record at Brough Haven (River Humber VC61) on 23/10 [Rosemary Roach]. As Clouded Yellows take just 6 to 10 weeks to move from freshly laid egg to emerging butterfly it is possible that, given good weather, at least two generations of offspring can result from May/June arrivals in Yorkshire and sometimes even three, with each successive generation producing bigger numbers than previously. As a result, numbers in Yorkshire are usually highest in the autumn. In poorer years later arrivals may be the offspring of earlier arrivals in southern Britain. In other years there may be successive waves of butterflies arriving from different sources.

WORLD STATUS: Widespread, common, polyvoltine resident and migrant: 0-1600m (to 3000m+ as migrant). Range: S Spain and N Africa through S Europe & Middle East to W Asia. Also annual or occasional migrant to British Isles (inc Orkney & Shetland) and N Europe, as far north as S Baltic coast, but further north as one moves eastward: rarely in Norway, occasionally in Sweden and Finland, and in N Russia westward to central Urals. May occasionally survive mild winters in southern part of migratory zone as far north as south coast of Britain. Breeds continuously (summer & winter) around Mediterranean and occasionally builds up huge populations, which head north in spring or summer to provide memorable 'Clouded Yellow Years'.

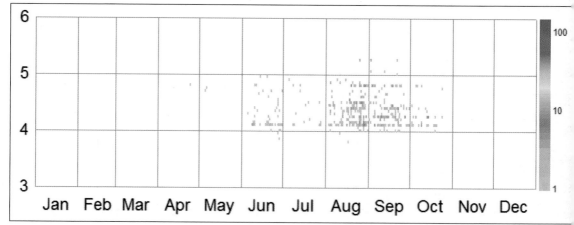

Jan Feb Mar Apr May Jun Jul Aug Sep Oct Nov Dec

ID NOTES: Only two species of yellow butterfly are likely in Yorkshire: Clouded Yellow and Brimstone. The former is relatively small (Small White size), the latter distinctively large. Both invariably perch with wings closed. Brimstone's prominent wing veins and leaf-like wing points make it clearly different, whilst the Clouded Yellow's figure-of-eight spot on the lower wing is also distinctive. In flight the male Clouded Yellow's rich mustard-yellow upperwings can be picked out, as can the female's deep orange-yellow. By contrast, the Brimstone male is a bright, very noticeable, citrus yellow, whilst the female is a greenish-tinged white, easily overlooked due to similarity to Large White. Clouded Yellow males have solid black margins to all four upperwings. Females are similar, but the black margins are dotted with yellow spots. In bright sunlight these margins can often be seen through the closed wings of a perched butterfly. A fresh male's underwings have a more greenish tinge than a female's. Around 10% of female Clouded Yellows have pale, white to grey upperwings, instead of yellow, (the *helice* variety). The closed-wing view looks the same, although a hint of white may show through the upper closed wing. The *helice* can give rise to confusion with the Pale Clouded Yellow *Colias hyale* (not definitely recorded in Yorkshire since 1900) and Berger's Clouded Yellow *Colias alfacariensis* (only separated as a species in 1945, and never recorded in Yorkshire). See under Pale Clouded Yellow for further discussion of these related ID problems. The Clouded Yellow can be quite variable in colour and also interbreeds with the Eastern Pale Clouded Yellow *Colias erate* in E and SE Europe, which makes it difficult to reliably distinguish some examples from its near relatives (especially in the field, but sometimes even with dead specimens!).

PHENOGRAM: Yorkshire 1995/2003. Indicates this species mostly seen in low numbers with sightings mainly in June and Aug/Sept.

Above left: male, mustard yellow, black wing tips. Lower left: female, orange yellow, yellow blotches in wing tips. Above right: pale *helice*, female.

HMF courtesy private collection.

CONSERVATION ISSUES: It is probable that in the 19th century the number of butterflies arriving in good years was higher than today due to the prevalence of small farms and hay meadows on the continent. Also the relatively small number of observers and difficulties of travel would have meant many would have been overlooked. Fortunately, this butterfly's foodplants remain common and the species is one of few, which is able to survive in modern grass leys where the limited species mix often includes clover. However, the size of future arrivals may be increasingly subject to changing agricultural patterns on the continent and particularly in France. In 2002 France was growing in the region of 385,000 hectares of lucerne as a break crop or for silage. Therefore, even in the most open prairie landscapes (as in the Paris basin) there are habitats which can be seething with Clouded Yellows, in spite of the fact that two or three cuts a year may be made. By contrast, in more rural parts, the hay meadow is becoming a thing of the past. Land is either being abandoned and is scrubbing over fast, or it has already been ploughed out and incorporated into modern crop units to gain higher subsidies. The future size of Clouded Yellow invasions may well depend in some degree on the outcome of proposed CAP (Common Agricultural Policy) reforms which France and its farming community are currently resisting. In addition, a warmer climate could be opening up the possibility of the zone of continuous breeding extending northward and increasing the volume of butterflies available to move north in any given year.

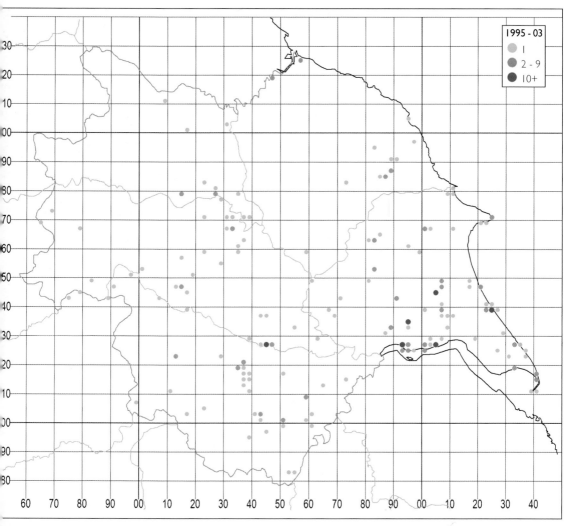

Clouded Yellow: Yorkshire Tetrad map 1995-2003

MAP NOTES 1995-2003: Recorded in 156/3319 recorded tetrads (ie 3.1%) and out of 4120 tetrads in the county. **Ranked 26th most widespread** out of 36 breeding species in the county. Bearing in mind that this is a migrant butterfly and that the map sums up successive arrivals over a 9yr period the key factor indicated is its greater presence in the S and SE, with red dots, particularly along the Humber Estuary, resulting from one or more generations of offspring. The spread of dots may also lend weight to the theory that this species often arrives on the east coast and moves inland along the Humber Estuary, (Payne 1985).

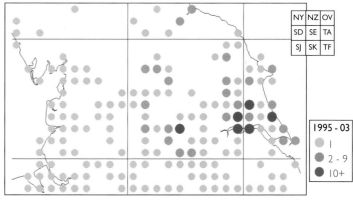

Clouded Yellow: 10km distribution North of England

● = 1 or more records out of county 1995-1999

LIFE STORY

Clouded Yellows courting. Coverack, Cornwall, Sept 2000. Probably the only time this species perches with open wings. Note brighter than normal yellow forewings and greyish hindwings, suggesting the rarer form *helicina*.

The Clouded Yellow is a periodic immigrant to Yorkshire from the Mediterranean area where it breeds more or less continuously, summer and winter. From around Feb onward, the species moves northward into central France and similar latitudes to the east. Occasionally individuals may arrive in southern Britain from Feb onward, but more typically the first arrivals along the South Coast (and in Yorkshire) are in May and June. These may have come directly from the Mediterranean or be offspring from earlier immigrants to central France. Recent warmer years have also seen small numbers successfully wintering along the South Coast, eg in the Bournemouth area 1998/9 (Skelton 2000), where up to 8 locally hatched butterflies were counted in March/April 1999. Such attempted colonisation may explain early Yorkshire

records like the single individual seen at Warmsworth (nr Doncaster VC63) in poor weather conditions on 18/05/1999 [Hugh Parkin]. It was the year's only Yorkshire record of this species, in a year noted for minimal immigration of both moths and butterflies. In addition, the northern demarcation between continuous breeding, and breeding dependent on immigration, may be moving north in France, increasing the chances, and perhaps the numbers, of Clouded Yellows reaching Britain. At the same time, the species suffers at larval and pupal stages from excessively cold or wet weather, so is likely to remain only a very marginal resident in southern Britain in the foreseeable future.

However, in good immigration years large numbers can reach Yorkshire and if this is as early as May or June, at least two generations are possible given reasonable weather, with offspring typically appearing in July/Aug and Sept/Oct and even Oct/Nov. Eggs are bottle-shaped, initially yellow white, turning to pinkish orange and then to leaden grey the day before hatching after 7/10 days. Each female is capable of laying 600+ eggs which are placed singly on the tops of the leaves of clovers, vetches and other pea family members. Tolman & Lewington (1997) suggest females tend to use a single plant species on any given site. Most of the eggshell is eaten, then, for the first few days, the larvae feed on the cuticle of the leaves without perforating them. Later they strip the whole leaf. Larvae are dark green with yellow and orange streaks on each side, and short white hairs. The larval stage passes through 5 instars in three to six weeks (but may develop much more slowly in winter). The pupa is yellowy-green with a few black dots. It is attached with silk to the stems of foodplants and develops in two to three weeks. Each new generation may head further north, giving rise to the possibility of offspring and new immigrant appearing together, but around late Aug/Sept onward there is an increasing tendency for a reverse southward migration to take place. It is possible that the success or failure of this return to the Mediterranean area may affect the numbers available to move north in the following year.

Barry Spence

Clouded Yellows: mating pair. Spurn NNR 16/08/04.

The **Clouded Yellow** was first described by Mouffet (1634). Petiver (1703) named it the **Saffron Butterfly** *Papilio croceus*, a name also adopted by Ray (1710) but with the feminised Latin *crocea*, still used by some authors today. In 1717 Petiver further described the male and female **Clouded Yellows** as two species: the **Saffron** (male) and the **Spotted Saffron** (female). Wilkes (1741, 1742) was first to use **Clouded Yellow**, but confusions continued and even Linnaeus mixed up the **Clouded Yellow** *croceus* with the **Pale Clouded Yellow** *hyale*, placing both species together as *hyale*. Lewin (1795) altered the name to **Clouded Orange** *Papilio electra*, a change accepted by Donovan (1798) who also introduced a new Latin name: *P. edusa*. **Clouded Orange** failed to catch on, but *edusa* remained in use until some 40 years ago when scientific precedence demanded a return to *croceus*. Haworth (1803) thought the *helice* variety was a separate species, which he called the **White Clouded Yellow**. Rennie (1832) tried unsuccessfully to popularise **Clouded Saffron** but **Clouded Yellow** has now become standard. In the current Latin, *Colias* is a place name associated with Aphrodite (Venus), the goddess of beauty, whilst *croceus* is related to 'crocus' and refers to the saffron yellow ground colour.

19th century entomologists were largely unaware that butterflies could migrate, so the Clouded Yellow was originally considered a resident. Duncan (1844) summed up the national distribution as follows: *'The butterfly occurs in the south of England in considerable plenty in particular years, while in others, scarcely an example is to be met with. It seems to*

Clouded Yellow resting in sand dune, Spurn NNR 06/08/1983.

prefer the vicinity of the sea, having been found more copiously than elsewhere along the south-east coast, particularly in the neighbourhood of Dover. It is likewise seen occasionally in the midland counties.'

The pattern of Clouded Yellow arrivals has always been erratic. A few are recorded nationally in most years. Larger numbers sometimes occur in localised areas in other years, whilst more widespread large numbers appear in around 20 individual years in each century, with two of these better years being spectacular in each of the last two centuries, namely: **1826, 1877, 1947** and **1983**. The list below (collated from a wide range of sources) gives years noted nationally as good for the species. They were probably (but not necessarily) also good in Yorkshire. Where this is known for certain, the year is indicated in blue or dark red and starred. Some Yorkshire reports include *helice* specimens, but these are not noted here as their value is doubtful. The earliest Yorkshire sightings so far discovered are in Morris (1853) who refers to 1833 and 1834.

Clouded Yellow Years: 1797, 1804, 1808, 1811, 1818, 1822, **1826*** (One of the best ever.), 1831, 1833 & 1834 (*'a few in Heslington Fields, nr York'* VC61) both years (Morris 1853), 1835, **1842*** (47 seen Heslington Fields, York VC61 Morris (1853). Officially noted for the first time ever in Scotland), 1852 (Good numbers in Scotland), 1858, **1859***, 1864, 1865, 1875, 1876, **1877*** (A spectacular year. Noted in Yorks from 03/06 to 30/09. CB Williams (1958) collated and mapped records which included some 22 Yorks reports from the north, south and east of the county. YNU noted 30+ sites. Carter (1904) wrote: *'Occurred in vast swarms all over the British Isles, with a goodly number…in the Bradford (VC63) district, even in close proximity to the smoky furnaces of Low Moor, truly not a very tempting spot for sun-loving creatures of any species,'* c20 at Flamborough Head on 27/06/1877-WB Turner. Several hundred Scottish records as far north as Orkney.), 1889, **1890*** (*'Quite common in the E of the county'*, Porritt 1904), **1892*** (A few reached Scotland. 1 at Spurn VC61 on 25/08/1892. *'Common in Aug'* in Doncaster area VC63.), **1895***, 1899, **1900***, (Lots in Scotland. *'A remarkable year'* in Doncaster VC63 area, 1 in Scarborough-J H Rowntree), **1913*** (Occurred Bridlington, Hull, Spurn VC61, and Robin Hood's Bay VC62). 1919/21 (3 relatively good years in Northumberland and Durham), **1922*** (Records from Beverley and Allerthorpe VC61), **1928*** (3 in Holderness), **1933***, 1937, **1941*** (*'The great Clouded Yellow Year for Northumberland & Durham'*. Noted in many parts of Yorks 24/06 to 09/09. About 70 records in Scotland. Almost certainly under-recorded due to the war. Several other wartime years were vaguely reported as good, but not detailed.), **1947*** (The best year of the century in one of best summers on record, following one of the worst winters ever. **An estimated 36,000 butterflies on the wing nationally.** 261 records from 18 Scottish counties. *'Common all over the Scarborough district'* with 3 broods noted by GB Walsh. ND Riley estimated 150 on sand dunes at Redcar VC62.), **1949***, 1950, 1955, 1969, (Then a long gap with few records, leading many observers to fear that the modernisation of agriculture on the continent was sounding the death knell to future immigrations.), **1983*** (Warmest July in 100yrs. **Some 15,000 butterflies reported nationally of which 1041 were counted in Yorks across 99x10km squares** and collated by Joyce Payne (1985). First Yorks record: 08/06; last 10/10. Evidence of some reverse migration at Spurn VC61 in Sept & Oct. Around 600 butterflies reported from Sheffield area (Sorby Nat Hist Soc VCs 57 & 63), 122 seen in the Doncaster area VC63 and c100 around Harrogate VC64. Barnham & Foggitt (1987) noted that captured specimens in 1983 were noticeably smaller than those taken in 1947.), **1992*** (A 'Clouded Yellow Year' on the west side of Britain and in Scotland & Ireland. Recorded in 300x10km Scottish squares! Some Yorks records (14 in S Holderness) inc first and last arrivals at Spurn VC61: 15/05 and 05/09), **1996***, **1998***, **2000*** (Last 3 years detailed earlier.).

Marie-Christine Frost

1546 BRIMSTONE *Gonepteryx rhamni* (Linnaeus 1758)
Family: Pieridae, sub-group Coliadinae ('the Yellows').

Busy White Cross Roundabout, (Holderness VC61). Untypical Brimstone colony site!

UK BAP Status: *Not listed.*
BC Priorities: National: *Low.*
N of Eng: *Low.* Yorkshire: *Low.*
European status: *Not threatened.*

WORLD STATUS: Long-lived, nomadic, hibernating resident, 0-2000m+. Usually one brood (Jun/Jun in S; Jul/Jul in N). Possible partial 2nd brood in far south of range. May fly in any month of year. Can emerge from hibernation for short periods when warm enough and return when cold weather dictates. Range: NW Africa to C Norway and east to W Siberia and Mongolia. In Britain range extends only to N England with occasional vagrants reaching Scotland. A separate subspecies *gravesi* Huggins 1956 is found in Ireland. The species is currently extending its range northward in Britain but may be limited by foodplant availability from any further major extension.

YORKSHIRE STATUS 1995/2003:

Very mobile, hibernating resident. One brood, with butterfly stage lasting up to 12 months (approx Jul/Jul). The northern limit of the species in Britain lies across Yorkshire and Cumbria, and has swung back and forth over the years. The latest northern range expansion began around 1982 (Sutton & Beaumont 1989) and still continues. Before 1982, the species was largely confined to VC63 and southern parts of the Vale of York. It is now strongly present in central and eastern parts of VC63; in the Lower Derwent Valley NNR (VC61); in and around Hull (VC61) and the southern edges of the Yorkshire Wolds; in the Howardian Hills and across the southern escarpment of the N York Moors, and in the N York Moors Forest District inc Newton Dale (VC62). The majority of tetrad records represent single sightings of wanderers, whilst tetrad clusters indicate areas of foodplant availability where regular breeding takes place. The northern edges of both the foodplant range and the butterfly's range correspond approximately with the northern edge of OS 100km square SE. The Brimstone is a butterfly invariably seen one or two at a time and even in its hotspot areas site counts (covering up to 1km square) are rarely above the 10/30 range. The butterfly has been recorded in every month of the year in the 1995/2003 period and increasingly reported earlier (Feb/Mar) and later (Sept/Oct). **Earliest record 1995/2003:** 15/01/2002 from Kildale (VC62) [J Leeman] and **latest:** 08/12/2001 in Knaresborough (VC64) [Mike Barnham].

Brimstone

Egg laying.

Sean A Clough

Freshly laid egg.

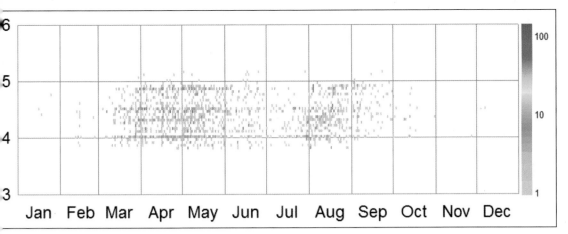

	Jan	Feb	Mar	Apr	May	Jun	Jul	Aug	Sep	Oct	Nov	Dec

D NOTES: Our only **large** yellow butterfly: Large White size. The male is distinctively citrus yellow, the female much paler. Confusion with the Clouded Yellow is possible, but that species is smaller (Small White size) and a much richer orange or mustard yellow. The Brimstone has a small, single, yellowish eyespot on each side of each wing, making the Clouded Yellow's darker upperwing spots and figure of eight lower wing spots distinctive features. The female Brimstone is pale enough to be dismissed as a Large White in flight. In closed-wing view the Brimstone is remarkably leaf-like, with the male yellow and the female creamy white and both sometimes tinged with green. Variation is uncommon with less than 30 aberrations described. Suffusions of orange are possible on the upperwings, and these could give rise to confusion with the Cleopatra. However, such aberrations are extremely rare. Yorkshire reports of the Cleopatra are described in the Rare Species Section of the book.

imstone pupa: Front view. A 'beak' and 'eyes' ake it look pretty dangerous to predators! Hull ly 1996.

PHENOGRAM: Yorkshire 1995/2003. Indicates two showings: spring emergence from hibernation and a summer brood, coupled with a long life and an appearance in every month of the year, albeit very small in the winter months.

Sean A Clough

Brimstone larva: poised to reduce shadow. Shadows attract predators. Hull, July 1996.

Sean A Clough

Brimstone pupa: side view.

CONSERVATION ISSUES: In the 1950s it was thought that Brimstone distribution in the county was always going to be severely limited by the distribution of its foodplants, which were also on the northern edge of their natural range across the county. Garland (1981) summed up the received wisdom of the time: *'The foodplants of the Brimstone are near their northern limit in South Yorkshire, so it follows that the butterfly is similarly restricted, although wandering males are often recorded away from established colonies.'* It now appears that Buckthorns are much more widespread than in the past, having been quite widely planted in gardens; as part of amenity and conservation plantings, and as part of agricultural and forest management. They are not uncommon in hedges and scrubby areas on the Wolds and are found in many parts of the Vale of York, both to the north and south of York. Anyone involved in conservation or amenity planting work can help to improve this situation further by including Buckthorns in any plantings, whilst enthusiasts can valuably add a shrub or two to their gardens (bearing in mind they can grow into medium sized trees if not clipped as hedging plants!). Purging Buckthorn occurs as male or female plants and hedgerow planting should include 1 male to every 5 or 6 females to ensure a supply of berries, which will also attract birds. In turn the birds will spread the species around the neighbourhood! Shrubs can be propagated from fruits and grown on for 2 years before planting. However, to ensure the correct sex, it may be better to take semi-hardwood cuttings with a heel in late summer. Regular records from the Shipley area VC63 during the 1995/2003 period appear to be entirely the result of planting Buckthorns in gardens. Brimstones seem to be able to find and to utilise quite isolated shrubs. The Brimstone is included in Hull City Council's Local Biodiversity Action Plan and 2000 Alder Buckthorns have been planted in various parts of the city in 2003/04 to encourage this species.

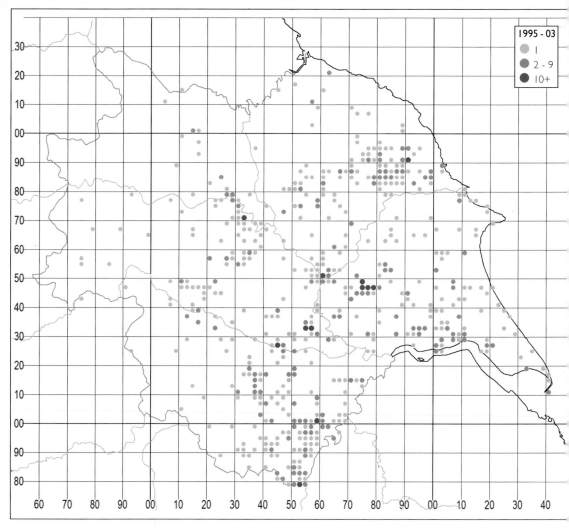

Brimstone: Yorkshire Tetrad map 1995-2003

MAP NOTES 1995-2003: Noted in **525/3319** recorded tetrads (ie 15.8%) and out of 4120 tetrads in the county. **Ranked 20th most widespread** out of 36 breeding species in county. Brimstones tend to be found where their foodplant trees and shrubs are concentrated, hence the clusters of dots on the maps, with red and brown indicating strong colonies, and yellow dots showing wanderers.

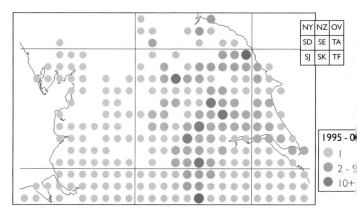

Brimstone: 10km distribution North of England

= I or more records out of county 1995-1999

LIFE STORY

HABITAT: Wanderers can and do turn up in every corner of the county. However, breeding concentrations are only found where the foodplants Common (also known as Purging) Buckthorn *Rhamnus catharticus* or Alder Buckthorn *Frangula alnus* (formerly *Rhamnus frangula*) are present. Purging Buckthorn usually grows into a tree 3-10m (10-30ft) in height. It is found along woodland edges and in scrubby areas and hedgerows, thriving best on poor, dry, chalk and limestone soils but also able to grow on other soils. By contrast, Alder Buckthorn is acid-loving, being found in damp, marshy areas or as an under storey in open woodlands. It grows mainly as a shrub, only occasionally reaching as high as 5-7m (15-20ft). Typical sites on which to find the Brimstone include: **VC61:** Pocklington Canal Head, and Allerthorpe Common, both popular sites. The White Cross roundabout, a busy junction on the Hull/Bridlington road in Holderness is an unlikely setting for a colony which became established following the planting of Buckthorns as part of a County Council amenity project c1990; **VC62:** The species is well-established in the big forests such as Dalby and Langdale and along Newton Dale. It is also found further to the west in the Howardian Hills (eg Yearsley Common); **VC63:** There are many woodland and wetland sites from the eastern edges of Sheffield and Rotherham across to the Doncaster area where Potteric Carr, Sprotborough and Thorne and Hatfield Moors produce regular annual counts; **VC64:** Bishop Wood (nr Selby), Fairburn Ings (RSPB NR) and various sites around Harrogate and Knaresborough produce regular sightings; **VC65:** Both foodplant and butterfly are found in the northern part of the Vale of York up to Northallerton and into the eastern edges of VC65.

Egg laying sites are carefully selected for warmth and shelter and may be over 4m above the ground. Pale bottle-shaped eggs are placed on the undersides of foodplant leaves or on twigs or buds if leaves not yet open. Most sources indicate that the Brimstone only lays on Buckthorn species. However, the accompanying photos illustrate a surprising exception when a female was caught laying on Dock *Rumex* sp in Kirk Dale (nr Kirkbymoorside

VC62) by Neil Rankin on 04/06/1998. Unfortunately, the eggs were not monitored, but the sighting raises some interesting questions. Was it a one-off mistake? Or could it just possibly indicate an overlooked strategy where wanderers caught out, away from their regular foodplants, could temporarily breed on another group of plants? Could this even be a way ahead for expansion beyond the range of its foodplants?

Eggs are laid from April to July and hatch after about 10 days. Dark green larvae take around a month and 5 instars to mature and

Brimstone emerging from pupa. Hull, July 1996.

Sean A Clough

usually leave their buckthorn to pupate in low vegetation. Adult butterflies emerge after about 2 weeks and can remain active until the end of Sept or later, building up reserves for hibernation. The species shows a strong preference for purple flowers when nectaring, and its long proboscis is well-adapted to feeding on flowers like Teasel *Dipsacus fullonum*. Brimstones often hibernate under evergreen leaves, especially Holly *Ilex aquifolium* or Ivy *Hedera helix*. They may test the air on warmer winter days and visit 'Pussy' Willow catkins *Salix* sp or early Dandelions *Taraxacum hamatum* in search of a top-up nectar feed. A sheltered dandelion-rich meadow on Allerthorpe Common (VC61) proved a good place to find early specimens during the Survey period.

Neil Rankin

Neil Rankin

Brimstones are thought to lay eggs singly, although small clusters are sometimes found and assumed to be the work of several females. Neil Rankin photographed this speciment (left) laying on dock *Rumex* sp in Kirk Dale (VC62) on 04/06/1998. It proceeded to lay a cluster of eggs (right).

Tradition has it that the species was once referred to as **the butter-coloured fly** or **Butter Fly,** and from that came the general name 'butterfly', although not everyone agrees. It was first illustrated by Mouffet in 1634, and referred to as the **Brimstone** by Petiver in 1695, a name used consistently ever since, except for an unsuccessful attempt by Rennie in 1832 to change it to the **Primrose** (a plant on which it often nectars). In the current Latin name *Gonepteryx* refers to the angled wings, and *rhamni* to the buckthorn with which it is associated.

The species was known in the first half of the 19th century in S Yorkshire and parts of W Yorkshire. It declined in the second half of the 19th century and almost disappeared from the county during the cold years (1879/95). A slight increase was evident around 1925/30 but the species remained quite rare until the 1970s, since when it has expanded to occupy a greater range than was thought possible due to the limitations imposed by foodplant presence.

Duncan (1844) noted that it was *'generally distributed over southern parts of England: it likewise occurs pretty far to the north as it is abundant at York....'* A likely York area site would have been Askham Bog (VC64). Morris (1853) noted it was found as far north as Yorkshire and Newcastle *'but not by any means so plentifully as in the more southern parts of the country'*. Rimington (1992) describes *'a satisfactory presence'* around Doncaster (VC63) in the early 1800s. The species was recorded in Wath-upon-Dearne (Anon 1832); was abundant throughout the neighbourhood of Askern (Lankester 1842), and *'swarmed'* in Edlington Wood in 1875 (all VC63). Fryer

Brimstone, very fresh and very green. France 1996.

& Lucas (2001) note that in the Huddersfield area (VC63) Hobkirk (1859, 1868) listed it from Lepton, Lockwood, Honley Moor, Farnley Woods and Almondbury Bank. But by the end of the 19th century it had virtually disappeared with only a single Skelmanthorpe record about 1880 and one or two reports from Elland in the early 20th century. Similarly, there were hardly any Doncaster area reports between about 1880 and 1930. Re the Scarborough area (VC62) Walsh (1952) recalled that Thomas Wilkinson (who died in 1876) used to record it in Forge Valley and Yedmandale (probably in the 1860s) and Theakston's Guide (probably 1871) noted: *'Larva breeds on Buckthorn, both of which grow in the neighbourhood'* (ie of Scarborough). However, Tetley (1915) didn't include it at all in his Scarborough area synopsis.

Porritt's (1883) comment: *'Of general occurrence (except in the coal districts of the West Riding, where it is rare)'* was corrected in 1901 to *'Widely distributed, but apparently not nearly so common as my former record would lead one to suppose'*. Porritt's habit of assuming that a report indicated a permanent presence even if that report was 50 yrs old seems to have drawn criticisms here! He fails to distinguish between breeding areas and the one-off records of wanderers. In fact Robson (1902) writing about Durham and Northumberland gives us more detail about this species in Yorkshire than does Porritt! *'So far as I know,* he says, *'G Rhamni does not occur in any portion of Yorkshire which adjoins or approaches the southern portion of the county of Durham and I have been unable to obtain any evidence of its occurrence in the North Riding at all, nor do I think the Butterfly ranges much to the north of central Yorkshire.'* Robson notes just two sightings of wanderers, both from 1889, one seen by LS Brady in Newcastle-upon-Tyne, and the other seen by himself in Hartlepool. The rarity of such observations appears indicative of the fact that the species was also at a low ebb in Yorkshire at this time.

Stainforth (1919) commenting mainly on specimens in the Thomas Stather collection, (probably obtained in the 1860s and 1870s), indicates a Hull area Brimstone presence in Newbald and Gilberdike (VC61). He notes one specimen labelled *'caught in Hedon Road, Hull, 1875.'* and others from Pearson Park and Queen's Road (1887). He continues: *'Ramnus catharticus grows near Everingham and South Cave and I have seen it in hedgerows near Barmby, so there is no reason why specimens of rhamni [the Brimstone] should not be truly natives of the Gilberdike and Newbald districts. Rhamnus frangula is not uncommon in hedgerows near Cottingham'*. When Porritt updated the Hull area list in 1922, he still only had the 1887 records noted above.

JH Seago commented in the YNU Lepidoptera Bulletin No10 (01/06/1958) that the Brimstone *'exists chiefly along the borders of the county with Lincs and Notts'*. Walsh (1952) noted, *'In the Scarborough district it is very rare, and there are few records (except of occasional wanderers) probably owing to the local scarcity of its foodplant...A Smith reports it from the York area in good numbers in 1947/48 but none seen this year, and HW Dobson records a single specimen from 29/09/1945.'* The YNU 1967/70 Report noted that the Brimstone was *'Thinly distributed mainly in the East Riding [presumably at Allerthorpe and the Lower Derwent Valley] and the extreme southern parts of the county. The former flourishing colony at Askham Bog [VC64] must now be regarded as at a very low ebb'*. Heath et al (1984) indicate that by the 1970/82 Survey, the species was already turning up in the N Yorks Moors Forest District where it was not known in the 1950s but has since become well established. Sutton & Beaumont (1989) detected a temporary increase in Yorkshire distribution in the fine summer of 1976, followed by a retraction, before a further spread got underway around 1982, which continues today.

Marie-Christine Frost

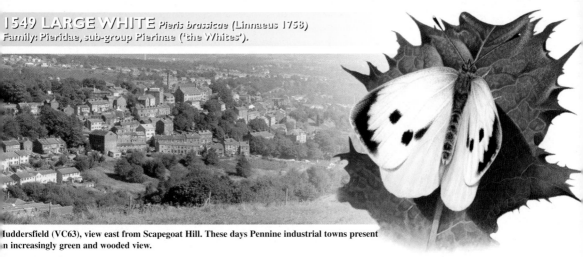

1549 LARGE WHITE *Pieris brassicae* (Linnaeus 1758)
Family: Pieridae, sub-group Pierinae ('the Whites').

Huddersfield (VC63), view east from Scapegoat Hill. These days Pennine industrial towns present an increasingly green and wooded view.

SPECIAL NOTE: Together with the Small White this species is also given the general name **Cabbage White**.

UK BAP Status: *Not listed.*
BC Priorities: National: *Low.*
N of Eng: *Low.* Yorkshire: *Low.*
European status: *Not threatened.*

WORLD STATUS: Common and widespread resident and migrant, 0-2600m. A pest of cultivated cabbage crops. Up to 4 broods possible according to height/latitude (Mar/Nov). Probably an annual migrant in most northerly part of range and a partial migrant elsewhere. Range: N Africa to N Norway and eastward across Asia to Himalayas. Naturalised in Chile, and introduced to Australia, but later eradicated by a parasitic wasp. Widely distributed in British Isles (except in highest areas) as far north as Shetland. In suitable conditions, may be seen flying at any time from Feb to Nov.

Large White

YORKSHIRE STATUS 1995/2003:

Widespread, common, mobile resident, and regular migrant. It should be recorded in every lowland tetrad and many higher ones. Therefore, the accompanying tetrad map shows weaknesses in recording coverage rather than any discontinuous distribution. Usually 2 broods and (in good years) a partial 3rd, with generations often overlapping (Apr/Jun, Jul/Sept, Sept/Oct).

Overlaps can result from immigrants arriving out of phase with resident stock. Immigration may come from southern Europe via a Channel crossing; from the south from other parts of England; or from the south-east, east, or north-east, over the N Sea. Movements through southern and central England tend to reach Yorkshire on a broad and thinning front. Arrivals from N Sea crossings may be localised and quite densely packed. Occasional observations indicate some southward movements in late summer and autumn, and arrivals from the N Sea in August (thought to come from Baltic countries) may be part of an attempted southward return.

The species is commonest in lowland areas, less so on open moors and higher ground where it is mainly seen passing through. Most observations have been of single figures (often ones and twos) with 1st brood site counts generally in the 10/30 range, and second brood 20/300. Third brood numbers are invariably small, usually with 1 to 3 being seen on any one site. The largest 1995/2003 site count was made by Filey Brigg Ornithological Group on 14/08/2001 when over **1500** were logged on Filey's North Cliff (VC61). Such a large coastal count suggests recent immigration from the N Sea direction.

Earliest 1995/2003 record: 17/03/1997, Knaresborough (VC64) [Robert Chandler]; **latest:** 27/10/1999 from Sandal (nr Wakefield VC63) [John Laws]. March and October records have figured in all the years since (and including) 1997.

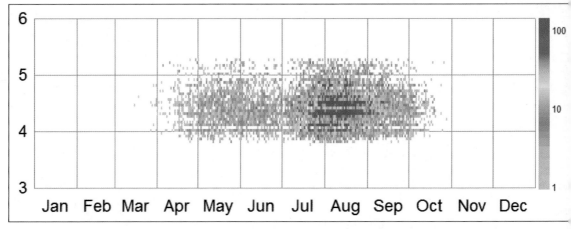

PHENOGRAM: Yorkshire 1995/2003. Shows a smaller spring brood followed by a larger and longer summer brood which probably extends into a partial 3rd generation without any discernible break.

ID NOTES: Although a well-known butterfly, it is often confused with Small White and Green-veined White. All three species vary considerably in size and may just about overlap, so be wary of judging on size alone, although the largest Large Whites (usually 2nd brood females) are distinctively larger. Wing tips are the most diagnostic feature and with practice can often be picked out in flight. Second brood specimens are more strongly marked than those of the 1st. Around 30 aberrations have been described, including a rare sulphur yellow variety ab *flava* Kane and a pink-tinged specimen ab *carnea* Gross-Smith.

CONSERVATION ISSUES: Times have changed since Adrian Haworth suggested in his *Lepidoptera Britannica* of 1803 one answer to controlling this pest: *'In enclosed gardens sea-gulls, with their wings cut, are of infinite service'*. Many would see today's apparently diminished population as an improvement on the past. However, the Large White is a very beautiful butterfly and, in spite of its pest potential, it is a species we would not want to lose. As it is very fond of nasturtiums, some people plant these to give it a place in the garden, or even in an attempt to draw it away from cabbage crops, as an alternative to using sprays. Others pick off and kill larvae from cabbage crops by hand, rather than use chemicals. In this way a few can be left to carry on the population without completely devastating the crops. One cannot help but admire a species which continues to be successful in spite of all that is thrown at it!

WHITES: WING-TIP ID

Many observers overlook recording whites because they can't easily distinguish species. Getting your eye into wing-tip differences will help. But once mastered you also need to take note of the many seasonal differences described in ID books.

LARGE WHITE: Male, summer. Note strong black wing tip with *curving* base, and black *extending* a long way along wing edges.

SMALL WHITE: Male, summer. Note small black wing tip. Usually a flattish bottomed, blotchy patch, often greyish. Rather variable in amount and sometimes almost non-existent. Second brood usually bigger and more strongly marked than first.

GREEN-VEINED WHITE: Male summer. Closed-wing view distinctive. Veins also usually visible on upperwings, though variable. Look for them extending as points from wing tips.

ORANGE-TIP: Female. Note white spots on black wing-tip edge.

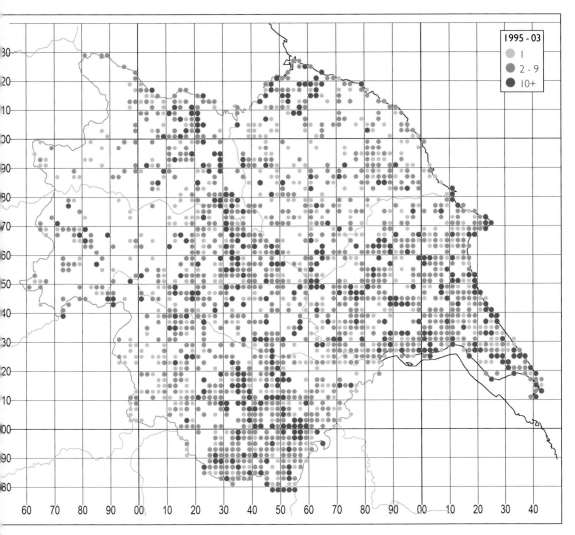

Large White: Yorkshire Tetrad map 1995-2003

MAP NOTES 1995-2003: Noted in 1899/3319 recorded tetrads in the county. Ranked 5th most widespread out of 36 breeding species in Yorkshire. Although one of the most widespread butterflies in the county, the tetrad map indicates much thinner populations on the higher areas of the Pennines and N York Moors, although with a presence along river valleys as shown by lines of dots. Thinner areas of distribution in parts of the Vales of York and Pickering result from under-recording.

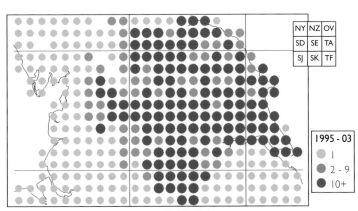

Large White: 10km distribution North of England

● = 1 or more records out of county 1995-1999

LIFE STORY

Large White egg-laying on nasturtium.

Larvae on nasturtium.

Using their antennae, female Large Whites are able to detect the strength of mustard oil in potential larval foodplants and seek to choose plants with the greatest concentration. The oil (a burning irritant) makes larvae distasteful to predators, particularly birds, which is a useful protection. Eggs are then laid in batches of c50 on a wide range of wild and cultivated cabbage family plants. Pale yellow when laid, they eventually turn dark orange and hatch after one to two weeks. Larvae eat their eggshells, then the leaf on which they were laid, before moving on to other leaves or plants. They usually only eat the plant's outer leaves (compared to Small White larvae which mainly specialise on the inner leaves). They grow to c4.5cm/2ins through 5 moults. Pale green, yellow striped and black-spotted, the larvae are initially gregarious and quickly turn the outer part of their foodplants to skeletons. Later, they usually move away individually, searching for somewhere to pupate. This often involves amazing climbs up structures such as tree trunks, pylons or house walls (where they often pupate under the eaves!). Pupae are variable in colour, usually in shades from green to brown, and speckled with black dots. Winter is spent in the pupal stage fixed in position with hooks and a silken girdle. The butterfly emerges when the weather is warm enough, usually around the end of April in Yorkshire, although recent warmer years have also seen a thin scatter of March sightings.

As a potential pest, the Large White is widely controlled by chemical poisons on both commercial and domestic sites. It is also periodically decimated by a tiny wasp *Apanteles glomeratus*. The wasp injects eggs just below the skin of the larvae, enabling the resulting grubs to develop without killing their hosts until just before pupation. As many as 80 wasps may develop on each larva! Thomas & Lewington (1991) indicate that in some years these wasps account for 80% of the population and therefore have much to do with population variations over the years.

First illustrated by Mouffet in 1643, but not given an English name until Petiver (1703) called it the **Greater White Cabbage Butterfly**. Thereafter, it was given a range of similar but slightly different names including the **Large White Garden Butterfly**, the **Great White Cabbage Butterfly** and more simply, the **Large Cabbage** or just the **Cabbage**. The **Large White** was introduced by Haworth (1803) but did not become the standard name until adopted by South in 1906. The general public still call Large White and Small White by the generalised name of **Cabbage White**. In the Latin *Pieris* comes from the Pierides or Muses of Mount Pierus (nr Mt Olympus), and *brassicae* refers to the foodplants (the cabbages).

The noted abundance of the species over the last 200+ years has meant that until recent times, it has been taken for granted and often not distinguished from Small and Green-veined Whites. Details of population swings have been little recorded. Porritt (1883) simply noted, *'Abundant everywhere'*, although in his Hull area summary (1922) he does say, *'Some years very common, other years very rare'*. The YNU 1967/70 Report was no more detailed: *'Usually very common, though scarce in some years'*. The boom years probably correspond to migratory

Large White, pausing to nectar on migration. Spurn 28/08/1982.

arrivals and/or low wasp infestation levels. Garland (1981) highlights an 1819 observation from Ecclesfield (N of Sheffield VC63) when there were, *'the most white butterflies ever remembered by any person'*. These would have presumably included Small Whites as well.

Robson (1902), although not writing about Yorkshire, provides one of the most graphic N of England descriptions of Large Whites coming in from the North Sea close to our northern border. It occurred on a hot day in July 1867 at Hartlepool (just about 4 miles north of South Gare (VC62) on the northern side of the Tees Estuary). Robson noticed *'an unusual number of white butterflies in the street'* at 9am. *'As the day wore on the numbers steadily increased and by 11am a dozen or twenty might be seen flying down the street'* at any one time. *'By noon they were flying in hundreds'* and by 2pm *'there were thousands of them to be seen at once, all flying in one direction from east to west.... Their white colour, and somewhat irregular flight, made them exactly resemble a heavy fall of large flakes of snow'*. This immigration continued until about 5pm when a thunderstorm brought a dramatic end and many butterflies were *'pelted to death by the rain or floated in hundreds along flooded channels'*. Local fishermen confirmed that the butterflies had flown in from the east over a dead calm sea, and they had been surprised to see some of them resting awhile on the water before flying off and continuing their journeys. *'Next day there was a very large number about the streets, but they flew in a desultory manner, and entirely without the steady purpose-like flight of the day before'*.

Butterfield (1925) wrote in the *Naturalist*, *'On 22nd of Aug near Rycroft, Keighley [VC63] white butterflies were so numerous that they gave the impression it was raining butterflies'*. Walsh (1952) points out that the species was common in the Scarborough area (VC62) in 1909, 1926 and 1937. He notes: *'In some years of special abundance it is heavily parasitised – up to 98%, so that such a year may be followed by years of scarcity eg 1927 and 1928'*. He goes on to report that *'WJ Clarke on one occasion observed thousands coming in from the sea; the swarm stretched for some miles along the coast. In the middle of August 1940, there was another swarm of immigrants and a procession of many butterflies flew for some days up the Ramsdale Valley, Scarborough, which runs up from the sea.'* Whiteley (1992) referring to the Sheffield area (VC63) notes, *'Migration north takes place early in the year, and there is some evidence of return migration in summer, eg visible migration studies at Redmires recorded over 600 moving S-SW on 6th Aug 1988, with similar observations at Middleton Moor and Oughtibridge (K Clarkson)'*. Barry Spence (1991) notes that at Spurn (VC61) occasional large-scale movements are seen as early as May (eg 24/05/1979). Some southerly movement usually takes place in August at Spurn with females sometimes laying eggs as they pass through. Such movements generally involve Small and Large Whites together and are usually small scale, but occasionally large, as on 11/08/1979, when both species passed through the reserve for some time at a rate of about 1500 per hour.

In 1955 continental immigrants brought with them granulosis virus, which may have been introduced to protect continental cabbage crops, and may still be affecting the species. Since then, numbers have reportedly never been as high as in the past. Sutton & Beaumont (1989) summed up the regime we still have today: *'Widespread and common throughout the lowlands, but less so than formerly'*.

Adrian Johnson

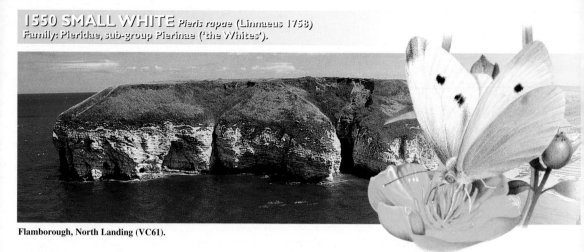

1550 SMALL WHITE *Pieris rapae* (Linnaeus 1758)
Family: Pieridae, sub-group Pierinae ('the Whites').

Flamborough, North Landing (VC61).

SPECIAL NOTE: Together with the Large White this species is also known as the **Cabbage White.**

UK BAP Status: *Not listed.*
BC Priorities: National: *Low.*
N of Eng: *Low.* Yorkshire: *Low.*
European status: *Not threatened.*

Small White on dandelion. Sept 1981.

Small White

YORKSHIRE STATUS 1995/2003:

Common, widespread resident and migrant. Probably, the commonest Yorkshire butterfly. Often the first of the non-hibernating species to be seen on the wing in spring and the last in autumn. Usually 2 broods, plus a partial third in warmer autumns (Mar/Jun, Jul/Sept, Sept/Oct). Subject to seasonal fluctuations, and immigration from further south or the continent, giving the impression of a continuous flight season from Mar to Oct. The 2nd brood is usually (but not always) more numerous than the first. In years boosted by immigration, the difference can be marked, but in years like 2002, where immigration appeared to be minimal, peaks were roughly the same in both generations. In most years there is a wide range of variation in success and failure across the county.

Being such a common butterfly, it does tend to be taken for granted and not systematically identified, recorded or counted, which is a pity! Typical 1st brood site counts tend to be in the 10/100 range, and 2nd brood 10/250 with occasional higher peaks (usually estimated), eg **450** at Goldsborough (nr Harrogate VC64) on 13/08/2001 [Mike Barnham] and **1000** at North Cliff Filey (VC61) on 14/08/2001 [Filey Brigg Ornithological Group]. In most years there are occasions when Small Whites can be seen almost everywhere at the same time, and drift movements can be discerned moving N or S across the countryside according to season. The **earliest** 1995/2003 records were of 2 seen at Husthwaite (N of York VC62) on 24/01/2002 [Mrs MB Duffield], and 1 on 19/02/2002 at Clifton (York VC62) [Mrs B Skerritt]. Jan and Feb 2002 produced some notable warm

WORLD STATUS: Common, widespread resident and migrant, considered a pest of cultivated cabbage family plants. Up to 5 overlapping broods (Feb/Nov) according to latitude/height. Breeds 0-2100m (occasionally seen up to 3500m, probably as a passage migrant). Range: N Africa to N Norway and eastward across Asia to Japan. Probably migratory on northern edge of range. Introduced to N America in 1860 and now common and widespread inc Hawaii. Also introduced to Australia (1939) and Tasmania and New Zealand. Widespread in British Isles, but thinner distribution in Scottish Highlands and largely absent from Orkney and Shetland Isles. Declines noted on the continent in Albania, Finland, Malta and Sweden, balanced by increases in Canary Islands, Netherlands and NW Russia.

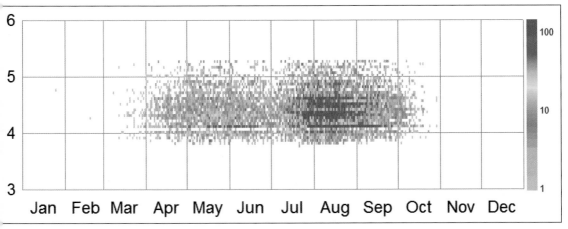

ID NOTES: See diagram on p84.

ID NOTES: See diagram on p84. Readily confused with both Large and Green-veined Whites. Large White usually (but not always) bigger. Summer generation Small Whites are larger than the spring brood and just about overlap in size with smaller Large Whites. Small White has smaller dark wing tip patches, which don't curve far round the wing. 1st brood is paler than second and 1st brood male wing tips can be very pale, almost lacking in colour. Female Small White is more strongly marked than the male, with two spots on each upperside forewing compared to male's single spot. Around 40 variations have been described with a very yellowish form ab *flava* Ter Haar, which in flight might be mistaken for a Pale Clouded Yellow. Occasionally females show the two upper forewing black spots joined up, forming a black bar: ab *fasciata* Tutt. Morris (1853) points out that the black spots on the upperwings are very variable and no two specimens in his collection were the same.

PHENOGRAM: Yorkshire 1995/2003. Two overlapping broods are indicated with the summer generation probably extending into a partial 3rd brood and giving the impression of almost continuous generation.

spells. The main emergence in the county is more usually seen in April and May with a scatter of Mar records in warmer springs. The **earliest** of those has been 10/03/1997 at Blackburn Meadows (Rotherham VC63) [John Law]. Sept numbers drop off fairly steadily on most sites, to ones and twos by the end of the month, followed by a slight rise to threes and fours if Oct produces warm enough weather. **Latest records**, (all singles), have been: 28/10/1997 Harrogate (VC64) [Angela Mettam]; 28/10/1999 and 28/10/2001 Knaresborough VC64 [Mike Barnham]; and 28/10/2001 Spurn NNR (VC61) [Barry Spence]. Regular reports have been received from Grange Moor (Pennines VC63) at 200/300m [Pam Sykes].

Freshly arrived immigrants at Spurn (VC61), Aug 1973.

Typical yellow colouring on fresh specimen. Aug 1996.

CONSERVATION ISSUES: As a pest of cabbage-family crops it would be easy to dismiss the species as unworthy of conservation consideration. However, a few years ago we never imagined that at the beginning of the 21st century we would be seeing the House Sparrow disappear from whole areas of the S of England. We should be wary of taking too much for granted. We need to be alert to the population trends in all our common butterfly species by regular monitoring. The Small White might be a pest, but it is also an important part of the ecological balance in our gardens and countryside in that it provides a food supply for many other creatures, not least the House Sparrow, which eats both eggs and larvae. Larvae are also taken by Song Thrushes and Titmice, as well as being eaten by various species of beetle and harvest spider. Asher *et al* (2001) point out that using chemicals to control pests like the Small White also kills the butterfly's invertebrate predators. In addition, more butterflies quickly move in, and take advantage of laying a new crop of eggs on sites which now have minimal predator protection! An untidy, unsprayed garden with weedy areas can harbour plenty of predators and may well produce cabbage crops with less 'Cabbage White' damage than those which are protected by sprays!

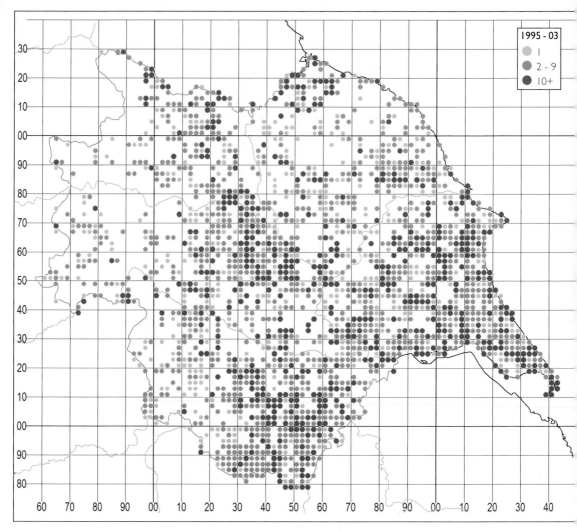

Small White: Yorkshire Tetrad map 1995-2003

MAP NOTES 1995-2003: Noted in **2061/3319** recorded tetrads (ie 62.1%), and out of 4120 tetrads in the county. **Ranked 3rd most widespread** out of 36 breeding species in Yorkshire. Many observers tend to ignore this species in their general recording, therefore it is certainly more common and widespread than these maps and figures suggest. Any gaps in distribution in lowland areas are due to under-recording, therefore the 10km map gives a better impression of distribution than does the tetrad map. However, breeding populations in higher areas are much more dispersed and gaps here are expected.

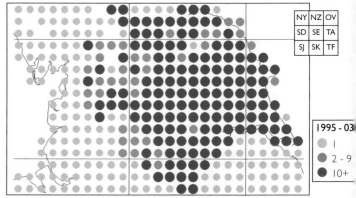

Small White: 10km distribution North of England

● = 1 or more records out of county 1995-1999

LIFE STORY

Small Whites: Mating pair. Withernsea (VC61) 2003.

Eggs laid singly, usually on the undersides of foodplant leaves. Sites chosen for laying are often selected for warmth and shelter with the result that farm cabbage crops may only be infested around the edges of fields. Whitish eggs change to yellow, then grey, and hatch to straw-coloured larvae, which eventually become blue-green covered with tiny black dots and with a line of yellow dots along the sides. Small Whites lack the Large White's protection of an unpleasant taste

White bells provide early spring nectar. Withernsea (VC61) April 1982.

and all stages are eaten by birds. Larvae are strongly attacked by harvest spiders and ground beetles as well as parasitic wasps such as *Apanteles rubecula*. Virus diseases also take a toll, especially in cool, wet summers. The larval stage lasts about 20 days and passes through 5 moults. Larvae on cabbages usually burrow into the centre of the plant where they do a great deal of damage. First brood larvae may pupate on other foodplants, attached to a stem by a silken pad and girdle. Later broods tend to climb tree trunks, buildings and other structures in similar fashion to the Large White. Pupae are well disguised, varying in colour from green to brown, but they are still searched for and eaten by birds. Small Whites pass winter in the pupal stage and can react quickly to early spring warmth, occasionally even emerging during a midwinter mild spell. Once emerged, Small Whites are very active butterflies. Howard Frost (pers comm.) was surprised to find a Small White already busily inspecting his allotment cabbages at 5.55am one warm July morning. Others have been seen after 8pm in the evening. A single larva dislodged from a sprout plant in the writer's garden at Aldbrough (on the Holderness coast VC61) on 09/03/2004 and again a couple of weeks later raises some intriguing questions! Anyone observing a similar occurence should also be wary of the Cabbage Moth *Mamestra brassicae*, the larvae of which have been recorded in every month of the year.

Some researchers (eg Baker 1969) think that Small Whites tend to move northward on an annual basis in spring and return southward in late summer. This may involve movements of British butterflies alone or be added to by immigrants from the continent. Not everyone agrees with the theory, which would be an interesting subject of further study in Yorkshire. Seasonal movements have been noted casually in the county but it is unclear as to whether or not they occur annually and irrespective of any immigration.

First illustrated by Mouffet in 1634 and described by Merrett in 1666. Petiver (1703) gave it the name **Lesser Cabbage Butterfly** and many later authors used different but similar names based on the same theme: eg **Small Common White Butterfly** (Ray 1710), **Small Garden White Butterfly** (Wilkes 1747-49), and **Small Cabbage Butterfly** (Samouelle 1819). **Small White** became the generally accepted name after being introduced by Haworth (1803). In the Latin name, *Pieris* comes from the name of the Greek Muses, the Pierids who were reputed to live on Mount Pierus (nr Mt Olympus, in Greece) whilst *rapae* refers to the wild turnip *Brassica rapa*, one of the Small White's foodplants.

The species appears to have been equally common and widespread for 200yrs or more, so much so that its distribution has invariably been dismissed in general terms by a majority of writers. The 19th century national distribution was summed up as: *'very common in all parts of the country and in most quarters of Europe'* (Duncan 1844); *'very abundant and there are three broods'* (Morris 1853); *'seen during nearly the whole of the summer, and is found almost everywhere'* (Coleman 1860). Yorkshire comments add little: *'Abundant everywhere'* (Porritt 1883); for the Scarborough District (VC62), *'common throughout the district'*, (Walsh 1952); regarding the Sheffield area (VC63): *'has always been very common with variable numbers dependent on migrants'* (Garland 1981); *'has always been well distributed around Doncaster'* (Rimington 1992); and for the Huddersfield area (VC63): *'it has always been widespread'*, (Fryer & Lucas 2001). For the Hull area (VC61) Porritt (1922) noted, *'Common in gardens'*.

Along the way there are hints nationally, that the species may sometimes have been present in bigger numbers than today. Morris (1853) and others describe an *'extraordinary migration'* which took place on 05/07/1846 and was reported in a Kent newspaper the *Canterbury Journal*. Morris writes: *'such was the density and extent of the cloud formed by the living mass, that it completely obscured the sun from the people on board the continental steamers on their passage, for many hundreds of yards, whilst the insects strewed the deep in all directions.* (Note Coleman (1860) uses the same newspaper source but gives *'strewed the **decks**'*, which seems more likely. *'The flight reached England about twelve o'clock at noon, and dispersed themselves inland and along the shore, darkening the air as they went. During the sea passage of the butterflies, the weather was calm and sunny with scarcely a puff of wind stirring, but an hour or so after they reached 'terra firma', it began to blow 'great guns' from the SW, the direction whence the insects came. The gardens suffered from the ravages of their larvae, even at the distance of ten miles from Dover'.* (It is surprising that despite occasional reports like this, few lepidopterists of the time realised that migration was such a notable feature of the butterfly world.)

In their detailed study of the Huddersfield district Fryer & Lucas looked in vain for any indications that the Small White had suffered in the same way as so many other species towards the end of the 19th century. They concluded: *'It has been present in the area since recording began, but as any decline in resident stock would be made good by immigration, its apparent immunity from whatever caused the local extinctions of several species in the late 19th century, may be misleading.'* Sutton & Beaumont (1989) considered it, *'Probably the most common white over much of the County with a similar distribution to P. brassicae [Large White]'*. Whiteley (1992) said it was *'A difficult species to assess accurately because it is under recorded'*. He reports a flight period in the Sheffield area running from 26/03 to 14/10 with occasional individuals seen in Feb and early March.

Spence (1991) in summarising the lepidoptera recording at what is now Spurn National Nature Reserve noted that the first recorded sighting at Spurn was on 03/08/1919 [J Porter]. He points out that Small Whites and Large Whites often migrate together, with the former being more numerous. Such movements are, he says, *'often only small scale, though can be quite large, as on 11th August 1979, when check counts showed they were passing at a rate of 1,500 per hour. Very occasionally, there have been north-west movements in August as well, as on the 16th August 1979, when large numbers of 'whites' came in from the south-east'*.

Adrian Johnson

Small and Green-veined Whites feeding on sheep droppings, N Wolds (VC61).

Countryside around Ingleborough (VC64).

UK BAP Status: *Not listed.*
BC Priorities: National: *Low.*
N of Eng: *Low.* Yorkshire: *Low.*
European Status: *Stable.*

Worn Green-veined White. Note upperwing veins.
26/08/1981 Burnby Hall (VC61).

YORKSHIRE STATUS 1995/2003:

Resident. Usually 2 overlapping broods (Apr/Jun and Jun/Aug); with a small partial 3rd in warmer years (Sept/Oct). Higher areas may only produce 1 brood (Jun/Jul). Single brooded populations are thought to remain single brooded even in warmer years. This deserves further research, especially in the Dales (VCs64/65). Single brooded populations are also thought to be more sedentary than their lowland cousins. Although Green-veined Whites are less mobile than Small and Large Whites, the double-brooded variety does wander, and although not generally considered migratory, occasional long-distance movements are suspected. In this respect sudden build-ups sometimes observed at traditional migration hotspots along Yorkshire's east coast deserve more study.

By tetrad count this species is the second most widespread Yorkshire species after the Small Tortoiseshell. Typical site counts are generally in the 1 to 10 range, with observed peaks around 20/30 in the 1st brood and 20/250 in the 2nd. Highest site counts in the Survey Period have included: **VC61: 250** at Spurn NNR on 19/07/1998 [Barry Spence], **VC62: 215** at

Green-Veined White

WORLD STATUS: Mobile resident with uncertain status as a migrant. Up to 4 overlapping broods depending on latitude, height and weather (Mar/Oct). Range: NW Africa to N Scandinavia and eastward across Asia and N America (where it is known as the **Veined White** or **Mustard White** *Artogeia napi.*) A very variable species across its range, controversially split into many subspecies. Tolman (1997) suggests it is in *'an active state of evolution'.* Pyle (1981) referring to N America notes, *'It may well consist of more than one biological species'.* Found throughout British Isles except Shetland, with 3 subspecies described, but confusion over subspecies names and ranges! English specimens currently referred to subspecies *sabellicae* Stephens 1828, or *septentrionalis* Verity 1916. At some point north of Yorkshire the English subspecies gives way to a more strongly marked subspecies *thomsoni* Warren 1968, which (according to Thomson 1980) is found right across Scotland. However, not everyone agrees. Some suggest that *thomsoni* is restricted to Perth, Fife and Stirling. Subspecies *britannica* Müller & Kautz 1939 is found in Ireland and is similar in looks to the Scottish race. Increases noted in Netherlands and Romania.

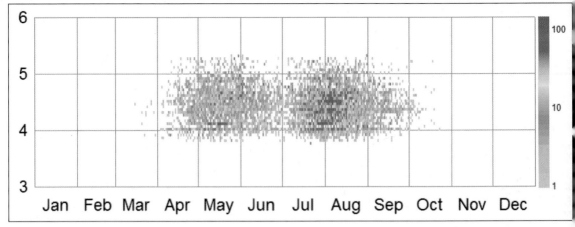

ID NOTES: See diagram on p84. Usually a medium sized, white butterfly, easily confused in flight with Small White, Large White and female Orange Tip. Size can vary considerably from half-sized miniature editions with similar wingspan to Common Blue, to 'giants' close in size to Large White. Summer brood is on average larger in size than spring brood. Closed-wing view of a resting butterfly is usually distinctive, with fuzzy, grey-green veins against a mainly yellowish background (although background colour is quite variable). Upperside wings have less well-marked dark veins in male, and more strongly marked in female. Upper forewings have dark wing tips broken by white strips of varying width. Very variable species with around 80 aberrations described. Ab *sulphurea* Schöyen has pale citrus-coloured upperwings and might be mistaken for a Pale Clouded Yellow.

CONSERVATION ISSUES: At first sight there seems little to be concerned about over such a widespread species able to wander sufficiently in search of new sites and able to use quite marginal, damp habitats. Drought years are known to be a problem, but in recent times (eg following the very hot summer of 1976) it has shown itself able to spring back within a year or two of any losses. Nonetheless, global warming is of potential concern, particularly for the one-generation upland form. It would be valuable to study the extent of this form in Yorkshire and to monitor its success separately from the species at large.

PHENOGRAM: Yorkshire 1995/2003. Shows two generations, both with a tendency to peak later in the North. Additional peaks mid-Sept/Oct probably indicate a partial 3rd brood.

Strensall Common YWT NR on 30/07/2000 [Pat & Jim Bone], **VC63: 106** at Hatfield on 12/08/2000 [Ken Woolley], **VC64: 250** at Aubert Ings, Cattal on 29/07/1997 [Mike Barnham], **VC65: 40** at Hunton 01/08/1999 [Charles Chandler], and **41** at Foxglove Covert, Catterick on 05/08/2003 [Sam Ellis]. **Earliest** records are usually in early Apr, but a scatter of Mar appearances have also been noted, the earliest being 19/03/1998 at North Cave [Rosemary Roach]. Prior to the 1990s, **last sightings** often came quite abruptly at the end of Aug, even in the warmer parts of VC61. Between 1996 and 2003 last records have been between 16/09 and 24/10, the latter at Wombwell (VC63), in 2001 [Dean Stables]. This seems to indicate the development of a regular partial third brood. However, autumn numbers remain small with sightings mainly in single figures.

A sudden shower. Butterfly drops into cornfield, but keeps wings open. Wolds (VC61) 2001.

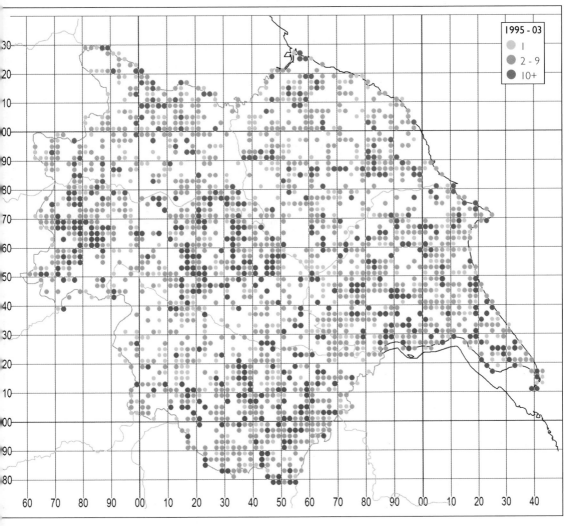

Green-Veined White: Yorkshire Tetrad map 1995-2003

MAP NOTES 1995-2003: Noted in 2109/3319 recorded tetrads (ie 63.5%), and out of 4120 tetrads in Yorkshire. Ranked as 2nd most widespread out of 36 species breeding in the county. Although generally less numerous than the Small White, its ability to utilise both highland and lowland habitats makes it marginally more widespread. The tetrad map reveals under-recorded areas in the Vales of York and Pickering where the species is actually very much at home in the damper habitats along ditches, streams and rivers.

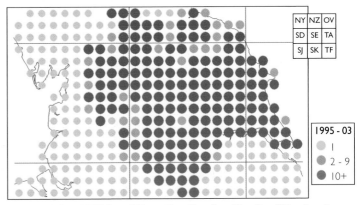

Green-Veined White: 10km distribution North of England

= 1 or more records out of county 1995-1999

LIFE STORY

HABITAT: Although widespread, the species is localised by a need for damp and humid areas. It uses a wide range of cruciferous plants, but its main foodplants tend to be: Lady's Smock *Cardamine pratensis*; Garlic Mustard *Alliaria petiolata*; Hedge Mustard *Sisymbrium officinale* and Watercress *Nasturtium officinale*. Typical habitats are found in association with marshes, bogs, canal and river banks, slow moving streams, lush ditches and damp meadows. The butterfly also favours sheltered woodland edges and rides where males can often be seen patrolling quite high up along the lines of trees. It is also found along road and rail verges, especially where hedges or trees give rise to shadier damper sections. Although a regular visitor to gardens, numbers are usually low, and probably represent wandering individuals. There have long been colonies at Spurn NNR which seems a somewhat untypical habitat comprising a line of sand dunes sandwiched between the N Sea and the Humber Estuary. The butterfly is also found up to 300m in sheltered valleys west of Sheffield and on moors above Huddersfield and Ripponden (all VC63), and up to 450m in the Stang forest (VC65). Barnham & Foggitt (1987) report seeing it on the summit of Little Whernside 604m/1982ft. The species is one of the commonest in the Yorkshire Dales and on the North Yorkshire Moors where additional rainfall gives rise to plenty of suitably damp areas.

Green-veined White: mating pair.

day). Thin-skinned pupae go on to produce another generation within as little as 10 days, whilst thick-skinned varieties will hibernate for 7-11 months. Up to 40% of pupae appear to be killed by a virus during hibernation.

Males usually emerge a few days before females and patrol habitats in search of mates. They shower potential partners with a chemical, which smells like Lemon Verbena, and is strong enough to be picked up by humans. This action is usually followed by a chase and then by pairing. Finally, the male smears another chemical on the female, which dissuades other males from pursuing his female. However, this effect only lasts a few days so the female later goes on to attract and mate with other males, apparently to get more smears of anti-male chemical, which help to provide her with quiet periods in which she can concentrate on laying eggs. Adult males often land on the muddy edges of puddles or on animal droppings to suck up sodium and essential minerals.

Eggs laid singly and well scattered on the undersides of leaves of cruciferous plants such as those mentioned above. Sutton & Beaumont (1989) include a report by AMR Heron on the occasional use of aubretia as a foodplant in gardens. However, the species mainly uses wild plants and is not a pest. Eggs hatch after about a week. Larvae eat their eggshells then begin to tackle foodplant leaves. They pupate after two to three weeks and 5 instars. Pupae occur in brown, green or mixed colour forms and are hidden away near ground level and very difficult to find. Every pupa has the possibility of being thin-skinned (if produced when there are 12 or more hours of daylight, or thick-skinned (when daylight hours are waning, with less than 12 hours in the

Small and Green-veined Whites feeding on sheep droppings. (Thixendale VC61).

HISTORICAL REVIEW:
Green-veined White

First illustrated in 1634 by Mouffet, and named the **common white veined-Butterfly** by Petiver in 1699. Then, for a while, 3 similar names were circulated because it was thought there were 3 similar species: **the common white veined Butterfly with single spots**; **the common white veined Butterfly with double spots**, and **the lesser, white, veined Butterfly**. Albin (1720) used **Green Veined Butterfly** whilst Lewin (1795) was first to introduce **Green-veined White**. Stephens (1828) also thought there were two species, which he called the **Turnip** and the **Colewort**. Fortunately, the more attractive Green-veined White or just the **Green veined** (Morris 1853) won the day. In the Latin, *Pieris* was one of the Muses associated with Mt Pierus (nr Mt Olympus) in Greece, and *napi* is derived from the plant name, Rape *Brassicae napus*.

It appears from the general comments of past authors that the species has been common and widespread in the county over the last 200yrs and more. Unfortunately, as a result, there are few detailed comments or dated records. Duncan (1844) noted, *'This butterfly is one of the most common species both in this country and throughout Europe'.* Morris (1853) wrote: *'The Green-veined White is another of our most common native species. It occurs about the middle of May, and also in July, and is found in all situations – gardens, woods, lanes and fields'.* He illustrates a remarkably small specimen, which he caught himself. Porritt (1883, 1907) simply wrote, *'Abundant everywhere'*, and for the Hull area (1922): *'Common in lanes'.* Walsh (1952) writing of the Scarborough area, commented: *'Common throughout the district, especially in woods and dales.'* Interestingly, he goes on to say, *'In favourable years its numbers are increased by immigration'.* However, Sutton & Beaumont (1989) express the opinion that *'there is little immigration in this species'.* Fryer & Lucas (2001) highlight an interesting record in Frohawk (1934). Apparently, considerable migrations of this species were observed in 1933 in Cumberland (at over 600m) and Northumberland, both on the same day. Barnett *et al* (2003) report an influx of 50 seen arriving at Steepholme, an island in the Bristol Channel in 1990. It certainly seems that occasional migrations cannot be ruled out. The YNU 1967/70 Report noted the species, *'Generally common in all districts'*, whilst Sutton & Beaumont (1989) commented that it was: *'A very hardy species, being the most common white of the higher ground to the north and west of the County'.* They add that it was also found *'over most of the rest of Yorkshire, but much less frequent in suburban gardens'.*

Fryer & Lucas, in their study of Huddersfield butterflies, discuss the history of the Green-veined White since the end of the last Ice Age. They consider suggestions that the single brooded population may have spread across from Europe when the North Sea was still a land bridge, whilst the multi-brooded variety is more likely to have arrived later from the warmer south. The single brooded colonies can survive in cold climates, which is why they are so successful in our highest areas. The multi-brooded specimens prefer lowland warmth. Neither appears to interbreed with the other, although this is an area which needs further study, especially in the Yorkshire Dales. If they really are so independent of one another, the question must arise as to whether or not they could represent a separate species. Current opinion suggests this is unlikely. Fryer & Lucas point out that Porter & Geiger (1995) sampled the genetic content of several Scottish populations plus one from lowland Yorkshire. However, the results, say Fryer & Lucas, *'were confusing and ambiguous'.* It confirms that, right around the northern hemisphere, this is a challenging species!

Adrian Johnson

Left: Nectaring on knapweed. Centre: Nectaring on hawthorn blossom. Right: Freshly emerged inside a commercial greenhouse.

1553 ORANGE-TIP *Anthocharis cardamines* Linnaeus 1758
Family: Pieridae, sub-group Pierinae ('the Whites').

High Force (Teesdale VC65) on the traditional Yorkshire border (Yorkshire to left, Co Durham to right).

UK BAP Status: *Not listed.*
BC Priorities: National: *Low.*
N of Eng: *Low.* Yorkshire: *Low.*
European Status: *Not threatened.*

WORLD STATUS: Resident, 0-2200m. Single brood (Mar/Jul). Range: Mediterranean (except southern parts of Spain & Portugal) to C Scandinavia and eastward across Asia to Japan. Ssp *britannica* Verity 1908 in Britain; *hibernica* Williams 1916 in Ireland. Widespread in Britain and Ireland except Scottish Highlands where it is more localised. Absent from Outer Hebrides, Orkney and Shetland. A 40% increase by 10km squares noted in Britain since the 1970/82 Survey. It is spreading on the northern edge of its range in Britain and Europe.

Orange-tip

YORKSHIRE STATUS 1995/2003:

Widespread, common resident. Single brood: usually May/June but May and Jul records not infrequent. Exceptionally late records noted in Whiteley (1992): Sheffield area (VC63) 02/08/1981, and Frost & Winter (2001): Grosmont (VC62) 19/10/2000 [R McLaren] may indicate attempts at a 2nd brood. (Aug and Sep records are reported from S England from time to time. Emmet & Heath (1989) are unsure as to the status of such sightings. However, as the species is single-brooded throughout its range a 2nd brood seems unlikely. See further comments below.)

Making sense of the tetrad distribution is complicated by the fact that there are gaps in known under-recorded areas such as the Vales of York and Pickering, although sample counts along roadside verges indicate the species is relatively common in both regions. Unfortunately, weather in May and June is often cool and changeable and does not encourage observers to make long journeys to check out this species. Although there has been an overall increase in distribution, especially in the west of the county, it is probable that there have also been some local retractions in more open situations, due to inclement weather. Populations in Pennine dales and in the higher parts of the N York Moors may well be thin due to height, but probably not quite as thin as the map appears to indicate. Recorder coverage is simply not big enough to check out the huge area occupied by this species on an annual basis.

Most observations are of males in ones and twos. Females tend to be more sedentary and are generally overlooked. The following summaries are included to typify the seasonal variations of our 1995/2003 recording period, although 1995 has not been included as the data for that year was rather limited. FR = first record of the year. LR = last record. HC = highest count of the year.

1996: FR: 04/05 Low Bentham (VC64) [Terry Whitaker].
HC: **32** (03/06) Ottringham (VC61) [Chris Frost].
LR: 17/07 Raindale (VC62) [John Hume, D Hardcastle].

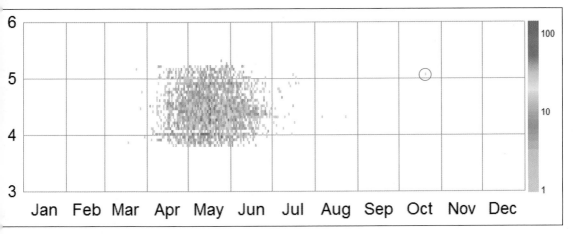

6													100
5													
4													10
3													1
	Jan	Feb	Mar	Apr	May	Jun	Jul	Aug	Sep	Oct	Nov	Dec	

ID NOTES: Male distinctive, being a white butterfly with orange wingtips. Female lacks orange and is easily overlooked as it looks like a Small White, although flight often less determined. Both sexes show a mottled pattern on lower wing in closed-wing view. This is made up of black and yellow scales, yet gives a greenish-grey effect. Males relentlessly patrol territories whilst females spend much time sitting and waiting. A very variable species with over 50 aberrations described including males with yellow rather than orange wing tips. Very small specimens can also be found.

CONSERVATION ISSUES: Damp meadows with lady's smock are a key habitat for this species, but one which has been steadily disappearing in the interests of improving pastures. Wherever possible such meadows should be preserved. But even where they are preserved, grazing or mowing needs to be delayed until larvae leave their foodplants. The fact that Orange-tips are so widespread on county roadside verges, may well owe its origins to modern approaches to maintenance. Restricting cutting to a metre strip allows the foodplant garlic mustard to grow unhindered, especially where hedgerows provide suitable protection. In fact the general trend towards re-instating hedgerows may actually be creating additional Orange-tip habitat and encouraging the species to spread further. Unfortunately, some farmers cut the whole roadside verge adjoining their fields which destroys the habitat required by this species.

PHENOGRAM: Yorkshire 1995/2003. Clearly single brooded and showing a remarkably synchronous emergence from S to N. The rather strange Oct record is explained in the text.

1997: FR: 30/03 Potteric Carr (VC63) [Ken Woolley].
HC: **60** (02/05) Wintersett (VC63) [Wintersett Wildlife Group].
LR: 18/06 Tophill Low (VC61) [David Woodmansey],
and S Kirby (VC63) [Richard Sunter].

1998: FR: 20/04 Wheldrake (VC61) [Craig Ralston].
HC: **30** (15/05) Elland (VC63) [P Martin].
LR: 29/06 Wassand (VC61) [Brian Mallison].

1999: FR: 03/04 Roche Abbey (VC63) [Bill Ely].
HC: **40** (27/05) Fulford, York, (VC61) [Pat Bone].
LR: 19/07 Bedale (VC65) [Charles Chandler].

2000: FR: 10/04 Preston-under-Scar (VC65) [E Green].
HC: **52** (20/05) Fairburn Ings RSPB NR (VC64) [P Stephenson].
LR: 13/07 Gundale (VC62) [B Blake, B Ingram].

2001: FR: 21/04 Sprotborough (VC63) [Dave Booth].
HC: **120** (24/05) Sheffield (VC63) [Cheryl Gibson].
LR: 08/07 Ellis Lathe (VC63) [Wintersett Wildlife Group].

2002: FR: 01/04 South Woundales Beck (VC65) [MJ Osgood].
HC: **60** (11/05) Bishop Monkton Ings (VC64) [Mike Barnham].
LR: 05/07 Ripon Parks (VC64) [Jill Warwick].

2003: FR: 17/03 Rotherham (VC63) [Bill Ely].
HC: **43** (18/04) York Cemetery [Pat & Jim Bone].
LR: 16/07 Wakefield [Andrew Bedford]

Orange-tip: mixed gynandromorph (= male & female features mixed up in same specimen). Denaby Ings NR, 21/05/2001 (Mexborough, VC63), courtesy HE Beaumont collection. Upperwing view left, underwing right.

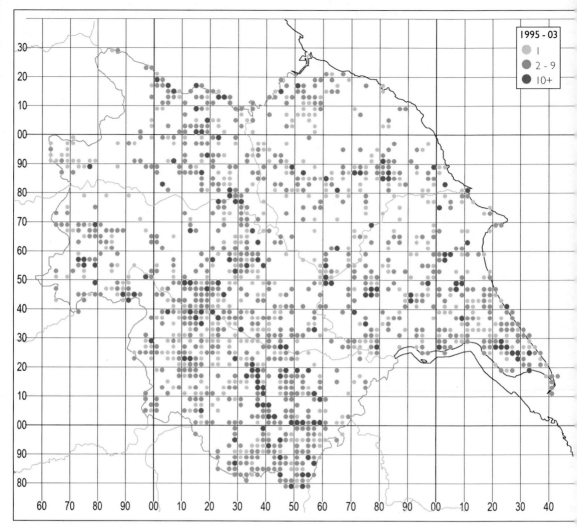

Orange-tip: Yorkshire Tetrad map 1995-2003

Noted in 1386/3319 recorded tetrads (ie 41.8%), and out of 4120 tetrads in Yorkshire. Ranked 8th most widespread out of 36 breeding species in the county. The maps appear to indicate a somewhat uneven presence, but this may well be a false impression resulting from under-recording. The Orange-tip is a common road verge species in lowland areas, especially along country lanes, but many observers only record on nature reserves or in hotspot areas. Spring visits by the editor to the Vale of Pickering in 2004 revealed the species as common there as elsewhere.

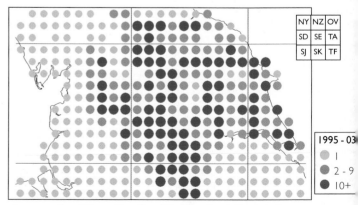

Orange-tip: 10km distribution North of England

◔ = 1 or more records out of county 1995-1999

LIFE STORY

HABITAT: Damp meadows, marshy areas, ditches or river banks, with Cuckooflower/Lady's Smock *Cardamine pratense*, or rail or roadside verges, field margins or forest rides with Garlic Mustard/Jack-by-the-Hedge *Alliaria petiolata*. Whilst these appear to be the main foodplants, over 30 other cruciferous species have also been noted as being used by this species. *The Naturalist* (1941 p248) carries a report of Orange-tip larvae noted on Nasturtium *Tropaeolum majus* at Cawood (VC64) on 12/07/1941. Orange-tips tend to be more localised in the north than in the south. Sightings from VC65 included 1997 observations in a garden near Leyburn at c270m/c800ft [Judy Brown] and from Marrick at c330m/1000ft [Hilda Hodgson]. The species also visits gardens and may lay on Honesty *Lunaria annua*, Rocket *Sysimbrium* sp or Arabis *Arabis* sp. On cool, bright days in May when northerly winds provide a last hint of winter chill, this species may be quite active, hidden below ground level in the micro-climate warmth and shelter of deep ditches.

Spindle-shaped eggs are laid singly on cruciferous plants in May and June. The female is able to apply a chemical test via her feet to ensure the plant she chooses contains mustard oils, which make the butterflies unpalatable to birds. The male's orange tips serve as a warning of that fact. Eggs hatch after 1 to 2 weeks into dark green larvae, which feed on the developing seed heads of the plant. Each larva needs the benefit of a whole plant and in the rare event of additional eggs having been laid on the same plant, the strongest larva will eat any opposition. Larvae are subject to attacks from invertebrate predators, from birds and from a parasitic fly *Phryxe vulgaris*. After 3 to 4 weeks they leave their foodplants and travel for up to 30hrs to pupate in brown, or more rarely green, forms, deep in protective vegetation and possibly quite high up. Winter is passed in the pupal stage. Emmet & Heath (1989) draw attention to the fact that occasionally this may last through a second winter. Such a possibility may also be linked to the odd late appearances noted above, where something triggers an interruption to a second winter hibernation. Adults emerge in spring usually during the first warm spell in April or May. Males usually appear about a week before the first females.

Butterfly emerging from pupal case.

Sean A Clough

Orange-tips: mating pair.

Dean Stables

Larva on Lady's Smock.

Orange-tips: courting pair.

Sean A Clough

First called **the white marbled Butterfly** by Petiver (1699). Dutfield (1748) later called it the **Wood Lady** or **Prince of Orange**. Wilkes (1747-1749) introduced **Orange-tip Butterfly** but several names circulated well into the 1800s before **Orange-tip** became generally accepted. In the current Latin name *Antho* means a flower, and *charis* grace, used perhaps in the sense of the butterfly adding beauty to the flowers. The species name *cardamines* refers to the bitter-cress family to which it is linked by foodplant.

The Orange-tip appears to have been quite widespread in the first half of the 19th century. Duncan (1844) noted that it *'seems to occur in considerable plenty in all parts of Britain and it is not infrequent in Ireland'*. Then it appeared to suffer a serious crash across the northern half of Britain. Robson (1902) commented in relation to Durham and Northumberland: *'For some years this pretty species has all but disappeared from our district, but it has since resumed its usual numbers again. The disappearance was simultaneous with that of other species'*. Dunn & Parrack (1986), referring to Robson's comment, note: *'The decline referred to here seems to have started in the 1860s or 1870s in VC66, with some resurgence by the time Robson finished the first part of the Catalogue in 1899'*. However, the species continued to disappear from many Durham and Northumberland sites in the early 1900s and numbers remained low until the 1960s. Thomson (1980) notes similar declines in Scotland in the 1880s and 1890s with the species continuing at a low ebb there until the 1950s when a slow recovery began which continues today and has recently become quite notable. Early records suggest that

Foodplant flower Jack-by-the-Hedge showing why it got its name!

there was also a retraction in Yorkshire around the same time, although wi[th] a patchy survival on sheltered sites.

Rimington (1992) produces Yorkshire's earliest reports: Wath-upon-Dear[ne] (Anon 1832); *'Abundant'* at Askern (Lankester 1842); Adwick [JW Dunni[ng] 1846]; Roche Abbey 1858 (Smith 1858); Edlington Wood 1871 [W Burma[n] and 1888 [AE Hall]; Wadworth Wood (1888); Wheatley Wood (1898); Ne[w] Park Spring Wood (1899) (A Whitaker diaries) (all VC63). The A Whitak[er] diaries also indicate that the species had become scarce around Barnsley b[y] 1900. Fryer & Lucas pick up a similar story of reduction around th[e] Huddersfield area (VC63): *'it was certainly rare or absent from most of t[he] Huddersfield area towards the end of the 19th century and continued to be s[o] for some time after.'* They quote Butterfield (1911) who referred to an *'almo[st] total disappearance'* around Bradford. By contrast, Garland (1981) suggest[s] that in the Sheffield (VC63) area *'populations and range appear to have bee[n] always about the same'*. Tetley (1915), writing about the Scarborough (VC6[2?] area, noted the Orange-tip *'very scarce near Scarborough'* but *'common [at] Thornton Dale and further west'*. It would seem fair to conclude that the co[ld] years (1879/1895) affected Yorkshire populations, but without wiping the[m] out. As far as can be deduced from generally scant details, the majority [of] published Yorkshire records from the 1890s into the early 20th century appe[ar] to be from woodlands or sheltered valleys. It may well be that the bad weath[er] years removed the species as a butterfly of the wider countryside. Population[s] in the Doncaster (VC63) area appear to have remained about the same lev[el] until a slight increase was noticed around 1940. Porritt (1883 & 1907) ad[ded] little to our knowledge, writing the same comment in both lists: *'General[ly] common throughout the county, but less so in some parts of the West Riding[.]* Stainforth makes no comment for the Hull (VC61) area but simply lis[ts] Birkhill Wood, Riplingham and Cottingham as Orange-tip sites (in the mi[d] 19th century). Porritt's 1922 Hull area list noted the species as: *'Common[.]* These various comments seem to indicate that Yorkshire was on a boundar[y] in the late 19th century, between severe losses of this species to the north, an[d] more stable populations to the south. Rimington (1992) points to the fact tha[t] populations in Lincolnshire, Nottinghamshire and Derbyshire appeared [to] have changed little in the second half of the 19th century, whilst those to th[e] west and north of Yorkshire were affected in some degree. Even so, the[re] appears to have been a patchwork of survival and a YNU visit to Grassingto[n] in Wharfedale on 20/06/1891 (*Naturalist* 1891 p265) recorded the species i[n] its report.

Recovery was initially slow, beginning in the 1940s when a sighting at Austwic[k] Moss reported in *The Naturalist* (1940 p213) was noted as *'unexpected'*. Wals[h] (1952), referring to the Scarborough area, wrote, *'It has definitely grow[n] commoner of recent years and can now be seen regularly every year in Forg[e] Valley, Pickering etc.* The YNU 1967/70 Report noted: *'Although varying i[n] numbers from year to year, and to some extent local, it may be regarded [as] generally common, less so in industrial parts of the West Riding.'* Sutton [&] Beaumont (1989) highlighted an expansion gathering momentum: *'There ha[s] been a considerable range extension since the early 1970s.....first noted in 197[?] when it was plentiful at Castleford (VC63) and the first for about 30yrs was see[n] at Muston [nr Filey] (VC61)'*. They also commented that it was *'widespread [in VC65] between Leyburn and Bedale, less frequent westwards of Leyburn, b[ut] common in Sedbergh. Also reported as far west as Lawkland and Austwic[k] Mosses (VC64) in 1985'*. Barnham & Foggitt (1987), writing about th[e] Harrogate area, noted it was by then *'widely distributed...in lowland areas. [It] seems to penetrate no further up our dales than Gouthwaite and Leighto[n] Reservoirs and it is not found on the moorland'*. In the 1990s the species ha[s] continued to expand to the point where it is now becoming difficult to separa[te] growing distribution from growing recorder effort.

Marie-Christine Fros[t]

Green Hairstreak habitat on hillside above Holm Industrial Estate, Ovenden, Halifax (VC63).

UK BAP Status: *Not listed.*
BC Priorities: National: *Low.*
N of Eng: *Medium.* Yorkshire: *Medium.*
European status: *Not threatened.*

WORLD STATUS: Resident: 0-2300m. Single brood (Mar/Jul). Range: N Africa to N Norway and eastward through Turkey, Russia & Siberia to Amur. Europe has a very similar second member of the *Callophrys* family: Chapman's Green Hairstreak *Callophrys avis* (N Africa/SW Europe). N America also has a range of close relatives which look very similar and might even include *rubi* under a different name. Widespread but local throughout mainland Britain and Ireland.

Green Hairstreak

YORKSHIRE STATUS 1995/2003:

Very local resident: one brood, (late Apr/mid-Jun). Found mainly in upland moorland areas, with Pennine sites forming a vast complex of colonies extending southward into Derbyshire and Cheshire, westward towards the Forest of Bowland, and northward into County Durham. The species is also widespread on the N Yorkshire Moors and there are a few scattered colonies in lower areas eg Cottam/Cowlam on the Wolds (VC61), Strensall (VC62) and at Spurn NNR (VC61). The Spurn colony is unusual in that it appears to represent a recent northward expansion along the Lincolnshire coast, which would have involved the butterflies crossing 5 miles of open estuary water. Following a first sighting on 31/05/1983 [Steve Lister], and a further single sighting on 04/06/1993 [Barry Spence], a small gorse based colony (established in 1993/94) has survived in a sand-dune habitat at the tip of the 4 mile long peninsula producing max counts of 5 or 6 butterflies throughout our Survey period (and up to 16 in 2004). In upland areas it is usually found in relatively small numbers, typically in the 10-20 range, but with larger populations in certain areas of heather moorland where the growth of bilberry is also extensive. Estimates of **1000+** were made by Dave & Stuart Wise on hillsides between Sowerby Bridge and Ripponden (VC63) in May 1997 and at Queensbury (VC63) in 2001. Graham Foggitt reported similar numbers in Nidderdale: Woo Gill (VC64) in May 1997, and the writer counted around **550** at Stock Beck Moor (VC64) in May 1990. The **earliest record** known was on 30/03/2003 when 2 were seen at Eldwick (VC64) [Susan Stead]. Typical **latest records** include 17/06/2002 at Bastow Wood (VC64) [Dave and Rosemary Howson], and 18/06/1997 at Spurn [Barry Spence]. One exceptionally late record was made on the N York Moors on 19/07/1997 [Joyce Payne]. Steve Graham had an unusual experience on 03/05/2002 near Langsett Reservoir (in the Dark Peak area of S Yorkshire VC63) when he came across 5 Green Hairstreaks already on the wing at 07.40hrs on a sunny morning but with the air temperature only c3°C.

Increasing records of this species in recent years suggest a real increase in abundance since the 1950s, although the lack of previous records could have been due to under-recording in the inaccessible places this butterfly prefers. Whilst climatic change may have influenced a population growth, it is also possible that the spread of intensive sheep grazing (which also began in the 1950s) may have had a greater effect. The heather is eaten

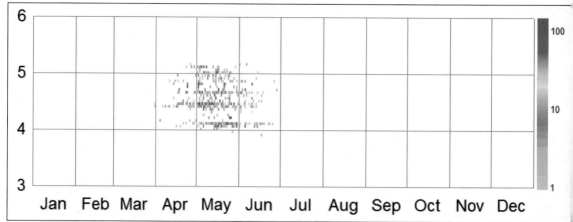

6

5

4

3

| Jan | Feb | Mar | Apr | May | Jun | Jul | Aug | Sep | Oct | Nov | Dec |

100

10

1

ID NOTES: An unmistakeable bright, metallic green butterfly, unlike any other in Britain. Underwings green, upperwings brown, showing golden bronze when fresh. Always settles with wings closed, showing green, and resembling the bright green spring foliage of bilberry etc, providing excellent camouflage. In flight appears an inconspicuous, drab, olive green-brown blur. Male and female similar in appearance, with 'tailed' hindwings not very obvious. The green, closed-wing view is crossed by a variable curved line of white dots, ranging from a full set across both wings (ab *punctata* Tutt), to no dots at all (ab *caecus* Geoffroy). The highly dotted form may be more of a feature of the northern races of the Green Hairstreak than those in the south (Haworth 1973), and, in the experience of the writer, often accounts for 5-10% of Yorkshire individuals. True ab *caecus* forms (with no dots) are rare, but many entomologists use ab *caecus* to describe specimens with a single dot as well, and these are much more common, again accounting for some 5-10% of individuals. The distribution of these various forms in the county deserves further study (see p48). Only 15 variations have been described, mainly involving the variable dot patterns. The green colouring may occasionally be brown or show brown areas (ab *brunnea* Tutt). Specimens collected and photographed by the author at Roulston Scar (Sutton Bank VC62) in May 1981 (see photo) show what is thought to be a previously undescribed expansion of the white dots producing stubby rays across the underwings.

PHENOGRAM: Yorkshire 1995/2003. Contrary to the pattern in most species this appears to indicate earlier peaks in the N than the S and an earlier appearance on highland sites than on lowland.

back by the sheep and this allows the bilberry to become the dominant plant. In view of the butterfly's preference for remote moorland locations, as well as its early and inconspicuous appearance, it probably remains significantly under-recorded in the county.

Variation from Roulston Scar, Sutton under Whitestonecliff (VC62, May 1981). Available reference sources do not include this form, so it might qualify as ab *radiata* Barnham! (Editor).

CONSERVATION ISSUES: The species has been given a *medium* Yorkshire & N of England priority by Butterfly Conservation due to uncertainties about the real strength of its populations, and therefore the need for further monitoring. Numbers appear to fluctuate considerably from year to year and between 1986 and 1996 Co Durham has seen 6 colony extinctions partly balanced by 2 new colonisations. In addition there have been 4 extinctions and 4 colonisations in Northumberland. The situation in Yorkshire has been less closely monitored, but circumstantial evidence suggests similar fluctuations. It is possible that fluctuating colonies are a norm for this species as it often occupies marginal habitats, which are successional and will eventually become unsuitable, eg open rides in young woodland, which eventually become too shady. The current success of the species in upland areas is possibly linked to intensive sheep farming which grazes down the heather to the benefit of the bilberry. Intensive sheep grazing is now being seen as a damaging influence on the ecology of the Pennine region and plans are afoot to introduce lighter cattle grazing on an experimental basis. This may have ramifications for the future success of the Green Hairstreak. There is a need to look at the species' relationship with ants, and to bear in mind the need to avoid damaging or disturbing pupae, which are spending winter at ground level or underneath the ground. The Biodiversity Action Plan for Bradford includes the Green Hairstreak and aims to increase the number of known colonies by 10% above baseline survey levels by 2005, and 20% by 2010, by encouraging natural colonisation. Key colonies within the Bradford Urban Wildlife region are being notified as 'Bradford Wildlife Areas'.

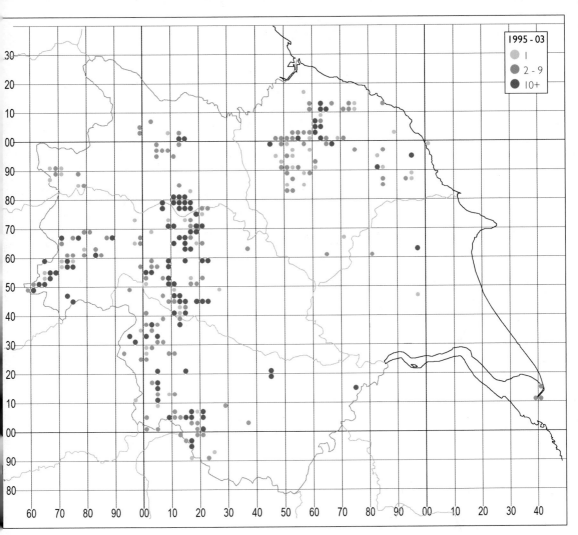

Green Hairstreak: Yorkshire Tetrad map 1995-2003

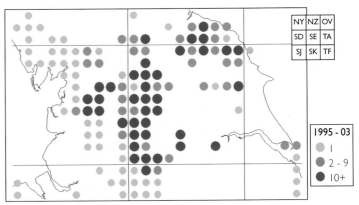

Green Hairstreak: 10km distribution North of England

⬤ = 1 or more records out of county 1995-1999

LIFE STORY

HABITAT: A species of rough, scrubby grasslands in cuttings, quarries, woodland rides etc, also found on moors, bogs and heaths. In Yorkshire, the butterfly is mainly found on upland moors in association with Bilberry *Vaccinium myrtillus*. The county's few lowland colonies appear to use Gorse *Ulex* spp. and perhaps Bramble *Rubus fruticosus*. A wide range of other foodplants has been recorded in Britain, but not in Yorkshire, including Bird's-foot Trefoil *Lotus corniculatus*, Broom *Sarothamnus scoparius*, Buckthorn *Rhamnus catharticus*, Common Rock-rose *Helianthemum nummularium*, Dogwood *Swida sanguinea* etc. In moorland areas, sheltered, sunny slopes are favoured, particularly where there are ruts, hollows, incised streams, gullies, and nearby walls, scrub or trees on which to perch. Although preferring sheltered sites, in warm still conditions, individuals will range extensively over open moorland where a light growth of bilberry often occurs amongst the heather. Many of our strongest colonies are found where sheep graze the bilberry really hard, and where the growth of bracken gives protection later in the year. Overgrown bushes of bilberry appear to be less attractive, as at Brimham Rocks in Nidderdale, where the butterflies are few and only found at the edges of the site. The species also occurs in certain bilberry-rich bogs and mosses as at Austwick and Malham Tarn (both VC64). Colonies at Spurn, on the Wolds and at Strensall use patches of gorse, whilst a colony at Staveley (VC64) observed for several years in the 1990s, appeared dependent on bramble.

Green Hairstreaks: mating pair. Upper Skell Ghyll (VC64) May 2001. Note variations in spotting.

Eggs are laid in the young tips of growing shoots or flower buds of the foodplant and hatch within 7-10 days. Green and yellow larvae are woodlouse-shaped and well camouflaged. They are solitary and cannibalistic. By Jul/Aug they are fully grown and wander away from the foodplant to pupate. Pupae attract ants by making audible squeaks and producing tasty secretions. It is thought that in most cases winter is spent within the shelter of ants' nests. The pupal stage lasts 8-10 months. The male is highly territorial and will fly aggressively at other insects, often circling away into the sky in an aerial battle, before returning to a regular perch. Courtship and mating occur throughout the flight period and pairs may be seen perched on low vegetation or on the ground. Females are more elusive, travelling more widely in search of foodplants, and settling and crawling on them to find suitable egg-laying locations. Although a fairly sedentary species, wandering butterflies may sometimes be found many miles from any known colonies, especially in years when populations are high, (eg 15 miles from nearest known colonies in the Harrogate area (VC64), there have been 7 reports from gardens, wasteland or woodland over a period of 20yrs).

Les Rush

Left: Specimen with reduced spots. Sutton Bank (VC62), 15/05/1988. Right: Specimen with strongly marked spots. Skrikes Wood, Bewerley, (VC64).

First noted in Britain by Merrett in 1666. Early collectors called it the **holly under green** or the **holly butterfly**, as the first recorded observation had been on holly. Wilkes 1747/49) named it the **Green Butterfly**, whilst Harris (1766) used the **Green Fly** ('fly' being a common abbreviation for 'butterfly') or the **Green Papillon** ('butterfly' in French), or the **Bramble**. Lewin (1795) was the first to use **Green Hairstreak**. The Latin name *Callophrys* means 'beautiful eyebrow', perhaps referring to the metallic green scales between the eyes, whilst the specific name *rubi* refers to 'bramble', which was thought by early lepidopterists to be the main larval foodplant.

Duncan (1844), referring to national distribution, noted, *'It is not a common species, but its ascertained localities indicate that it is pretty generally distributed throughout England and the southern division of Scotland'* . He quotes George Wailes as reporting its presence in *'Keswick and some of the Yorkshire Wolds'*. Morris 1853) wrote: *'This petite species is not uncommon, though only of local distribution. I have taken it in tolerable plenty at Buttercrambe Moor near Stamford Bridge, Langwith, Stockton and Sand Hutton, Yorkshire'*, (all VC62 just E of York). Porritt (1883) listed only 5 sites:

This butterfly appears to become even better disguised after a few bird pecks reveal bits of brown upperwing! Sutton Bank (VC62) 5/05/1988.

Pickering Valley (VC62) (presumably Newtondale), Pontefract and Sheffield (VC63), Askham Bog (nr York VC64), and Barden Moors (Wharfedale VC64) where it was considered rare. Porritt (1904) added a number of N Yorkshire Moors sightings (VC62) from Battersby-in-Cleveland, Glaisdale (where it was *'abundant'* in May 1901), and Helmsley. He also added Skelmanthorpe (Huddersfield VC63) in the name of Ben Morley, which Fryer & Lucas (2001) consider is an error resulting from confusion with another undated and isolated sighting from Cannon Hall Park (in the SE of the Huddersfield area), and reported in Brady (1884). Fryer & Lucas note that except for this one record, the well-documented Huddersfield area failed to produce any other sightings until Geoffrey Fryer's own observation in the early 1950s. Porritt (1907) summarised the county distribution as, *'widely distributed but not often common, except for some localities in the Cleveland district'*.

Tetley (1915) wrote, (as a fairly new resident of the Scarborough VC62 area): *'Callophrys rubi is a moorland butterfly here, its larvae feeding on bilberry. I once saw hundreds at the head of Beedale, resting on stunted mountain ash trees growing among the heather'*. Walsh (1952) also referring to the Scarborough area makes a similar comment: *'This is generally distributed on the moors, sometimes occurring in swarms, especially in the localities where there is plenty of bilberry'*. Rimington (1992) noted that the butterfly had declined from its former fairly widespread distribution in the neighbouring areas of Nottinghamshire (from 1900), Derbyshire (from 1940) and Lincolnshire (from 1950). Duddington & Johnson (1983) said that it was frequent in many localities in Lincolnshire up to 1960, but then *'disappeared from N Lincs and many of its previous haunts, and is now mainly found in a belt of scrub dune lands along the East Coast (eg Theddlethorpe and Gibraltar Point')*. Theddlethorpe (VC54) is about 15 miles south of Spurn Point (VC61) where the species turned up in 1983. Rimington could find no historical records for the Doncaster area (VC63). The only sightings date from quite recent times with a single seen at Roman Ridge in 1970 and a small colony apparently having become established at Thorne Moors for a period of at least 7 years from 1983. However, it is not impossible that this colony had been previously overlooked.

Fryer & Lucas (2001) describe in some detail the steady expansion of the species in the Huddersfield area from the 1950s (when there were a couple of isolated sightings and the discovery of a single colony near Langsett) to the 1990s (when there were several dozen colonies and site counts in excess of 300 butterflies). Garland (1981) notes that the species has been found in the higher areas to the west of Sheffield throughout its recorded history but expanded its range in the late 1950s. Whiteley (1992) referring to the same area, draws attention to the fact that 54 additional 1km squares were added to the species' range between 1981 and 1992, more than doubling its previously recorded distribution in the Sheffield region.

The YNU (1967/70) Report somewhat vaguely summed up the distribution as, *'Locally common in a variety of habitats in many parts of the county'*. Sutton & Beaumont (1989) provided more detail noting only one recent record for VC61 (Spurn 1983) and few records for VC63. Elsewhere (VCs 62, 64, 65) it was *'found in many small, well defined colonies, mainly in moorland and heathland localities where bilberry abounds'*. It seems fair to conclude that this species has expanded in upland areas over the last 50yrs but remains scarce and very local in lowland areas, although it is not impossible that it is being widely overlooked.

Mike Barnham

Mike Barnham

Cardale, (Harrogate VC64).

UK BAP status: *Not listed.*
BC Priorities: National: *Low.*
N of Eng: *Medium.* Yorkshire: *Medium.*
European Status: *Not threatened.*

WORLD STATUS: Resident: 0-2000m+. Single brood (Jun/Sept). Range: N Africa to S Scotland and S Scandinavia, and eastward through Asia to S Urals and Kazakhstan. In Britain found mainly south of a line from Humber to Mersey, becoming increasingly localised north of this line, but also apparently spreading in Yorkshire and Co Durham. Isolated presence in S and C Scotland. Local and sparse in Ireland. Protected in N Ireland. Declines reported from Austria, Belgium, Latvia, Luxembourg, Romania, S Russia and Ukraine. Also expanding northward with increases in Britain, Finland and Central Russia (Asher *et al* 2001).

YORKSHIRE STATUS 1995/2003:

Resident. Single brood (early Jul/early Sept). The butterfly appears to have expanded dramatically over the last 30+yrs. The 1970/82 Survey recorded its presence in just two Yorkshire 10km squares compared to at least 88 recorded between 1995 and 2003. There is little doubt it has been expanding, but as it is easily overlooked, it is difficult to assess how great an expansion has actually taken place, as it is probable that few people searched for it until the latter part of the 20th century. Since 1995 many observers have taken up the challenge to look for this insect in the early evening and as a result it has been found in every part of the county, from lowland areas to the borders of upland moors. The distribution is more extensive than has ever been documented previously also extending into Durham & Northumberland where 7x10km squares had been recorded up to 1985 and no fewer than 20 additional 10km squares were added in 2003 but not yet included on our maps (Pers comm. Mike Hunter).

During the present Survey the **earliest** record was 16/06/2003 from Skelbrooke (NW of Doncaster VC63) [Mike Lockwood], and the **latest** 16/09/2001 from Odsal Woods (VC63) [Dave & Stuart Wise]. Observations have mainly been of low numbers in the 5 to 10 range but with some higher counts in every VC, eg Burton Constable Woods (VC61 with **122** on 01/08/1999 [Adrian Johnson], Strensall Common (VC62 with **185** on 25/07/2000 [Pat & Jim Bone], Notton Wood (VC63) with **155** on 28/07/2002 [Ralph Hibbert & Chris Parkin], Harrogate (VC64) with **45** on 26/07/2000 [Mike Barnham], and Eryholme (on our northern boundary SE of Darlington, VC65) with **c100** on 29/07/1999 [Mike Barnham].

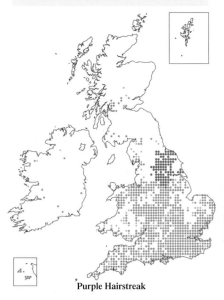

Purple Hairstreak

Purple Hairstreak larva, Ambleside, Cumbria, 23/05/2002.

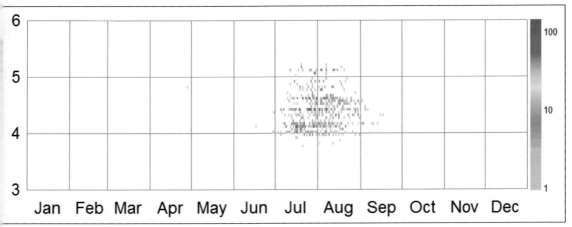

6

5

4

3

100

10

1

Jan   Feb   Mar   Apr   May   Jun   Jul   Aug   Sep   Oct   Nov   Dec

ID NOTES: A treetop butterfly strongly associated with oaks (of any species) although it will also feed in neighbouring trees, particularly ash. It is close to Small White size, with silver-grey underwings and dark, almost black upperwings, which have an overall purple sheen in the male and iridescent purple patches on the upper forewings of the female. The species will readily bask with wings open. The closed wing view shows a jagged white line top to bottom and two orange spots, one with a black centre close to a small hindwing 'tail'. Although the occasional Purple Hairstreak may be encountered nectaring at ground level, particularly on hot afternoons, most remain static, high in the trees, for long periods. Binoculars are needed to make a thorough search, and a 20min watch on likely trees will usually reveal an occasional movement if the butterfly is there. In flight it produces a characteristic flashing silver-grey appearance, but this needs to be distinguished with care from the White-letter Hairstreak (which usually looks a little darker), and also from the Holly Blue which may occasionally wander round the same trees and look very similar. Although Purple Hairstreaks can be seen at any time of the day from about 10am onward, they often become more active in the early evening (6pm to dusk), especially on still, warm evenings, when the biggest numbers may be seen, flying and chasing around the treetops, and from a distance, looking rather like grey moths. In any given locality in which you can spot one or two in mid-afternoon, you may well find 50 or more around 7pm, and even then, that may represent only a small fraction of the actual population. Aberrations are not very common. Haworth (1973) refers to 17 described variations, mainly in females.

PHENOGRAM: Yorkshire 1995/2003. Emphasises that this species appears to be less common (or less well recorded) in the N half of the county.

Picture taken along a woodland track nr Langres (France), 05/08/2003 when temperature exceeded 40°C and Purple Hairstreaks were descending to ground level en masse in search of shade. *'At times we walked through clouds of them, a strange feeling! In the deepest shade, several Hairstreaks, like the one just visible in this picture, were pushing whole leaves aside with their antennae, and probing the ground underneath, perhaps for dampness, salts or both? We were amazed at their dexterity and the way they could use their antennae as arms to manoeuvre leaves many times their own size.'* (Pers comm. Howard & Christine Frost)

CONSERVATION ISSUES: The species has been given Butterfly Conservation's *medium* status in the N of England and in Yorkshire due to the need to better understand the reasons for its apparent increase so that we may encourage this further. The butterfly is dependent on a reasonable abundance of oaks in the countryside and it is important to ensure that this is maintained. The recent spread of disease in oaks is of great concern as it threatens to be as serious as Dutch Elm Disease was in the past. Other threats include: habitat loss and habitat change (where inappropriate woodland management replaces native trees with conifers etc). Many oaks appear to be old and in need of management. Where felling is involved, projects should be phased over a period of years in order to provide continuity of habitat, with fresh oak plantings allowed time to grow, before older trees are completely removed. The Local Biodiversity Action Plan for the Bradford area has included the butterfly in its Oak Woodland Habitat Action Plan. Butterfly Conservation has produced an advisory leaflet about management for this butterfly in Yorkshire.

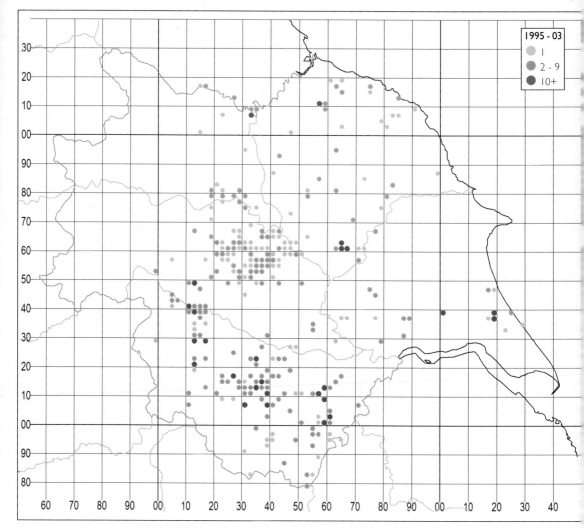

Purple Hairstreak: Yorkshire Tetrad map 1995-2003

1995 - 03	
⬤	1
⬤	2 - 9
⬤	10+

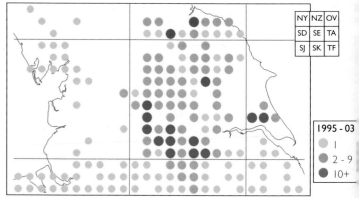

NY	NZ	OV
SD	SE	TA
SJ	SK	TF

1995 - 03	
⬤	1
⬤	2 - 9
⬤	10+

Purple Hairstreak: 10km distribution North of England

⬤ = 1 or more records out of county 1995-1999

LIFE STORY

HABITAT: Found wherever Oak trees *Quercus* spp grow singly or together. Even quite young trees 3-7m (10/20ft) in height may be used. Egg-laying has occasionally been recorded on Ash *Fraxinus* spp and even on Sallow *Salix* spp and Spanish Chestnut *Castania sativa*, but such variations may be accidental rather than intentional. In Yorkshire, the insect occurs wherever there is a good growth of oak in forests, woods and copses, also in parklands, along hedgerows, railway cuttings and embankments, and in stands of trees alongside roads. The butterflies favour warm, south-facing and protected locations, such as occur among the boughs of large trees, along rides and woodland edges sheltered from prevailing winds, and where trees grow in naturally sheltered spots as in narrow valleys and on undulating hillsides.

Purple Hairstreaks resting at ground level in shade of nettles, France 05/08/2003. (See text.)

Eggs are laid on the twigs of oak and around the base of flower buds in sheltered, sunny positions at all heights in Jul and Aug. The young larvae develop within a few weeks, but stay inside the egg until the following spring. Eggs are fairly conspicuous and provide a way for the naturalist to hunt for the insect even during wintertime. They are whitish grey, round, and the size of a pinhead. A significant number are parasitised by chalcid wasps *Trichogramma* spp, but a higher mortality occurs in the pupal stage for reasons not presently understood. Larvae emerge in early April and burrow inside the expanding oak buds. Later they emerge to live within a loose tent of silk that entraps leaf scales and debris to provide shelter, and feed at night. The larva is shaped like a woodlouse and well camouflaged in brown covered in paler triangular markings, resembling the emerging leaf tissues of the oak.

Purple Hairstreak pupa (bred from captive larva).

There are uncertainties about where larvae pupate. Some sources suggest in the tree (eg in crevices on trunk and branches), others, on the ground under leaf litter, or in an ants' nest. When on the ground, it is unclear as to how they get there. Do they crawl down the trunk, or simply drop, or even use silken threads to lower themselves more gently? Both larvae and pupae produce secretions, which attract ants, and pupae are also able to make a squeaking sound by rubbing abdominal segments together to catch the attention of ants. Pupae have been found inside the nests of red ants *Myrmica* spp and preliminary data suggest this might be the normal location at this stage of this hairstreak's life cycle. The ecology of ants in the neighbourhood of oaks might be an important factor in the local distribution and strength of Purple Hairstreak colonies.

The butterflies feed mainly on honeydew (from aphids) and will congregate on other tree species such as ash, aspen, birch and sycamore, as well as oak, in their search for a food supply. Freshly emerged specimens may sometimes be found perched in low vegetation, although after hatching they have an instinct to fly up to the safety of the trees, where they spend their time basking or crawling around. Females may descend within an observer's reach when laying eggs on lower boughs, whilst others may come down to feast on honeydew-spattered vegetation beneath the trees or even on moisture on the ground. They may also occasionally come down to ground level to nectar on flowers such as bramble, thistle and hemp agrimony but this is unusual. Frost & Frost (2003) describe a situation in France in 2003 where whole populations descended to rest at ground level because it was too hot in the canopy when shade temperatures exceeded 40°C. Even in Yorkshire, very hot days may occasionally bring butterflies to lower levels. Large numbers of Purple Hairstreaks can be active in the evening between about 1800hrs and 2000hrs or later. Howard Frost (pers comm.) has noticed that on suitably warm evenings activity carries on until it is too dark to observe, and Jill Warwick has actually caught a specimen in her moth trap (although not in Yorkshire). It may be that this butterfly remains active through the night when conditions are right. Little has been observed of its mating habits, so there is much yet to discover. In hot summers when the butterflies are numerous the writer has seen them occasionally crossing open land or flying along hedgerows at some distance from any oaks. In good years with warm springs and summers, numbers may occasionally explode and, exceptionally, (in the S of England) mass migrations have sometimes been observed as Purple Hairstreaks leave woodlands in search of new sites.

First mentioned by Petiver (1702) and described by Ray in 1710. Petiver initially called it **Mr Ray's purple streak** and later in 1717 **Mr Ray's blue streak**. Albin introduced the definitive name **Purple Hairstreak** in 1720. In the Latin *quercus* refers to the oak, making it the 'oak tree butterfly'.

The inconspicuous nature of this butterfly makes it difficult to know how much faith to place in the comments left behind by past entomologists. Duncan (1844) painted the national picture as follows: *'The most common species of Thecla* [ie hairstreak] *in this island, especially in southern districts of England, where it may be found abundantly in every oakwood. It extends northwards in considerable plenty as far as Newcastle in the neighbourhood of which, Mr Wailes informs us that it is far from uncommon. Beyond that locality, however, it seems to become scarce'.* However, Duncan appears to have misquoted George Wailes who only knew one site in Co Durham, but in his 1857 'Catalogue' covering Durham and Northumberland noted: *'I know of no other locality for it though doubtless, if looked for at the right season and in its lofty abode, it would be found generally diffused over our oakwoods'.* Robson (1902) commented, *'Mr Wailes' idea as to its more general occurrence has not yet been substantiated'.* In fact there were only 3 reported sightings for Durham and Northumberland in the whole of the 19th century! Morris (1853)

also wrote a national assessment, but from the point of view of having lived in Yorkshire: *'It is common throughout England in most parts of the country. I have met with it at Nunburnholme in Brant Wood* [probably today's Brat Wood VC61/SE84]*, and at Buttercrambe Moor* [VC62]*, and it also occurs a Sutton-on-Derwent Wood* [VC61] *and Raincliffe Wood near Scarborough* [VC62] *and Sandal Beat Wood* [nr Doncaster VC63]*, all in Yorkshire...* Porritt (1883) failed to note any VC61 records, but listed Scarborough and Whitby (VC62) noting two exclamation marks for Whitby to indicate 'abundant'; Doncaster, Pontefract, Sheffield and Wakefield in VC63; and Askham Bog (York), Bishop Wood (Selby), Bramham (nr Wetherby) and Leeds all in VC64. Porritt (1904) added Forge Valley (nr Scarborough VC62) in 1901. Walsh (1952) includes further detail re the latter record, which he abstracted from Peter Inchbald's Lepidoptera list in Theakston (1871): *'Recorded from the east side of Forge Valley by T Wilkinson* [d1876] *and by Tetley as having been taken once by HW Head in Raincliffe Wood in some year prior to 1902, and by RH Barker as having been taken by Head in Forge Valley in Aug 1901; these probably refer to the same specimen. It ha not been seen there since that date, but A Smith records it on several occasion from Buttercrambe Woods near York'.* Stainforth (1919) referring to the mid 19th century Thomas Stather collection noted a record from Gilberdike (west of Hull VC61) which he reported as: *'The only East Riding record'* indicating he was unaware of Morris's VC61 records.

Rimington (1992) noted only 6 Doncaster (VC63) records: Sandall Beat Wood (c1830s) where Hawley (1866) also reported it *'used to be plentiful'* Maltby (1858); Wheatley Wood (c1870), Roche Abbey (prior to 1896) and Rossington (1911). Rimington adds that the species appears to have been quite common in neighbouring counties to the south and east prior to 1900 but then seemed to be at a low ebb until the 1970s. No records were reported for the Sheffield area after Porritt (1883), until Whiteley (1992) mentioned a discovery at Whitwell Wood in 1992, followed by a 1993 record for Canklow Wood, Rotherham. The YNU 1967/70 Report gives only 4 reports: Bishop Wood (VC64 1915); Buttercrambe (VC61 1942); Strensall (VC62 1959) and Skipwith Common (undated VC61). Sutton & Beaumont (1989) report *'a comeback in the last few years'* giving VC61: Dunnington (nr York) 1984/86 Aughton Common (Allerthorpe) 1987; VC62: Strensall 1977/88, Bulmer 1983, Gate Helmsley 1984, Beningbrough Hall 1984; VC64: Goldsborough Woods (Harrogate area) 1983. Subsequently Barnham and colleagues (1993) reported on the remarkable spread of the species westward and northwards in the Harrogate district, whilst Fryer & Lucas (2001) detailed a similar colonisation of the Huddersfield area from 1996 onward.

By 2002 Beaumont (2002) was able to note the species now *'far more common and widespread than previously realised'* with *'a general consensus that there has been a national expansion of the species over recent years'*, a conclusion borne out by the results of Butterfly Conservation's 1995/1999 Millennium Atlas Butterfly Survey.

In summary, it appears that the species was relatively common in the early 19th century, but became less so by c1900, perhaps another victim of the 1879/1895 cold years and the growing effects of industrial pollution. Whilst there were hints of a recovery to the south of Yorkshire in the 1970s this wasn't picked up in the county till the 1980s, but has certainly gathered momentum in the 1990s. It is unclear if the species remained unnoticed on widely separate sites throughout the 20th century and then began to expand from many focal points; or whether it died out in most parts of Yorkshire and has since re-colonised as part of a range expansion from the south. It is even possible that both scenarios have occurred simultaneously.

Mike Barnham

Derek Parkinson

Female Purple Hairstreak (captive reared).

1558 WHITE-LETTER HAIRSTREAK *Satyrium w-album* (Knoch 1782)
Family: Lycaenidae, sub-group Theclinae ('the Hairstreaks').

Roadside Wych Elm sucker growth. Burton Constable Woods (VC61).

UK BAP Status: *Not listed.*
BC Priorities: National: *Medium.*
N of England: *Medium.* Yorkshire: *Medium.*
European Status: *Not threatened.*
Protected in Great Britain for sale only.

Young, (and therefore pale) White-letter
Hairstreak larva. Scotton Banks (VC64), 1980.

White-letter Hairstreak

YORKSHIRE STATUS 1995/2003:

Resident. Single brood (late Jun/mid-Aug). Secretive treetop butterfly, often overlooked, and probably much under-recorded. Current distribution as mapped appears to be strongly influenced by the location of experienced observers. Although the species was thought to be on the verge of extinction through loss of elms in the 1970s and 1980s, it is clear that the butterfly is now flourishing throughout much of its former range (such as Teeside and Cleveland VC62, Doncaster and Barnsley VC63, and Harrogate and Ripon VC64). There is also evidence of an actual spread into previously unrecorded areas in the east of East Yorkshire VC61 (Holderness), Huddersfield, Bradford and Keighley VC63, and Ilkley VC64. The species is found mainly in association with Wych Elm *Ulmus glabra* which has been less prone to attack by Dutch Elm Disease, but where it has suffered and been felled, strong secondary growth from around the trunk has produced conditions in which today's butterflies thrive.

White-letter Hairstreaks are usually on the wing in the county from late Jun to mid-Aug, with the **earliest** on 15/06/2003 (and 13/06/2004!) at Potteric Carr YWT Nature Reserve (VC63) [Potteric Carr Recording Group] and the **latest** on 21/08/1997 at Burton Constable (nr Hull, VC61), [Howard & Chris Frost]. Numbers observed are usually fairly small, typically in the 1 to 20 range. Adults lead a sedentary life in the trees and are generally several times more numerous than they appear from casual observation. Highest counts have been **32** on 13/07/2003 at Burton Constable Woods (VC61) [Adrian Johnson], and **46** (on 26/07/2002) and **61** (on 16/07/2003) at Hugset Wood (nr Barnsley VC63) [Ralph Hibbert & Chris Parkin]. Count sizes have risen during the Survey period partly in response to appeals for more population data, but probably also as a result of a series of warm summers.

WORLD STATUS: Resident 0-1700m. Single brood (mid-Jun/late Jul, later in north). Range: N Spain, S France, Italy - northward to N England, S Scandinavia and eastward across Europe and Asia to Japan. Widespread in Britain as far north as Lancashire, Co Durham and the southern edge of Northumberland, (two 19th century records for Scotland). British status badly affected from 1960s onward when Dutch Elm Disease decimated many foodplant trees. However, the species now appears to be recovering. Decreases also noted in Austria, Belgium, France, Luxembourg and Netherlands, but a spread observed in Finland.

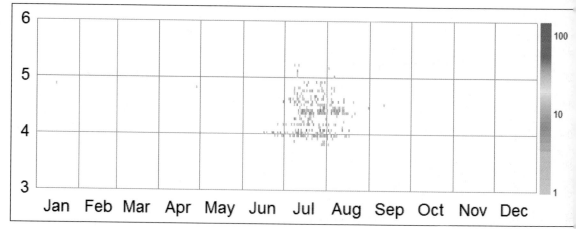

6
5
4
3

Jan Feb Mar Apr May Jun Jul Aug Sep Oct Nov Dec

100

10

1

ID NOTES: A treetop butterfly rarely seen close-to, and best observed with the help of binoculars. Occasionally descends to take nectar from flowers or to shelter from high winds. At rest it keeps wings closed, showing dusky brown crossed by a thin white 'hairstreak' line. On the hindwing the line zigzags to produce the 'w' shape which gives the butterfly its name. There is a distinct white-tipped 'tail' on the lower border of each hindwing, longer in the female than the male, but these often break away as the insect becomes worn. The edge of the hindwing shows a row of orange crescents, most prominent near the tail, and these join to form a short wavy band. Males are a little smaller than females and are a deeper brown on the upper surface. In flight the butterfly appears dark and drab as it darts about the upper branches of trees, sometimes silhouetted against the sky. It will perch and walk about on the leaves of high boughs with tightly closed wings. When freshly emerged it may have a sheen which glints in the sun at certain angles. Easily confused with Purple Hairstreak, and also Meadow Browns and Gatekeepers, which may take to the treetops on occasion. Aberrations are rare with only 7 variations described.

PHENOGRAM: Yorkshire 1995-2003. Shows a relatively short flight season which starts early in the S than the N.

Older (and therefore darker) White-letter Hairstreak larva.

White-letter Hairstreak. Note intact wing 'tails'. Goldsborough Woods VC64 1988.

CONSERVATION ISSUES: The species has been given Butterfly Conservation's 'medium' status due to a need to monitor its progress in a somewhat uncertain situation. The insect appears able to maintain itself on naturally regenerating elm growth, a proportion of which may succumb to another bout of Dutch Elm Disease. So, periodic lopping of infected trunks to encourage fresh regeneration may be important in maintaining a status quo for the butterfly. Particular threats which may arise include: a) removal of elms in hedgerows which might be acting as stepping stones between colonies; b) inappropriate management of hedgerows containing elms (eg through simultaneous layering of elm suckers); c) not including elms in planting schemes because of concerns about them becoming diseased. The butterfly could benefit from woodland management which encourages the natural regeneration of elms, and from woodland planting schemes which use disease-resistant strains of wych elm. The butterfly will also adapt to Japanese Elm *Ulmus japonica*. White-letter Hairstreaks have been included in the Local Biodiversity Action Plans for Wakefield and Bradford, and in the latter area all identified colonies are designated 'Third Tier Sites', indicating a priority status.

Mike Barnham

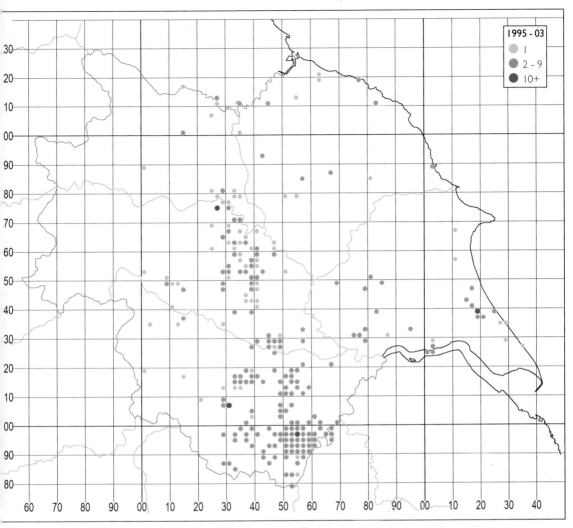

White-letter Hairstreak: Yorkshire Tetrad map 1995-2003

MAP NOTES 1995-2003: Noted in **248/3319** recorded tetrads (ie 7.5%), and out of 4120 tetrads in Yorkshire. **Ranked 24th most widespread** out of 36 breeding species in the county. Easily overlooked but presence can also be picked up by winter egg searches which partly accounts for the density of dots in the south of the county. The species appears widespread in lowland areas and in sheltered valleys in hillier parts. Similarities to Purple Hairstreak distribution may be linked to observer effort rather than to any specific correlation between the two species.

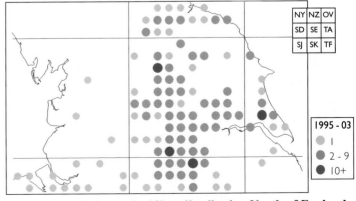

White-letter Hairstreak: 10km distribution North of England

= 1 or more records out of county 1995-1999

LIFE STORY

Another egg view. Unlike the butterflies, eggs stay still and can be spotted in winter!

HABITAT: Found principally in well-wooded areas but also in urban parks, churchyards and gardens wherever elms still flourish, even singly and in isolation. Less frequently found in intensively farmed lowland areas, or in the more exposed uplands of the Pennines, Moors and Wolds. Can utilise any species of elm, including hybrid forms, but in Yorkshire appears to have a strong preference for Wych Elm *Ulmus glabra*. There have also been Yorkshire sightings around surviving specimens of English Elm *U. procera* and Smooth-leaved Elm *U. minor*, but we need further study to find out how important these might be in the county. Larvae are reported to eat Lime *Tilia* spp in captivity, but there is no evidence that this happens in the wild.

Eggs laid singly in sheltered positions and at any height, around annual rings, nodes and bud bases of elms. The central dome of the egg turns chocolate brown, surrounded by a pale rim and is fairly conspicuous to the practised eye, enabling searching and recording to be carried out throughout the winter months. Eggs are often found on lower branches, and a walking stick can be useful for hooking branches to bring them closer for examination. Larvae develop inside the egg, but don't hatch out until the following spring. A significant number are parasitised at an early stage by chalcid wasps *Trichogramma* spp. Larvae usually feed on flower buds as they open out, and later move on to leaf buds and developing seed clusters. In the final moult, they eat and rest on the under surface of elm

Spot the egg! It's pale, tiny and hat shaped.

leaves, producing a characteristic dark silhouette to an observer looking up from beneath. The woodlouse shaped larvae are green and yellow with oblique pale stripes and lilac markings. They finally pupate on the underside of an elm leaf, or on a twig, or fork on a bough, hanging by a pad and girdle of silk. Pupae are speckled brown and hairy, resembling an elm bud. They are able to produce a faint rasping 'song' as do other hairstreaks, although they don't appear to be dependent on ants in any way.

For about a week, fresh adults tend to stay close to the trees on which they emerged, after which they become increasingly prone to wander, probably as a means of developing new colonies. This may be the explanation behind an unexpected sighting on Withernsea promenade (VC61) on 19/07/1999, miles away from any known colony [Howard & Christine Frost]. In most cases colonies on mature trees are stable and persistent over many years.

On still, sunny mornings, butterflies may be on the wing from 08.30hrs, and if conditions remain suitable, will fly throughout the day until 1900hrs. They may be spotted in flight, zigzagging rapidly about, weaving and fluttering around the boughs, darting over the top of the tree canopy, or with a rival, spiralling away together into the sky, before making their separate ways back to the tree. This is a species which needs warmth and sunshine. Adults are often seen taking up a slanted position as they perch, to best absorb the rays of the sun. They are reluctant to fly in cold, windy or dull conditions. Aphid honeydew is their main food and butterflies may visit other trees to find it (eg ash, oak, birch and sycamore). When this is in short supply, the butterflies may descend (especially in the early morning or late afternoon) to take nectar from Creeping Thistle *Cirsium arvense*, Bramble *Rubus* spp, Ragwort *Senecio* spp, Privet *Ligustrum* spp, Rosebay Willowherb *Epilobium angustifolium* etc. High ground level counts have been reported from S England, but rarely from Yorkshire: Roy Bedford found a remarkable 35 nectaring in Hugset Wood (VC63) on 16/08/1996, whilst the author observed 10 to 15 lining up on bracken stems in a woodland clearing at Scotton Banks (VC64) in 1979. It was thought that the attraction might have been a female. Little is known of this hairstreak's mating habits, but the author saw a pair in tandem, perched on a leaf in the high bows of an elm tree on the afternoon of 12/07/1989.

First mentioned by Petiver in 1703 as the **Hair-streak**. Moses Harris (1775) called it the **Dark Hairstreak**, whilst Donovan (1808) referred to it as the **Black Hairstreak** *Thecla pruni*. Today's Black Hairstreak was not discovered in England until 1828, after which the English and Latin names for the White-letter Hairstreak were transferred to the 'new' species, leaving the White-letter apparently without a name until *w-album* was introduced by Humphreys & Westwood in 1841. Morris (1853) referred to it as the **White-W Hairstreak**, but in the later 1800s several authors returned to using Black Hairstreak, calling the real Black Hairstreak the Dark Hairstreak, and leaving behind a legacy of confusion over the historical records of both species! Kirby (1896) introduced **White-letter Hairstreak** and has been followed by authors since then. The Latin family name *Satyrium* comes from satyr and may reflect the dancing flight of the hairstreaks in general, whilst *w-album* refers to the 'white w'.

So not only is this one of our most elusive butterflies, but there is also difficulty in estimating the accuracy and adequacy of many of the early records. It is probable that the Black Hairstreak has never been a Yorkshire butterfly, therefore early reports under old names may be accepted as White-letter Hairstreaks. Duncan (1844) assessed the national situation as: *'Of late years it has occurred in great plenty in some districts, but in general it may be accounted scarce, particularly in northern parts of the kingdom'*. In fact, for two centuries the species has been on the northern edge of its

Adult in Tilery Wood, Castle Eden Walkway (Co Durham) 27/07/2002.

range in Yorkshire although there are two isolated and undated Scottish records (reported in 1859 and 1885), which suggest that it might once have extended much further north. Rimington (1992) refers to the Doncaster area (VC63) as being *'the traditional Yorkshire home'* of this species, with many records between 1837 and 1908 including Melton Woods (1837), Edlington Wood (1830s/1908), Wadworth Wood (1890/1908), Maltby (1856), and Roche Abbey (1858 and 1884). Interestingly, Rimington draws attention to the fact that Hall (1895) reported the species as scarce in its usual Doncaster haunts in 1891 (1890 was one of the ten coldest summers in the 19th century and 1891 was also pretty poor), but in the early 1900s many observers point to a notable abundance.

Morris (1853) noted, *'I have captured this pretty species in numbers at High Melton Wood near Doncaster and Nunburnholme Brant Wood'* [VC61]. 'Brant Wood' is presumed to be the same as today's Bratt Wood (SE8448k). Porritt (1883) noted its abundance at Edlington Wood where it was also found *'in adjoining lanes and field sides'*. He reported it as common at Roche Abbey [WH Smith] and recorded at Sheffield and York. In 1904, he added Wheatley Wood, Doncaster (*'larvae in profusion in 1901'*), and from VC62: Helmsley, and Kilton Woods (Cleveland) [Thomas Lofthouse]. For the Scarborough area (VC62), Tetley (1915) noted that it occurred at Sleightholmdale to the west of Pickering (nr Helmsley). Walsh (1952) adds: *'Porritt [1904] records this as having been taken at Helmsley by S Walker of York. There were no other [Scarborough area] records until, in 1935, I beat larvae in small numbers from wych elm in moorland valleys running north. It is obviously extremely local. A Smith reports it from localities near Malton and Kirby Moorside'*. It seems possible that the northern front of the species pushed further north in the early 20th century with Kilton Woods (almost in Middlesbrough) representing its most northerly attainment in Britain at that time.

However, after 1908, reports across the county suggest the species became less common until the 1960s/1970s. Then, just as Dutch Elm Disease was threatening the butterfly's extinction in S England, populations in Yorkshire showed signs of increasing, perhaps a result of warming summers. The disease didn't have much effect on Yorkshire populations until the late 1970s/early 1980s, partly as a result of wych elms being less affected. Where they were felled, sucker growth quickly developed and by the 1990s this was being widely utilised, bringing the butterflies to a more suitable height for observation. The YNU 1967/70 Report noted: *'Not often reported in recent years, but some colonies must still survive'*. Records were reported from **VC61:** Hull area 1956, **VC62:** Pickering and Kirkbymoorside *'widely distributed'*, **VC63:** Doncaster *'formerly common...numbers now much reduced'*, **VC64:** Bishop Wood, Fountains Abbey and Knavesmire Wood (all 1955). Sutton & Beaumont (1989) wrote: *'Despite (or possibly as a result of) many elms being destroyed...this species has spread considerably since 1970'*. They also noted that although recorded in all five VCs, the majority of records seemed to be associated with the N/S band of Magnesian Limestone. However, so also are human populations, resulting in certain areas being intensively searched over many years whilst more distant regions have been neglected. It is probable that we have many more sites to discover.

It is interesting to note that in recent years the butterfly has pushed its northern front beyond Yorkshire and into Co Durham (VC66) where it had never been previously recorded. Dunn & Parrack (1986) noted that following D Horsfield's report of a re-appearance in Kilton Woods (VC62) in 1978 and its arrival at other N Yorkshire sites close to the Durham border; the butterfly was finally discovered in VC66 in 1982. By 2003 it had spread even further northward, right through Co Durham and into southern Northumberland, with 65 tetrads recorded so far (Hunter & Norman 2003).

Mike Barnham

Wheeldale Moor (VC62). Large patches of Sheep's Sorrel are created by managed heather burning for game shooting.

BAP Status: *Not listed.*
BC Priorities: National: *Low.*
N of Eng: *Low.* Yorkshire: *Low.*
European Status: *Not threatened.*

Paul W Forster

Small Copper, Danby (VC62), with a hint of blue spotting.

Small Copper

YORKSHIRE STATUS 1995/2003:

Fairly mobile resident: 2/3 broods (sometimes overlapping), with partial 3rd appearing in good years: Apr/Jun, Jul/Aug, Sept/Oct. **Earliest record:** 14/03/2003 Heslington (York, VC61) [J Leeman]. **Latest:** 11/11/1998 York VC61 [Pat Bone]. Widely distributed in lowland and upland areas except in NW (Yorkshire Dales VC65) where height, exposure and higher rainfall may be inhibiting factors. Populations fluctuate widely from year to year, with warm, sunny and fairly dry conditions being advantageous, but cold, wet, or drought conditions, disadvantageous. 1997 stood out as an exceptionally good year with counts over 100 at Allerthorpe Common (VC61) [**104** on 13/08: John Killingbeck, **175** on 16/08: Howard & Christine Frost] and Troller's Gill (VC64) [**100+** CJ Coupland]. Such large numbers are, however, exceptional and sightings of ones and twos are more commonplace. Although difficult to quantify, it seems that the overall population trend has been downward over the last 100yrs, largely as a result of habitat loss. However, over the last 25yrs of the 20th century the loss has only been about 1% by 10km squares (Ellis 2000). Had it been possible to make comparisons by tetrad or 1km square scales, a greater loss might have become apparent. The current tetrad map shows many gaps, especially in the Vales of York and Pickering, although some of this could be due to under-recording. The Small Copper is an elusive butterfly and easily missed where it exists in very small colonies. A few have been recorded across the region every autumn between 1996 and 2003, suggesting the occurrence of a regular, though small, partial 3rd brood, and occasional Nov records raise questions as to the possibility of a 4th appearance. First and last records over the Survey period (discounting 1995 for which we had insufficient data) were: **1996:** 24/05 to 21/10; **1997:** 09/04 to 22/10; **1998:** 03/05 to 11/11; **1999:** 18/04 to 12/10; **2000:** 06/05 to 18/10; **2001:** 10/05 to 03/11; **2002:** 27/03 to 24/10; **2003:** 14/03 to 30/10.

WORLD STATUS: Resident, 0-2700m. Up to 4 broods (Feb/Nov). Range: N Africa to N Norway and across Asia and N America (where it is known as the **American Copper**). Generally widespread and common across range, but although not under threat, some declines noted in Europe. Widely distributed in British Isles except in highest areas of N England and Scotland, and on Western Isles of Scotland. Many racial variations across range including *eleus* (Fabricius 1798) in Britain and *hibernica* Goodson 1948 in Ireland. It is probable that the overall British distribution has not altered significantly over the last 200yrs but population numbers have declined.

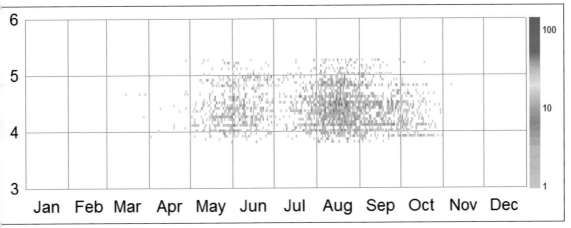

ID NOTES: A small, very active and fast-flying butterfly (about same size as Common Blue) with bright copper-coloured upper forewings and black spots and margins. Hindwings are dark with copper-coloured black-spotted lower margins. Female slightly larger than male with less pointed forewings and narrower copper-coloured hindwing band. Conspicuous at rest, often basking on low herbage or open ground. Easily overlooked in closed-wing view, as drab brown colours provide notable camouflage. A very variable species with 140 described aberrations, several of which occur regularly. The most striking, perhaps, is the white form ab *schmidtii* Gerhard or ab *alba* Tutt, in which the copper-coloured areas are replaced with white. This is thought to occur where colonies are inbred having been founded by single females. As a result the white forms tend to recur from year to year until the colony receives new blood. Somewhat less striking is ab *cuprinus* Peyerimhoff, which is a pale variety; and easily overlooked are ab *radiata* Tutt, where the copper hindwing band is replaced by streaks, and ab *caeruleopunctata* Rühl, which has blue spots on the upper edge of the hindwing copper band. These may vary considerably in their visibility.

PHENOGRAM: Yorkshire 1995-2003. Appears to indicate an overall pattern of two main broods and a partial third in late Sept/Oct.

David Howson

Two views of a white form of Small Copper, ab *schmidtii* Gerhard, from Bradford (VC63).

CONSERVATION ISSUES: Asher et al (2001) draw attention to a N Wales study which indicated a 90% Small Copper population decline since the beginning of the 20th century. The ability of the species to exist in very small, and sometimes erratically occupied colonies, tends to mask any downward population trends. Transect counting may enable us to learn more about its welfare, but we need additional transects to get a better understanding across the county. Conservation managers need to be aware of the importance of sorrel to this species, especially Sheep's Sorrel, which is particularly favoured. Sorrel growth in sunny areas with short vegetation and bare patches of ground is good for this species. The practice of burning patches of heather moorland appears particularly beneficial in that it promotes the growth of Sheep's Sorrel as a colonising plant of bare areas. Small Coppers also nectar on the heather. The widening of rides and clearing of conifers to open up heathland at Allerthorpe Common (VC61) (Forestry Commission/YWT volunteers) is already proving extremely successful in building up Small Copper populations. However, the project has also shown that heather and sorrel growth alongside rides rapidly becomes shaded out by regenerating tree and shrub growth, and the benefits to the butterfly are lost after 2 or 3 years without further maintenance. The Small Copper has also become a species increasingly found on brownfield sites, the reclamation of which represents a serious management issue. In many ways the Small Copper is dependent on periodic land disturbance as its foodplants are amongst the first colonisers of bare patches of ground.

Small Copper ab *radiata* Tutt. WE Rimington collection.

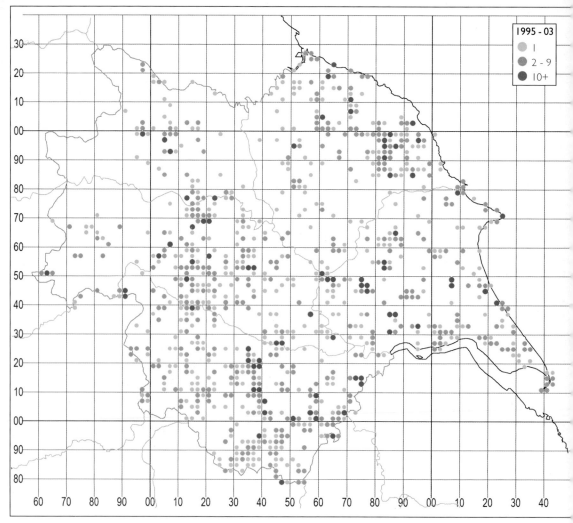

Small Copper: Yorkshire Tetrad map 1995-2003

MAP NOTES 1995-2003: Noted in **890/3319** recorded tetrads (ie 26.8%), and out of 4120 tetrads in Yorkshire. **Ranked 14th most widespread** out of 36 breeding species in the county. Easily overlooked as it may occur in very small numbers on any given site and its fast flight can defeat the eye. Appears largely absent over much of the higher NW Pennines (the Dales), although gaps in lowland areas are more likely to result from under-recording. Peter Robinson, checking an unrecorded Vale of Pickering area in 2004, discovered a major overlooked site on the verge of a country lane!

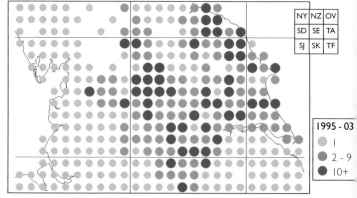

Small Copper: 10km distribution North of England

● = 1 or more records out of county 1995-1999

The Butterflies of Yorkshire

HABITAT: Rough grassland and disturbed habitats where the foodplants Common Sorrel *Rumex acetosa* or Sheep's Sorrel *R. acetosella* occur. Other Dock species may also be used occasionally. The butterfly favours open, sunny areas with low, rather sparse vegetation in compressed soils containing patches of bare ground. Examples of preferred habitat include railway embankments, disused rail tracks, riverbanks, cliffs, meadows, sheltered moorland hollows, disused quarries, roadside verges and patches of waste ground. The species is fairly mobile and can turn up almost anywhere including parks, gardens and cemeteries. In **VC61** large numbers can often be found nectaring on heather at Allerthorpe Common. Good counts can also occur in Yorkshire Wolds valleys such as at Millington and Bishop Wilton, also at Northcliffe Wood YWT NR in the Vale of York, and along disused railway lines including the Hudson Way Leisure Trail on the Wolds and the Withernsea/Hull and Hornsea/Hull (Trans Pennine Trail) routes in Holderness. Wharram Quarry YWT NR, Thixendale (Wolds Way), Pocklington Canal, Weedley Springs, Tophill Low NR and Spurn NNR are all potential sites for this species. In **VC62** there are sites on the N Yorks Moors where periodic heather burning provides strong new growth of Sheep's Sorrel, eg on Wheeldale Moor. The butterfly has also been reported from Danby in Eskdale, around Guisborough, at Ellerburn Bank, Crabdale, Bransdale, Fulford Low Moor, Jugger Howe, at South Gare on the Tees Estuary and at Strensall Common YWT NR near York. In **VC63** there are productive sites near Wakefield including the canal meadows of Haw Park and Walton Nature Park; reclaimed industrial areas near Wath, Carlton Marsh near Barnsley, Grange Moor near Huddersfield, Denaby Ings near Rotherham, Potteric Carr near Doncaster, Austerfield near Bawtry and last but not least Thorne Moors NNR where some of the highest counts in the county have been made, eg 393 in 1991 (Rimington 1992). Some of the best **VC64** sites include: Baildon Bank (Shipley), Denton Moor, Lower Barden reservoir, Midgely Wood, Skellgill Bridge, Fairburn Ings RSPB NR and Plumpton Rocks. There have been fewer sightings in **VC65** but the species has been seen at Turfmoor Hush, Fremington (nr Reeth), Carperby, Grinton Mill and Thorpe Perrow Arboretum. Observers visiting VC65 are encouraged to look out for this species and to report every sighting.

Small, but bright, the Small Copper stands out like a jewel when fresh. This blue-spotted form was seen along a track on Allerthorpe Common (VC61).

White eggs, which look like miniature golf balls, are laid on the underside of food plant leaves and hatch after 7-14 days. In spring, females show preference for larger plants up to 30cm, whilst in summer much smaller plants are preferred. Slug-like green larvae are often edged and lined in purple helping them to merge into the colours of the foodplants. They pupate after 25-30 days becoming brown, dumpy sacs hanging from vegetation by silken pads. This stage, lasting about a month, is rarely observed in the wild. Larvae from eggs laid by summer or autumn brood butterflies remain as larvae throughout winter and continue to feed when mild, but become dormant during cold spells. They usually begin to feed more actively in March and pupate later that month to emerge as butterflies from early May onward. Recent years have seen an increase in April sightings of adults and even the occasional March appearance. In Yorkshire the 2 or 3 broods tend to overlap giving the impression of a continuous flight season from Apr or May through to Oct. It is assumed that this butterfly is quite mobile, yet some small colonies seem very sedentary. Thomas and Lewington (1991) mention a sighting on a lightship 7 miles off the Sussex coast. This may have been a specimen accidentally blown offshore, or it could indicate that the butterfly occasionally migrates. We have a lot more to learn about this species especially as to how its populations can suddenly mushroom after several lean years.

Small Copper, blue-spotted form. Harrogate (VC64) Oct 2000.

Michael P Laycock

HISTORICAL REVIEW:
Small Copper
Polyommatus phlaeas in Porritt (1883)

The early history of the Small Copper is somewhat muddled, suggesting to some that it may not have been as familiar, and therefore as common a butterfly, as today (Emmet & Heath 1989). Petiver (1699) referred to it as the **small golden black-spotted Meadow Butterfly**. Lewin (1795) was first to call it the **Small Copper** but his contemporaries also used the **Copper,** the **Common Copper** or the **Small Common Copper**. It took until the end of the 19th century before Small Copper was the generally accepted name. The meaning of the current Latin family name *Lycaena* is uncertain. One of many theories suggests a connection to the Lyceum (a Greek gymnasium) where the lively activities of participants could be compared to the lively flights of the Coppers. The species name, *phlaeas,* is probably derived from a word meaning 'to blaze up', an appropriate reference to the copper colour.

Commenting on the national distribution Duncan (1844) simply noted: *'It is rather common in all parts of Britain and seems to breed several times a year'.* Morris (1853) added little: *'It is a common insect with us, and generally distributed throughout the country'.* Coleman (1860) commented: *'This little, but lively representative of the genus, is one of our commonest and most widely distributed butterflies, flashing about in the sunshine, joining in a dance with the no less lively blues, or settling on the lilac flowers of the scabious &c, whose soft tones set off to the best advantage the metallic effulgence of this little gem.'* The earliest Yorkshire record appears to be that in an anonymous list for 1832 from Wath-upon-Dearne (VC63) (Rimington 1992). Fryer & Lucas (2001) note that it was reported from Storthes (VC63) in 1846 and according to Hobkirk (1859, 1868) was common in the Huddersfield area (VC63) in the 1840s and 1850s. They suggest a decline began around 1865, quoting Porritt (1918) (who was born in 1848), *'In my early days Polyommatus phlaeas was in my experience quite a rarity in the Huddersfield district'.* Nonetheless, in his 1883 volume Porritt also notes *'The white variety schmidtii occasionally occurs; one in my own cabinet was taken in Huddersfield in 1871'.* In the same work he reports the species to be *'Commonly distributed throughout the county'.* However, Fryer & Lucas (2001) indicate that many observers between 1901 and 1918 specifically noted that the species had re-appeared after a long absence. Although they argue that the main reason for the disappearance was probably connected to industrial pollution, which coated plants with soot and reduced the strength of the sun, it seems equally likely that such conditions were made even worse by the exceptionally cold weather between 1879 and 1895. Fryer & Lucas go on to chart the 20th century ups and downs of this species in the Huddersfield area in considerable detail, drawing attention to the fact that there were many variations in local populations over the years, and many variations between sites, perhaps due to increasing habitat loss or deterioration, rather than unsuitable weather alone. For the Scarborough area (VC62), AS Tetley (who recorded in the early 1900s) noted, *'I have never found this butterfly common. Isolated specimens all over the district'* (Walsh 1952). Walsh himself, in the same article adds, *'In 1947 four broods occurred. It is now common all over the [Scarborough] district'.* In the Hull area (VC61) Stainforth (1919) simply records its presence *'at Riplingham'*, whilst Porritt (1922) noted it as *'occasional'* around Hull.

The rather thin historical information available suggests that except for the end of the late 19th century, when cold weather, pollution or both, affected this species, the general distribution has remained much the same, albeit with regular ups and downs in response to weather conditions from year to year. At the same time actual population numbers may have declined due to loss or degradation of habitat in some areas, balanced in more recent years by the growing availability of derelict industrial sites resulting from the axing of railway lines in the 1960s, and the abandonment of mining and other industries.

The YNU Report (1967/70) simply commented *'Generally common, occurs in all districts'.* Sutton & Beaumont (1989) added, *'Generally widespread and common on both moorland and lowland localities in VCs 61 to 64, but more local and much rarer in VC65'.* They point out large fluctuations in numbers in the mid-1980s when an estimated 15-fold reduction was reported from the Harrogate Naturalists' Society recording area. Fortunately, the species appears to be able to recover fairly readily from such setbacks.

Peter A Crowther

Paul W Forster

Small Copper: closed-wing view.

1572 BROWN ARGUS *Aricia agestis* (Denis & Schiffermüller 1775)
Family: Lycaenidae ('the Blues').

NORTHERN BROWN ARGUS hybrids *Aricia artaxerxes x agestis*

1573 NORTHERN BROWN ARGUS *Aricia artaxerxes* (Fabricius 1793)
Family: Lycaenidae ('the Blues'). Also known as the MOUNTAIN ARGUS.

View N near Burdale (N Wolds VC61) where Brown Argus is found on the steep grassy slopes of the higher valleys.

BROWN ARGUS:
UK BAP status: *Not listed.*
BC priorities: National: *Low.* N of Eng: *Uncertain.*
Yorkshire: *Medium*
European status: *Not threatened.*

NORTHERN BROWN ARGUS:
UK BAP status: *Priority species.*
BC priorities: National: *High.* N of Eng: *High.*
Yorkshire: *High.*
European status: *Not threatened.*
Protected from sale in GB.

Northern Brown Argus

Brown Argus

SPECIAL NOTES:

Status: These two similar and closely related species have been placed together to avoid repetition in discussing their unusual status. For 300yrs entomologists have puzzled over this issue and wondered if there were one, two or even three Brown Argus species. For much of the 20th century it was widely accepted there was only one. Then in the 1960s they were divided into two: double brooded Brown Argus *agestis* in England as far north as Anglesey and Lincolnshire, and single brooded Northern Brown Argus *artaxerxes* from the Peak District and Yorkshire Wolds northward into Scotland (Jarvis 1966, 1969). It was thought that the Northern Brown Argus was Britain's only endemic species (ie one not found anywhere else), which gave it a very special conservation standing. However, it has since become apparent that the work of Jarvis did not fully explain the variability found in N of England colonies, which one school of thought now sees as bearing the hallmarks of hybrid populations between *agestis* to the south and *artaxerxes* to the north. Over recent years, the problem has prompted statistical studies of wing pattern features (Smyllie 1992, 1996, 1998) and genetic analysis (Aagaard 2002, Wynne in prep. 2002) all of which suggest a final solution may be closer, although yet to be fully agreed. This chapter summarises the current state of affairs.

Latin names: Writers discussing the Brown Argus/Northern Brown Argus problems invariably use Latin names and we have used them here for brevity and clarity. The Brown Argus is called *Aricia agestis* but the genus name *Aricia* can be dropped and the species name *'agestis'* used on its own. The Northern Brown Argus/Mountain Argus is *Aricia artaxerxes* or just *'artaxerxes'*. Northern Brown Argus specimens from Castle Eden in Co Durham were long ago given a sub-species status with the name *salmacis* (Stephens 1828). Over the years this has been extended by usage to describe many other N of England (and Yorkshire) sites where wing patterns are variable. Subspecies names come third, so the full Latin name would be *Aricia artaxerxes salmacis*, but *'salmacis'* can be used on its own. The North European continental race (the Mountain Argus) is usually *Aricia artaxerxes allous* or just *'allous'*, (but some authors prefer *'inhonora'*). The Northern Brown Argus in Scotland (sometimes known as the Scotch or Scottish Whitespot) is now thought to have been formed from the Mountain Argus on the continent, so it is *Aricia artaxerxes* subspecies *artaxerxes*, which at least means we can still call it *'artaxerxes'*. There are also many other subspecies or named varieties in Europe including a southern form *'cramera'*, found in N Africa, Spain and Portugal. (Editor).

WORLD STATUS: Brown Argus:

Resident, 0-1700m: 1 to 3 broods according to height, weather, and latitude (May/Jun, Jul/Sep or Apr/Oct). Present in 35 European countries: declined in 7, and listed as a Red Data Book species (RDB) in 9. **Northern Brown Argus:** Resident, 0-2800m: usually 1 brood, but small partial 2nd appears possible in good years even in Scotland (mid-Jun/late Jul, Aug/Sep). Recorded in 30 European countries: declines reported in 8, and listed as an RDB species in 9. As a result of difficulties over status throughout its range, there are doubts about which part of the genus occurs in various localities, therefore, the range of the whole Argus/*Aricia* genus is summarised here: it includes the Canary Islands, the Atlas Mountains in N Africa (Morocco to Tunisia), Iran, the whole of Europe, and eastward through the northern half of Asia to Siberia and Amur. In Britain the Brown Argus is mainly found east of a line from the Severn to the Humber, with a scatter of mainly coastal colonies in the west as far north as N Wales. The Northern Brown Argus ranges from Lancashire, Cumbria and the northern Pennines in Yorkshire, into SW and E Scotland.

Bill Smyllie

David & Stuart Wise

Above: illustrates variation in the 'colon' dots (see ID section), with one dot reduced to a white spot. (Coombs Dale, Derbyshire, 19/05/1990). Below: an apparently malformed female with over-emphasised lunules (from a S Yorkshire VC63 site), presumed to be from recent immigrant stock. Note the varying discal spots.

YORKSHIRE STATUS 1995/2003:

In Yorkshire there are three groups of the Argus/*Aricia* family to consider:

1) **Brown Argus resident populations:** These fairly small, and apparently sedentary colonies (formerly thought to be *artaxerxes* but now considered *agestis*) are found on the chalk grasslands of the northern Yorkshire Wolds (VC61) (c100-200m) in such places as Sledmere, Burdale, Fordon, Cowlam, Nine Springs Dale, Cottondale, Fridaythorpe and Thixendale. No detailed survey has been undertaken, but numbers seen on casual visits are invariably in single figures, with considerable variation in the amount of white spotting noted over the years. These populations are based on Common Rock-rose *Helianthemum nummularium* as foodplant and are usually single brooded (May/Jul) but may produce a partial 2nd brood in good years (Aug/Sept).

2) **Brown Argus colonisers:** The bulk of the *agestis* population in Britain has 2 broods (May/Jul, Aug/Sep) using common rock-rose on limestone areas, Dove's-foot Cranesbill *Geranium molle* (and other geranium species) on non-limestone soils, and Common Stork's-bill *Erodium cicutarium* on coastal dunes. In the early 1990s populations in central and eastern England began expanding northward, utilising geranium species and spreading rapidly into many new habitats. The expansion corresponded to some exceptionally warm years, and to the regime of set-aside fields under the Common Agricultural Policy reforms begun in 1992. Non-rotational set-aside seems to have been particularly beneficial in promoting the growth of these alternative foodplants. Tyszka (1994) notes that the species had been considered extinct in Lincolnshire since 1960 but 1994 produced VC54 records from Thurlby Fen and Ancaster. Over the next few years several other localities were recorded as far north as the south bank of the Humber, including Gibraltar Point NNR, (on the coast south of Skegness). The first hint that an expanding population might colonise Yorkshire came in 1997 when a small outpost was established in a modified sand dune habitat at the tip of Spurn NNR on the old military parade ground [Mick & Martin Stoyle]. It is assumed that this resulted from immigrants flying across 5+ miles of open estuary from Lincolnshire. In fact, one individual was actually seen arriving and flying up the beach on 02/08/2002 [Dave McAleavy] on a day on which Holly Blues were also flying in from the Humber Estuary. The colony has remained small with maximum counts around **5 or 6**. A few individuals have spread a short distance northward along the peninsular, producing sightings in two other tetrads. A presence survives in 2003 but remains very small with no more than 2 butterflies seen at any one time. VC61 has also produced other sightings which appear to be colonisers, eg on the southern edge of the Wolds at Weedley Springs in 2000 [Sean Clough] and at Allerthorpe Common in 2002 [Christine Frost].

1999 saw the first recently recorded VC63 records at Warmsworth (just west of Doncaster) where **6** were seen on 17/06 [Martin Roberts]. In 2000 further 'arrivals' were noted at Lindrick Common [Ben Keywood], Potteric Carr [up to 11 seen by Ken Woolley], Sprotborough [Dave Booth] and Limpool [Martin Greenland]. Since then, reports have increased annually, until by 2003 some 30 VC63 tetrads have produced records, although many of these appear to be 'one-offs' with the species disappearing as suddenly as it arrived. The butterfly also appears to have jumped northward to Fairburn ings RSPB NR in VC64 where it was recorded on 20/08/2000 [Philip Stephenson]. However, it has been suggested that some of the VC63/64 sightings may have resulted from private introductions. The sudden appearance of c40 specimens at Brockadale YWT NR (VC63) in 2002 appears unnatural. At a time of general expansion it would be a great pity if unauthorised introductions from unnamed sources were to obscure what is happening naturally. In 2003 (a year of record warmth) colonising populations emerged on 25/05 and flew until 22/06. A second brood emerged around 27/07 and flew until around mid-Aug. Then Spurn (VC61) and Brockadale (VC63) produced isolated Oct records with just 1 seen at Spurn on 02/10 and 3 at Brockadale on 16/10, suggesting the possibility of an exceptional partial 3rd brood.

3) Northern Brown Argus resident populations: These appear to be sedentary

one-generation populations linked to common rock-rose on limestone grassland/limestone pavement habitats, and spread across 3x10km squares on the N Yorkshire Moors (VC62) and 12x10km squares in the northern Pennines (VCs64/65). During our 1995/2003 Survey, counts on N Yorkshire Moors sites have been mainly in single figures, the highest being **41** at Ellerburn Bank in 1999 [John Mackenzie]. In the Yorkshire Pennines 33 colonies have been distinguished, mainly in the Ribblesdale/Ingleborough, Wharfedale/Littondale, Wensleydale, Malham and Swaledale areas (170-460m). Most of these populations are small (ie 14 colonies with less than 100 adults), or medium (10 colonies with 100-500), but 6 colonies are large (500-1000) and 3 are very large with over 1000 adults (Ellis 2003). Although *artaxerxes* is generally single-brooded a small partial 2nd generation can appear on N York Moors sites in good years. In fact, current indications (detailed below) suggest the N Yorkshire Moors populations may be considered as predominantly *agestis*, whilst Pennine populations are thought to be hybrids. In 2003 VC64 Pennine populations were first noted flying on 31/05 at Kettlewell [Derek Parkinson] and last recorded at Buckhaw Brow Quarry on 30/07 [Brian & Elizabeth Shorrock]. Pennine flight periods sometimes extend into mid-Aug but usually peak late Jun/mid-Jul (Ellis 2003). Also in 2003 Ellerburn Bank (nr Pickering VC62) recorded two apparently overlapping broods: (numbers of butterflies in bold) 10/06-**1**, 22/06-**6**, 04/07-**9**, 07/07-**2**, 09/07-**10**, 12/07-**2**, 16/07-**3** and 26/07-**1**, 03/08-**2**, 24/08-**7**, 31/08-**2**. [Graham Jackson, Peter Robinson, Graham Sigsworth, David Woodmansey, Ken Woolley]

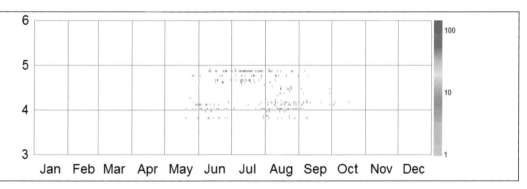

Brown Argus PHENOGRAM:Yorkshire 1995-2003. Shows two or even three broods in S (the colonisers), and mainly one brood in the Wolds and Moors (the long-time residents) with a partial second (in some years).

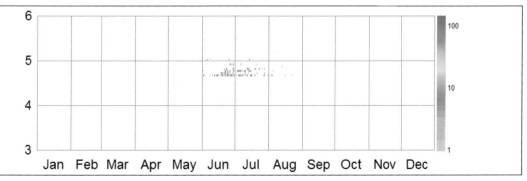

Northern Brown Argus PHENOGRAM:Yorkshire 1995-2003. Shows one brood flying mainly in Jun/Jul. (However, it is probable that the species is rarely searched for in the Dales in Aug/Sept as it is not expected to be found!)

Northern Brown Argus: Yorkshire Tetrad map 1995-2003

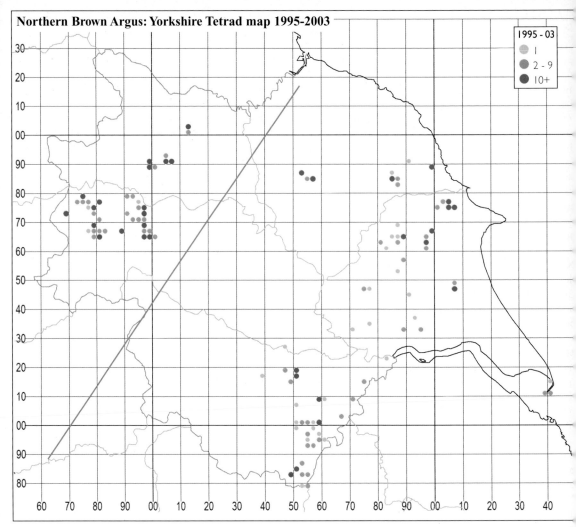

Brown Argus: Yorkshire Tetrad map 1995-2003

Northern Brown Argus

MAP NOTES 1995-2003: The divisions on these maps are based on the most recent information we have regarding these two species, with Brown Argus in southern Yorkshire, on the Wolds and probably on the N York Moors, and N Brown Argus on the NW Pennines. Brown Argus has been noted in **75/3319** recorded tetrads (ie 2.3%), and out of 4120 tetrads in Yorkshire. It is ranked the **28th most widespread** out of 36 breeding species in the county. N Brown Argus has been noted in **42/3319** recorded tetrads (ie 1.3%) and is ranked **31st**.

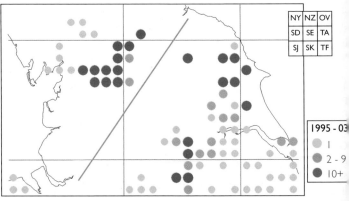

Brown Argus: 10km distribution North of England

◯ = 1 or more records out of county 1995-1999

ver recent years two strands of
vestigation have developed in search of
esh answers to the problems created by
ese two species. The first approach
ndertaken by the present writer since
87) has been to study the variation in
e number of orange spots or 'lunules'
und on the upper forewing, using
atistical analysis. The second, and more
cent approach has been to examine the
tual genetics. The statistical research
as based on the hunch that there could
links between the genetic constitution
a butterfly and its wing pattern (see
ijhout 1989). It is generally accepted
at *agestis* is well lunulated, the north of
ngland race more variable, and *allous* is
oorly lunulated but within any given
olony there is some variation. These
udies indicate that British colonies can
classed according to the degree of
nulation over whole colonies rather than
individual butterflies. Although the
eory is yet to be fully proven, the degree
f correspondence between the two types
f study is considerable and indicates that
nulation studies can make a valuable
ontribution to our understanding of these
roblems. The genetic studies were
ndertaken as a joint project between the
orwegian Institute for Nature Research
d the University of Birmingham which
vestigated colonies in many parts of
W Europe, including one in Yorkshire.
he findings were reported in Aagaard *et
l* (2002). An as yet unpublished and more
mplex genetic analysis was also
ompleted recently and is expected to
ed further light on the general situation
the N of England (pers comm. Ian
ynne).

he statistical study started with the Peak
istrict colonies and extended to many
ther sites in mainland Britain, as well as
museum collections in Britain,
ermany, Switzerland and Spain.
ttention has concentrated on males,
ince their more variable upper forewing
nules (ufl) are better able to show up
ifferences. In this approach a trace of a
nule counts as a full one. Any colony
can have individual males or females which vary between 0 and 6 ufl (upper forewing lunules) on each wing. The differences lie in the relative frequency of well-lunulated (say 5&6 ufl) and very poorly lunulated (0 ufl) males. For example, in Britain, colonies from S England to the Yorkshire Wolds have around 80% (or 4 out of 5) males with 5&6 ufl, whereas the 0 ufl portion is very low, under 1%. By comparison, the females have around 95% with 6 ufl, and a similar (or even lower) 0 ufl content. However, in the vicinity of Pickering, the 5&6 ufl male content drops to under 50%, whilst the 0 ufl proportion stays low, and the proportion of females with 6 ufl stays high (although some of the females have smaller lunules towards the wing-tips). The colonies in NW Yorkshire can be regarded as part of a band stretching from N Lancashire to the Durham coast. Their lunulation is quite variable, not only for different colonies, but also for the same colony in different years. The 5&6 ufl male content is in the range 10-45%, with a significant 5-35% 0 ufl presence. In NW Yorkshire, a colony sampled from museum specimens labelled Grass Wood (nr Grassington VC64) had 17% of males with 5&6 ufl and 33% with 0 ufl.

Another aspect of this study relates to 'phased emergence', referring to the way not all butterflies in a colony emerge at the same time. Instead, their appearance is phased over several weeks. What is intriguing in the Argus group is the way that male ufl drifts downward through any flight period. Males emerging early may have high 5&6 ufl figures (85-100%) whilst those appearing later are much lower (50-65%). This suggests that later specimens have a different genetic content to those appearing earlier and the timing of their emergence is related to inclinations towards one or two generations. The conclusion is that *agestis* colonies not only contain an element of *artaxerxes* (the occasional 'whitespot' can even be found in S England, and 2 out of 3 southern females contain one or more white discal scales), but they also appear to have an element of the southern Brown Argus *cramera*. (Colonies in Tenerife and the Iberian peninsula can have 60-100% of males showing 6 ufl, whilst *agestis* males in England have only 30-45%.) In the Pickering area (VC62) previously considered *artaxerxes*, only 40% of 44 males examined had 5&6 ufl, which was **well below** the statistical minimum of 70% for *agestis*, whilst none had 0 ufl, which is what one might **expect** from *agestis*. It can be argued that these results are part of a sequence of changes in a range of hybrids between *agestis* and *artaxerxes*. There are colonies with similar statistics in Germany and Denmark and they have been labelled *agestis*! The lunulation variation due to phased emergence coupled with increasing evidence of variation in colonies from Pickering northward certainly make life difficult regarding any attempts to find out what is really happening.

As a result of the author's studies (Smyllie 1992a, 1992b, 1997, 1998, 2004) it has been postulated that: a) The mainly single brooded colonies in the Peak District, at Eyarth Rocks in North Wales, and on the Yorkshire Wolds, are *agestis*; b) colonies near Pickering can be considered to be *agestis* due to the absence of 0 ufl specimens; c) colonies between the N York Moors and the Scottish border (inc the N Pennines) are composed of a variable range of hybrids between *artaxerxes* and *agestis*; d) Looking at the whole of Britain, there also appears to be a limited penetration of *artaxerxes* into *agestis* and vice-versa, indicated by the occasional appearance of well-lunulated males in *artaxerxes*, and poorly lunulated males in *agestis*; e) Scottish *artaxerxes* is very similar to the continental *allous*, except that *allous* usually has black discal spots. However, *allous* will produce white discal scales in response to the experimental introduction of low temperatures early in the pupal stage; f) All this is part of a larger system with 0 ufl males up to 100% in N Scandinavia and 6 ufl males up to 100% in the Canaries.

The genetic studies, reported in Aagaard *et al* (2002), involved sampling 18 populations in Britain and Scandinavia, including Fordon Bank (Yorkshire Wolds VC61), Thrislington (Co Durham), Smardale Gill (Cumbria, close to Yorkshire's NW border), and Coombs Dale and Cressbrook Dale (Derbyshire). The investigating team argue that *'given the available data'* the following conclusions can now be drawn: a) *artaxerxes* in Britain is the same species as *allous* in Scandinavia and is, therefore, not endemic to Britain; b) Wolds populations, formerly thought to be *artaxerxes* due to being mainly single brooded, are actually *agestis*; c) Populations in NW England are *artaxerxes*; d) Peak District populations produced conflicting results and may therefore be of hybrid origin. This survey did not include any N Yorkshire Moors data.

The statistical and genetic studies show considerable agreement. Both indicate that Wolds colonies are not *artaxerxes* as previously thought, but *agestis*. Both agree that the Scottish *artaxerxes* populations are related to the Mountain Argus *allous* on the continent. Aagaard *et al* were unable to confirm the presence of hybrids except possibly in the Peak District where contradictory results could indicate hybridisation. However, the Aagaard team did not examine specimens from the N York Moors, whereas a later as yet unpublished genetic study by Ian Wynne (pers comm. 2002) is expected to confirm the existence of hybrids in N of England colonies. So far, all samples for genetic analysis appear to have been taken on single visits to each colony, so do not allow for the possibility that phased emergence might have had a bearing on the results. In other words in a potentially hybrid population, specimens taken early

in the flight season might be expected to show an affinity with *agestis* (this flies earlier), and specimens taken later, a stronger link with *artaxerx* which flies later. The Aagaard study covered only one site in Yorkshire (the Wolds at Fordon Bank) leaving many county sites yet to be examine Wynne's forthcoming paper may fill in some of the gaps, but there is like to be a need for further genetic studies before any apparent discrepanci between DNA analysis and lunulation are finally explained.

View of typical Northern Brown Argus habitat near Kettlewell (Wharfedale VC64).

CONSERVATION ISSUES: The **Brown Argus** is given *medium* priority by Butterfly Conservation (BC) in Yorkshire as it is probably a rarer butterfly in the county than the Northern Brown Argus! In fact, the scientific interest of the Wolds' populations deserves special consideration and a more detailed population study. The **Northern Brown Argus** has been intensively studied in recent years. In particular, management issues are addressed in a survey report of the Yorkshire Dales organised by BC's N of England Regional Officer, Sam Ellis (Ellis 2003). Further management ideas are discussed in Ellis (1997) and BC has also produced a Species Action Plan for the Northern Brown Argus (Ravenscroft & Warren 1996).

In both species, over-grazing or use of fertilisers could cause population crashes and extinction. Tree-planting is a threat to some Dales sites and possibly also to some on the Wolds. Healthy populations can be maintained by light grazing using sheep, cattle or horses. The ideal site is one where luxuriant common rock-rose growth can co-exist with other vegetation forms, either with or without limited grazing. Un-grazed sites will eventually scrub over, but can be restored, either by physical scrub clearance or a light grazing regime. Well-spaced scrub can be beneficial in providing shelter, but needs to be controlled on a 10-15yr rotation. The ideal sward height is 6-10cm or very slightly higher to accommodate the foodplant height typically attained on any given site. Fragmentation of colonies needs to be avoided as this can lead to extinctions. The Northern Brown Argus is listed as a priority species in the Biodiversity Action Plan for the Dales National Park, and efforts are being made to manage all suitable unoccupied habitat within 5km of known colonies.

ID NOTES:

Key issues are:

a) separating both Argus species from similar brown female Common Blues (which also have black discal spots and variable numbers of orange lunules): see diagram for diagnostic features. The Argus tends to be smaller, and in Brown Argus usually has a warmer, richer brown, ground colour to the upperwings, and more striking white wing margins when fresh. (But be wary of very small Common Blues which sometimes occur.)

b) separating *agestis* from *artaxerxes*: The commonly accepted method of using upperwing discal spots to separate *agestis* (with black spots), *artaxerxes* (with white spots) and *salmacis* (with black and white spots) is unreliable. White scales, and even the all white discal spot, can occasionally appear throughout the Brown Argus range becoming more frequent as one heads north. Likewise, within the former *salmacis* range, a proportion of butterflies still show black discal spots. The number of white scales appearing in either group varies from a single scale to a white patch or even a complete ring of scales around the black discal spot (ab *snelleni* Ter Haar). *Agestis* tends to be more strongly marked than its northern counterpart, with more prominent orange lunules, and bigger black spots in the dot pattern of the underwings. The upperwing ground colour also tends to be a more reddish brown in *agestis* compared to a much darker brown in *artaxerxes*.

However, the range of variation means that **individuals** cannot be cited as having diagnostic features either in Yorkshire or elsewhere. For the time being, identification is best made on a geographical basis: we can say that the colonising specimens in the southern half of the county and the resident populations on the Yorkshire Wolds are Brown Argus; populations on the northern Pennines are Northern Brown Argus (probably hybrids), leaving those on the N Yorkshire Moors yet to be finalised, but probably as *agestis*.

Over 40 Brown Argus variations have been described including ab *pallidior* Oberthür with yellow upperwing lunules replacing the orange ones, or ab *graafi* Ver-Huell where the lunules are white. Only a dozen specific aberrations have been described for the Northern Brown Argus, mainly covering variations in amounts of white around the discal spot, (although some aberrations described for Brown Argus also apply). Occasionally all four upperwings carry a white discal spot (ab *quadripuncta* Tutt).

Above: Brown Argus: In this view note spot free area on lower part of upperwing (diagnostic). Note also, the 'colon' – 2 spots near the centre of the upper edge of the lower wing, and at right angles to the edge. (Similar spots in Common Blue are usually at a sharper angle to the edge, and more widely spaced. This is a good guide but subject to variation). Second spot of colon can be reduced. Body hairs more silvery grey than blue, but a slight hint of blue is sometimes possible.

Below: Common Blue: Note extra spots on lower part of upperwing, and colon dots usually well separated. Body hairs often quite strongly blue, but can be much paler and almost identical to silvery grey of Brown Argus.

PHOTO STRIP: This selection illustrates some of the variations found in Britain from North (top) to South. 1 to 3 are *artaxerxes*, 4 is uncertain but probably *agestis* (Pickering area), and 5 and 6 are *agestis*. 1: Scottish Whitespot (Perthshire 07/2001 *Paul Kirkland*). 2: Almost a 'whitespot'. Hart Warren (Durham Coast 03/07/1990 *Bill Smyllie*). 3: No upperwing lunules, Gait Barrows (N Lancs 07/1989 *Les Hall*). 4: Another near 'whitespot', Ashberry Pastures (N York Moors 19/06/1998 *Neil Rankin*). 5: Very well-lunulated female (6ufl), with white scales round black discal dot (or eyespot), Coombs Dale (Derbyshire 22/07/1990 *Bill Smyllie*). 6: Typical male agestis with black discal spots and fairly well-marked lunules (Coombs Dale 29/06/1990 *Bill Smyllie*).

LIFE STORY

Brown Argus/Northern Brown Argus egg from Ellerburn (VC62).

Paul W Forster

Northern Brown Argus egg x120 magnification from Kettlewell (Courtesy Sheffield University Sorby Centre).

Eggs are laid singly, usually on common rock-rose leaves but occasionally (as at Spurn) on species of wild geranium as noted above. *Agestis* tends to lay eggs on the underside of leaves, whilst *artaxerxes* places them on the upper surfaces. However, although the Wolds race is now considered *agestis*, eggs are usually laid on the upper surface in spite of the fact that further south the reverse is true. It would appear, therefore, that the major influence on egg placement is climatic rather than genetic, although one visitor to Coombs Dale described a female which laid one egg on the upper surface, and then followed with another underneath! Eggs appear as squat, whitish circles, found from mid-June on low-lying sheltered situations in the south of the county, and from early July further north and higher up. Microscopic examination reveals that eggs have a very variable reticulated surface structure. (See photo.)

Larvae hatch out after about two weeks, and crawl to the underside of the leaf, where they eat small areas, leaving the upper leaf surface intact. The affected surface of the leaf tends to turn yellow after a short time, and the general effect on rock-rose is indicative of *Aricia*. Woodlouse-shaped larvae are similar in both species, being green with well-marked darker green chevrons and black heads. *Agestis* tends to be slightly smaller with a green dorsal line (down the middle of the back) compared to *artaxerxes* with a purple line, but such lines vary significantly. The sub-spiracular line, (low down on both sides) varies from white, with purplish pink above and below the white, to white with virtually no colours on either side. Such variation seems to be another pointer towards hybrids, but it is interesting to note that well-coloured larvae do not necessarily produce well-lunulated butterflies.

In autumn, larvae hibernate at the bottom of the foodplant or under a leaf and become active again in early spring probably in March. Pupation takes place on or near the ground and ants may attend both larvae and pupae. Larvae are thought to attract the ants by 'singing' (ie producing a sound) and by the production of honeydew. Pupae may be carried off by the ants and guarded underground. We know little about the part played by ants in Yorkshire. Sam Ellis (1997) has observed *Formica lemani* attending larvae of Northern Brown Argus on a Durham site, but inferred this was probably a fairly rare occurrence. There is scope for further study here.

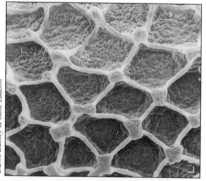

Dawn Bussey & Jane Ladson

Surface of Northern Brown Argus egg from Kettlewell at x400 magnification. (Courtesy Sheffield University Sorby Centre)

derivation of *agestis* is not known, but Emmet (1991) suggests a possible corruption of Argestes, the god of the NW wind; Artaxerxes is the name of several Persian kings; Salmacis was a Naiad who fell in love with Hermaphroditus.

The Brown Argus was first named **the Edg'd Brown Argus** by Petiver (1704). It later became the **Argus Blue** (Harris 1775), and the **Brown Blue** (Lewin 1795). Haworth (1803) simplified it to the **Brown Argus**, whilst Morris (1853) expanded it to **Brown Argus Blue**. Samouelle (1819) used **Black-Spot Brown** and **White-Spot Brown** to distinguish the two varieties. The first scientific effort to describe the Northern Brown Argus came when Fabricius gave the scientific name *artaxerxes* to examples taken from Arthur's Seat, Edinburgh, in 1793. Lewin (1795) then called it the **Brown Whitespot**, whilst Haworth (1803) used **Scotch Argus** (the present butterfly bearing that name not having yet been discovered). However, not everyone accepted the division. Morris (1853) considered both forms as one species. Newman (1871) introduced the name as **Scotch Brown Argus**, whilst South (1906) re-christened the Scottish form as the **Scotch White Spot** (a name still sometimes used, but more recently written as **Scottish Whitespot**). Heslop (1959) lists *A. artaxerxes* as the **Scotch Brown Blue**. The distinct forms in Northern England were long ago thought to be a subspecies and Stephens (1828) bestowed the additional subspecies name *salmacis*, initially to describe the examples found at Castle Eden Dene in Co Durham, which were later called the **Durham Argus** (Rennie 1832) or the **Castle Eden Argus** (Newman 1871). Rennie decided there were three species to contend with, the **Brown Argus Blue**, the **Durham Argus** and the **Scotch Argus**. Dale (1830) rejected the subspecies idea, insisting that the specimens found in the Durham area were *'mules, or hybrids between the two species'*, (ie between *agestis* to the south and *artaxerxes* to the north in Scotland). 170yrs later his ideas are gaining ground! In the Latin *Aricia* is the name of an ancient town; the

Duncan (1844) described 3 species: the **Brown Argus**, the **Durham Argus** and the **Artaxerxes Butterfly**. Regarding the latter two he comments, *'The examination of an extensive series of specimens of the two preceding insects, will probably lead most people to the belief, that the marks which have caused them to be regarded as specifically different, are far from being stable or satisfactory.'* Morris (1853) wrote, *'The changes in the markings on the wing of this insect, in different latitudes of the country, are certainly very curious; but though described as three separate species, there seems every reason to believe, or rather, in fact no reason to doubt, but that they are all referable to one and the same butterfly.'* Coleman (1860) describes the **Brown Argus** and the **Artaxerxes Butterfly**, noting, *'There has been a great deal of discussion among entomologists, as to whether this be a distinct species, or only a variety of Agestis. I believe it to be the latter, but do not attach much importance to the question; and as this butterfly is found under the name of Artaxerxes, in almost every cabinet, and is rather a famous little insect, I have thought it best to give it a separate heading under its usual title, and collecting readers may still label it in their cabinet either as above, or as Polyommatus Agestis or as 'P. Agestis, var, Artaxerxes', and probably will be equally right either way.'* He goes on to argue, *'Against the idea of Agestis and Artaxerxes being one species, it has been objected, that the former is double, the latter single brooded. What of that? Plenty of species that are double-brooded in the south of Europe are well known to become single brooded in a more northern situation.'*

The *Aricia* have never been common in Yorkshire. Porritt's earliest records are for York 1842 (exact site and VC not known) and Boston Spa (VC64) in 1856 (both quoted from entomological magazines of those dates). His 1883 'List' also gives Scarborough (VC62), Ledsham (VC64) and Richmond (VC65). Regarding the latter record he notes: *'Mr John Sang informs us that the Richmond specimens are of the form Salmacis (Steph).'*

Contrasting specimens from Ellerburn Bank (VC62). Left: Burnished brown example of male (09/07/2001 *Bill Smyllie*). Right: Much greyer individual (28/05/2004 *Paul W Forster*).

Porritt's 1904 'Supplement' adds Sledmere (VC61), Gormire (VC62), Grassington (VC64) and Redmire (VC65). Porritt (1907) adds no new sites, but removes the York and Boston Spa records. Stainforth (1919) notes that, *'Lycaena agestis is plentiful at Riplingham,'* [just west of Hull VC61]. *'The only other East Riding locality for this species is Sledmere. Mr A S Tetley says it swarms on the Wolds near Pickering'.* This is incorrectly quoted. Tetley (1915) actually wrote, *'Of the Blues I have taken only Polyommatus icarus and Aricia medon [= agestis], which swarms on the Wolds and near Pickering, where I have taken a specimen very near to var. salmacis.'* Walsh (1952 & 1956) looked back on the previous 50+ years of recording in the Scarborough area (VC62). He notes that Porritt's earlier reference to Scarborough was probably derived from a report of a sighting in Forge Valley by A Tyers. He also notes that Tetley mentioned the species as very common at Haugh Rigg near Pickering (VC62) in June 1914, whilst in Aug of that same year, one or two examples of a second brood were noted! Walsh commented that the species still occurred on this site in the 1950s but, *'Its chief haunts, however, are on the chalk Wolds [VC61]; it is common at Cowlam and Thixendale and occurs in numbers in a valley off the Driffield road on the Scarborough side of Foxholes. It is generally common in suitable localities such as High Fordon, Allerston and Langdale.* (Note: Allerston and Langdale are not on the Wolds, but on or towards the southern edge of the N York Moors VC62.)

The YNU Report (1967/70) only considered one species, Brown Argus *Aricia agestis*, and classed it as *'local but usually common where it occurs.'* The main sites were given as: **VC61**: Burdale, Cowlam, Sledmere and Thixendale; **VC62**: Gormire, Newton Dale, Pickering and Scarborough; **VC64**: Arncliffe, Buckden, and Grassington; **VC65**: Redmire and Richmond. Garland (1981) writes that the 'Northern Brown Argus' was recorded in the Maltby area in the 1800s and near Worral (VC63) in the

A selection of Pennine specimens from Wharfedale VC64 (all from Skirethorns except bottom R from nearby Bastow) illustrating the variety of upperwing patterns found in these *artaxerxes* colonies. All above photos *David Howson*.

1945/55 period. Whiteley (1992) accepts that Derbyshire Northern Brown Argus colonies were then considered to be Brown Argus and points out that in 1987, stock from Coombs Dale in Derbyshire was privately introduced to Lindrick (VC63) and survived until at least 1989. Sutton & Beaumont (1989) discuss the difficulties concerning the *Aricia* and mention the following localities: for *agestis* in **VC61**: at Sledmere and Fordon; for *artaxerxes* ssp *salmacis* in **VC61**: at Cowlam, Fordon, Fridaythorpe, Muston and Thixendale; in **VC62**: at Ashberry Pastures, Caydale, Dalby Forest, Ellerburn Bank, Gundale and Hutton Common; in **VC64**: at Buckden, Grassington, Kettlewell and Threshfield.

The work of Jarvis and Høegh Guldberg in the 1950s/1960s seemed to bring final clarification to the *Aricia* problem, separating Brown Argus *agestis* from Northern Brown Argus *artaxerxes* and cutting out intermediate forms. However, the way such forms turned up in many N of England colonies continued to puzzle some observers resulting in the new studies and discoveries outlined in the status reappraisal section above.

Bill Smyllie

1574 COMMON BLUE *Polyommatus icarus* (Rottemburg 1775)
Family: Lycaenidae, sub-group Polyommatinae ('the Blues').

Hawnby Hill viewed from Murton (N York Moors VC62).

UK BAP Status: *Not listed.*
BC Priorities: National: *Low.*
N of Eng: *Low.* **Yorkshire:** *Low.*
European status: *Not threatened.*

WORLD STATUS: Common, widespread, resident: 0-3000m. Up to 3 broods. Possible continuous generation in warmest climates (eg Canary Isles). Range: N Africa to N Scotland, and E across Asia. Some decreases in W Europe and expansion in W Russia. Voltinism varies, even year to year on same site, according to latitude, height, locality and weather. Single brood populations fly longer (Jun/Aug); double broods May/Jun & late Jul/Sept; 3rd broods – Sept/Oct. UK populations usually bivoltine in S, univoltine in N, with Yorkshire a transitional zone between the two.

Common Blue

YORKSHIRE STATUS 1995/2003:

Fairly common and widespread resident where suitable grassland habitats still exist, but vulnerable to habitat loss and drought. Many sites lost to intensive farming in recent years. Also suffered in the dry years of the early 1990s, but recovered in the wetter period around 2000/2002. A line drawn from Scarborough (VC62) to Skipton (VC64) forms an approximate boundary between tendencies towards 2 generations to the south and 1 to the north, although lowland or sheltered sites to the north often produce 2 broods. A usually small, partial 3rd brood appears to occur in some years, particularly on the southern edges of the county. However, this may actually result from the fact that a usually large proportion of 1st brood larvae overwinter, whilst the rest produce the 2nd generation. Warm autumns may trigger some of these overwintering larvae to become active and hatch out. So what appears to be a 3rd generation is really an extended 2nd. This also explains why the first brood (May/Jun) generally (but not always) produces larger counts than the summer brood, and sometimes has 2 peaks, as an often high proportion of 2nd generation larvae do not hatch out until the following year. Therefore the spring brood is made up of offspring from the previous year's 1st and 2nd broods which may develop at slightly different rates.

Our 1995/2003 Survey drew attention to the generally **early emergence** in the south of the county, eg in VC63: 03/05/1997; 08/05/1998; 25/04/1999; 14/05/2000; 10/05/2001; 23/04/2002 and 16/04/2003. First records in VC61 have been around 10/05 in this period with no Apr records. Emergence tends to be later as one moves northward and upward, but with exceptions on sheltered sites eg in Deepdale (N York Moors VC62) on 03/05/1999 [Len & Norma Auckland]. 1st brood usually ends late Jun/early Jul, but in some years and on some sites, both generations overlap and can only be distinguished by peaks. In the Dales (VC65), the single brood usually emerges mid-Jun/early Jul (occasionally even early Aug), but there are also lowland VC65 sites (eg Nosterfield NR SE28) where 2 broods occur regularly and **last records** can be as late as 12/09/2002 [Jill Warwick]. The Coatham Sands/ South Gare area (VC62/NZ52) is in the extreme north of the county beside the Tees Estuary, and regularly produces 2 broods with an occasional hint of a 'partial 3rd'. Singletons were noted by IW Reynolds on 23/09/2002 at nearby Corus Steelworks, and by

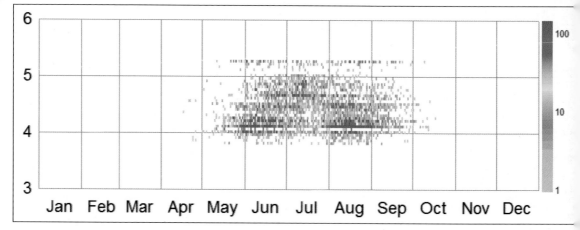

Jan Feb Mar Apr May Jun Jul Aug Sep Oct Nov Dec

PHENOGRAM:Yorkshire 1995-2003. Shows 2 broods merging to become one as we move north, but with a return to 2 broods in lowland areas to N (Middlesbrough/S Gare). The situation on the ground is probably more complicated and variable than this diagram indicates.

ID NOTES: Uppersides: male - violet blue; female – a variable number of orange lunules on brown, blue/brown or violet blue background. 'Blue' females are very distinctive and look like a different species. (The tendency towards blue females is thought to increase from south to north, and is strongest in Ireland and NW Scotland where some sources allocate the subspecies status *mariscolore*.) Most colonies in Yorkshire produce varying proportions of blue or blue/brown females. Undersides: both sexes similar with patterns of black and white spots and orange lunules on greyish (for male), or brownish (for female) backgrounds. Can be confused with Holly Blue (undersides with black spots only), or brown female with Brown Argus. Latter usually smaller and more active with notable white fringe to wing when fresh. (See p139 for further discussion on differences.) An extremely variable species with over 200 aberrations described.

Howard Frost a little further west at the Tees Barrage (NZ41) on 28/09/2001. **Latest records** in the Survey period: **1996:** 13/10 Walton Nature Park (VC63) [Roy Bedford], **1997:** 18/10 Walton Nature Park (VC63) [Roy Bedford], **1998:** 01/10 Farnham Gravel Pits (VC64) [Leonard Ratliffe], **1999:** 05/10 Shipley (VC63) [Susan Stead], **2000:** 10/10 Fairburn Ings RSPB NR (VC64) [Philip Stephenson], **2001:** 16/10 Methley (VC63) [John Martin], **2002:** 09/10 Carlton Marsh NR (VC63) [Carlton Marsh Recording Group], **2003:** 12/10 York (VC62) [B Skerritt].

Across the county, typical site counts are in the 2 to 20 range. Highest 1995/2003 Survey counts: **c600** at Spurn NNR (VC61) on 01/08/1999 [Barry Spence]; **611** Walton Nature Park (VC63) on 15/08/1997 [Roy Bedford]; **c300** at Wharram Quarry YWT NR (VC61) on 03/07/1998 [MN Rankin]; **353** at Duck St Quarry, Greenhow (c400m) (VC64) on 11/07/2002 [Mike Barnham] and **169** at Coatham Marsh (Nr South Gare VC62) on 01/06/2002 [P Lees]. It is unclear as to whether the very thin distribution in central parts of the northern half of the county is a result of genuine absence, or of under recording. The latter is suspected, although it is also possible that colonies are more scattered and not easy to pick up on casual visits.

CONSERVATION ISSUES: Many observers feel the Common Blue has declined in numbers over the last 50yrs. This is difficult to quantify, as the butterfly is still quite widespread and has even extended its range in some areas (eg the West Riding). Ellis (2000) suggests a decline of only 1% by 10km squares over the previous 25yrs. However, the general cleaning up of the countryside has greatly reduced the number of sites available. Although it may still be present in any given 10km square, it may not be present on as many sites within that square as previously. In some areas, the development of nature parks on old mining tips and the building of new roads has resulted in Bird's-foot Trefoil being planted with the grass mix used to sow meadows and verges. Roy Bedford's transect through such an area at Walton Nature Park (near Wakefield VC63) has shown very large Common Blue populations can develop on such sites. However, Bird's-foot Trefoil is a colonising plant, which will progressively disappear as the grassland matures, unless bare patches are regularly re-introduced either by grazing or by physical disturbance. Cattle or horse grazing is particularly useful in that feet create scuffs and scrapes where Bird's-foot Trefoil can colonise. However, the level of grazing should be light as Common Blues thrive best where sward height varies. Rabbits seem to do the job really well. Disused railway tracks are often excellent habitats for this and many other species, but after some 40yrs of disuse, tracks axed in the days of Beeching are now becoming increasingly over-shaded by tree and shrub growth. Without drastic cutting back, their value for butterflies will be lost. Ideally, such habitats should have an ongoing programme of patchwork clearance aimed at creating plenty of habitat variation. Butterfly Conservation has a small nature reserve at Shipley Station (VC63) managed with this species in mind.

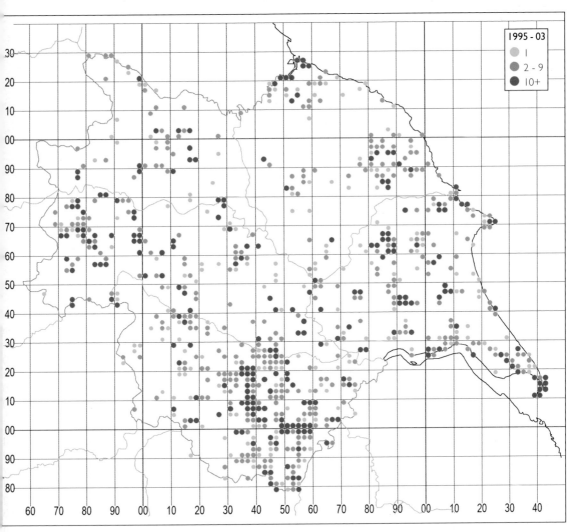

Common Blue: Yorkshire Tetrad map 1995-2003

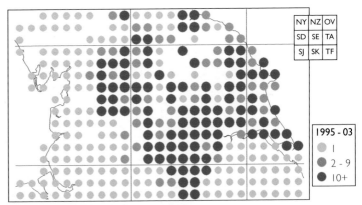

NY	NZ	OV
SD	SE	TA
SJ	SK	TF

Common Blue: 10km distribution North of England

= 1 or more records out of county 1995-1999

LIFE STORY

Common Blue: mating pair (Coatham Marsh VC62 31/05/2004).

White eggs are laid singly on upper surfaces of leaves near the top of leguminous foodplants. Eggs hatch into green larvae after about 10 days. Where there are 2 broods it is thought that only a minority of the 1st generation feed up to become 2nd generation. Most grow slowly until ready to hibernate at the 3rd instar in late Sep/early Oct. Second generation larvae reach the same point at the same time! These combined generations usually ensure that the following year's early summer peak is much higher than the mid-summer peak. This is borne out in Roy Bedford's transect counts at Walton Nature Park (nr Wakefield VC63) where in 2002 the spring peak on 10/06 was 318, but the summer peak on 21/08 was only 51. However, exceptionally, during our Survey years, 1999 produced a reverse, at both Spurn NNR and Walton Nature Park (Spurn: 29/05 = **250**, 01/08 = **600**; Walton 15/06 = **49**, 22/08 = **67**.) Where the species is single brooded, the flight season is usually later but longer (Jun/Sept). During the winter, larvae hibernate and hide away in the leaf litter or in the lower part of a thickness of plants. Feeding usually resumes Mar/Apr. Larvae may be milked by ants and are capable of 'singing' (below human hearing) to attract attention. As a result, some larvae are thought to spend winter safely protected within anthills. Larvae pupate after 5 instars and spend about 2 weeks as greenish coloured pupae also capable of attracting ants with long periods of noise described as being like a clicking ratchet (Thomas & Lewington 1991). Red Ants *Myrmica sabuleti* have been observed at Butterfly Conservation's Shipley Station NR, which is managed for the Common Blue, but searches for larvae and pupae inside nests have not been successful. In Yorkshire adult butterflies usually begin appearing in Apr/May and often roost communally. Some adults wander in search of new territories and can be encountered nectaring in places where they are not normally resident, including parks and gardens.

Left: Common Blue females vary from all blue (Biesbos, Netherlands 02/08/1981), to Right: all brown individuals with only a hint of blue round the body (Cowden VC61, Jul 2000).

HISTORICAL REVIEW:
Common Blue
Formerly *Lycaena alexis* Hübner in Porritt (1883)

Petiver (1704) named the male the **Blue Argus** and the female the **Mixed Argus**. In 1717 he further deduced a 3rd species from variant females, which he called the **Selvedg'd Argus**. It is unclear as to which form he had in mind. Wilkes (1741/42) used **Ultramarine Blue**, but later changed it to the **Blue Argus**. Harris (1775) introduced **Common Blue** and this won the day in spite of Brown (1832) calling it the **Caerulean Blue** and Rennie (1832) opting for **the Alexis**. In the Latin *Polyommatus* means 'many-eyed', whilst *icarus* refers to Icarus, son of Daedalus, who was given wings attached with wax which melted when he got too near the sun.

Duncan (1844) commenting on the national distribution noted it *'a very abundant insect...distributed over the whole country'*. Morris (1853) made a similar comment: *'one of the commonest of our native species...appears to be distributed throughout the kingdom'*. Coleman (1860) wrote: *'This very pretty little insect is the blue butterfly one sees everywhere, abounding in meadows, on heaths and downs, and not at all confined to chalky soils, like some other blues.'* In Yorkshire the Common Blue always appears to have been common enough not to attract much comment or attention. Porritt (1883/1907) noted it *'Generally distributed, but very scarce in some parts of the West Riding'*. The YNU 1967/70 Report quotes Porritt and adds: *It is interesting to note that his remarks made so long ago still apply more or less exactly today'*. Rimington (1992) highlights some of Yorkshire's earliest VC63 records from the Doncaster area, including Wath-upon-Dearne 1832, Askern (Lankester 1842) and Adwick 1846 (JW Dunning). Peter Gibson (pers comm.) drew our attention to an early reference for VC62 in Belcher (1836) who mentions 'Blue Argus' specimens in the collection of Mr Hartas of Rosedale, which were probably taken locally.

Garland (1981) suggests that in the Sheffield area, *'Its distribution seems to have remained relatively constant throughout the last one hundred and fifty years'*. Rimington (1992) notes that Doncaster area records from the 19th and early 20th centuries are *'generally scarce, but with no reference to a marked decline in the district'*. Fryer & Lucas (2001) investigate the Huddersfield area distribution in considerable depth from about 1850. They note that Newman (1870/71) judged the Common Blue to be present everywhere in England *'except in a few localities in Yorkshire'*. Stainforth (1919) fails to note it for the Hull area in respect of Thomas Stather's collection made prior to 1878, although Boult (1899) and Porritt (1922) indicated it was common in the Hull region. For the Scarborough area, Tetley (1915) makes only a passing reference to having caught one. Walsh (1956) describes it as *'Generally distributed and common'* around Scarborough. Moseley (1883) writing about the Huddersfield area only knew it on *'Mollicar Pastures formerly'*. Fryer & Lucas report that the species appeared to be largely absent from the Huddersfield area from the late 1800s until the 1940s, although with odd records here and there, indicating that it had never quite disappeared completely. An increase became evident from c1945, probably extending westward along the Calder Valley and a more general Huddersfield area increase was noted in the 1980s and 1990s. Sutton & Beaumont (1989) also noted a general increase in many parts of the county in the early 1980s, followed by a decline after several poor summers (1985/1988). The warmer 1990s were not necessarily better for the species as in some years, periods of drought affected foodplant growth.

Howard M Frost & Derek Parkinson

Middle of the range blue female (Kent 1983). Note: hint of white scales around discal dots similar to Brown Argus.

Aberrant male. Cowden (VC61) 2003.

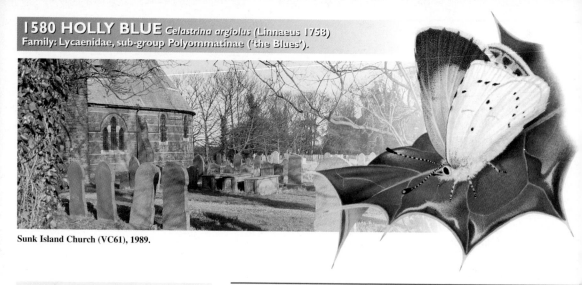

1580 HOLLY BLUE *Celastrina argiolus* (Linnaeus 1758)
Family: Lycaenidae, sub-group Polyommatinae ('the Blues').

Sunk Island Church (VC61), 1989.

UK BAP Status: *Not listed.*
BC Priorities: National: *Low.*
N of Eng: *Low.* Yorkshire: *Low.*
European status: *Not threatened.*
Protected in Northern Ireland.

WORLD STATUS: Mobile resident, 0-1900m in Europe, 0-2600m in Africa, 2 broods (possibly 3). Range: N Africa to N England and S Scandinavia, and eastward across central Asia to Japan, and N and Central America. Also present but less widespread in Ireland and parts of N Scandinavia. Stable or expanding across range. 89% increase by 10km squares in Britain since 1982 (Asher *et al* 2001). British race considered separate subspecies *britanna* (Verity 1919). In N America: called the **Spring Azure**, formerly *Celastrina argiolus* but now *C. ladon*, may embrace more than one species!

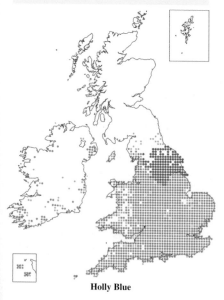

Holly Blue

YORKSHIRE STATUS 1995/2003:

Immigrant and coloniser. Periodically invades from the south (and east?) in warmer years, establishing semi-permanent populations, which then disappear in colder years. A long-standing colonisation developed around 1978 between York, Harrogate and Nidderdale (all VC64). The population was considered univoltine around Nidderdale (presumably due to the height and a cooler, cloudier climate), but bivoltine towards York (Barnham & Foggitt 1987). This isolated colonisation has survived into our survey period but has been overlapped by a more widespread invasion dating from 1990, a year which saw the first of several recent invasions from areas to the south of Yorkshire. Frost & Frost (1992) describe a notable 1991 spring generation in VC61 followed by a huge offspring in summer with 180 sightings collated for 9x10km squares in South Holderness alone. In addition, dramatic immigrations at Spurn (**300+** butterflies on one day in 1991 and **150+** in 1992), Yorkshire sightings of butterflies flying in from the sea, and records from oil and gas rigs up to 50 miles off the east coasts of both Lincolnshire and Yorkshire, all raise as yet unanswered questions about the butterfly's abilities to migrate and the possibility of arrivals from, or departures to, the continent! However, it seems more likely that considerable numbers sometimes head northwards into the North Sea from N Norfolk, then veer westward towards the Yorkshire coast. Large numbers of butterflies have been involved, with the biggest arrival at Spurn NNR, in 1991, being in excess of 300 on one day. Smaller coastal arrivals have continued into our survey period with the most recent being Dan McAleavy's observation of at least **40** in the sand dunes at the tip of Spurn on 02/08/2002. Some of these were observed flying in up the beach.

In 1996 the **earliest** Yorkshire record was registered fairly typically in mid-May on 13/05. Since then the trend has been to much earlier sightings: 25/03 in 1997, 22/03 in 1998, 25/04 in 1999, 25/04 in 2000, 01/05 in 2001, 29/03 in 2002 and 17/03 in 2003. Probably **the earliest ever** recorded Yorkshire sighting was from the Sheffield area (VC63) on 04/03/1992 (Whiteley 1992). Between 1990 and 1996 the **latest records** for this species were usually noted in Aug, the last record for 1996 being a fairly typical 27/08. A rapid change has occurred since then with the number of

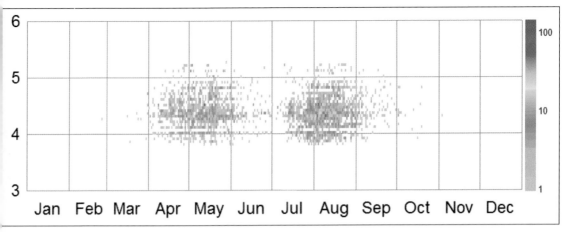

PHENOGRAM: Yorkshire 1995-2003. Shows two clear generations plus the hint of a partial 3rd in Oct.

ID NOTES: A small silvery-blue butterfly often first seen flying fairly high around trees and shrubs, especially in gardens, parks and churchyards. It will descend to ground level to nectar on flowers including buddleia. It will also seek nutrients from damp mud and animal dung. Can be confused with Common Blue, which is generally (but not always!) found in more open grassland habitats, flying closer to the ground. In closed-wing view Holly Blue reveals black dots on a silvery blue-grey background, quite different to the Common Blue's bands of orange-centred lunules. Holly Blue usually perches with wings closed or only partially open to about 90°. Male Holly Blue has mid-blue all over whilst female is similar but with strong black margins to upper forewings and, less obviously, to upper hindwings. First brood females are less strongly marked than 2nd brood. Variation is uncommon, although at least 35 aberrations have been described.

CONSERVATION ISSUES: The mobility of this species ensures that when conditions are right it can invariably find suitable habitats for itself. Its continued success in the north will depend on the degree of future climatic swings, the butterfly's parasite, and perhaps the maintenance of holly and ivy in such places as parks, gardens and churchyards. Holly is often quite a scarce plant in the open countryside so it would be valuable if the species could be included in more of the growing number of hedge-planting projects seen today, bearing in mind the need to include male and female plants.

autumn records increasing steadily and the last records becoming much later: 18/10 in 1997, 12/10 in 1998, 21/09 in 1999, 02/10 in 2000, 17/10 in 2001 and amazingly, 02/11 in 2002 (when Louise Howard recorded what must be Yorkshire's latest-ever Holly Blue in the middle of Hull, VC61), and 15/10 in 2003. Some late records into Sept may be delayed second brood emergence, but later records into Oct suggest a partial third generation, as is found in southern Europe, and very occasionally in the south of England. That this could happen as far north as Yorkshire was undreamed of just a few years ago! Yorkshire sightings are typically in ones and twos with occasional concentrations on prime sites like York Cemetery Nature Reserve (VC62/SE65) [eg 20 on 15/08/1998 Pat Bone], and Haw Park nr Wakefield (VC63/SE31) [eg 28 on 09/08/1998 Roy Bedford]. In 2002 the species was recorded in 251 tetrads spread across 88x10km squares, the majority south of a line from Flamborough Head to Ripon, with particular concentrations in the S and SE of the county.

Holly Blue: Note position of proboscis and the way this butterfly has apparently found a way of tapping an unusual nectar source! Great Ayton (VC62) Aug 2003.

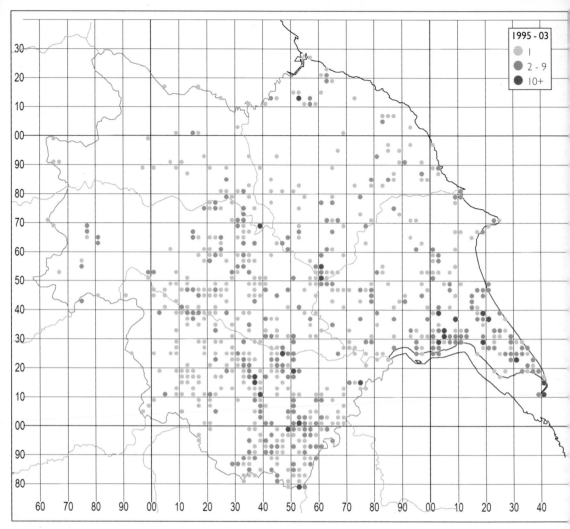

Holly Blue: Yorkshire Tetrad map 1995-2003

MAP NOTES 1995-2003: Noted in **724/3319** recorded tetrads (ie 21.8%), and out of 4120 tetrads in Yorkshire. **Ranked 18th most widespread** out of 36 breeding species in the county. It is a butterfly which is expanding northward as indicated by the colour grading on the 10km map where numbers decline from the densest populations in the SE towards NW. The map appears to indicate the main expansion front lying across the northern half of the county, but in fact, by 2003 the species had also moved into Durham and Northumberland where it was recorded in 24 tetrads to the north of our map (Hunter & Norman 2004).

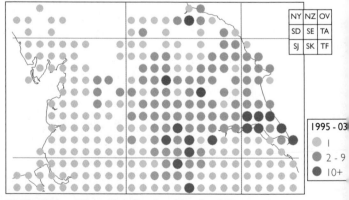

Holly Blue: 10km distribution North of England
● = 1 or more records out of county 1995-1999

LIFE STORY

HABITAT: A nomadic and wide-ranging species, at home anywhere it can find its main foodplants, Holly *Ilex aquifolium* and Ivy *Hedera helix*. Hence it can be found in city centres and open countryside. It is particularly at home in parks, gardens and churchyards, as well as woodland rides. Although butterfly literature emphasises the link between holly for the spring generation and ivy for the summer, the Holly Blue is not absolutely dependent on these. In fact Willmott (1999) listed over 200 species of foodplant used by the species worldwide. Observations in the British Isles indicate the use of dogwoods *Cornus* spp, gorse *Ulex* spp (sometimes by both generations), bramble *Rubus* spp, snowberries *Symphoricarpus* spp and even Heather *Calluna vulgaris*. We know nothing about the range of foodplants used in Yorkshire so this would be a valuable area of future study. In 1996 Sean Clough found eggs on Alder Buckthorn *Frangula alnus* growing in his Hull (VC61) garden. Morris (1853) includes Common Buckthorn *Rhamnus catharticus* in his list of Holly Blue foodplants.

Eggs are small but visible, pale discs, laid at the base of unopened flower buds. They hatch after about 2 weeks. Larvae develop through 4 instars and can appear in at least 3 forms: the commonest being green, a second having maroon dorsal and lateral stripes, and a third having similar stripes but in pink. Larvae first eat the flower buds and later the insides of the developing fruit in which they leave a trail of distinctive holes. Those unlucky enough to be laid on male holly shrubs

Holly Blue larva (Hull VC61) Aug 1996.

Holly Blue female on Ivy, showing how readily this species can merge into the dappled light it favours. (Kent 1983).

survive on tender terminal shoots. A proportion of larvae may be attended by ants, which are attracted to larval secretions. Thomas & Lewington (1991) suggest that association with ants is minimal in Britain, because there are fewer tree-climbing species than on the continent. However, it appears that no-one has reported seeing the pupal stage in the wild, suggesting that this occurs either high up in trees or shrubs, or low down, possibly underground, where they may be looked after by ants, and perhaps given some protection against the parasitic wasp *Listrodomus nycthemerus*. This wasp appears to play a major part in the butterfly's life cycle, causing the cyclical boom and bust pattern in its populations. The wasp injects an egg into a first instar larva, which then develops inside the larva without killing its host until it emerges as a wasp from the pupal shell. The Holly Blue passes winter as a pupa and it is assumed that wasp eggs laid on 2nd or 3rd brood larvae also overwinter inside the pupa, which is not killed until just before the wasp emerges the following year. A few days before this event the pupa becomes discoloured in patches. (Revels 1994). We know nothing about the success of this wasp in Yorkshire and whether the butterfly's one-generation adaptation in Nidderdale might help to reduce the effects of such parasitism. However, since the butterfly arrived in 1990 it has gone through the typical population cycles that are known in the south and thought to be associated with the predations of the wasp, which builds up its population with that of the butterfly until the wasp virtually destroys the butterfly and itself! A tiny remnant population of butterflies is usually left to start re-building its numbers almost free of the wasp in its earliest years but quickly matched by increasing wasp numbers once again. In Yorkshire the process has been taking about 5 years, although complicated by successive influxes of the butterfly from the south. From the 1990 arrival the population built up for two years then began to dwindle in 1993 and was at its lowest ebb in 1995. It then built up to another peak by 1998 but crashed in 1999, with 2000 being a notably poor year. 2001 saw a recovery and 2002 was one of the best years ever. 2003 saw a downturn in numbers although with a long season (17/03 to the 15/10) and three generations.

Described by Ray in 1710, and named by Petiver in 1717 **the Blue Speckt Butterfly** (male), and **the Blue Speckt Butterfly with black Tipps** (female). The butterfly was not referred to again for some 50yrs, prompting Emmett & Heath (1989) to suggest it may then have been rarer than today, perhaps a result of the cooler years of the latter part of the Little Ice Age (1300-1850). Berkenhout listed the species in 1769 but only by its Latin name. Harris (1775) called it the **Azure Blue** a name accepted by most writers for the next 100yrs or more (and reflected in the N American name **Spring Azure**). Morris (1853) introduced **Holly Blue**. *Celastrina* is 'Holly', and *argiolus* a diminutive of *argus* (= 'many-eyed'), referring to the tiny black dots or eyespots on the underwing.

The history of this species in Yorkshire is one of periodic comings and goings on the northern edge of its range. Arrivals appear to be triggered by periods of warm dry springs to the south of the county. The earliest county record may be deduced from a watercolour painted by Sabine Winn of Nostell Priory (nr Wakefield VC63) dated 12/06/1780. 19th century records correlate fairly well with the century's weather. The period 1805/1820 was one of the coldest in the so-called 'Little Ice Age' (1300-1850) and 1816 was the coldest summer ever recorded in the previous 192 years (Fagan 2000). All our butterflies must have suffered and it is unlikely that Holly Blues would have been tempted northward at that time. However,

Peter Waterton.

Holly Blue female.

the next 20 years to 1840 were notably warm, with 1826 the warmest summer between 1676 and 1976! Duncan (1844) sums up the national distribution of the Holly Blue around this time as of *'frequent occurrence* in southern England, *'but rather scarce in the north, although* (surprisingly!) *'found not infrequently near Newcastle in places where hollies abound and also in Castle Eden Dean'*. Morris (1853), noting that *'In Yorkshire it is not uncommon'* also adds Northumberland. This could be explained by a postulated northward surge of the species through Yorkshire and into Durham around 1826. Dunn & Parrack (1986) note that the Holly Blue disappeared from Durham and Northumberland in the 1840s and was not seen again until 1948, a hundred year gap!

Rimington (1992) includes early Doncaster area records from: Wath-upon-Dearne (VC63/SE40) in 1832, Askern *'about the Mount'* in 1842 (Lankester 1842), and Owston (VC63/SE51) in 1846. Fryer & Lucas (2001) re the Huddersfield (VC63/SE11) area note it was common at Storthes Hall in 1847 and found around Honley, Woodsome and Castle Hill in the 1850s (which were fairly mild years). Stainton's Manual (1857) indicates sightings at York at some point prior to 1857. 1868 was a hot summer and the species was discovered in May as being *'not uncommon in the hollies in Raincliffe Wood'* Scarborough, (VC62/SE98) (Theakston 1871). Then it was not recorded again around Scarborough until 1946. Porritt (1883) comments that it *'was usually not uncommon where holly grows freely'* and lists 10 areas (some already detailed) including Rotherham, Sheffield, and Wakefield (VC63); Ledsham (E of Leeds), Leeds and Ripon (VC64); and Richmond (VC65). The 1870s were rather average, cooler years, unlikely to have produced a major surge. Garland (1981) mentions that the species was already scarce in Wharncliffe Woods, Sheffield (VC63/SK39) in 1874. The period 1879 to 1892 was dramatically cold. It seems unlikely any Holly Blues would have survived, although in 1884, the one warm year sandwiched in the middle, there is a surprising record as far north as Guise Cliff, Pateley Bridge (Yorkshire Dales VC64/SE16) on 17/05 [William Storey] (Barnham & Foggitt 1987).

A scatter of turn of century VC63 reports indicates a further return to the south of the county. Garland (1981) suggests Canklow Wood (Rotherham VC63/SE49) was the *'principal Yorkshire locality'* at this time. Boul (1899) reports one in Hull (VC62/TA03) in 1897. Garland (1981) mentions Cudworth (nr Barnsley VC63/SE30) in 1898. Between 1900 and 1910, the weather was on the cool side with 3 notably cold summers. From this point on, until 1946, there were only odd sightings, including a single record from the Sheffield area in 1934, which followed the particularly warm spring and summer of 1933. A mild winter followed by a warm spring in 1943 heralded a series of warm springs, leading to the re-appearance of the Holly Blue in Sept 1946, when it was seen on Seamer Moor, nr Scarborough (VC62/TA08) [Eric Owston]. The following year, 1947 (and in spite of the spectacularly cold winter), the species spread rapidly in the Doncaster and Sheffield areas, no doubt helped by the memorable summer of 1947, and in the years up to 1951 it became established as far north as Scarborough (VC62), York (VC61/62) and Harrogate (VC64). Walsh (1952) gives VC62 records for High Langdale End (SE99) in 1947/48, Burniston (TA09) in 1949/50 and Bickley (SE99) in 1951. The 1950s saw a fairly sharp decline, and except for one or two vagrants, the species was absent in the cooler wetter decade of the 1960s. Then came the first-ever sighting reported for Spurn (VC61/TA41) on 25/07/1971, and another in the same year at Husthwaite (VC62/SE57). Scattered records followed in most years in the 1970s, leading up to colonisation around York and Harrogate around 1978.

Howard M Frost & Derek Parkinson

1582 DUKE of BURGUNDY *Hamearis lucina* (Linnaeus 1758)
Family: Lycaenidae, sub-group Riodininae ('the Metalmarks').

Colonising primrose on N Yorkshire Moors Railway (photographed with permission courtesy NYMR).

UK BAP Status: *Species of Conservation Concern.*
BC Priorities: National: *Medium.*
N of Eng: *High.* Yorkshire: *High.*
European status: *Near threatened.*
Protected in GB for sale only.

Imperfect female, Pexton (VC62) 19/05/2002.

Duke of Burgundy

YORKSHIRE STATUS 1995/2003:

Resident: 1 brood (May/June). Overwinters as pupa. One of the county's rarest species, found in two areas only, around Helmsley and Pickering (VC62) with c20 colonies representing 10% of the national colony strength. Survey work co-ordinated by Robert Parks, Steve Kirtley and Sam Ellis between 1992 and 2003 identified c18 breeding colonies in the Helmsley area up to 300m (based mainly on cowslips on limestone grassland, but with 5 sites including primroses in woodland margin locations). Most of these colonies are 'small' where only 2 to 6 adults might be seen on a good day, and only one is 'large' where more than 20 might be seen. The Pickering area holds c4 further colonies (based mainly on primroses along woodland rides). Woodland colonies are nationally rare with only about 20 left in the whole country. Since 1999, there have been unexpected fluctuations in population levels at various sites, with declines and probable extinctions in some, including the main site with public accessibility, at Ashberry Viewpoint (nr Rievaulx Abbey VC62) where the last reported sighting was on 17/06/2000 [Dennis Giggal]. Collecting is reported to be a factor here, although similar declines, for reasons that are unclear, are also apparent on other sites. Dan McAndrew carried out a survey of the Helmsley area in 2000 and established a presence at 13 of the 17 known sites. It is probable that all these colonies constitute a single metapopulation, which has since become fragmented and isolated by changes in land use, reducing both the area of suitable habitat, and the

WORLD STATUS: Resident, 0-1700m. 1 or 2 broods (May/Jun or Apr/Jun and Jul/Sept). Range: occupies a broad band northwards from Spain, S France, central Italy, and central Greece, to S England, N France, central Germany and eastward to Japan. Isolated outliers found to the north and south of this band, inc N England, S Sweden, N Central Spain and Sicily. Declining in many parts of range, although some evidence of range extension in the north (Sweden) and range contraction in the south (Spain). In Britain once distributed as far north as S Scotland but apparently disappeared in the 1860s: northern limit now in England, lying along northern edges of OS 100km squares SD in Cumbria and SE in Yorkshire. Population mainly confined to chalk downlands of southern central England (eg Cotswolds, Salisbury Plain and the North and South Downs). There are also isolated locations around Peterborough (inc 3 Lincolnshire colonies), and in Cumbria, as well as along the southern edge of the N Yorks Moors (VC62). The species is declining nationally with c200 colonies left in total.

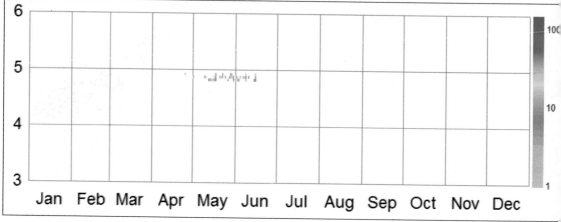

6												100
5				'd.li,ji.i								
4												10
3	Jan	Feb	Mar	Apr	May	Jun	Jul	Aug	Sep	Oct	Nov	Dec	1

number of 'stepping stones' between them. Various locations around Pickering were colonised in the past, including the deep-set, glacial overflow valley of Newtondale (or Newton Dale). A survey co-ordinated by Howard Frost in 2000 found a very thin presence covering 6 out of 26x1km squares surveyed between Pickering and Levisham. The butterfly appears to use the track of the North Yorkshire Moors Railway, which runs the length of the valley, as a corridor linking sites. There may also be a small amount of egg laying and nectaring at track verge 'hotspots' where primroses re-colonise areas cleared by annual applications of weedkiller but the main colonies appear to be on the valley sides. The Newtondale population was once described as, 'very large', with up to 25 butterflies recorded on one site in 1984, but the recent Survey observed an average density of only 3 butterflies per

PHENOGRAM: Yorkshire 1995-2003. The limited distribution and the May/June flight season show well in this diagram.

1km square. Unfortunately, the planting of conifers, with very narrow rides, has shaded out many favoured hot-spots, whilst former meadows have been allowed to revert to scrub, which has grown beyond the successional stage required by this butterfly. In addition, Newtondale often channels cold northerly winds along much of its length in May, which is probably why most of the small colonies left, have developed in sheltered areas. Past colonies were known in neighbouring Gundale and on Haugh Rigg but there have been no reports from these areas since 1982. Two butterflies were seen near Lockton village in 1996 (Len & Norma Auckland), but subsequent searches in the Lockton/Levisham areas have drawn a blank. Ellerburn Bank held a colony up to the 1990s but this seems to have failed around 1992/3 probably due to overgrazing. Peter Cawdell recorded 11 eggs here in 1996, but no butterflies were seen in 1997. There have been other sightings since, particularly from 2000 onward, but there are indications these might have resulted from unauthorised introductions.

Peter Waterton

Duke of Burgundy.

CONSERVATION ISSUES: In the light of national and regional concern about the future of this species a great deal of survey work has been undertaken since 1992. An English Nature Species Action Plan was drawn up in 1996, and in 2001 a North Yorkshire Moors Butterfly & Moth Action Group was set up under the auspices of Butterfly Conservation and the N York Moors National Park, to bring together representatives of statutory bodies, landowners and relevant groups to help develop a strategy to preserve this and other species. Many of the most important sites are isolated areas of marginal grassland, which are too steep to plough or plant with trees, and have ceased to be used as pasture. Such habitat is subject to rapid scrub succession. Controlled grazing would provide the best management, but this is often not available. Therefore, since 1995 there has been a winter programme of management on key sites using volunteer groups. This work was increased in 2003 with the help of National Park volunteers and an Employment Task Force team who created 7 glades on three sites. More work and monitoring is planned for future years with the aim of improving existing sites and creating habitat patches which could act as stepping stones between colonies. Oates (2000) provides a useful discussion of the management needs of this species. Ellis (2002) describes management plans for each site in the N Yorkshire Moors National Park.

ID NOTES: Looks similar to a fritillary with a pattern of spots and blotches in dark brown and orange, but is much smaller than any British fritillary being about the same size and shape as a Blue. Although it once carried the name Duke of Burgundy **Fritillary**, it is not a Fritillary. Until recently it was placed in the Riodinidae family or **Metalmarks**, the Duke being the only European member of this large tropical group of butterflies now considered a sub-group of the Lycaenidae or Blues. Viewed with wings closed, there are two bands of white cells across the lower wing and the underwings are paler with more orange visible than on the upperwings. Males are usually slightly bigger than females, and darker, with the forelegs reduced in size. They are seen more often than females as they perch openly on plants and shrubs to defend territories and engage in aerial chases with rivals. Dukes from woodland areas tend to be a shade darker than Dukes found in open grasslands.

Duke of Burgundy female laying.

Duke of Burgundy eggs on underside of leaf.

Steve Kirtley

Duke of Burgundy larva.

Duke of Burgundy typical larval leaf damage.

Steve Kirtley

MAP NOTES 1995-2003: Noted in only 13/3319 recorded tetrads (ie 0.4%), and out of 4120 tetrads in Yorkshire. **Ranked 33rd most widespread** out of 36 breeding species in the county. No tetrad map has been included as most sites are on private land and not open to the public. The scarcity of this formerly much more common species is emphasised by the restricted area now occupied.

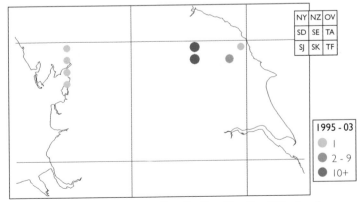

NY	NZ	OV
SD	SE	TA
SJ	SK	TF

1995 - 03
● 1
● 2 - 9
● 10+

Duke of Burgundy: 10km distribution North of England

● = 1 or more records out of county 1995-1999

LIFE STORY

HABITAT: Requires Primroses *Primula vulgaris* in woodland clearings, (eg on wide rides, permanent glades, new plantings or coppiced areas, all of which need to be warm and sheltered). Also uses Cowslips *P. veris* on lightly grazed limestone grasslands where sward height is 6-20cm. In Yorkshire the Duke is most commonly found in areas of sun-facing, rough limestone grassland, interspersed with hawthorn scrub (providing shelter) and patches of cowslips. Duke of Burgundy colonies are often small and need to be linked by rides or patches of grassland habitat to enable periodic interchange. Anyone wishing to observe this species must be prepared to walk quite long distances along public footpaths, especially in Newtondale where the search should be along sheltered, sunny, woodland rides on valley sides.

Duke of Burgundy: mating pair.

Most Duke of Burgundy colonies are quite small in size with only 5 or 6 butterflies likely to be seen at any one time on a typical site. Woodland populations generally occupy a series of small linked breeding sites, spread along rides, tracks and pathways. Yorkshire emergence varies from year to year according to weather conditions. The height of the N York Moors makes them often cloudier and cooler than neighbouring areas, but the butterfly is quite tough and can tolerate less than perfect conditions by being active in the odd hour of spring sunshine that might occur in an otherwise dismal day. (That said, the species does seem to have suffered from some particularly cold springs in recent years.) Typical emergence is in mid-May with a flight season extending from 3 to 5 weeks but recent years have seen a shift to a week or so earlier eg 08/05 in 1999, 11/05 in 2000 and an all time Yorkshire record of 30/04 in 1997 (on a grassland site in the Helmsley area). Emergence on southern England grassland sites is reported as being 10 to 14 days earlier than those in woodlands, but as yet we do not have sufficient Yorkshire data to make such comparisons. Emergence in S England has also been earlier recently, increasingly starting in April, with 10/04/1997 being the earliest yet (Oates 2000).

Individual butterflies only live for 5 to 7 days, which makes small colonies easy to overlook. Males are highly territorial, selecting a small bush or grass tussock in a favoured hot-spot clearing or ride. There they await the arrival of a female and keep a lookout for rival males, which are pursued in high-speed spiralling flights. Females are more elusive, spending much of the day resting with wings closed, which makes them difficult to spot. Once mated (an act which generally takes place briefly and without much ceremony between 10am and 2pm), they tend to become nomadic wanderers in search of suitable patches of cowslips or primroses. They are very selective, seeking out well-grown plants in semi-shade, which are not likely to become dried out later in the summer. However, where the choice is more limited, as in Newtondale, egg laying has been noted on less than perfect plants, but still the best of those in view. Eggs are laid on the undersides of primula leaves, usually singly or in small clusters of 2 or 3, very occasionally in bigger groups. Cowslip, primrose or their hybrid form, Oxlip *P. veris x vulgaris*, are all used, usually with cowslips on grassland sites and primroses in woodland. Occasionally, eggs are laid on other foliage adjacent to the foodplant. They hatch after 7 to 21 days and pale brown larvae eat a distinctive pattern of holes, leaving the skeletal structure of the leaf intact. Searches for eggs or skeletal leaves can provide a useful indication of the Duke's presence. Larvae feed under cover of darkness on dry nights, and after 4 instars lasting around 6 weeks, they crawl into the protection of a mat of vegetation or into a dry patch of chalk or limestone rubble, and pupate. This stage lasts around 9 months until the butterfly hatches the following spring.

Males are darker than females with the degree of darkness variable.

HISTORICAL REVIEW:

Duke of Burgundy
Formerly: *Nemeobius lucina* (in Porritt 1883).

William Vernon captured the first specimen recorded for Europe in Cambridgeshire in the 1690s. It became known as **Mr Vernon's Small Fritillary**, but Harris (1766) refers to it as the **Duke of Burgundy Frittillaria**. He appears to be describing a name already widely accepted as he explains that it was often called **the Burgundy**. The origins of this titled name remain a mystery. Rennie (1832) shortened it to **the Duke**, an affectionate abbreviation still used today. In the current Latin name *Hamearis* means 'spring' and *lucina* 'light' or 'childbirth', from Lucina the Goddess of Childbirth.

Past records say little about sites and give only the most generalised indication of where sightings occurred. 'Scarborough' could mean anywhere within a day trip of the town by rail, which might mean Pickering! During the 1800s, the species was more widespread and occurred along the Magnesian Limestone Ridge from the Doncaster/Sheffield area (VC63) to Bramham (nr Tadcaster VC64) where Porritt (1883) says it was *'common'*. Coleman (1860), Morris (1853), Porritt 1883), Garland (1981) and Rimington 1992) between them give VC63 records from Melton Wood (SE50) and Tickhill SK59) in the 1830s; Sandbeck Park

Duke of Burgundy eggs and larval damage.

(SK59) in 1842; Maltby (SK59) in 1858 and c1875; Roche Abbey (SK58) in 1858, where WH Smith took 60; Doncaster (SE50) in the 1860s; and more specifically Hawley (1866) refers to it being found *'on the 'out moor' beyond Edlington Wood'* (SK59) where it was known until the 1870s. Newman (1871) indicates Leeds as a site, which could have been the Bramham area. The species continued to be recorded in VCs63/64 up to the 1870s, after which no further dated records appear. It seems likely that the Duke was yet another victim of the 1879/1895 period of severe weather perhaps combined with growing industrial pollution and considerable land use change.

All subsequent records have come from the southern edge of the N Yorkshire Moors (VC62) where a band of Jurassic limestone stretches from Sutton Bank nr Helmsley in the west, through Kirkbymoorside and Pickering, to Scarborough in the east. Although the butterfly may once have been more widespread throughout this whole area, Parks & Kirtley (1994) concluded that all the known historical records came from 4 areas: Helmsley, Kirkbymoorside, Pickering (including Newtondale and Thornton Dale) and the Scarborough district. Helmsley area records date from 1913, whilst the known presence in Kirkbymoorside is limited to a YNU field trip report for 1954 and a single record from Hutton Common in 1956 when the site was already perceived as becoming unsuitable. Walsh (1952) states that *'JH Rowntree recorded it as abundant at Pickering in 1868; it is still common there* (in 1952) *and also in the woods on the west side of Newtondale'* as well as being seen in Thornton Dale. The main area in which the butterfly was recorded was around a tributary valley to Newtondale called Gundale where in 1970 it was described as being *'probably more abundant than in any other location north of the Trent'*. But then tree felling and the planting of conifers resulted in a severe decline and the last record for this neighbourhood came from Haugh Rigg in 1982. The butterfly has been recorded historically at various locations in Newtondale particularly in the complex of tributary valleys around Lockton and Levisham where it was seen in the 1970s and early 1980s, but only once in the 1990s. Many of the former grasslands here have been invaded by scrub and no longer appear suitable for the butterfly. It is presumed that Walsh's 1952 reference to Thornton Dale refers to Ellerburn Bank in the valley of Thornton Dale (near the village of Thornton-le-Dale). Thornton Dale runs roughly parallel to Newtondale and in places the distance between the two valleys is only 1.5 to 2km. So it may once have been part of the same metapopulation. The Duke's presence was recorded regularly up to 1989 but since then has become increasingly sporadic. Newman (1871) noted that Edwin Birchall had recorded the species in the Scarborough area. It is generally assumed that this would have been close to the town, but it is not certain, and Pickering, only about 18 miles away might have been attainable within a day trip. However, records from Langdale End [DW Bevan 1922] and Silpho Quarry [Roger Key 1978] suggest there were colonies in the area in the past although widespread searches in more recent times have failed to find any continued presence. The only known records outside the 4 areas detailed above are from Cropton Forest (1977) and Deepdale in Dalby Forest (2002) both presumed wanderers, although the latter may have been an unauthorised release.

Robert Parks

1590 RED ADMIRAL *Vanessa atalanta* (Linnaeus 1758)
Family: Nymphalidae, sub-group Nymphalinae (the 'Nymphalids' or 'Vanessids').

View south from Scarborough to Filey Brigg.

UK BAP Status: *Not assessed.*
BC Priorities: *Not assessed.*
European Status: *Not assessed.*

WORLD STATUS: Resident, 0-2500m, and wide-ranging migrant with 1 or possibly 2 generations. Capable of partial (or short-term) hibernation. Range: Azores and Canary Islands, to Scandinavia and east across Europe and N Africa, through Asia to N America. Mainly migratory in northern part of range to approx 68°N, and an annual visitor to British Isles, Denmark, Scandinavia and occasionally even to Faeroes and Iceland. Also found in Guatemala, Haiti and New Zealand.

Red Admiral

YORKSHIRE STATUS 1995/2003:

Long-lived, annual immigrant from Mediterranean region, which may occasionally attempt to winter in Britain and possibly in Yorkshire Sightings can occur any month of year, but in Yorkshire mainly May-Oct/early Nov and occasionally small numbers Feb-April. **Earliest:** 13/02/1998 (see below), **latest:** 25/12/2002 Bingley (VC63) [AP Josephs] Generally widespread reaching all parts and heights, and recorded in 50% to 70% of 10km squares each year, with greatest density of reports from S and SE of county. Being a migrant it can turn up anywhere, although distribution invariably thins towards the NW (Dales VC65). Around the Mediterranean, it flies continuously through the winter months in suitable weather, but can go into short-term hibernation for a week or two when cold, and can probably pass winter in any stage. Yorkshire may receive several waves of arrivals, the earliest often direct from the Mediterranean or N Africa, followed later by offspring of earlier arrivals in France, central Europe or even southern England. Occasionally, immigrations come across the N Sea from Scandinavia or E Europe.

In recent years overwintering appears to have been increasing, mainly in S England, but larvae have been observed in winter diapause as far north as the Midlands. Circumstantial evidence suggests small numbers may winter in Yorkshire as hibernating butterflies, but no absolute proof. Overwintering has also been reported historically, but is generally dismissed as resulting from incorrect reporting due to people wrongly calling Small Tortoiseshells, 'Red Admirals', or mistaking hibernating Peacocks for Red Admirals. Overwintering Red Admirals need to wake up every week or two to feed when nectar sources in Yorkshire are virtually non-existent. They can feed on tree sap, animal dung and rotting fruit and can survive low temperatures, but probably only for short periods. Feb records from reliable observers occurred in **1998:** Barwick in Elmet (VC64) 13/02 [David Blakeley], and Esholt nr Shipley (VC64) 15/02 [Les Barrett], **1999:** Fulford, York (VC61) 23/02 [Pat Bone], and **2000:** Fulford York (VC61) 20/02 [Pat Bone], and two sightings in Haw Park nr Wakefield (VC63) on 26/02 [Wintersett Wildlife Group]. However, it is still possible that Feb sightings could be immigrants from further south. Indeed, immigrants from the continent have been known to arrive on the south coast of England in Jan and Feb.

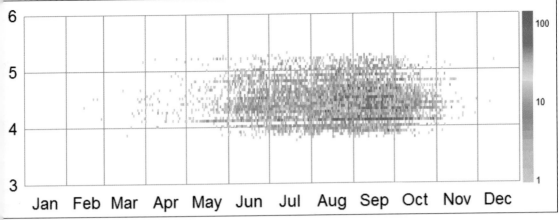

Jan Feb Mar Apr May Jun Jul Aug Sep Oct Nov Dec

PHENOGRAM: Yorkshire 1995-2003. Indicates a pattern of continuous arrival and assumed single generation produced by each arrival, with Oct peaks a result of migratory concentrations heading south, particularly along the coast.

ID NOTES: Beware: Small Tortoiseshell often wrongly called Red Admiral. Former usually smaller, and noticeably orange-brown. Red Admiral is dark brown/**black**, with bold poster-red admiral's stripes down the upper wings, and poster-red trailing edges to lower wings. Also note striking white patches on black wing tips. Closed wings cryptically patterned, offering near perfect disguise. With practice can be picked out in flight by a distinctive blur of black, white and red. Females usually larger than males. Variation uncommon (although over 30 aberrations described) except for regular occurrence of a small white spot in each of the red stripes, more often seen on females than males. Variety *klemensiewiczi* Schille has fuzzier pattern and orange stripes.

Voltinism (the number of generations) is uncertain and may vary according to latitude. Lafranchis (2000) indicates one **or two** broods in France. In Britain it is assumed to be a single-brooded species, but with a more or less continuous stream of arrivals possible, it is often seen on the wing throughout summer (weather permitting), giving a probably false impression of continuous generation. Although the butterfly may be widespread it is also generally thin on the ground and usually seen only in ones and twos in the first half of the year. From mid-Aug onward it starts heading S/SE and numbers may build at key nectaring spots such as parks and gardens. Numbers may also rise along the coastline where visible migratory flows occur, especially along Spurn Peninsula. A combination of light SW winds and warm sunshine often promotes a movement of Red Admirals and other insects on the east side of the dunes, which make up the peninsula. This occurs below the dune tops and usually 2 to 3m above the beach so the observer can watch a stream of butterflies, dragonflies, bees, hoverflies and other insects, from above. The peak of such movements is usually around the middle of Sept and used to end around mid-Oct, but in most years of the 1995/2003 Survey it has carried on into Nov, albeit in small numbers, up to a record 22 observed on 03/11/2001,

Rare white Red Admiral: Ilkley (VC64) 08/09/1997. Probably ab *millierei* Cabeau, although with a hint of the straw-yellow form ab *flavescens* Fritsch.

CONSERVATION ISSUES: Not threatened as long as the humble stinging nettle remains common. Over the longer term, populations could be affected by shifting weather patterns or changing approaches to land-use and agriculture across Europe.

and a late single on 15/11/2001 [Barry Spence]. It is possible that migrations from Scandinavia arriving on easterly winds along the coastline of Northumberland or Durham may account for some of the movements seen along the Yorkshire coast.

Red Admiral well-disguised in a rainstorm, hiding in hawthorn. Beacon Lane, Kilnsea (VC61), autumn 1994.

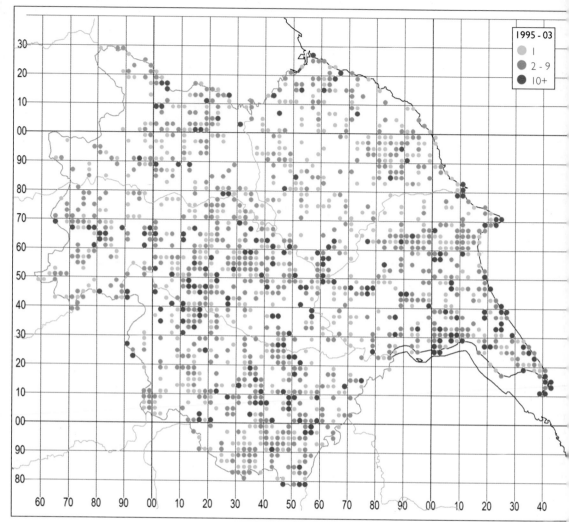

Red Admiral: Yorkshire Tetrad map 1995-2003

MAP NOTES 1995-2003: Noted in **1508/3319** recorded tetrads (ie 45.4%), and out of 4120 tetrads in Yorkshire. **Ranked 7th most widespread** out of 36 breeding species in the county. However, it should be noted that the Red Admiral is mainly an annual immigrant and the maps sum up 9 years of annual arrivals. The actual presence from year to year fluctuates a great deal, eg in 2002 it was only recorded in 335 tetrads. Nonetheless, the map does highlight the fact that this is often our most common immigrant, and one which can turn up in any part of the county, although usually more frequent in the southern half.

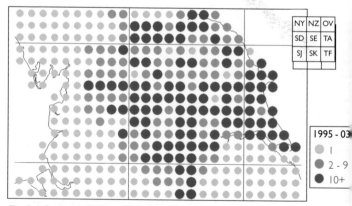

Red Admiral: 10km distribution North of England

⬤ = 1 or more records out of county 1995-1999

HABITAT: This strong-flying migratory species can turn up anywhere. Males defend territories, often in sheltered areas like gardens, tracks, or woodland rides. Eggs usually laid on the uppersides of young leaves of Common Nettle *Urtica dioica* (and occasionally other related plant species). Red Admirals around nettle beds are invariably females. They prefer strong-growing nettles on well-manured or damp sites, or isolated clumps in sunny positions. Parks, gardens, meadows and grasslands with nectar-rich flowers attract the species in high summer, whilst gardens, orchards or woodlands with rotting fruit (apples, pears, plums, brambles, figs, tomatoes etc) or sap, are typical autumn habitats, where, even in Yorkshire, Red Admirals may still be flying in Nov and occasionally Dec.

Mike Barnham

Red Admirals feeding on fruit: Knaresborough (VC64), autumn 1995.

Small pale-green eggs laid singly are fairly easy to spot in spite of small size (<1mm) being paler green than surrounding nettle leaves until just before hatching, when they darken. They hatch after 1 to 5 weeks depending on weather. Larvae are pale greenish-buff at first, turning to brown with black heads and occurring in pale and dark forms. Blackish spikes develop in 2nd instar. Larvae are parasitised by various wasps and flies and turn sickly yellow if affected. They live in individual tents made by tying two leaves together with silk. The final tent is usually made by chewing part way through the top of the nettle stalk (about 15cm/6ins down), causing it to flop over. Tent then secured

with silk threads, and larva changes into grey to pale brown pupa, blotched with varying amounts of gold. Pupal stage may take $2\frac{1}{2}$ to 4 weeks.

The lives of adult Red Admirals are still imperfectly understood. Tucker (1991, 1997) suggests adults breed around the Mediterranean throughout winter. Numbers build and expand northward April/Aug (sometimes earlier) leading to a virtual emptying of the species from the Mediterranean. At the same time, from approx Lat 45/47° N (across central France) southward, the species can usually survive winter in a state of semi-hibernation. This group breeds in early spring, perhaps laying as early as Feb, to produce fresh adults which may head further north to breed in later summer. Immigration to Britain is usually triggered by S/SE winds from the Mediterranean (more rarely by E winds from E Europe or NE winds from Scandinavia) with butterflies arriving individually and well-spread out, or occasionally in streams. Arriving females appear to be already mated, yet males set up temporary territories for a week or so at a time, but we have no evidence of courting or mating! Mystery! Are we missing something which goes on at night? Or high up in trees? Or do these males fail to mate? The only (!) reported British observation of mating in the wild, was observed in Dec (!) 1984 in Cornwall (Archer-Lock 1989). From Aug-Nov (in Yorkshire) Red Admirals head south, presumably intending to return to southern Europe. Could these end up breeding around the Mediterranean in winter? How far does the success of the Mediterranean population depend on a return migration? Southward flows at Spurn have been estimated at up to 500 individuals per day at peak times (1995/2003), eg on 28/09/1999 and 22/09/2000, [Barry Spence]. Fryer & Lucas (2001) note an observation by F Crawshaw and his brother who saw *'large numbers'* heading south (08/09/1960) over Buckstone Moss (VC63) at a height above c500m/1500ft, indicating that southward movements are not confined to the coast. It is presumed that when adverse weather/wind direction dictates, returning Red Admirals attempt semi-hibernation, usually in the open, on trunks and branches of large trees in the shelter of woodland, where they are almost impossible to see. They may also use sheds, houses and other buildings on occasion. A further Red Admiral mystery centres on their ability to fly at night, resulting in fairly frequent catches in Yorkshire moth traps. Brian Morland (Morland & Morland 2000) recorded a moth trap catch of 17 Red Admirals at Bellflask NR (River Ure VC64/65) on 26/08/2000!

Red Admiral showing common variant with small white spot in red bar.

Originally **the Admiral Butterfly**, probably dating from the 1600s. Later apparently corrupted to **The Admirable** (mid 1700s). Returned to **The Admiral** in the early 1800s and soon after re-christened the **Scarlet Admiral** to distinguish it from the White Admiral. Later (from Donovan 1799 onward) it became the **Red Admiral**. It was also occasionally known as **the Alderman Butterfly** (1750/1850 approx). *Vanessa* is taken from Dean Swift's poem, *Cadenus and Vanessa*, whilst 'Atalanta' was a Greek beauty and athlete.

For much of the 19th century, the Red Admiral was considered a resident butterfly, which some thought hibernated and others didn't. No one imagined it could migrate! Duncan 1844 wrote, *'But V. atalanta appears only in the autumn, not as a preserved creature, but as a recent introduction; and hence we can ascertain the duration of its life to be comprised only of Sept to the end of Oct.'* In spite of the mysteries associated with it, the species seems to have been taken for granted in Yorkshire and most writers and recorders have noted only the most generalised comments about it. Morris (1853) wrote: *'The perfect insect appears in June, July and August, and many individuals live on to the winter, and even survive until the following spring, when they appear again...In Yorkshire it is found plentifully near Nunburnholme and Nafferton,'* (VC61).

Fryer & Lucas 2001 mention that it was recorded throughout the 19th century in the Huddersfield area VC63, with Dunning noting it as abundant at Storthes Hall in 1846 and Hobkirk (1859) listing it as common. Mosley (1883) considered it less common than formerly (in the Huddersfield area) which may have been connected to bad weather and growing industrial pollution, although the key factors controlling Red Admiral numbers would be elsewhere. Huddersfield Naturalists' Society recorded it as abundant again in 1899 and the Halifax Scientific Society noted it to be more plentiful than usual in the same year. Garland (1981) reported that the species was extremely abundant in 1900, whilst Rimington (1992) points out that good Yorkshire years generally coincide with good years nationally and the best years have been: 1900, 1901, 1903, 1913, 1914, 1917, 1920, 1921, 1924, 1933, 1945, 1949, 1950, 1952, 1955, 1969, 1973, 1976, 1982, and 1990. Porritt (1883 and 1907) considered it *'common throughout the county'*. Stainforth (1919) noted just one site indicated by the Thomas Stather collection, namely Gilberdyke (VC61 SE82). Walsh (1952), writing about the Scarborough area (VC61), noted that *'immigrants reach this district every year and in autumn their descendants are to be seen all over the countryside.'* He also recorded that in Sept 1951, Athol Wallis saw *'a thin stream of these butterflies flying south at Filey Brigg and Spurn, there being a gentle wind from the SW at the time'*. The YNU 1967/70 Report summed it up as *'generally common in all districts, but not every year'*, which comment is probably a good summary for the last 200 years! Jackson (1983), reporting on the years 1975 to 1980, noted that 1975 was a poor year, whilst 1976 was the best in the period, with Spurn records starting on 10/04/1976 and ending on 07/11/1976. Peak 1976 counts at Spurn were **150** on 05/08, **80** on 03/09 and **100** on 10/10. In our 1995/2003 Survey period we have been trying to develop ways of better quantifying the annual Red Admiral immigration, although any figures produced are always related to the number of recorders (varying between about 200 and 400 each year - 1997 to 2003). First and last dates with the number of flight days recorded across the county are as follows: **1997:** 23/04 to 16/11 (**144**); **1998:** 13/02 to 11/11 (**171**); **1999:** 23/02 to 19/11 (**166**); **2000:** 20/02 to 28/11 (**164**); **2001:** 01/04 to 15/11 (**152**); **2002:** 21/03 to 22/11 (**172**); **2003:** 14/03 to 28/10 (**163**). Judging from the memories of individuals, it would appear that over the last 50 years the Red Admiral in Yorkshire has changed from being a mainly July to Sept butterfly, to one which is occasionally seen in almost every month of the year and may be attempting to overwinter.

Howard M Frost

Warming up via direct and reflected sunshine!

1591 PAINTED LADY *Cynthia cardui* (Linnaeus 1758)
Family: Nymphalidae, sub-group Nymphalinae (the 'Nymphalids' or 'Vanessids').

Scarborough, Castle Hill (VC62), a sheltered site for coastal migrants (1973).

UK BAP Status: *Not assessed.*
BC Priorities: *Not assessed.*
European Status: *Not assessed.*

Painted Lady: faded arrival at Spurn (VC62, 1988).

Painted Lady

YORKSHIRE STATUS 1995/2003:

Annual immigrant from N Africa, usually arriving June/Aug, occasionally earlier or later. Arrivals on English south coast can be as early as Jan and Feb. **Earliest** Yorkshire record (1995/2003): 02/05/1997, 2 at High Birstwith (VC64) [Richard Walton]. **Earliest-ever** reported county record: 06/04/1985 at Spurn VC61 (Spence 1991). Some arrivals come direct from N Africa (with the butterfly capable of travelling 150km per day and continuing its flight through the night), others come via an intermediate generation in continental Europe or southern England. In some years, successive waves occur, and may come from different sources. Most arrivals cross the English Channel and head northwards along coastlines or up through the centre of the country. More unusually, arrivals come in from the N Sea, and even more rarely, such arrivals may have originated in central and southern Asia rather than N Africa. First arrivals are often along the east coast, especially in the SE corner at Spurn NNR or along the southern edges of the county between Doncaster and Sheffield (VC63). In some years the northward movement gets little further north than this. In most years fewer Painted Ladies are seen as you move NW.

Once in Yorkshire, Painted Ladies are fast breeders and can, in theory, move from egg to new butterfly in around 4 weeks, although in the weather conditions this far north, the timescale is often longer. (In 1996, Mike Barnham noted that it took 56 days from the arrival of the first butterfly in the Harrogate area VC64, to the sighting of the first of the new generation.)

WORLD STATUS: Polyvoltine resident in N Africa and similar latitudes around the world. Long distance migrant northwards in spring, sometimes as far as Arctic Circle and Iceland. Numbers migrating vary considerably from year to year, from few, to millions. No set pattern to good and bad years which are thought to be explained by complex inter-relationship between weather, parasite attack, nectar availability and foodplant defoliation in resident areas, as well as helpful wind and weather conditions for northward journeys. Can winter successfully in European Mediterranean area and sometimes further north, even as far north as S England (eg Cornwall 1997/8), but population still dependent on annual build-up in N Africa. Range worldwide ('Perhaps the most widespread butterfly in the world,' Pyle 1981.) except for Australia and New Zealand (where it is replaced by related *Vanessa kershawi*), and S America (although some sources indicate a presence on that continent as well).

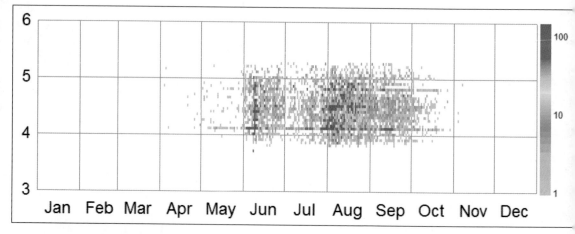

ID NOTES: Usually a large butterfly which looks dark orange in flight. Inexperienced observers sometimes confuse it with a Fritillary. May explode away from your feet and disappear before you have time for a proper look! Male and female are similar, with females tending to be slightly larger. On emergence, it has a notable salmon-pink suffusion, but this quickly disappears after a few days. Some specimens (presumed to have come direct from N Africa) look remarkably washed-out. It is not certain if this results from a long flight, or from living along the desert edges of N Africa where blown sand may act abrasively on the colour scales. Thomas & Lewington (1991) suggest oxidation of pigments under a desert sun could cause colours to fade. Paleness may therefore indicate an older butterfly. Occasional specimens (from larvae which it is assumed have not fed very well) can be exceptionally small, even smaller than an average sized Small Tortoiseshell. Typical flight pattern is made up of several flaps and a long glide (also found in the other Vanessids). There are at least 32 named variations none of which are common and many of which are variable in themselves. The American Painted Lady *C. virginiensis* (not to be confused with the normal Painted Lady which also occurs in N America) is very similar in looks and occasionally turns up in the western half of Britain and in Ireland. (See p267)

PHENOGRAM:Yorkshire 1995-2003. Illustrates the increasingly typical pattern of arrivals in June producing widespread offspring in Aug. Hidden within this pattern are additional arrivals in Jul and Aug and further offspring in late Aug/Sept, given suitable weather.

Even so, in favourable years at least two generations are possible from a May/Jun arrival, eg in Jul/Aug and Sept/Oct with numbers peaking in Jul/Sept. In some years, a small third generation may be possible with offspring appearing in Oct/Nov. The butterfly has certainly been seen into Nov in recent years with **latest** known record 06/11/2001 from Leeming (VC65) [Jean Lilley].

Small autumn accumulations of Painted Ladies often occur along the E coast of the county perhaps indicating some attempt at reverse migration. Alternatively, these could be arrivals from the continent across the N Sea on the same easterly winds that bring in migrant birds. They may still be en route southward. Odd individuals are sometimes seen heading southward in a linear migration stream with other insects (often including Red Admirals, Small Tortoiseshells, bees and hoverflies etc) along Spurn peninsula when light SW winds blow from about mid-Aug onward. However, although CB Williams (1958) indicated there was plenty of evidence of reverse migration across Europe, more recent authors suggest there is only minimal evidence for any meaningful return. This area deserves more documented study in Yorkshire, especially at Spurn. Painted Ladies are known to travel at night and sometimes appear in Yorkshire moth traps. Could this butterfly be migrating southward by night? Could it even be flying so high that it is being overlooked?

In the 1995/2003 period more than 100 Painted Ladies were seen in Yorkshire each year. (Over the last 200 years there have been many years when fewer than this have been reported nationally.) 1996 saw what was possibly the largest immigration in 300 yrs or more, with assessments of *'many millions'* nationally, and an observed Yorkshire arrival in excess of **50,000** butterflies, with Jul/Aug offspring reaching a similar recorded figure. The total Yorkshire numbers must have been huge, possibly many millions. The first sighting came on 29/05 at Fairburn Ings RSPB NR, (VC64), [Robin Horner]; and the last at Filey (VC61) on 19/10 [Filey Brigg Ornithological Group, Jack Sanderson *et al*]. The year 2000 was a more normal 'good year' with 1047 reports logged, and **1** to **122** butterflies per report seen between 07/05, Hollym (VC61) [Frank Josephs] and 04/11 Spurn NNR, (VC61), [Barry Spence].

CONSERVATION ISSUES: Being a common and widespread species, able to utilise a wide range of foodplants on many types of habitat, there are no relevant conservation issues to consider in the British Isles. However, global warming and climate change could affect habitats in N Africa on which this species currently depends, and any sustained move to a wetter climate in W Europe (as hinted at by the summer 2002 floods across many parts of Britain and Europe) could have ramifications for successful larval development.

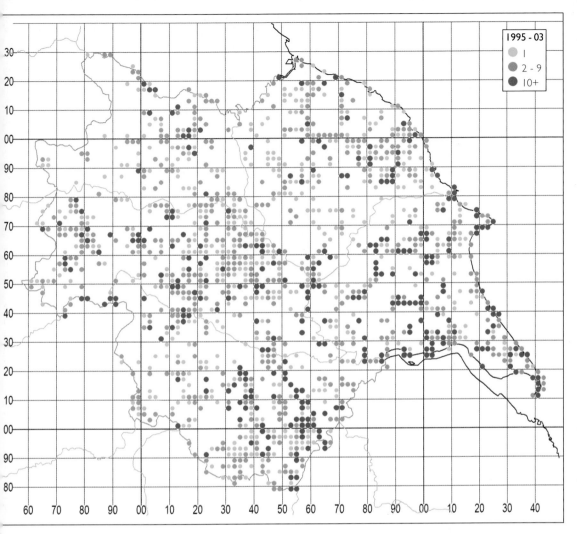

Painted Lady: Yorkshire Tetrad map 1995-2003

MAP NOTES 1995-2003: Noted in 1348/3319 recorded tetrads (ie 40.6%), and out of 4120 tetrads in Yorkshire. **Ranked 9th most widespread** out of 36 breeding species in the county. This is an annual immigrant from the Mediterranean and the map sums up 9yrs of successive arrivals. Numbers vary enormously from year to year, with widespread arrivals in some years, and presence restricted to coastal or southern areas in others. Gaps in the tetrad distribution probably result from under-recording, as suitable habitats are widespread.

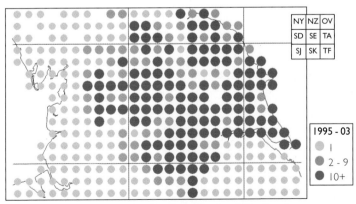

Painted Lady: 10km distribution North of England

⬤ = 1 or more records out of county 1995-1999

HABITAT: Being a wanderer, this butterfly can appear anywhere, though favouring dry, open areas such as sand dunes, heathlands, brownfield sites, and grasslands, particularly where there are good growths of thistles *Cirsium* ssp and *Carduus* ssp for foodplants and nectaring. Many other species are also used for egg laying. Lafranchis (2000) indicates 30 species from 7 families observed in France, including mallows *Malva* & *Athaea* ssp, Artichoke *Cynara scolymus*, Viper's Bugloss *Echium vulgare*, nettles *Urtica* ssp etc. The species is a common visitor to parks and gardens where buddleias *Buddleia* ssp are a great attraction for nectaring. Jenny Joy (BC *News* 63, 1996) suggested that Painted Ladies may indulge in 'hilltopping', a form of courtship activity also known in some other butterfly species, involving males congregating on prominent landmarks such as hills or tall trees where they are more likely to meet up with females. She reported several instances of Painted Ladies occurring on Shropshire hilltops. The writer has observed similar behaviour on the higher Wolds (VC61) where a combination of good chalk grassland along a roadside verge, and suitable height, appeared to account for a concentration of about a dozen butterflies. On 23/08/2003, Mike Barnham (pers comm.), walking the N York Moors (VC62), noted quite a few Painted Ladies, which *'were reliably (and nearly exclusively) found at the highest points of hills, around cairns and trig points'.* This is an aspect of the Painted Lady's lifestyle that deserves more study in Yorkshire.

Painted Lady emerging.

Light green eggs turn grey before hatching after 7 to 10 days. Larvae are black and hairy, covered in tiny cream dots, with almost continuous yellow lines along the sides. They feed in silk webs on leaf undersides and later make tents of folded leaves using silk threads. Larvae need warmth and sunshine for success. Rain and cloudy conditions can spell disaster. They can pupate after developing through 5 instars in about 7 days although this will be longer in less than ideal conditions. Pupae hang from leaves and come in two attractive forms, one brown with a golden sheen, the other silver-grey. The butterfly emerges after about two weeks, though longer in cooler weather.

The species is thought to be continuously brooded in N Africa where huge numbers can build up during our winter months. At some point this triggers a northward movement, occasionally even in winter, and arrivals in Jan/Feb/Mar can occur along the south coast of England and occasionally reach further north, though not recorded for Yorkshire. It is assumed they invariably perish on arrival due to our unsuitable temperatures and lack of nectar sources. The species has been thought to be incapable of hibernation having a life of only 2 to 4 weeks, but a recent discovery (Wacher 1998/9) has raised questions about the real status of this butterfly. A specimen caught on 23/10/1997 in Cornwall was colour-marked and released next day. It re-appeared on 07/04/1998 and was still flying on 19/05/1998! It appears that hibernation and long life are possible in this species after all.

Mike Barnham

Painted Lady: larva, Birstwith (VC64) July 1996.

Painted Lady migrations occur in various ways from broad fronts 100 miles across, to bands a few metres wide but many miles long, and linear streams, with butterflies passing one behind the other for hours at a time. The mating behaviour of the species seems to be largely unobserved, to the extent that it is unlikely that any reader has seen a mating pair of Painted Ladies in the wild! It is presumed that as with other Vanessid butterflies this takes place in trees or shrubs under cover of darkness but there is still a lot to learn about this relatively common species.

HISTORICAL REVIEW:
Painted Lady
Formerly: *Vanessa cardui*
(in Porritt 1883).

To Petiver (1699) the **Painted Lady** was already the familiar name for this butterfly. At the time its Latin name was rendered as *Papilio Bella Donna* (the Beautiful Lady Butterfly) indicating a link to the plant 'belladonna' or deadly nightshade *Atropa belladonna*, which was also used as a base for a cosmetic. Women painted an extract onto their eyes to enlarge them and make themselves look more beautiful. Someone made a link between these cosmetically improved ladies and the striking ringed eye patterns on the lower underwings of this attractive butterfly! Lewin (1795) tried to re-name it the **Thistle Butterfly** in deference to the Latin name *cardui* bestowed by Linnaeus. It didn't catch on in Britain, but is still sometimes used in N America where it is also called the **Cosmopolite**, the 'worldwide butterfly', or **the Junkbug**, in reference to its amazing abundance in some years! In the Latin, *Cynthia* was the birthplace of Diana and *cardui* = thistle, the foodplant.

The Painted Lady was generally considered a resident until the early 1900s. Duncan (1844) noted, *'This species is generally scarce, but appears in certain indefinite periods in considerable numbers.'* He goes on, *'We once saw*

Painted Lady: adult resting in privet during rain.

several individuals in the Edinburgh Botanical Garden, at the end of March, which had evidently just issued from their winter retreat.' (Little did he realise the rarity of March sightings in Edinburgh! However, as the butterfly can arrive in Jan and Feb in southern England, this is not impossible.) Morris (1853) records that, *'In the year 1828 an immense swarm passed over parts of Switzerland in such vast numbers that their transit occupied several hours'*. Even so, he fails to make the link that this is a migratory species, simply noting that it is *'very uncertain in its appearance, at least in any numbers. In Yorkshire I have taken it not infrequently at Nafferton, also at Nunburnholme'* (both VC61). Yorkshire sources of information about good Painted Lady years are rather sparse. Nationally good years were probably good in the county although such a correlation may not always be true. In fact, as you go north into Scotland the correlation appears to become less true, with some very good years in Scotland corresponding to poor years in England. This can happen when wind conditions cause England to be bypassed to the west or when arrivals come in from the east across the N Sea.

Duncan (1844) mentions **1826** as a good year in the London area. Williams (1958) analyses reported sightings for the years 1850 to 1962. Clearly, such numbers reported nationally in those days would only have represented the tip of an iceberg, but looked at comparatively they serve to highlight the better years. In the 1800s, key years with over 500 butterflies reported (with number in brackets) were: **1858** (724), **1868** (503), **1879** (2568), **1883** (682), **1884** (1240), **1880** (691), **1892** (2980). Porritt (1883) says little about the species: *'Occurs periodically all over the county,'* and *'was very common everywhere in 1879'*.

In the 1900s important years deduced from William's list (where over 1000 butterflies were recorded) were: **1903** (3280), **1906** (1130), **1928** (2588), **1931** (1041), **1936** (1050), **1939** (4500), **1941** (1450), **1943** (3800), **1945** (6224), **1946** (2450), **1947** (12,000), **1948** (30,000), **1949** (5,500), **1952** (6700)(big arrival noted at Spurn on 03/07), **1958** (12,682), **1962** (4733). Whiteley (1992) gives more recent nationally good years (without totals) as **1966**, **1969**, **1980** (big arrival at Spurn 30/07), **1982** ('very good around Sheffield'), **1985** and **1988**. Frost & Frost (1995) noted that in 1985 a total of 410 Painted Ladies were recorded in South Holderness (VC61) alone (inc Spurn), over a period of 84 days. 1988 was less remarkable in S Holderness though noted as *'good'* around Sheffield. Whiteley also notes **1991** as a good year, although only an average year in S Holderness. Then came **1996** with national numbers larger than anyone could remember. Asher *et al* (2001) speak of *'many millions'* arriving in late May and early June, and similar large figures were seen in many other European countries. It is probable that over a million reached Yorkshire with many passing through and heading further north. Offspring numbers were equally high with almost every garden in the county experiencing counts of tens, and many with a hundred or more.

In CB William's 1850/1962 analysis there are 15 years in the 1800s with no recorded British sightings, but only one (1916) in the 1900s. An element of this will relate to the lack of coverage in the early days and increasing awareness and coverage in the 20th century. However, it is interesting to speculate that the Little Ice Age (1300/1850) may have reduced the Painted Lady's ability to get as far north as today, and in the numbers that we see today. Harris (1766) expected a 'good' year roughly once in every 10 to 12 years. We are now seeing a good year every 4 or 5 years even as far north as Yorkshire. If this is indeed the trend, we might expect to see spectacular years like 1996 more often.

Howard M Frost

1593 SMALL TORTOISESHELL *Aglais urticae* (Linnaeus 1758)
Family: Nymphalidae, sub-group Nymphalinae (the 'Nymphalids' or 'Vanessids').

Peter Waterton

Scugdale (N York Moors VC62).

UK BAP Status: *Not listed.*
BC Priorities: National: *Low.*
N of Eng: *Low.* Yorkshire: *Low.*
European Status: *Not threatened.*

WORLD STATUS: Mobile, hibernating, resident and partial migrant. 1 to 3 broods according to latitude, height, weather. Appears Mar/Apr (or earlier): 1st brood Jun/Jul, 2nd Aug/Sept, 3rd Sept/Oct. Breeds 0-2500m, flies to 3400m+. Range: Spain to N Norway and eastward across Europe & Asia to Pacific coast. Common & widespread in British Isles but pop. thinner in Central Ireland and Scottish Highlands & Islands. Lafranchis (2000) notes now rarer in N France and uncommon in Mediterranean area. Expansions reported for Netherlands, Russia, Sweden and Slovenia, but notable contraction in Slovakia.

Small Tortoiseshell

YORKSHIRE STATUS 1995/2003:

Mobile hibernating resident and partial migrant. Usually emerges from hibernation Mar/May although there has also been an increase in winter sightings (Jan/Feb) in recent years due to mild periods with unusually high temperatures up to 16°C. During Survey Period, brood situation appears to have been variable, with up to two generations plus a small partial 3rd in the south of county, whilst towards north there are two broods with the second tending to be partial. Situation is complicated by migratory movements, which may come from the continent or from S England. There are also regular but more local movements, NNW in spring and early summer, reversing to SSE around mid-Aug. Both kinds of movement can cause accumulations at nectar sources, which on paper may look like a local emergence. Butterfly lives for 10 months or more and during the Survey was recorded flying in every month of the year. **Earliest** records were on 10/01/1998 at Spurn National Nature Reserve [Barry Spence] and 13/01/2001 at Aldbrough (both VC61) [Jeanette Johnson]. **Latest** was on 08/12/2001 at Low Bentham (VC64) [J Jarrett]. Midwinter sightings can easily be the result of butterflies being disturbed whilst hibernating, especially as Small Tortoiseshells have a tendency to hibernate in homes and get woken up when the heating is turned up. However, in 1998 warm weather caused an exceptional awakening, with 44 reports totalling 66 butterflies seen on 14/02. In most years typical site counts (inc some garden counts) are in the 20-50 range and occasionally in multiple hundreds. The species is Yorkshire's most widespread, having been recorded in 2131 tetrads out of 3319 visited (1995/2003). It is also one of the commonest visitors to gardens and readily attracted to buddleias, French marigolds (single varieties), Michaelmas daisies, sedums etc.

Late summer SSE drift movements sometimes lead to steady streams of butterflies heading south along the coast. In 1997 between 2000 and 5000 Small Tortoiseshells were seen daily at Spurn between 21/08 and 09/09. Initially the movement was northward, but on 22/08 butterflies were observed moving in both directions at the same time. Howard & Christine Frost (pers comm.) observed the following unusual movement: *'Two linear streams of butterflies were moving along exactly the same track but in opposite directions. We observed the movement about half way along the 4-mile long peninsula looking down from the top of a sand dune. Spurn*

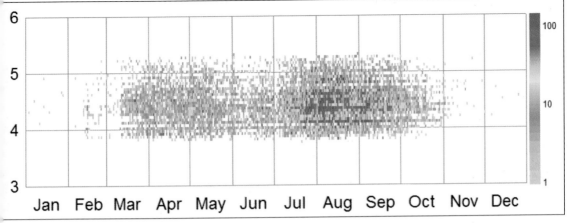

PHENOGRAM: Yorkshire 1995-2003. Shows spring emergence from hibernation and a long summer flight season with Dec/Feb records indicating the effects of increasingly warm winters on hibernation.

ID NOTES: A well-known species, long admired by gardeners and country lovers for its colourful upperwings, richly patterned in orange and yellow, and edged with blue lunules. Confusingly though, many people mistakenly call it the Red Admiral (a larger butterfly easily distinguished by its poster-red bars on a dark, almost black, background). In closed-wing view, the Small Tortoiseshell is dark and drab, enabling it to disappear into the shadows (especially in hibernation), and if danger threatens it can flick up its upper wings to reveal a silhouette eye pattern on the dark underside. Sexes are similar, with females usually being slightly larger. Males are likely to fly up and attack anything passing above them, whilst females remain disinterested.

A very variable species with over 100 aberrations described. Ab *pallida* Frohawk has an almost white ground colour whilst ab *ignea* Raynor is red. Ab *semi-ichnusoides* Pronin is very dark, with the orange reduced to flashes on the upperwings. Hotter summers tend to produce brighter specimens with less melanin, whilst cold weather, or a colder climate, leads to greater melanin, producing darker specimens and darker aberrations. In turn, the darker colouring is better for absorbing the available heat, and lighter or brighter colours better at reflecting it.

CONSERVATION ISSUES: Being a highly mobile species using an extremely common foodplant this butterfly is able to find suitable habitats throughout the British Isles. However, land managers of all kinds are urged to bear in mind the importance of nettles **in full sunshine** for this and other vanessid species. The butterfly is attracted to beds of nettles rather than isolated clumps, a situation which can be created in

runs roughly N/S and in a fresh westerly wind the butterflies were flying low over the sea beach in the shelter of the dunes. From time to time individual butterflies coming from opposite directions almost crashed. They would then spiral around one another heading upwards until they hit the wind current, which was so strong it swept them eastward and out to sea! In 1½ hours 113 flew south, 238 north and 23 disappeared seaward. Interestingly, a 24th butterfly blown out to sea managed to tack back to the shore from about 500m out. It came in very low over the water at an angle of about 45° to the wind.'

Large numbers of Small Tortoiseshells and other vanessids sometimes accumulate on Sea Asters *Aster tripolium* which grow on the salt marshes of the Humber Estuary, particularly around Spurn Bight (VC61). Although no large counts have been made in the Survey Period, previous years have seen estimates in the 10,000/15,000 range. It is thought that these butterflies eventually head on southward down the east coast, but visible movements are rarely noticed, so this is an area that would benefit from further study.

larger gardens, school wildlife areas, parks and nature reserves. Cutting and removing patches of nettle growth in June (taking care to avoid any remaining active webs) can promote young growth for a later generation. Every flower garden can be an invaluable source of nectar. Allowing dandelions and thistles to grow in sheltered hotspots can provide major nectar sources. One Yorkshire Butterfly Conservation member managed to persuade his allotment society to take a lenient view of dandelions and nettles to encourage this species, resulting in much less spraying, and more butterflies surviving!

Dean Stables

Courtesy H.E. Beaumont

Small Tortoiseshell ab *semi-ichnusoides*: above - a possible partial form (Brampton Bierlow VC63, 2004), below - (West Melton VC63, 17/09/1997).

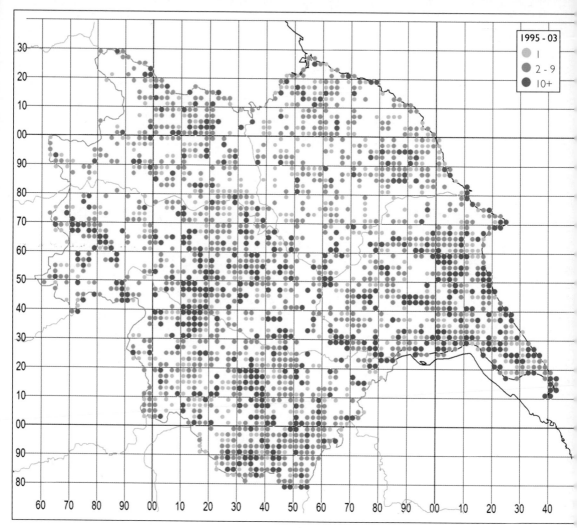

Small Tortoiseshell: Yorkshire Tetrad map 1995-2003

MAP NOTES 1995-2003: Noted in **2131/3319** recorded tetrads (ie 64.2%), and out of 4120 tetrads in Yorkshire. **Ranked 1ˢᵗ and therefore the county's most widespread** species out of 36 breeding species. The 10km map probably sums up the distribution even better than the tetrad map. Sample counts made in 2003 and 2004 in the Vales of York and Pickering indicate the species to be just as common in those areas as elsewhere.

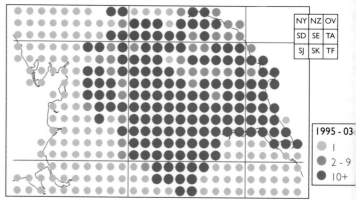

NY	NZ	OV
SD	SE	TA
SJ	SK	TF

Small Tortoiseshell: 10km distribution North of England

⬤ = 1 or more records out of county 1995-1999

LIFE STORY

Male (behind) in process of courting female by drumming on her wings with antennae.

HABITAT: Anywhere and everywhere! Being very mobile it probably visits or passes through every tetrad in the county. Its main larval foodplant is the humble Stinging Nettle or Common Nettle *Urtica dioica*, a species which thrives on nitrogen-rich soils and can even tolerate the edges of muck heaps. It is probable that modern farming methods have increased the amount of breeding habitat available, including accidentally fertilising areas bordering fields. Male Small Tortoiseshells set up territories, which are often on or near patches of nettles. They also need to recoup energy after hibernation and can often be found wherever there are dandelions, even on busy roadsides or roundabouts. Amidst such strong colour they are inconspicuous. They may also visit willow catkins, celandines, blackthorn and hawthorn and any other nectar source available. From year to year, the emphasis may be on different plants depending on availability at the time of emergence. The summer brood often visits gardens to nectar and will utilise many different species. In the wider countryside, Creeping Thistle *Cirsium arvense* provides one the strongest attractions and where this plant is cut in hayfields it will produce an extra late summer growth, which is often covered with Small Tortoiseshells.

After emerging from hibernation and finding a nectar source on which to feed, many Small Tortoiseshells use suitable weather to move on. They tend to feed in the early morning, and migrate in the middle of the day (10.00-14.00hrs) with males setting up a territory in the afternoon in the hope of intercepting a passing female. When a female arrives the male attempts to become her defender and will creep up behind her when she is at rest with wings open. He drums on her hindwings with his antennae and follows her about for the rest of the afternoon. If she remains receptive she will lead the male to roost in a nettle bed, where the two will copulate all night on the underside of a leaf, unseen (and rarely photographed!). The next day may see the two butterflies move on (weather permitting). Specially marked individuals have been shown to migrate up to 150km, travelling short distances each day, often less than 1km, but sometimes up to about

4km, for each hour of sunshine available. Green eggs are laid in clutches (up to c100) on the undersides of nettle leaves. (Small Nettle *Urtica urens* is also given as a foodplant by some authors, but no specific references relating to its use in Yorkshire have been found.) The female invariably chooses nettles in full sunshine, and often, young plants on the edge of a clump. Several females may deposit eggs on the same leaves resulting in up to 1000 being found in a single cluster! Eggs hatch after about two weeks and larvae build a communal home using silk threads to tie leaves together into an untidy bunch. Large clusters of larvae break up into smaller groups and each community will periodically move on to another plant and build a new communal home. Being gregarious they are able to benefit from the combined body warmth of the group and cope with cooler conditions better than many other species. Surprisingly, they are also better adapted to surviving in warmer conditions, in which they can grow more rapidly. Young larvae are greenish-yellow with fine black hairs. They develop through 5 instars into darker specimens with lateral yellow lines and dark spines, and are poisonous to many creatures, although still parasitised by ichneumon wasps and tachinid flies. When disturbed they can jerk heads in unison or regurgitate a ball of green fluid around their mouths. In the last instar they disperse up to 50/60m and complete their feeding alone, before pupating a metre or more above the ground suspended by threads in a tall plant, shrub, hedgerow, or on a wall. At this stage they are vulnerable to predation by birds.

The number of generations produced appears to be controlled by the timing of emergence. Butterflies on the wing by the first week of Aug are able to produce another generation, but those emerging later are not usually reproductive. They may go into early hibernation or drift southward searching for suitable hiding places en route, whilst also stopping off at nectar sites on the way, to build up their fat stores in readiness for hibernation. Hibernation takes place in caves, hollow trees, dry-stone walls, haystacks and buildings, including barns and sheds. Problems arise when houses are used and butterflies fly in through open windows in late summer but can't get out on the first suitable day in spring. They may also awake in winter when it is warm enough inside, but not outside. Such butterflies should not be released outside as they will perish, but caught and placed in a cool protected place like a shed or garage where they can resume hibernation.

HISTORICAL REVIEW:
Small Tortoiseshell

First illustrated by Mouffet in 1634, and called the **Lesser Tortoiseshell** or **Common Tortoiseshell** by Petiver in the early 1700s. But then in 1717 Petiver gave the name Small Tortoiseshell to the Small Copper, and although Wilkes (1741/42) gave the name back to the Small Tortoiseshell, confusion continued for some time, until Harris (1766) called the Small Copper, 'the Copper'. Lewin (1795) tried to introduce the **Nettle Tortoiseshell** and Stephens (1856) simply used **Tortoiseshell**, but from the 19th century onward **Small Tortoiseshell** became standard, although Duncan (1844) points out that in S Scotland **Devil's Butterfly** or the **Witch's Butterfly** were also used. In the Latin *Aglais* = beauty or beautiful, and *urticae* = nettle.

Sean A Clough

Parasitic insect (probably a chalcid wasp) caught in the act of inserting an egg, or eggs, into the pupa of a Small Tortoiseshell, (Hull VC61, 2002). Photo approx. 4.5 times life size.

Common and widespread over the last 200yrs, although with periodic fluctuations just as today. Duncan (1844), summed up national distribution *'This is by far the most common insect of the genus, occurring abundantly in all parts of England and extending to the northern extremity of Scotland'*. Morris (1853) writes in similar vein. Coleman (1860) gives an interesting report from a Mr Banning who lived near Ballacraine, Isle of Man: *'Whilst standing in my farmyard on the day following Christmas Day (1855), it being unusually fine and warm, I was suddenly astonished by the fall of more than a hundred of the accompanying butterflies (V. Urticae). commenced at once collecting them, and succeeded in securing more than sixty. These I have fed on sugar spread over cabbage leaves and bran, until now, and, to all appearances, those which still survive (more than forty in number) are thriving well, and in good condition.'* Thomas & Lewington (1991) refer (without details) to a large immigration where hundreds of dead specimens were found off Flamborough Head.

Rimington notes that for the Doncaster area the species was not mentioned between 1832 and 1898, or between 1902 and 1936, probably because it was such a familiar butterfly that everyone took it for granted. The earliest record Fryer & Lucas discovered for the Huddersfield area was 1846 [JW Dunning]. It was described as *'very common'* by Hobkirk (1859, 1868) and Morley (1883) said it was *'abundant throughout the district'* until the early 1860s, but then by 1883, only occasional stragglers were to be seen. Porritt (1883) was able to note it *'more or less common all over the county'* although in the *Naturalist* (1900 p16) he wrote that it was *'now comparatively seldom seen here'*. However, Huddersfield Naturalists Society had recorded that it had *'swarmed through the district in 1895'* The implication seems to be that the 1879/1895 period of severe weather had affected the Small Tortoiseshell population considerably, but its ability to move northward every year would have helped it to recover quickly. Porritt (1904) noted that it was *'Apparently, becoming much more common in the south West Riding'*. Halifax Scientific Society recorded it *'more plentiful than usual'* in 1899, and Morley (1902) noted that it *'simply swarmed'* in Skelmanthorpe in 1901, although he also recorded that it became scarce again between 1915 and 1917.

Walsh (1952), referring to the Scarborough area reported it, *'Generally distributed all over the district and usually common; it was, however, rare in 1932 after heavy rains and floods in Sept 1931 and May 1932'*. For the Hull area, Boult (1899) said it was *'very common'*, whilst Stainforth (1919) ignored the species completely, and Porritt's Hull area update (1922) simply re-iterated Boult's earlier comment. The YNU 1967/70 Report said it was *'Always common, but less often seen in city gardens than V. atalanta [the Red Admiral] being more at home in the open country'*. City gardens of the past would have lacked the range of nectar flowers we see today and parks and cemeteries would have been so well kept that nettles would have been scarce. Sutton & Beaumont (1989) noted that the species had been *'badly affected by the recent wet, cold summers'* with numbers being particularly low in 1986. An improvement followed in 1987 and 1988. Whiteley (1992) notes 1982, 1984, 1989, 1990, 1991 and 1992 as good years in the Sheffield area, whilst 1981, 1986 and 1987 were notably poor years.

Roy Bedford

1597 PEACOCK *Inachis io* (Linnaeus 1758)
Family: Nymphalidae, sub-group Nymphalinae (The 'Nymphalids' or 'Vanessids').

Roadside dandelions: an ideal springtime nectar site. (Sunk Island VC61).

UK BAP Status: *Not listed.*
BC Priorities: National: *Low.*
N of England: *Low.* Yorkshire: *Low.*
European status: *Not threatened.*

WORLD STATUS: Hibernating, mobile, resident and partial migrant, 0-2500m. Usually 1 brood (Jul/Sept), (but up to 2 or possibly 3, according to latitude/locality - Lafranchis 2000). Observed in all months of year. Range: N Spain and Mediterranean (but not S Greece), to S Norway, S Sweden and S Finland, and eastward through temperate Asia to Japan. Widespread in Britain, but largely absent from N Scotland where it may only be an occasional migrant. Currently expanding on northern edge of range.

Peacock

YORKSHIRE STATUS 1995/2003:

Common, widespread, hibernating resident and partial migrant. Usually 1 brood (late Jul/early Sept) which hibernates and re-appears the following spring (Mar/May), with a few stragglers still flying into Jun and early Jul. Recorded in every month of the year, due to hibernating individuals waking up in winter as a result of disturbance, or warm weather. **Earliest:** 01/01/1999 Harrogate (VC64) [MP Laycock]; **latest:** 18/12/2000 Hornsea (VC61) [Gordon Hylands]. Recent years (1995/2003) have seen an increase in the number of apparently fresh Peacocks flying in Sept, Oct and even Nov, indicating the likelihood that a small 2nd brood has been occurring. In hot summers this happens occasionally in southern counties, but has not previously been reported for Yorkshire. Rosemary Roach (North Cave nr Hull VC61) spotted larvae in her garden in Sept 1999 and watched 8 pupate. The butterflies emerged between 29/10 and 08/11, with one still flying on 27/11!

During the 1995/2003 Survey the Peacock has been noted in every Yorkshire 10km square except for 1 in the high Pennines (VC63). The strength of the population seems to be in the S and SE of the county (VCs 61 & 63) and it becomes somewhat less common in higher areas to the W and NW, although recently, it has been reported as appearing in higher Pennine gardens than previously noted, and in 2003 record numbers of up to 80 were seen around Malham Tarn (VC64) c400m [Brian & Elizabeth Shorrock]. The tetrad map highlights the thinner distribution in the far W and NW and on higher exposed areas of the N York Moors. The species also appears to be less commonly recorded in the Vales of York and Pickering, but sample observations indicate this is almost certainly due to under-recording. Population success appears to fluctuate considerably from year to year. Typical garden counts in lower areas can easily be in the **20/30** range, especially in association with buddleia, although ones and twos were more usual in 2002 and 2003 except, strangely enough, in some higher areas. The forested valleys towards the southern edge of the N York Moors (VC62) currently support particularly large populations indicated by a record count of **605** in Deepdale on 18/08/2000 [John Hume].

The species tends to live on the move, heading NNW in spring and early summer, and returning SSE from mid-Aug onward, giving rise to

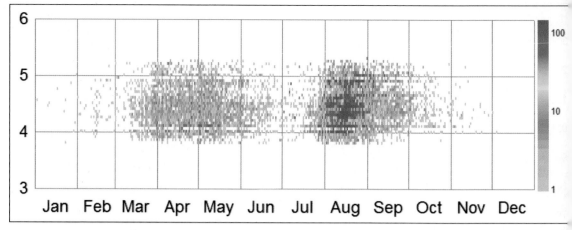

PHENOGRAM: Yorkshire 1995-2003. Note long emergence flight season, and south to north curve of peak colours indicating later peaks as you go north.

ID NOTES: Large red-brown butterfly with big, bluish, eye marks on each wing. Can give impression of a deep, purple-blue blur in flight. Underwings very dark, almost black, making butterfly difficult to spot in vegetation when wings closed. In flight at a distance, or high up, can appear extra large, and black, capable of confusion with extremely rare Camberwell Beauty, though lacking that species' pale wing edges. Sexes virtually identical, but females usually larger. Over 40 named aberrations including a 'blind' variety lacking blue eye marks (ab *belisaria* Oberthür), and one giving an impression of transparent wings, (ab *transparens* Beuret).

Viewed this way the hindwing eye pattern combines with the body to look very owl-like. By flicking its wings to suddenly reveal this pattern the Peacock may make a predator somewhat wary!

CONSERVATION ISSUES: Common enough not to require any help. The mobile nature of this species means it can search far and wide for suitable habitats and nectaring sites. The planting of nectar plants in parks and gardens, particularly buddleia, and the encouragement of nettle patches in sheltered places in full sun, can be of benefit to this species, as can allowing a patch of dandelions to flower in early spring when nectar plants are scarce.

concentrations on suitable nectar sites in the SE of the county. Highest site counts are invariably along the coast where butterflies accumulate and follow the coastline southward (eg 1188 counted in Filey Brigg Country Park (VC61) on 17/08/2002 [Filey Brigg Ornithological Group]. This sometimes develops into a small scale, but visible, southward migration best observed at the Narrow Neck, halfway along Spurn Peninsula (VC61). Movements invariably take place in late Aug on sunny days with a light SW wind. In these conditions Peacocks fly south along the beach, often in the company of Red Admirals, Small Tortoiseshells and other insects, such as bees, hoverflies and dragonflies. They can be seen leaving the tip of Spurn and heading out across 5 miles of open water towards Lincolnshire. It is not known how far these movements go, although Peacocks are not noted for long distance travel (c95km/60 miles being the currently recorded limit of known journeys). The species has also been recorded flying at night, as witnessed by the occasional catching of specimens in moth traps, eg in the Bell Flask/River Ure area (VC64/65), where Brian Morland caught 5 Peacocks on 26/08/2000, and up to 8 on five different occasions in 2001 (Morland 2000 and 2001). In addition, he describes a dramatic occasion on 18/08/2001 at 05.10hrs when it was still dark and he noticed several Peacocks flapping around an outside light above his head. He shone a strong lamp into the air like a searchlight and discovered *'Many hundreds of Peacocks were passing through, heading in a north westerly direction. Some were so high they appeared as dots in the beam of the lamp. The movement finished after about ten minutes.'*

Spot the butterfly! Well-disguised Peacock with closed wings, Burnby Hall Water Gardens, (VC61).

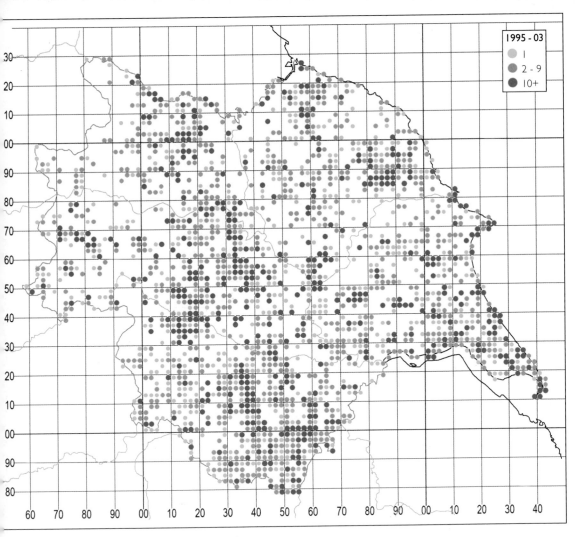

Peacock: Yorkshire Tetrad Map 1995-2003

MAP NOTES 1995/2003: Noted in 1922/3319 recorded tetrads (ie 57.9%), and out of a total of 4120 tetrads in Yorkshire. **Ranked 4th most widespread** out of 36 breeding species in the county. The 10km distribution map probably gives a more realistic idea of the Peacock's widespread presence than does the tetrad map, with only one unrecorded 10km square in the southern Pennines. The tetrad map highlights the thinner distribution in higher parts of the Pennines and N York Moors as well as in the Vales of York and Pickering, although sample counts in the latter areas indicate that these are simply under-recorded.

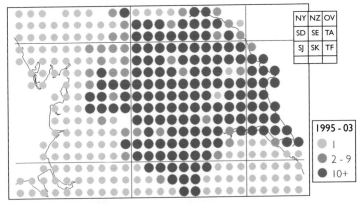

Peacock: 10km distribution North of England

= 1 or more records out of county 1995-1999

LIFE STORY

Peacock larvae

Peacocks usually emerge from hibernation Mar/May, with early specimens often found nectaring on dandelions, willow catkins and hawthorn blossom. A significant proportion of Peacocks are not properly resident on any given site. They constantly wander, heading northward in spring/early summer, flying about ½ km per day, with males holding different territories along the way. This implies that there is regular immigration into the county from the south and emigration to the north. The degree to which there is any immigration from the continent is unclear, due to difficulties in separating different kinds of movement. Local movements reverse around mid-Aug with a drift towards the S and SE.

Springtime males can often be seen spiralling high in the air in territorial arguments. A male may suddenly abandon a territory to follow a female across the countryside till she chooses a roosting site (probably high in a tree), where mating takes place, under cover of darkness and

unseen (and as far as we know un-photographed!). Once mated, females continue journeying, trying hard to shake off any pursuing males. Clusters of 300/500 eggs are laid on the undersides of nettle leaves (chosen for strong growth and sheltered, sunny position), usually around the middle of the day. Greenish-grey larvae hatch 1 to 3 weeks later, and develop through 5 instars into conspicuous hairy black larvae (Jun/Jul), speckled with white dots. They feed inside communal webs, periodically re-built on fresh nettle stems. Larvae usually pupate on nearby shrubs or tree trunks. Pupae are well hidden and difficult to find, hanging from silk pads for 2 to 4 weeks before hatching.

Summer emergence in Yorkshire is typically between 20/07 and 08/08, depending on weather conditions (but occasionally earlier or later). Butterflies sometimes hibernate after just a few days. By late Aug/early Sept they are generally moving less as they increase their searches for somewhere to hide, eg tree holes, garden sheds, garages etc. Odder places reported include: inside straw bales, under caravans, and 6m underground in an old military fortification at Paull (VC61). Barnham & Foggitt (1987) describe 20 Peacocks hibernating in a discarded cupboard in the Harrogate area (VC64). Churches offer many suitable hiding places, and extra warmth and light at Christmas midnight services sometimes produces unexpected Dec records!

Roosting or hibernating Peacocks may react to disturbance by flicking wings, revealing an owl-like, hindwing eye pattern. At the same time they can produce a creaking sound by rubbing their wings together. A communal roost reacting together can produce a hissing sound reminiscent of a snake! The eye patterns not only serve to frighten potential predators, but may also direct any attack at the wings rather than the body. Hence the summer sight of Peacocks with bites out of their wings, but still flying!

Peacocks may fly on warm days in any month, although in most years (1995/2003) there were less than 10 Jan/Feb sightings reported. 1998 was an exception with over 40 on 5 flight days in Jan, and 11 in Feb! Yorkshire statistics for 2000 provide a typical spread. The first figure (**bold**) shows number of flight days recorded, the second, the number of reports (ie where each report = 1, irrespective of the number of butterflies seen): Jan **1** (1); Feb **4** (5); Mar **14** (71); Apr **20** (199); May **26** (252); Jun **19** (57); Jul **11** (18); Aug **31** (651); Sept **27** (211); Oct **11** (31); Nov **2** (2); Dec **1** (1).

Feeding on grapes, France 1996.

HISTORICAL REVIEW:
Peacock *Vanessa io* in Porritt

Mouffet (1634) called it **The Queen of All**. Petiver (1699) referred to it as the **Peacock's Eye**. Wilkes (1741/42) simplified it to the **Peacock Butterfly** and general usage in more recent times has abbreviated it to **Peacock** alone. The Latin name *io* relates to Greek mythology and Io, the daughter of Inachis, in a story connected to Argus who had a hundred eyes.

Deducing the historical record is difficult, not just because of the paucity of records, but also because of the lack of detail in reports that do exist. Dunn & Parrack 1986) noted that in Northumberland and Durham it was considered *'common'* up to 1820, and *'common enough'* up to 1860. Then, following several years of cold summers (1860/63), it became much more rare. Robson (1902) also re Northumberland and Durham wrote, *'I have scarcely seen the insect since 1860, until 1893, when it was not uncommon'*. Dunn & Parrack further noted that between 1900 and 1939 only 6 or 7 specimens were reported in total for that region. Then there was a slow but steady recovery. This matches the Yorkshire experience. Duncan (1844) noted: *'Although abundant in most parts of England, there appear to be certain districts even in the south where it is not common and it gradually becomes scarce as we advance northwards. The most northern place where it has occurred in plenty is in the vicinity of York, and it probably does not extend beyond the Firth of Forth.* However, Thomson (1980) questions Duncan's accuracy regarding

Using a reflective background for warming up.

Scotland, as old records from 1766 onward indicate a permanent Scottish presence in southern Scotland and periodic boosts to Scottish populations (as in 1868), which hint at the arrival of immigrants. At the same time, Thomson gives no records for the period 1868 to 1900. Rimington (1992) suggests there was a *'severe retraction'* around 1860 when the species became rare or absent from the N of England and Scotland and showed little sign of any major recovery until the 1930s.

Regarding the Huddersfield (VC63) area, Fryer & Lucas (2001) note that Hobkirk (1859, 1868) described the Peacock as being common, but by 1883 Mosley was reporting it as rare. The scarcity carried on with some minor swings until the late 1960s. Porritt (1883) commented it was *'not so abundant as in many counties'*. He listed 24 areas from which he had received records (2 in VC61, 6 in VC62, 7 in VC63, 8 in VC64 and 1 in VC65). Porritt (1907) re-phrases his comments: *'Occurs occasionally in almost every district, but is only recorded as plentiful in Scarborough VC62, Bradford VC63 and Bramham and Knaresborough VC64'*. However, Walsh (1952) qualifies Porritt's comment: *JH Rowntree recorded this as common in Scarborough in the 1860s, but it became so scarce that the Scarborough Field Naturalists' Recorder for the Lepidoptera made a special note of when it occurred: 1878, 1917, 1918 and 1933'*. Tetley (1915), also writing of the Scarborough District noted: *'Vanessa io is very rare. I have only seen it once, in Langdale in the spring of 1912'* Taken together these various reports fit in with the theory that the 1879/1895 cold years may have been a cause of the Peacock's retraction. Rimington (1992) quotes Corbett (1918) referring to Peacocks in Doncaster in 1917 being: *'abundant after years of scarcity'*. Fryer & Lucas (2001) noted that Morley (1918) also reported a good year for Peacock in 1917 around Skelmanthorpe (VC63). Porritt recorded an increase for that year as well.

Rimington (1992) quotes several observers who noted a return of the species around Doncaster from 1931 onward. By 1939 this re-colonisation had moved right through Yorkshire and was being noted in Northumberland and Durham. By 1959 it was considered fairly plentiful in Doncaster (Hyde 1959) and this seems to have been the picture across lowland VC63. Sutton & Beaumont (1989) indicate that the butterfly was still rare in the early 1960s, but spread rapidly from 1968 onward, whilst the YNU (1967/70) recorded it as, *'widely distributed throughout the county'* but *'to some extent local'*. Walsh (1956) bears out the idea of local variation when he notes that it was formerly *'rare'* in the Scarborough district, but by the 1950s had become *'uncommon'* with a few specimens seen each year. The writer recorded butterflies in the Scarborough area between 1953 and 1957 and never saw a single Peacock. It appears that in the 1950s and 1960s the population strengthened in the southern central parts of the county, but presence elsewhere was patchy, particularly in the east. Philip Winter (*pers comm.*) recalls it was locally common between Scarborough and Pickering in the late 1960s and became more widely common around 1972/73. Barnham & Foggitt (1987) reporting on a Harrogate area survey for 1976/1985 considered the species *'widespread and profuse'*. By contrast, Frost & Frost (1995) indicated it to be relatively uncommon in S Holderness (VC61) in the late 1970s and early 1980s, with very poor years in 1986 and 1987. Sutton & Beaumont also noted a population drop in 1986. But from 1988 in S Holderness and elsewhere there was a steady upsurge in numbers, which continued through the 1990s, and by 2002 some observers were reporting the Peacock more common in gardens than the Small Tortoiseshell. It seems probable that the species is now more common and widespread than it has been for at least 150yrs.

Howard M Frost

Bridestones NR, N York Moors National Park (VC62).

UK BAP Status: *Not listed.*
BC Priorities: National: *Low.*
N of England: *Low.* Yorkshire: *Low.*
European status: *Not threatened.*

WORLD STATUS: Hibernating, mobile resident, 0-2500m+. Undergoing dramatic expansion in British Isles and northern areas but usually bivoltine: May/Aug and Aug/Nov. Range: from N Africa to central Norway and eastward through central Asia to Japan. Present in England and Wales but only recently begun reaching Ireland and Scotland. Only occasional in N Netherlands, Denmark and N Germany (even though it is found to the north of these countries!).

Comma

YORKSHIRE STATUS 1995/2003:

Hibernating resident with complex life story and usually 2 broods, the 2nd being partial. Populations in the county have waxed and waned considerably over the last 200yrs with virtual extinctions following clusters of cool or cold years. The latest expansion became evident in the 1980s and has recently taken the species to the northern county boundary and beyond, as far north as Scotland. There were no Yorkshire sightings between 1961, when one was seen in the Doncaster area [EW Smith], and 1969 when W Bunting found one in hibernation at Thorne (both VC63) (Rimington 1992). Only 3 further records were logged for the 1970s: Potteric Carr 1973 [SM Jackson]; Halifax 1974 [A Bannister]; and Bradford 1976 [RD Purnell]. Then records began to increase again from: 1980 onward in VC61 & 63; 1985 onward in VC62, and 1987 onward in VC64, when it was recorded as far north as Harlow Carr Gardens. The 1990s then saw a dramatic increase, eg in Holderness (VC61) from 1 or 2 sightings annually from 1984 onward to 29 sightings in 1992 (Frost & Frost 1995). Rimington (1992) counted 30 specimens in Owston Wood (nr Doncaster VC63) in May 1991. Whiteley (1992) notes Sheffield area records from 29x1km squares between 1980 and 1989, then a further 162x1km squares were added between 1990 and 1992. Numbers faltered a little between 1993 and 1996 but took off again in 1997 with nearly 500 sightings countywide.

In 1995 there were fewer than 100 reports but by 2003 we had 1398 records (involving 3429 butterflies seen). Our 1995/2003 Survey recorded it in over 150x10km squares and 1061 tetrads. Due to its habit of hiding away in woodlands it has almost certainly been under-recorded. Hibernated specimens will sometimes emerge on warmer winter days and six Feb appearances have been noted in our Survey Period with the **earliest** on 13/02/1998 when 2 were seen at Sprotborough (VC63) [Dave Booth]. Most individuals begin appearing from early Mar onward and fly until late May/early Jun. The 1st brood runs from mid/late Jun or early Jul to late Aug/early Sep. The partial 2nd brood appears from late Sep and can be on the wing until late Nov. **Latest records** in Survey Period: 11/11/1998 York (VC61) [Pat Bone]; 20/11/2000 Wakefield (VC63) [Roy Bedford];

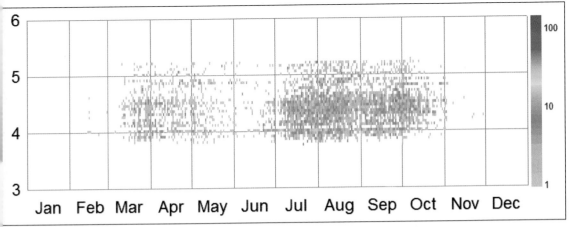

Jan Feb Mar Apr May Jun Jul Aug Sep Oct Nov Dec

PHENOGRAM: Yorkshire 1995-2003. Shows the spring emergence from hibernation and the two overlapping summer broods leading to a build up numbers in autumn (see text).

ID NOTES: Very similar in looks to a Small Tortoiseshell, but with scalloped wings and a more even orange brown coloration lacking blue spots. Can also be confused with Wall Brown and some Fritillaries. Undersides vary from dark brown to near black, with a marbling of ochre and bronze green, and the usually distinctive white comma mark on the hindwing. Sexes very similar, but females tend to be larger with less ragged edges and a more even dark coloration on the underside. Up to 40% of the 1st brood have brighter more golden orange upperparts and much paler underparts with less strongly scalloped wings. These are known as the *hutchinsoni* form, after Emma Hutchinson (b1820/d1906) who was first to breed them and discover that only this colour form produced the second brood. Although major variation is rare, over 30 aberrations have been described. Ground colour can vary considerably from almost white (ab *albus* Frohawk) or pale straw yellow (ab *dilutus* Frohawk), to examples where the dark markings join together (ab *suffusa* Tutt), or the hindwing is almost black (ab *reichenstettenis* Fettig). The amount of ochre and metallic green on the underside may vary as can the 'comma' mark in size or shape. More rarely it may even be missing (ab *extincta* Rebel).

26/11/2002 Knaresborough (VC64) [Mike Barnham], and 28/11/2002 Fairburn Ings (VC64) [John Laws]. This is a species usually seen in ones and twos only, but occasionally newly emerged butterflies may be found in temporary concentrations, which quickly disperse. These have resulted in counts in the 20s and 30s and on 25/09/1999 Pat Bone noted **71** in York Cemetery NR (VC62).

Comma pupa. Brampton Bierlow (Barnsley VC63) June 2004.

Dean Stables

Comma: note pale colours = *hutchinsoni* (Cornwall 14/07/1997).

Sean A Clough

CONSERVATION ISSUES: Given the widespread nature of the Comma's foodplants, and its ability to range widely in search of suitable habitats, there is little we can do to conserve this species, although maintenance of sunny forest rides and other edge of woodland habitats is clearly important. The continued planting and maintenance of wych elms may also have a bearing on this butterfly's success in the North of England. Scientists are not yet certain of all the triggers and controls behind its expansions and contractions, although climate swings seem to play the biggest role. The current warming trend appears favourable to the Comma, but future cooler periods could readily cause a further crash.

Comma: normal darker form. June 2004.

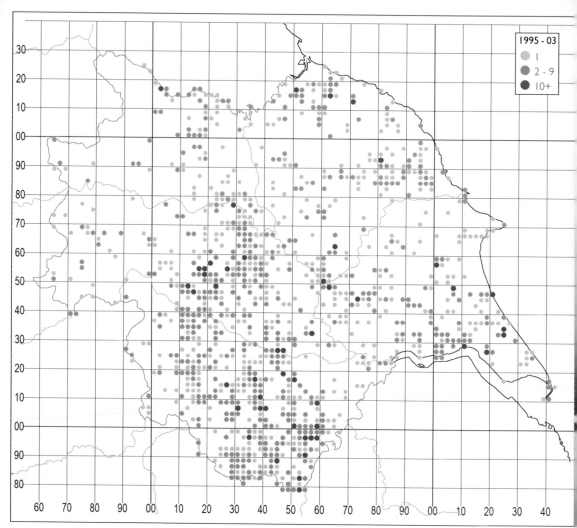

Comma: Yorkshire Tetrad map 1995-2003

MAP NOTES 1995-2003: Noted in 1061/3319 recorded tetrads (ie 32%), and out of 4120 tetrads in Yorkshire. **Rated 13th most widespread** out of 36 breeding species in the county, having been one of our rarer species in 1995. The spread of red and brown dots indicates larger numbers and more consistent presence in the southern half of the county. Even so, the species has also expanded into Durham and Northumberland where 437 tetrads were recorded between 1995 and 2003 (Hunter & Norman 2004).

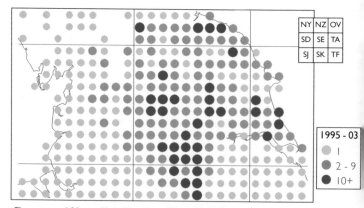

Comma: 10km distribution North of England
= 1 or more records out of county 1995-1999

LIFE STORY

Comma feeding on pear. (Neuilly l'Eveque, France), Aug 1991.

Hibernated butterflies may awake on warm, winter days in Jan/Feb, and nectar on 'Pussy' Willow *Salix capraea* and other species of catkins, but the majority are more likely to emerge from early Mar onward. As most Commas hibernate and breed in woodland areas, they are not as evident in gardens in spring as they are in autumn. Males establish territories and seek out females. Mating appears to take place unseen, high up in trees, perhaps at night. Females lay some 10 to 25 eggs on each suitable day and around 275 in a lifetime. Eggs hatch after 2 to 3 weeks, becoming drab, brown larvae with a white splodge helping to disguise them as bird droppings. The 1st brood larval period lasts

c4 to 7 weeks depending on which colour form is involved. Pupae resemble withered leaves and hang from a pad of silk under a leaf or branch of the foodplant.

First brood adults come in two forms: the normal dull brown form (offering better disguise during winter hibernation); and the lighter, brighter more golden-brown *hutchinsoni* form, with much paler underwings (better adapted to dodging predators in bright summer sunlight). The proportion of colour types appears to be determined by daylight length during the larval stage (although Emmet & Heath (1989) suggest succulence of foodplant also plays a part). 1st brood larvae, which develop before the solstice, are likely to be *hutchinsoni* (and destined to produce a second brood). Those developing as day length shortens will grow more slowly and emerge later as the normal darker form whose prime purpose is to hibernate successfully in readiness for mating the following spring. The proportion of *hutchinsoni* will vary from year to year according to weather conditions/latitude. An early emergence from hibernation is likely to increase chances of higher numbers of *hutchinsoni*. As one moves north the occurrence of a 2nd brood becomes more sporadic, and limited to exceptionally good summers. Where two broods occur, both may be on the wing at the same time in autumn, giving rise to a larger number of butterflies ranging widely in search of nectar and fruit to build up reserves in preparation for hibernation. Hibernation often takes place on tree trunks and branches, and occasionally in caves, hollows and open buildings. The butterfly looks like a dead leaf with the comma mark appearing to be a crack in the leaf, whilst the white legs can merge into the mosaic of lichens found on the bark. The Comma is often one of the last butterflies to be seen in late autumn and one of the first to appear in spring. Many sources suggest it does not appear to migrate across areas of sea. But its recent appearance on the Isle of Man and in Ireland, as well as a sighting 3.5km off the Cornish coast, and an occasional presence on the Isles of Scilly (Wacher *et al* 2003), suggest that past sea crossings may have been overlooked.

Comma larva.

Ray (1710) referred in Latin to *'the Tortoise-shell with jagged wings'*, whilst Petiver (1717) distinguished four types of **'Comma'**, indicating the name was already established. Wilkes (1741/42) specified **Comma Butterfly** and subsequent authors followed suit. In the current Latin name *Poly* means 'many' and *gonia* refers to the jagged edges of the wings, whilst *c-album* indicates the white c-shape (or comma) on the lower hindwing.

Comma populations have fluctuated over the years due to: climatic extremes, a decline in 19th century hop growing, and the introduction of burning hop bines after use (1880s), which destroyed pupae. The first recorded crash occurred just after the 1810/1817 cold period. Thomas & Lewington (1991) indicate the Comma's decline in southern counties dated from c1818/1820 (before any changes in the hop industry) and affected populations as far north as Lincolnshire.

Wallis (1769) (re North Durham & Northumberland) comments: *'The Tortoise-shell Butterfly with lacinated wings is not unfrequent in vale-meadows and gardens in August'*. If the Comma was present to the north of us in the later 1700s it seems likely it was present in Yorkshire at the same time. The evidence indicates a severe crash around 1816/17, with a recovery taking place in the 1830s, although Emmet & Heath (1989) suggest the recovery in the north was not matched in the south. In fact many southern counties experienced an almost complete loss from c1830 until 1930! Yorkshire records date from the 1830s and become more frequent in the 1850s and 1860s. Furthermore, Thomson (1980) points out that Commas were found in Scotland at this time as well, right up to the early 1870s.

Rimington (1992) notes our earliest records: Doncaster area (VC63/SE50) (Anon 1832), and Campsall Park nr Doncaster (VC63/SE51) (Lankester 1842). Duncan (1844) wrote: the Comma was *'by no means of frequent occurrence in Britain, at least in certain years, and does not appear to extend far north although we have heard of it being* seen in Fifeshire in Scotland. It has been found abundantly near Hertford, in Suffolk, in the neighbourhood of York, and occasionally in most of the Midland counties of England'*. Evidence of a rise in numbers in the 1850s and 1860s is indicated by an increase in reports eg: *'abundant in Rotherham* [VC63] *in 1856'* [W Thomas] in Porritt (1883); Pocklington (VC61) [AW Griggen] in Porritt (1883); Edlington Wood (VC63/SE59) *'I took eight in one day last Autumn and saw others,'* (Clark 1858); Doncaster (VC63) in 1866, *'rare and beautiful, but still remains with us'* (Hawley 1866). Morris (1853) wrote: The Comma *'has been noticed very abundantly two successive years by Mr Graham, of York, near Green Hammerton, Yorkshire* [W of York VC64] *alighting in hundreds on the blossoms of wild Scabious; and James Dalton Esq has taken it at Hackfall* [nr Grewelthorpe? VC64/65 border]*, so celebrated for its beautiful scenery. It also occurs at York. I have seen it occasionally near Doncaster* [VC63] *and Burnby, also in the garden of Nunburnholme Rectory, and by the side of the Brant Wood, also at Howsham Sutton-on-Derwent, Langwith* [all VC61] *and Buttercrambe Wood* [VC62] *and in other parts of the same county'*.

Newman (1871) reported it: *'common at York'* [TH Allis]; *'formerly taken at Raincliffe Woods nr Scarborough* [by Thomas Wilkinson in 1865] *but not of late years'*, [JH Rowntree]; *'rarely and singly'* in Huddersfield (VC63) [GT Porritt]; and, recorded at Halifax, Sheffield, Wakefield and Leeds (VC63/64) by Edwin Birchall. Stainforth (1919) reported specimens from Thomas Stather's Hull area (VC61) collection [Thomas Stather b1812/d1878] from Gilberdyke and a garden in Hull. By 1883 Porritt was able to comment that it was, *'Distributed, but only common in a few localities.'* He goes on to list 13 areas: Bishop's Wood (nr Selby VC64), Sheffield, Wakefield, Halifax, and Pontefract (all VC63), (plus others mentioned above) and Adel Blackmoor (nr Leeds VC64) [WH Taylor]; Green Hammerton, where it was *'sometimes abundant'* [John Hanson]; York where William Prest noted it at Askham Bog *'in the rough field adjoining the middle of the bog'*; Helmsley (VC62) where F Raine found it *'abundant on 05/09/1872,'* and Whitby (VC62) where it was recorded by WE Clarke. Robson (1902) suggests it was also common in parts of Co Durham around 1870.

There are no dated Yorkshire records from the 1879/1895 cold period when the species crashed once again nationally, and virtually disappeared except in an area centred on the counties of Gloucester, Hereford and Monmouth. There were few records in England between 1900 and 1913, but from 1914 onward it began to re-appear across southern counties, with a steady build-up in the 1920s. The general view has been that the species then re-expanded northward reaching Yorkshire in the 1930s/40s. However, it may not have completely disappeared from Yorkshire at all. The last dated county record was 1872 from Helmsley, but Walsh (1952) noted one taken at Helmsley by Thomas Lofthouse *'about 1902'*. Walsh also reports that, *'A Smith says it occurred there in Beckdale about 1918'*. Porritt (1904) added just one record to his 1883 list, an undated sighting by Arthur Angel, again at Helmsley. Tetley (1915) seems to confirm this presence when he notes, *'I have seen specimens taken at Helmsley'*. The first hints of a re-expansion into S Yorkshire came in 1921 and 1927, when it was recorded in Wheatley Wood (VC63/SE60) by EW Smith (Rimington 1992). By the 1930s/40s a more widespread appearance became evident as gleaned from Rimington and the YNU 1967/70 Report. **VC61:** Hull 1942, Skipwith 1947; **VC62:** Scarborough 1942, Pickering 1943, Allerston 1949, Goathland 1957; **VC63:** Hatfield Woodhouse 1939, Bradford 1942, Barnsley 1945/50; Elland, Cawthorne, and Wakefield all 1948; **VC64:** Harrogate 1946. The majority were autumn sightings, perhaps indicative of colonisers. However, any noticeable expansion came to an end by 1961 after which only 4 county records were logged until the early 1980s when the current expansion began.

Roy Bedford

View N: Newtondale from Skelton Tower. Levisham Moor on right, Cropton Forest to left.

UK BAP Status: *Species of Conservation Concern* **BC Priorities:** National: *Medium.* N of England: *High.* Yorkshire: *High.* **European Status:** *Not threatened.*

WORLD STATUS: Resident: 0-2200m. 1 or 2 broods (mid-May/late Jun, or early May/late Jun and mid-Jul/early Sept). Range: N Spain to N Norway and across Europe, Asia and N America, (but absent: Ireland, most of Italy, Greece etc). Stable in many countries, but declining in some, especially Belgium, Luxembourg and the Netherlands. In Britain mainly univoltine, with an occasional partial second brood in south, especially Devon and Cornwall (pers comm. Gary Pilkington). Once found throughout England, now largely absent from central and eastern regions. Still fairly widespread in Devon, Cornwall, Wales and Cumbria. More so in Scotland.

Small Pearl-bordered Fritillary

SPECIAL NOTE: In this section Small Pearl-bordered Fritillary is abbreviated to **SPBF** and Pearl-bordered Fritillary to **PBF**.

YORKSHIRE STATUS 1995/2003:

Scarce resident: 1 brood (June/July). Found in only 15x10km squares, and given *High* regional priority due to loss of many central Yorkshire sites during 20th century as well as threats to remaining sites. Survives in localized colonies in the western Yorkshire Dales and N York Moors, with Dales butterflies typically emerging c10 days later than those on the Moors, largely due to altitude, but also (more anecdotally) greater cloud cover and lower mean temperatures during earlier stages. Mean colony elevations: VC62: 130m, VC64: 171m and VC65: 240m. **Earliest** record: 31/05/1997 at Lownorth Camp (VC62) [Sean Clough]. **Latest** often in last week of Jul, especially in Pennine colonies. Occasional Aug records suggest possibility of token second brood in some recent years: eg 1 seen in Deepdale (VC62/SE99) on 19/08/1998 [John Hume]. Well-established on Moors where some colony site counts are regularly in **15/30** range. Colonies scattered throughout Cropton and Dalby Forests (VC62/SE79/SE88) including Keldy Castle, Raygate Slack, and Keys Beck Pond. Also occurs in nearby moorland valleys around Jugger Howe Beck, Wheeldale Gill, and Fen Bog/Eller Beck. Northernmost colonies are around May Beck and Biller Howe Dale. Pennine colonies usually listed as: Austwick, Lawkland and Cockett Mosses (VC64/SD76) and *'near Clapham'* (SD77). Recent surveying (Terry Whitaker & Brian Shorrock) has revealed the Clapham site to be made up of at least 14 populations spread over 2.5 square km on Newby Moor SSSI: a true metapopulation, and the only extensive network of sites now left in W Yorkshire. Maximum numbers on Pennine sites usually less than **20**, but **50+** possible on Newby Moor and Austwick Moss. Most sites considered 'small', producing less than 100 adults in a season but a few are 'medium size' and could number up to 1000 adults. Other colonies appear extremely isolated, which is of considerable concern as small isolated populations are statistically the most likely to become extinct (Hanski 1991).

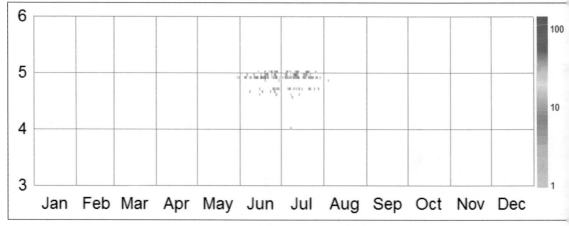

PHENOGRAM: Yorkshire 1995-2003. Indicates the limited population, the single brood and well-defined flight season.

ID NOTES: Can be confused with the much rarer PBF, although PBF is so restricted in its Yorkshire distribution that it is unlikely to be seen. Habitat is also a guide to ID in that the usually solitary PBF prefers drier sites whilst SPBF tolerates damp areas. SPBF usually smaller, but sizes do overlap. For diagnostic separation take note of closed-wing view. SPBF has thicker black lines dividing cells, giving richer, brighter, stained-glass window effect. PBF has lighter colours, suffused with ochre and pale mustard, and divided by finer lines. See also under PBF for further distinctions. SPBF has over 30 named aberrations including variations in ground colour ranging from white through cream and buff to darker melanic forms. One Dales colony consistently produces a high proportion of individuals with a darker dusting than normal. Scotland has its own more brightly marked form: *insularium*.

Newton Dale specimen.

Pennine specimen.

CONSERVATION ISSUES: The SPBF is given *high* priority in Butterfly Conservation's North East Regional Action Plan. It needs damp, grassy habitats with violets, in open sunny areas. Some N Yorkshire Moors forest sites appear to have become shaded out. Rides need to be widened and periodic clearings made to encourage violet growth. Removal of conifers could be of great value. Where the species is found in bracken covered areas a balance needs to be maintained between bracken and grassland to ensure violet growth. Scrub clearance needs to be considered in some areas. The SPBF is one of the species included in the remit of the N York Moors Butterfly and Moth Action Group formed in 2001 under the auspices of Butterfly Conservation and the National Park in co-operation with the Forestry Commission. A distribution study was carried out by the writer in 2003. The species has an Action Plan in the Yorkshire Dales National Park BAP aimed at providing conservation management on all known sites and on all suitable habitat within 5km of existing colonies. In the Dales, drainage improvements, re-seeding and fertilizer run-off are additional problems. Light grazing or selective Juncus cutting is considered important to reduce ranker vegetation. Removal of the cut biomass could help to reduce the effects of enrichment. The Forestry Commission has taken robust action in Gisburn Forest where, once notified about the species' importance, conifers, sallow and birch scrub were removed from the site in autumn 1999. Twenty-two of the Pennine sites are SSSIs but as the butterfly is not specifically mentioned in any of the site designations, site management for the species may not always be appropriate, something which needs to be worked on for the future.

Pennine specimen with extra patches of dark scales.

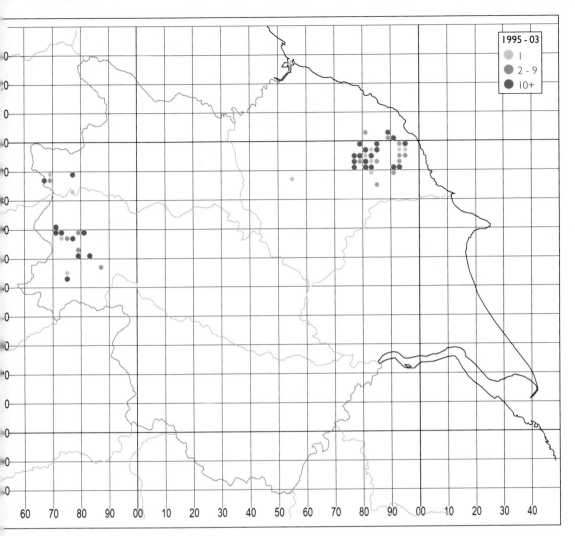

Small Pearl-bordered Fritillary: Yorkshire Tetrad map 1995-2003

MAP NOTES 1995-2003: Noted in 53/3319 recorded tetrads (ie 1.6%), and out of 4120 tetrads in Yorkshire. Ranked 29th most widespread out of 36 breeding species in the county. The rarity of this species is emphasized by the small number of squares in which it is present. Hopefully current conservation projects will help alleviate the decline in this species. (At least 4 new colony sites on the N York Moors were reported in 2004.)

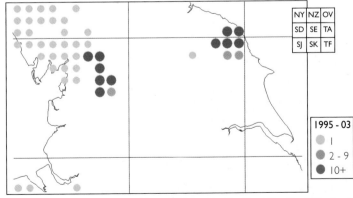

Small Pearl-bordered Fritillary: 10km distribution North of England

● = 1 or more records out of county 1995-1999

LIFE STORY

HABITAT: Uses woodland glades, mires, damp grassland and rush pasture, grassland with bracken or scrub and woodland edges with open glades, where violets *Viola* spp (particularly Common Dog Violet *V. riviniana* and Marsh Violet *V. palustris*) grow. In Yorkshire, marsh violet appears to support the butterfly on a majority of sites. In the west, Austwick Moss, Wharfe Woods (both VC64), Rise Hill (VC65) and other sites possess areas where the plant is abundant, but there are also patches of common dog violet occurring sparsely on adjacent drier land. In County Durham, egg-laying has been observed on common dog violet **adjacent** to mires containing marsh violet and is considered to be an important site component (Ellis 2000). However, the Yorkshire situation is unclear. Some N York Moors (VC62) sites are exclusively of common dog violet, which occurs in low densities on dry grassy bank edges, or amongst light bracken litter (eg the southern half of the Newton Dale population). Marsh violet sites are typically found on moorland mires, rush pasture or marshy grassland with a wet peaty surface and impeded drainage. The violets grow in discrete areas on the margins of the wettest mire habitats, usually within rush pasture and often on the sides of tussocks, which may be an important structural component in the ecology of both larvae and violets. On the N York Moors, this habitat is also found within coniferous forest, usually adjacent to a beck. In VC62 it is probable that in the past the butterfly was largely dependent on coppicing, but now exploits whatever suitable habitat remains. By contrast, in the west it seems to have been using the same mire habitats for two millennia (Whitaker 2002, 2003).

Left: SPBF pupa, (Devon early Aug 2000). Right: SPBF mating pair, Newton Dale (VC62) 25/06/1996.

Sticky eggs are placed singly, or dropped into vegetation near foodplant and hatch within about a fortnight. Small larvae feed until 4th instar (late Sept) when they enter hibernation. Emmett and Heath (1989), suggest larvae overwinter beneath leaves or in ground detritus, but this probably only applies to woodland sites. Hibernation sites in moorland mire populations are not known, but may be within *Juncus* or Purple Moor Grass *Molinia caerulea* tussocks. Feeding recommences in April and full-grown 5th instar larva is about 20mm long, blackish, with yellow spines, a brownish dorsal line and a pinkish lateral stripe. Two longer horn-like spines push forward over the head. Larvae are secretive, hiding in the shadier parts of the vegetation, and only emerging for feeding forays. The pupal stage begins late May in Yorkshire and lasts about 3 weeks. Brown pupae, dotted with metallic silver spots, are suspended from silk pads, low down on a plant stem or in the detritus.

Adults fly Jun/Jul. Males patrol almost constantly in suitable weather and copulation takes place as soon as virgin females are discovered, with no courtship involved (Sean Clough pers obs.). Mated females divide time between basking low in vegetation, nectaring, and searching for violets. When suitable foodplants found, female crawls as far as possible into nearby vegetation before curving her abdomen and dropping an egg into the growth below. Although Emmet & Heath (1989) suggest egg-laying takes place only in the afternoon, this has been observed in both morning (09.30-10.30hrs) and afternoon (14.45hrs) in VC62 (Sean Clough pers obs.).

The most commonly used nectar-source is Marsh Thistle *Cirsium palustre* although Ragged Robin *Lychnis flos-cuculi* and Cuckoo Flower *Cardamine pratensis* are occasionally visited and wild Raspberry *Rubus idaeus* is used at Raygate Slack. Although any small flower proud of the foliage can be picked out by the butterfly, it seems incapable of distinguishing those growing amongst leaves. To this end it has developed a technique, which involves crawling through the leaves and stalks, with proboscis unfurled and trailing beneath, in contact with the foliage, until a flower-head is encountered and the butterfly stops to feed. (Sean Clough pers obs.). At Deepdale Meadow, the most abundant flower on one visit was Common Cat's-ear *Hypochaeris radicata*, which was used on 13 out of 16 visits by two nectaring females (Sean Clough pers obs.).

Larva (Devon early Aug 2000).

Early lepidopterists counted SPBF and PBF as one species, but by 1717, Petiver was describing SPBF as the **April Fritillary** and the PBF as the **April Fritillary with few Spots**. Wilkes (1741/42) introduced **Small Pearl Border Fritillary**, but Lewin (1795) called it the **May Fritillary**, a change of month probably resulting from Britain's acceptance of the Gregorian calendar in 1752, which caused 11 days to be eliminated, thus changing a late April emergence into one in May! Samouelle (1819) suggested the **Pearly-bordered Likeness**, whilst Haworth (1803) was first to use **Small Pearl-bordered Fritillary**. The family name *Boloria* means 'fishing net', a reference to the wing pattern, whilst *selene* meaning moon, refers to the pearls.

The earliest known Yorkshire reference is found in Morris (1853) who notes, *'I have taken it in plenty'* at Edlington Wood (Doncaster VC63/SK5497), probably in the mid-1830s (Rimington 1992). Morris also recorded it at, *' Buttercrambe Moor, Langwith and Stockton',* ie Stockton on the Forest (all nr York VC62/SE65/75) and describes it (nationally) as having two broods: May/Jun and Aug/Sept. It is intriguing that he doesn't make any exception for York area sites with which he was familiar. Heppenstall (1842) recorded it as *'abundant'* in Sandbeck Park (Doncaster VC63/SK5590) in 1842, and Newman (1860) noted a report by JH Rowntree (of Scarborough) that the

species was *'plentiful on moors and plantations near Cloughton'* (VC62/SE99). Porritt (1883) and Rimington (1992) also refer to records around Bawtry (Doncaster VC63/SK69), probably in the 1870s. Rimington concludes that this site became extinct around 1875/80, and the species completely disappeared from the Doncaster area in the 1890s, almost certainly as a result of the loss of damp meadow and damp woodland habitats, and an end to coppicing, all perhaps exacerbated by the climatic extremes and industrialisation.

Porritt (1883) refers to additional sites at Askham Bog (VC64/SE54); Bramham Park and Tadcaster (VC64/SE44); York (which could have been Askham Bog, Buttercrambe, Sandburn, Strensall etc); Bishop's Wood (nr Selby VC64/SE53); Pontefract (VC63/SE42), and the Sheffield area (VC63/SE38). Reports in the YNU Card File indicate a presence in 1900/1902 at Castle Howard (nr Malton VC62/SE76); Sandburn Common and Strensall (linked sites nr York VC62/SE65); Ingleby Greenhow (nr Middlesbrough VC62/NZ5806), and at Wykeham (VC62/SE98). However, it wasn't until 1930 that the species was first reported from Wharfedale (VC64/SD96) by Rosse Butterfield. In a local guide book (Crowther 1930), Butterfield wrote about the natural history of Grass and Bastow Woods and noted, *'A little lower down the valley in heathy gills on gritstone slopes the Green Hairstreak and the Small Argent Moth are locally common and the two Pearl-bordered Fritillaries still survive'.* From that point until today, the species has been continually recorded at Austwick and Lawkland Mosses (both VC64/SD76). By 1932, the SPBF had also been discovered in Newtondale (which leads northward from Pickering (VC62/SE88/SE89), where a YNU report referred to it being *'numerous'.* In 1936 Ivy Thomas referred to it as being *'common'* around Hackness (VC62/SE99) and Roger Key found it still *'common'* in that area in 1978. JM Brown recorded it at Robin Hood's Bay (VC62/NZ90) in 1943.

These various reports suggest that in the 1800s the species was fairly widespread (and probably greatly overlooked) from Doncaster and Sheffield northwards, through the Vale of York to Tadcaster and York, eastward and northward into the Howardian and Hambleton Hills, and north-eastwards onto the N York Moors. This same population may have once stretched continuously into the Pennine Dales. By the end of the 19th century many of the lowland populations had disappeared although a few survived into the 1950s/60s. In 1944 WG Bramley noted that the SPBF was *'much scarcer than usual at Sandburn and Strensall, with only a few at Askham Bog'.* In the 1950s E Ramsden (YNU Card File) reported it *'common'* on the slopes of the Hambleton Hills from Kilburn (VC62/SE58) to Pickering (VC62/SE78), and at Castle Howard (VC62/SE76/77), Sand Hutton (VC62/SE75) and Skipwith Common (VC61/SE63). By the 1960s, Skipwith was almost the last known Vale of York site. The YNU (1967/70) summary stating the SPBF was *'locally common in VC61'* appears misleading and is not born out by any records. Only one other site has been indicated, in Heath *et al* (1984), where presence is mapped for VC61/SE74 (Pocklington Canal/Allerthorpe area) in the 1970/88 period. The species was probably extinct at Skipwith by 1970, but was later re-introduced in 1980 by SM Jackson with a handful of females taken from Lawkland Moss. The offspring from this release survived until 1992 (possibly 1993) after which it is suspected the site became too dry. Recent systematic searching (1995/2002) indicates that although the species is now confined to the N York Moors and Pennine Dales, it is probably more widespread in both areas than previously realised with the likelihood of yet more sites to discover, especially in VC65 where its presence was first hinted at by a 1982 report from Aysgarth (VC65/ SE08) [AMR Heron/YNU Card File].

Small Pearl-bordered Fritillary, Raygate Slack 1995

Sean A Clough

1601 PEARL-BORDERED FRITILLARY *Boloria euphrosyne* (Linnaeus 1758)
Family: Nymphalidae, sub-group Argynninae: ('the Fritillaries').

Sean A Clough

A Yorkshire colony site (VC62).

UK BAP Status: *Priority species.*
BC Priorities: National: *High.*
N of Eng: *High.* Yorkshire: *High.*
European Status: *Not threatened.*
Protected in Britain for sale only.

WORLD STATUS: Resident: 0-1900m.
One brood N Europe (May/Jul); partial 2nd
possible in S of range and occasionally
further N in ideal conditions (Apr/Jun,
Jul/Sept). Range: N Spain to N Scandinavia
and eastward through Asia. Once widespread
and locally common throughout England and
Wales, as a butterfly of rides and clearings in
ancient deciduous woodlands. Dramatic
decline in 20th century resulted from changes
in woodland management and cessation of
coppicing. Now largely absent from eastern
England except for isolated presence in
Yorkshire.

SPECIAL NOTE: In this chapter, Pearl-bordered Fritillary has been abbreviated to **PBF,** and Small Pearl-bordered Fritillary to **SPBF.**

YORKSHIRE STATUS 1995/2003:

Resident: 1 brood (early-May/mid-Jun). **Yorkshire's rarest species.** Only 3 linked colonies known, on S edge of N Yorkshire Moors (all on private land not currently open to the public). The sites are within about 1km of each other and thought to be part of a single metapopulation, based on a mosaic of well-drained, violet-rich grassland, with scrub and bracken, the latter producing a warm micro-climate for the larvae. The main foodplant, Common Dog-violet *Viola riviniana*, grows amongst the bracken and grass tussocks.

All three colonies are on one landholding and the owner has worked with Butterfly Conservation for some years, allowing regular monitoring and more recently (2002) agreeing to a programme of management to help conserve the butterfly. Work is organised under the auspices of the North Yorkshire Moors Butterfly and Moth Action Group, which represents the N York Moors National Park, English Nature, Defra (Dept of Food, Fisheries and Rural Affairs), the National Trust and other organisations.

Monitoring indicates the colonies are remarkably small, with site checks on one site often producing counts of only one or two butterflies. Peak counts on the other two sites are usually less than **30** for each colony, with one exceptional year (2001) when **60** were recorded on one site [Sam Ellis]. During our Survey period the earliest record was 09/05 and the latest 15/06. A management plan was agreed in 2001 and work to control bracken, remove felled trees and trim scrub was carried out in 2002 and 2003. Further work is planned for the future in the hope of extending the sizes of existing colonies and hopefully, encouraging the colonisation of a new area. The remote possibility of an overlooked colony in the Levisham/Newtondale area, where it was recorded in the past, cannot be ruled out.

Pearl-bordered Fritillary

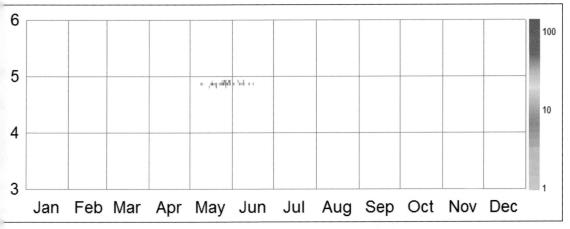

6

5

4

3

Jan Feb Mar Apr May Jun Jul Aug Sep Oct Nov Dec

100

10

1

ID NOTES: Similar in colour to Wall and Comma, which may be on the wing at the same time, but separable on their greater size and different wing shape. More readily confused with similar but more widespread SPBF, which may overlap in size with PBF. The two are best separated by comparison of closed-wing views. In PBF the silver-white 'pearls' towards the edge of the lower wing are lined with **reddish brown** chevrons, and there are just **two other silver white patches** away from the wing edge. In the more richly marked SPBF the chevrons are **black** and there are many silver-white patches on the rest of the wing. Quite a variable species with over 30 aberrations described. Ground colour may be lighter, ranging from yellow-ochre (as in ab *albinea* Lambillion) to almost white (ab *pallida* Spuler). A range of melanic forms have also been described, eg where there is a darkening of the wing bases as in ab *pillionii* Nitsche.

PHENOGRAM: Yorkshire 1995-2003. The limited distribution and relatively short flight season are clearly indicated here.

Mike Barnham

PBF: note typically elongated wing pose.

CONSERVATION ISSUES: As noted above, the PBF is a priority species in all UK categories and Butterfly Conservation (BC) has undertaken extensive research into bracken habitats and coppicing regimes as these are also of great importance to other fritillary species. The reinstatement of coppicing in woodland areas has been encouraged through the 'Coppice for Butterflies Challenge' grant scheme initiated by the Forestry Commission and BC in 1996. A Species Action Plan (Bourne & Warren 1995) has been published by BC. The species figures in BC's Regional Action Plan for North East England (Ellis 2000) and in various updates. BC has also published *The Conservation of the Pearl-bordered Fritillary on the North York Moors* (Ellis 2001), and the butterfly will be included in the forthcoming N Yorkshire Moors National Park Biodiversity Plan.

Bracken management relevant to Yorkshire colonies involves preventing scrub encroachment and balancing the build-up of too much bracken litter (which could shade out violet growth), against the larval need for enough litter to provide cover. Bracken litter may be cleared by hand, or by rolling, and heavy re-growth prevented by selective spraying or cutting in July. Livestock such as cows and ponies, which are heavy enough to poach the ground, can help prevent undue litter build-up and create patches of bare earth in which violet seedlings can germinate, but care must be taken over stocking levels. The action of rabbits, in grazing and creating scrapes can also help maintain suitable habitat as happens on one of the Yorkshire sites. Oates (2004) provides a valuable update on managing woodland sites, noting that ants play a part in the ecological balance by helping to disperse the violet seeds, which may have some bearing on the considerable, and potentially important, annual variations in the violet crop.

PBF: closed-wing view.

Shirley King

Roosting PBF. Easy to miss!

Front view.

Top view.

MAP NOTES 1995-2003: Noted in only **4/3319** recorded tetrads (ie 0.1%), and out of 4120 tetrads in Yorkshire. **Ranked 36**th **most widespread out of 36** breeding species in the county and therefore Yorkshire's rarest butterfly. We are unable to show detailed maps as the three colonies are on private land which is not currently open to the public.

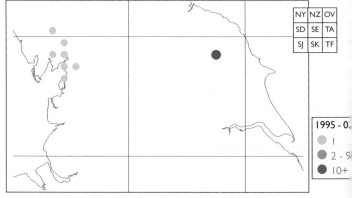

NY	NZ	OV
SD	SE	TA
SJ	SK	TF

1995 - 0.
○ 1
● 2 - 9
● 10+

Pearl-bordered Fritillary: 10km distribution North of England

○ = 1 or more records out of county 1995-1999

LIFE STORY

PBF mating ruck.

Sean A Clough

Eggs are deposited singly, on or near the foodplant, and most often simply dropped into leaf or bracken litter near violets (mainly Common Dog-violet *Viola riviniana*, but occasionally other species). Larvae emerge after 2 to 3 weeks and are all black with spines up to the 4th instar, after which, spines may develop lemon yellow bases. They feed on violet leaves and flowers, preferably the tender new shoots, and even use hidden plants, which have failed to grow through the litter (Oates 2004). Short periods of feeding are interspersed with longer periods of basking in the litter, although this is curtailed if temperatures remain high for a prolonged period, and larvae go into hiding. In Sept, larvae hibernate by hiding away in a curled leaf amongst the litter. They usually reappear in Mar and resume feeding and basking before pupating around mid-Apr. Pupae are silver-spotted, grey-brown, and look like dead leaves

PBF warming up.

hanging from a silken pad in a loose web. Butterflies emerge 2 to 3 weeks later. Males then tend to patrol suitable violet-rich areas searching for females, which often rest in low vegetation. Emmet & Heath (1989) suggest that copulation often takes place some height above the ground, such as in a nearby tree. Of two instances observed on Yorkshire sites, the first was in bracken litter about 30cm from the ground [Sean Clough 1997], and the second was on bare earth on a path [Sam Ellis 2001]. Both sites had scrub or nearby woodland edge which could have provided higher perches.

The butterfly has adapted to temporary habitats largely created by man's use of ancient woodlands for coppicing, a form of management in which trees are cut back on a 5 to 7yr rotation to produce poles, whips and fuel. Clearance allows a flush of under-storey flowers, including violets and Bugle *Ajuga reptans* (one of the butterfly's favourite nectaring plants). Litter from various trees (especially oak which is slow to break down) helps provide the ideal habitat. In the past, successive parts of a woodland would be coppiced each year providing a patchwork of suitable areas, allowing the butterfly to move on when an existing colony became shaded out after two or three years of coppice re-growth. Although relatively sedentary, a proportion of PBF individuals appear quite happy to wander, and a marked specimen has been recorded as far as 4.5km from its starting point (Oates 2004). It is increasingly thought that the butterfly's existence is dependent on a metapopulation structure, ie a series of linked colonies, and if this becomes too small the species may be unable to maintain itself. Coppicing fell out of favour towards the end of the 19th century causing many PBF losses; whilst in the 20th century many deciduous woodlands were felled and replaced with conifers. At first, the latter clearances provided more PBF habitat, but after about 10 years, colonies were increasingly shaded out by conifer growth. Losses were particularly noticed in the 1950s/1960s and have since become more marked. Asher *et al* (2001) indicate a 60% decrease in occupied 10km squares between the 1970/82 Survey and that of 1995/1999. Oates (2004) draws attention to the importance of grazing animals in creating suitable habitat and Heath *et al* (1984) indicate the loss of woodland rabbits to myxomatosis in the 1950s/1960s as a contributory factor.

HISTORICAL REVIEW:
Pearl-bordered Fritillary
Formerly: *Argynnis euphrosyne* in Porritt (1883).

PBF and SPBF were confused in the early days and treated as one species: **the April Fritillary** (See under SPBF for other details.) Harris (1766) introduced **Pearl Border Frittillaria** and both names continued circulating into the 1800s before **Pearl-bordered Fritillary** won the day. The Latin family name *Boloria* means 'fishing net', being a reference to the wing pattern, whilst Euphrosyne was one of the Three Graces, representing elegance and beauty.

In the past this species was far more common than today, both nationally and in Yorkshire. Duncan (1844) indicates: *'The butterfly is apparently distributed over the whole island'*, (ie Britain). Coleman (1860) refers to: *'This very common insect...'* In 19th century Yorkshire it was fairly widespread in the Vale of York from Doncaster and Sheffield northward to Bramham and York, as well as eastward from York through the Howardian and Hambleton Hills and along the southern escarpment of the N Yorkshire Moors to the Scarborough area. Rimington (1992) reports its VC63 presence in Wath-upon-Dearne (Anon 1832), Sutton Common (Lankester 1842), Adwick 1846 [JW Dunning], Roche Abbey 1858 (Smith 1858), Doncaster 1860 (Wragg 1860), c1875 [J Harrison in Porritt 1883], and Edlington Wood 1871 [W Burman]. There were no later records except for undated and unconfirmed references in

Peter Waterton

PBF VC62.

excursion circulars (1884 and 1897) and a single questionable 1906 Augu sighting (Hewett 1907). 2nd brood examples are the exception in Britain eve in southern England, although 19th century butterfly books often indicated was a double-brooded species! Whilst it is generally assumed that the speci began disappearing around this time due to an end to coppicing, t correlation with the cold years 1879/1895 raises the possibility that populations also suffered from the severe weather of that time.

Fryer & Lucas (2001) indicate it was known in the mid-19th centur Huddersfield area, from Storthes Wood (Hobkirk 1859,1868), and behir Castle Hill (Mosley 1883), but then there were no further records. Morr (1853) noted: *'It is plentiful in many places* [ie nationally] *among others Buttercrambe Moor nr Stamford Bridge* [VC62], *Stockton* [ie Stockton-o the-Forest just to the NE of York VC62], *Sutton-on-Derwent* [VC61] *ar Langwith, Yorkshire'*. Langwith Fields, just south of York appears to be 'lost' site, now probably part of Elvington Airfield (VC61/SE64). Porri (1883) reported that it, *'Occurs in many places, but is not often commor* He included: Goole (VC61 or 63), York, Castle Howard and Scarboroug in VC62; Doncaster, Huddersfield (very rare), Roche Abbey, Sheffield, ar Wakefield (rare) in VC63; Askham Bog, Bishop Wood and Bramha (VC64), and Richmond [John Sang] in VC65. Robson (1902) may b referring to the same record when he comments that: *'Mr Sang took it High Force* [Teesdale NY82] *on 28th Feb 1858'*. The early date suggests misprint or possibly a larval record, although it was a notably mild winte The Horbury School collection in Leeds Museum holds 4 PBFs date 06/1934 from Castle Howard and initialled ER (probably E Ramsder Porritt (1904) added: *'Common at Levisham in 1895 (YNU excursion* whilst his 1907 comment gave no hint of any changes noticed. A photocop of an annotated edition of Porritt (1904), with notes by Arthur R Smit (b1887/8, d1957), is held by New Walk Museum, Leicester, and carrie undated records from Strensall (nr York VC62) and Newtondale (VC62).

The earliest N York Moors reference appears to be that in Belcher (1836 *'The moors and vallies in this district* [Rosedale] *abound with mar beautiful insects. The intelligent son of Mr Hartas of Rosedale has a extensive collection of specimens of these and other natural productions the neighbourhood, and amongst them will be found the following: th pearl bordered fritillary...'* Theakston (1871) notes it was found *'in all th woods around Scarborough'*. Terry Whitaker drew our attention to a annotated copy of Porritt (1883/1904) with notes made by EOC (thought be EO Croft, a past president of the YNU). He indicates 2 PBF record *'Goathland* [VC62] *June 27th 1903 (season late)'* and *'Bishop Wood* [VC6 *June 3rd 1904'*. Tetley (1915) wrote: *'In all the dales* [ie the valleys on th S edge of the N York Moors] *Brenthis euphrosyne* [PBF] *and B. seler* [SPBF] *occur, the latter much the commoner and extending higher than i congener'*. Walsh (1952) provided an update on the same area: *'Here it confined to the dales and has been recorded as common at Pickerin (1886) and Levisham (1895) and still occurs there. E. Owston and N Ellison consider that it now equals the small pearl-bordered in abundanc a statement with which A. Smith* [Arthur R Smith of York] *agrees* Scarborough Field Naturalists' recorded it from Langdale in 1913 ar 1950, and from Raindale in 1968 [Philip Winter].

The YNU 1967/70 Report adds little to our knowledge: *Of simila distribution to the next species* [SPBF] *but more local; in one or tw districts, however, such as Pickering (62) and Levisham (62) it is ofte common.'* Sutton & Beaumont (1989) note, *'In Yorkshire it appeared to b in danger of extinction at the beginning of the 1980s, but has sinc appeared in a few sites around Kirkbymoorside and Newtondale (VC62)'*

Sean A Cloug

The Butterflies of Yorkshir

1607 DARK GREEN FRITILLARY *Argynnis aglaja* (Linnaeus 1758)
Family: Nymphalidae, sub-group Argynninae ('the Fritillaries').

Hole of Horcum (N of Pickering VC62), 02/03/2004, illustrating the harsh climate in which this species survives!

UK BAP Status: *Not listed.*
BC Priorities: National: *Low.*
N of England: *Medium.* Yorkshire: *Medium.*
European Status: *Not threatened.*

WORLD STATUS: Mobile resident, 0-2500m, 1 brood (Jun/Aug). Range: Morocco and N Mediterranean coast northward to N Norway, and eastward through Asia to China and Japan. Fairly widespread but local in British Isles, with marked decline in central and eastern England since 1960s. Although apparently stable in Europe, declines have been noted in 11 countries. Subspecies *scotica* Watkins 1921 is found in Ireland, W Scotland, Western Isles and Isle of Man.

YORKSHIRE STATUS 1995/2003:

Uncommon, localised resident and wanderer: largely confined to the western Pennines (Malham Tarn, Scar Close, Ribblehead area) (mainly VC64 but also a single colony in VC65) and N Yorkshire Moors (VC62) where there are colonies toward the western edge (Sutton Bank, Farndale) and around Dalby Forest, Lockton High Moor and Goathland Moors. There have also been records from the coastal area between Whitby and Redcar. The Harrogate district (VC64) continues to produce sporadic records, and occasional wanderers have been noted close to Yorkshire's S & SW borders near Sheffield (VC63), probably from centres of population in Derbyshire.

Single brood (usually 1st week of Jul to mid-Aug in VC62 and a week or so later in VC64). Late Jun records not unknown on N Yorkshire Moors: **earliest:** 21/06/2003 at May Beck [Terry Whitaker] and Ellerburn Bank [DW Wood] (both VC62), **latest:** Scar Close NNR (VC64) 01/09/2002 [Terry Whitaker]. Usually seen in single figures, with highest concentrations: **45** at Pexton Bank (VC62) on 12/07/1997 [John Mackenzie], and **41** at Scar Close NNR (VC64) on 08/08/2000 [Brian Shorrock].

Except for occasional wanderers (possibly misidentified), the species is absent from VC61, and since 1995 there have only been two reported VC63 records, both singles, at Dove Park Bridge, Denholme on 29/07/1999 [Alan Whitaker], and Potteric Carr on 12/07/2003 [Peter Greaves]. However, several other reports have come from counties adjacent to VC63, in 10km squares through which the traditional Yorkshire boundary passes. Following a decline in the early 1960s, which reached its lowest ebb around 1980, there appears to have been a slight recovery. Sutton & Beaumont (1989) date the beginnings of this from around 1982. During our Survey period around 50 tetrads have been recorded, of which about half appear to represent some kind of colonisation, the others being sightings of single wanderers.

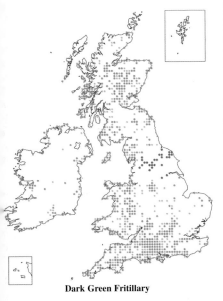

Dark Green Fritillary

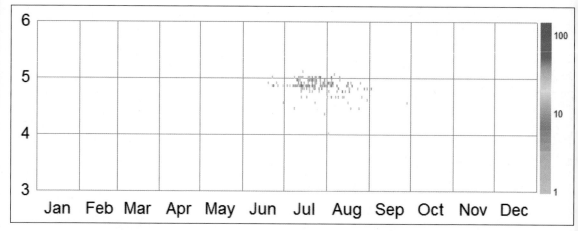

Jan Feb Mar Apr May Jun Jul Aug Sep Oct Nov Dec

ID NOTES: A large butterfly, fast and direct in flight, except for females investigating egg-laying sites. Similar to High Brown and Silver-washed Fritillaries, which are very rare, and unlikely to be found in Yorkshire. Upperwings typical of fritillaries in checkered orange-brown and black, bright and distinctive in sunshine. Closed-wing view is usually diagnostic revealing hindwing with large **silver-white spots** on a predominantly **olive green** ground colour. Inexperienced observers are sometimes confused by Comma, Painted Lady and Wall, which can appear similar in flight or in upper wing view, but lack the silver-white spots. Quite a variable species, with almost 100 aberrations described. Russwurm (1978) details: an albino where the black markings are silver-grey (ab *albomaculata* Rebel), and ab *charlotta* Haworth, where the silver spots on the base of the underside hindwings are joined into blocks.

PHENOGRAM: Yorkshire 1995-2003. Emphasises the limited population and the tendency of the species to wander.

DGF, N Yorkshire Moors.

CONSERVATION ISSUES: The Dark Green Fritillary can survive in cooler, wetter places than most other fritillaries. It prefers rich, lush violet growth in an 8 to 15cm sward. We still have much to learn about its needs. One of the difficulties about studying it is finding it! Most sightings appear to bear little relationship to where the butterfly might be breeding, and there are few areas where it can be reliably found from year to year. It seems probable that the species uses its mobility to travel around quite a large area and butterflies raised on one site may move away to breed on another. On the North Yorkshire Moors its survival appears to depend on a network of small colonies. The richer growth of violets it prefers is usually found in temporary stages of successional development and will only last a few years, therefore an ability to move on becomes essential. The butterfly appears to benefit from widened rides and clearings as well as rotational scrub clearance. It may temporarily benefit from clear felling where this produces a flush of violets, but commercial replanting will eventually shade out such sites and make them unsuitable again unless suitable rides and clearings are built into the planning. On grassland sites, overgrazing by rabbits or farm animals can damage violet growth and lead to site unsuitability. Light grazing can be of benefit. Winter management projects on sites known to harbour colonies should bear in mind the hibernating larvae hidden away in the leaf litter. Species Action Plans for the Dark Green Fritillary have been prepared by Butterfly Conservation for Biodiversity Action Plans in both our National Parks. The policy of widening rides in Forestry Commission woodlands (as at Allerthorpe Common VC61 and Yearsley Common VC62) could be especially beneficial to this species if it continues to expand.

DGF: female. Amount of green on the underwing can be variable.

Bill Smyllie

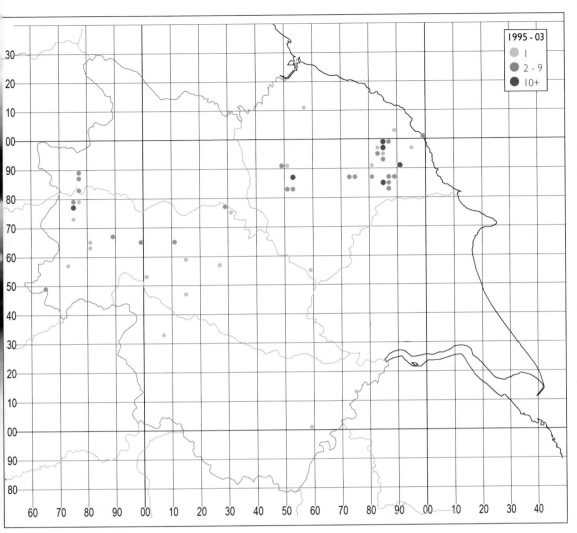

Dark Green Fritillary: Yorkshire Tetrad map 1995-2003

MAP NOTES 1995-2003: Noted in **50/3319 recorded tetrads (ie 1.5%), and out of 4120 tetrads in Yorkshire. Ranked 30th most widespread** out of 36 breeding species in the county. This butterfly is mainly found in those squares indicated by red or brown dots. It is a strong flyer and an inveterate wanderer, which probably accounts for the number of widely dispersed single sightings (yellow dots).

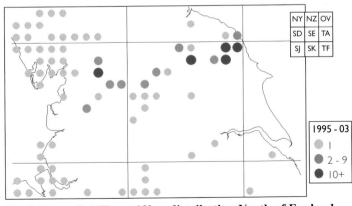

Dark Green Fritillary: 10km distribution North of England

⬤ = 1 or more records out of county 1995-1999

LIFE STORY

HABITAT: Uses a range of habitats containing violets, including flower-rich chalk or limestone grasslands, acidic bracken moorland, woodland rides and clearings, and even coastal dunes (but not in Yorkshire). The main foodplant is Common Dog-violet *Viola riviniana*, but other violet species are also used, including Marsh Violet *V. palustris* on wetter habitats. Tolerates cooler, damper conditions than many other fritillaries and prefers lush, strong-growing violets in a sward around 8 to 15cm with tree, shrub or bracken growth nearby.

DGF (left), Scar Close near Ingleborough (VC64).

Eggs laid singly on plants or litter in vicinity of foodplants. Larvae hatch after 2 to 3 weeks and go straight into hibernation in the leaf litter or grass tussocks. They become active again in the following spring and develop through 5 instars. Fully grown, they are dark, almost black, with lines of orange-brown dots along the sides. Pupation usually occurs late May/mid-Jun (in Yorkshire) and butterflies hatch out 3 to 4 weeks later. Males patrol over large areas in search of females, which tend to hide away in undergrowth where mating takes place. Butterflies may congregate to nectar in the early morning and evening, especially where patches of purple flowers like thistles and knapweeds occur. The species can be quite mobile with mark/recapture experiments recording movements up to 5km (Asher *et al* 2001). It is probable that clusters of smaller colonies (as in the N York Moors) function as a metapopulation. Yorkshire also produces

regular reports of single individuals seen long distances from nearest colonies. These are readily classified as *'dubious'* (ie possible misidentifications, unofficial introductions, or records based on incorrect map references). However, it is always possible that in ideal conditions the occasional wanderer makes a much longer journey than usual. It is also possible that there are as yet undiscovered colonies on some of our larger private estates or in little explored parts of the Pennines.

DGF, Ellerburn (VC62) 18/07/2004.

DGF on Knapweed, Scar Close (VC64)

HISTORICAL REVIEW:
Dark Green Fritillary
Argynnis aglaia (in Porritt 1883)

Although illustrated and described by Mouffet (1634) and Petiver (1717) no-one apparently gave it a name until Wilkes (1741-42) called it the **Darkned Green Fritillary**. Harris (1766) modified it to **Dark Green Fritillary** although some authors confusingly used **Silver-spotted Fritillary** around the turn of the 18th century, a name previously given to the High Brown Fritillary. The current Latin name derives from *Argynnus*, a lady loved by Agammemnon, whilst Aglaia was one of the Three Graces. There is probably a link in this choice between beautiful women and the silver 'pearls' on the underwing.

Rimington (1992) gives Yorkshire's earliest records: Wath-upon-Dearne (Anon 1832) and Sutton Common (Lankester 1842), both from the Doncaster area (VC63). Duncan 1844) summarised the national picture as: *a plentiful species in most parts of the country'*. Morris (1853) noted it: *'frequents heaths, woods, meadows and downs'*, and was found at Buttercrambe Moor (E of York VC62). Rimington indicates it was widespread in Lincs, Notts and Derbyshire until around the 1850s, but then declined, and except for reports from Barnsley (1871) and Maltby (c1875) [A Doncaster] the butterfly was not seen again near Doncaster until it appeared in Edlington Wood in 1917. Robson (1902) also considered it was becoming rare in Durham and Northumberland, having been recorded up to 1877, but with no recent records up to 1902. Porritt (1883) noted it was, *'Perhaps rarer'* than the Silver-washed Fritillary! He reported it from **VC61**: Flamborough Head, **VC62**: Scarborough, Whitby and York, **VC63**: Maltby, Sheffield, Pontefract and Wakefield, **VC64**: Selby. In 1904 he added: **VC62**: Helmsley, Ingleby Greenhow and Kirkbymoorside, **VC64**: Grassington. Fryer & Lucas (2001) could find no 19th century Huddersfield records. Garland (1981) re the Sheffield area, comments that it disappeared from Derbyshire some time after 1863, but was still present in Sherwood Forest (Notts) and in Wharncliffe, Maltby and Sheffield. However, few were seen in Sherwood Forest after 1890. Stainforth (1919) noted it had been recorded in the mid-19th century near Riplingham (S edge of the Wolds VC61).

The YNU Card File holds many 20th century records, indicating a similar but wider distribution to today, with an undefined presence on the Wolds (VC61) as well as colonies around Doncaster (VC63). Tetley (1915) presumably refers to the **VC61** Wolds when he writes about the Scarborough district: *'generally distributed on the moors and wolds and in the dales'*, ('dales' = valleys on the S edge of the Moors). Walsh (1956) may simply be echoing Tetley when he writes, *'Common near the head of most of the dales and in the Wold valleys'*. The only specific VC61 YNU Card File records are Filey 15/07/1922 in a cold NE gale [YNU visit], and *'common'* at Allerthorpe on 14/08/1922 [WJ Fordham]. The YNU 1967/70 Report also mentions a presence at Skipwith Common (VC61) in 1947.

VC62: Regularly found on patches of lowland heath from Buttercrambe (1941) through Sandburn (1957) to Strensall (1957) (last recorded years noted). A record from Hovingham in 1935 [YNU visit] may also indicate a past presence in the Howardian Hills (E of York) or a wanderer from the Moors. There were regular records from the Moors, the following being only a selection to illustrate similarity to today: Helmsley 1900 [Arthur Angel], Wykeham 1901 [YNU], Langdale End 1932 [Anon], Pickering 1933 [Arthur Smith], Hackness 1936 [Ivy Thomas], Hutton-le-Hole 1940 [E Dearing], Robin Hood's Bay 1945 [JM Brown], Haugh Rigg 1956 [E Ramsden], Ravenscar 1959 [LGF Waddington], Upper Rosedale & Gundale 1975 [AMR Heron], Ellerburn 1978 [BE Prater], Raindale 1978 [SM Jackson], Cropton Forest 1983 [Charles Critchley], Fen Bog 1984 [Mike Barnham], Appleton-le-Moor 1985 [SM Jackson], Ashberry Pastures 1987 [AMR Heron], Harwood Dale 1991 [Athol Wallis], and Bridestones NR 1993 [SM Jackson].

VC63: the species reappeared at Edlington Wood in 1917 and was recorded at Maltby in 1918. Rimington (1992) indicates it was not uncommon in the Doncaster area between the 1920s and 1960s, but then largely disappeared again. He lists Edlington and Wadworth Woods, Sandall Beat, Wheatley Wood, Little Smeaton, Bessacarr, Wentbridge, Crowle, Hatfield and Thorne Moors, and Wroot as sites of records in this period. After 1960 only odd sightings have been reported, including Anston Stones 1982 [JS Griffiths], Thorne Moors 1983, Crowle Moors 1984 [both Martin Limbert et al]. Elsewhere in VC63 it has occurred at Woolley (nr Wakefield) in 1946 [YNU], Buttershaw (Bradford) 1949 [R Overend], The Strines (S of Penistone) on 07/07, 14/07 and 24/07/1959 [IG Brown], Copley 1967 [per BD Cain], Rotherham 1975 [WL Barringer], and near Halifax in 1988 [BD Cain].

VC64: Records have been sporadic throughout 20th century with reports in the YNU Card File (or as given) from: Grassington before 1904, [F Booth], Hook Moor (Aberford E of Leeds) 1939 [JH Flint], Ledsham 03/07/47 [3 males in Horbury School collection/Leeds Museum ascribed to H Eddison and notified to us via J Dickinson], Lindley Wood (Washburndale, N of Otley) 1950 [CR Haxby & J Briggs], *'abundant'* at Walkingham Warren (N of Knaresborough) 1951 [CR Haxby & DM Jesper], Walkingham Hill (Copgrove, N of Knaresborough) 1953-1958 [CR Haxby et al], and Farnham, Knaresborough 1959 [W Beck]. Barnham & Foggitt (1987) note that it was common around Knaresborough in the early 1950s but then disappeared, with last sightings at Walkingham Warren 1957, Farnham Mires 1959, and Goldsborough Woods 1960. It began to reappear in the far west of the Harrogate Naturalists' recording area in 1984 when it was seen near Roundhill Reservoir; at Greenhow Quarry (W of Pateley Bridge); and on Braithwaite Moor to the SE of Greenhow. Scattered reports have continued since, but it is unclear as to whether source colonies around Harrogate are being overlooked, or sightings represent wanderers or even temporary colonisation, perhaps from colonies to the west. Surprisingly, there are no historic records from **VC65**, even though it is found in Durham and Northumberland, and further north into Scotland. However, a recent presence has been discovered in the far south west of VC65 close to other colonies found in VC64.

Sean A Clough

Drax Power Station (most easterly point of VC64), and home to Speckled Woods around the perimeter.

UK BAP Status: *Not listed.*
BC Priorities: National: *Low.*
N of England: *Low.* Yorkshire: *Low.*
European Status: *Not threatened.*

WORLD STATUS: Resident 0-2500m, 2 or 3 overlapping broods (Feb/Oct). Range: common and widespread N Africa to C Norway and across Asia to Urals, expanding northward in Europe. Discontinuous range in Britain, with southern population subspecies *tircis* (Godart 1821) extending to an expanding northern front: Cumbria to E Yorkshire, and separate populations in N Scotland (subspecies *oblita* Harrison 1949). Also present in Ireland.

Speckled Wood

YORKSHIRE STATUS 1995/2003:

Very mobile, rapidly expanding resident: 2 or 3 overlapping broods (April/Oct) with peaks usually May and June, Jul/Aug/Sept and Sept/Oct. **Earliest:** 23/03/2002, Brockadale YWT NR (VC63) [Ralph Hibbert & Chris Parkin]; **latest:** 30/10/2001, Wombwell [Dean Stables]. Rimington (1992) notes an even later record from Sprotborough (VC63) on 25/11/1986. Highest reported counts: **440** Hollins Wood (nr Barnsley VC63) 31/08/2003 [Ralph Hibbert & Chris Parkin]; **255** York Cemetery NR (VC62) 17/08/2003 [Pat & Jim Bone]. Yorkshire site counts more usually in the 10 to 40 range. The species was more common and widespread in Yorkshire in mid-19th century but crashed in late 19th century. Re-expansion began in 1920s, reached Yorkshire in 1940s and continues today.

Original thrust appeared confined to Magnesian Limestone ridge, but this no longer true. More recently it was assumed the species was moving eastward and westward from populations established on the ridge. The latest patterns of movement also suggest a series of five northward salients, which may not be inhibited by height and may or may not be combined with east/west movements:

1) West of the Pennines with sightings at Mewith Head (VC64) 22/09/2002 [Stephen Sutton], Settle (VC64) 10/09/2002 [Robert Starling], and Ingleton 06/09/2003 [Roger Neale] (probably originating from colonies recently established in the Lower Lune Valleys);

2) East of Pennines (possibly originating in part from long surviving colonies in S Yorkshire and in part from casual introductions of stock obtained from the south). This salient runs from Sheffield and Doncaster areas (VC63) and reached Tadcaster and Boston Spa (VC64) in 1989, Goldsborough Woods, W of Harrogate (VC64) in 1995 [Mike Barnham], Hutton Conyers (nr Ripon VC65) in 2000 [Charles Fletcher] and onwards beyond Yorkshire but in the same N/S line of 10km squares to Darlington and Winlaton (nr Gateshead VC66) in 2003 [Ken Dawson]. The species also appears to be moving westward from the main population into Pennine valleys, although it could also be heading directly north over higher land through Huddersfield, Shipley, Bingley and into middle Wharfedale reaching Grass Wood in 2002 [Tony Vittery] and Pateley Bridge in 2003

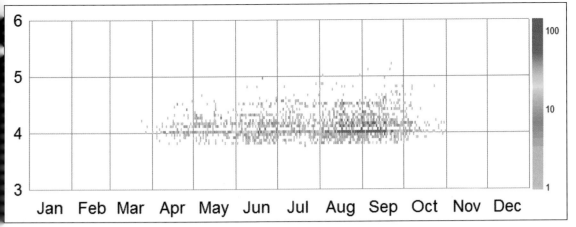

6

5

4

3

Jan Feb Mar Apr May Jun Jul Aug Sep Oct Nov Dec

100

10

1

PHENOGRAM: Yorkshire 1995-2003. Shows the strength of the population in the south of the county, and a tendency for more northerly records to occur in autumn.

ID NOTES: Medium-sized chocolate brown butterfly with pale yellow or cream blotches, single small eyespots on upper forewings, and 3 or 4 pupilled spots towards lower edges of upper hindwings. Female slightly larger with stronger markings. Overwintered pupae produce butterflies with larger, paler, yellow patches than overwintered larvae, although latter are usually bigger in size. Broods 2 and 3 tend to be darker than 1. Males very territorial and often perch on low branches in sunny parts of dappled shade habitats. Very likely to fly up and inspect any passing humans. Quite variable with over 30 described aberrations. Rarely, the pale yellow spotting may be replaced by a fulvous orange (ab *intermediana* Lempke), or be paler (ab *pallida* Tutt). Inexperienced observers might find initial confusion with Meadow Brown and Ringlet both of which occur in woodlands, but with practice, the overall pattern of spots and blotches is quite distinctive.

CONSERVATION ISSUES: The Speckled Wood is a very mobile butterfly able to utilise some of the shadiest deciduous woodland situations of any butterfly, as long as small patches of sunlight can percolate through to the edges of rides or tracks. It has the ability to spread through its own efforts and, climate allowing, should be able to expand throughout the county over the coming years. Such a natural expansion is fascinating to observe and should not be confused by casual introductions

[Howard & Christine Frost]. J Dale recorded the highest reported sighting from Lindley Moor (W of Harrogate VC64) at around 280m (850ft) in 2002.

3) Vale of York west: from Thorne Moors (VC63) through the Selby area (VC64) to Skipwith Common YWT NR (VC61), Acomb and Askham Bog (VC64) in 2002 [M Hammond] and York Cemetery NR (VC62) where 38 were recorded on 01/09/2002 and over 200 in 2003 [Pat & Jim Bone] (see above).

4) Vale of York east. This seems to have resulted from a surge through W Lincolnshire in 1999/2000 leading to a first record at Blacktoft Sands RSPB NR (VC63) in 2002 and a general occupation of tracks and copses in open countryside in the area of VC61 between Market Weighton, Bubwith and Goole.

5) East coast: East of the Wolds the Humber Estuary (40 miles from Goole to Spurn and 1 to 9 miles wide) may have been a barrier to northward movements until populations built up sufficiently in Lincolnshire. Occasional E Yorkshire sightings have been made since 1982. After the establishment of a small colony at Spurn (VC61) in 2000, coastal sightings have increased, with reports from Holmpton [Frank Josephs] and Withernsea [Martyn Johnson] in 2000, Aldbrough [Adrian Johnson], Hornsea [Joan Tottle] and Filey Brigg [Filey Brigg Ornithological Group] in 2001, as well as Flamborough Head in 2003 [Ian Marshall]. 2003 saw this coastal salient extend into VC62 with records from Staintondale, Whitby and as far north as Errington Woods (E of Middlesbrough) [Ian Miles].

Records have also increased around Hull and in Holderness (VC61) with first reports from Tophill Low NR in 2003. 2002 saw 102 tetrads added to the cumulative 1995/2001 county total of 201 tetrads recorded. Some private introductions have taken place eg Scabba Wood (VC63/SE50) in 1978 (Rimington 1986), and probably in E Yorkshire in the 1980s/90s but these seem to have been largely overtaken by events, with the natural expansion rapidly nullifying the effects of any introductions.

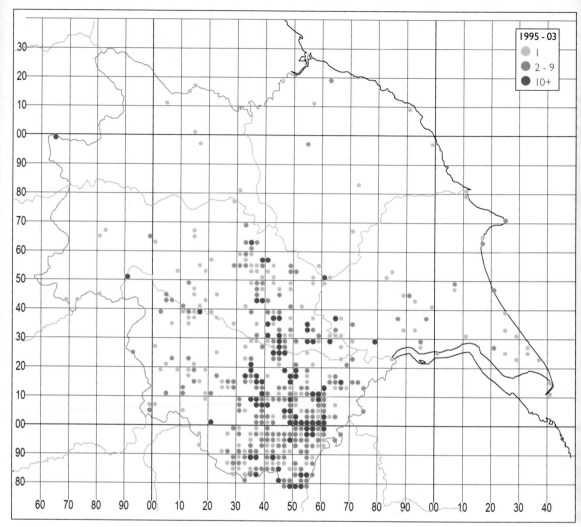

Speckled Wood: Yorkshire Tetrad map 1995-2003

MAP NOTES 1995-2003: Noted in **451/3319** recorded tetrads (ie 13.6%), and out of 4120 tetrads in Yorkshire. **Ranked 21st most widespread out of 36** breeding species in the county. A fast expanding species formerly confined to the southern edge of the county but now spreading steadily north especially in the Vale of York. It has been slow to cross the Humber Estuary from Lincolnshire in any numbers, but having done so recently is now racing up the east coast. The spread through Lincolnshire's open countryside also appears to have been slow and may account for the equally slow spread onto the Yorkshire Wolds.

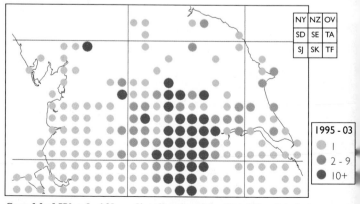

Speckled Wood: 10km distribution North of England

◔ = 1 or more records out of county 1995-1999

LIFE STORY

Brian Bull

Speckled Wood on rotten pear.

HABITAT: A species mainly associated with dappled shade in woodland or along lanes and tracks with high hedges. Also found in urban areas (parks, gardens, cemeteries, old rail tracks etc). Uses woodland or allied habitats where 40% to 90% of light is excluded (Thomas & Lewington 1991). Lays eggs on a wide range of grasses. Present in many of the larger woodlands within its range and also on the wetland heath of Thorne Moors (VC63), along shadier parts of old peat tramway banks. Found at the tip of Spurn Peninsula (VC61) in sand dunes with tall growth of Sea Buckthorn *Hippophaë rhamnoides* and Elder *Sambucus nigra*. In the frontal colonisation zone to the immediate west of the Yorkshire Wolds (VCs61/63/64: Goole, Selby, Market Weighton), where fields are wide and open, and woodlands few, the species is widely established along farm tracks, lanes and disused railway tracks where often short lengths of high hedge (as little as 50m in length) provide the shade. Banks of brambles are also a feature common to many of these sites.

Quite complex! Pale eggs laid singly on the underside of many species of grass blades, especially False Brome *Brachypodium sylvaticum*, Cock's-foot *Dactylis glomerata*, Yorkshire Fog *Holcus lanatus* and Common Couch *Elytrigia repens*. Sunny areas used in spring and autumn, but shadier sites in summer. Can spend winter in pupal or larval stages. In addition development is highly sensitive to temperature and may vary from site to site. Yellow-striped green larvae continue

feeding on and off through winter whenever temperature rises above 6°C (Lees 1962). Pupal stages vary from as little as 10 days in summer to several months (Oct to Apr/May) through winter. 1st brood in Yorkshire often has two distinct peaks resulting from different growth speeds of overwintered larvae and pupae. Cool weather in Jun, as in 1997 and 1998, can effectively separate these two peaks by inhibiting the emergence of the 2nd spring flight and extending its period into early Jul. This also has the effect of producing a later than usual peak emergence in Aug/Sept. A partial 3rd brood may occur in Oct/Nov. A proportion of males (often those with 4 upper hindwing spots, are territorial, perching on sunlit vegetation about 1m from the ground, watching for passing females and defending against patrolling males. Other males, (often the 3-spotted variety, and especially those from the summer brood) patrol through their breeding area searching for females (Shreeve 1986). Christine Frost (1996) described some intriguing behaviour observed in France (presumably between two males) where one attacked the other. *'One butterfly suddenly keeled over and lay flat on a leaf about 2m off the ground, appearing to be dead. The second landed beside it and vigorously pushed at the first with its antennae until it knocked it off the leaf. The falling butterfly spun like a dead leaf and landed gently but still flat on another leaf about a metre down and a metre off the ground. It lay seemingly dead for about 20 seconds during which period its rival flew off. Then the first butterfly suddenly jerked upright and flew off.'* A similar incident of 'playing dead' is recorded in the accompanying photograph, although this time at ground level and apparently between a male and female.

Females spend much time high in the canopy of trees except when egg laying. Males and females also feed high up on honeydew, although if this is unavailable they will nectar on flowers and also feed on fruit. Brian Bull, and Howard & Christine Frost (pers comm.) have observed the butterfly feeding on blackberries, and Brian Bull has had them feeding on pears in his Cheshire garden over several years (see photo). The butterfly also roosts in trees or shrubs.

Intriguing behaviour: worth watching out for! Butterfly on L appears to be a male (darker) courting a female (R). But seconds later female keeled over and looked dead, staying so until male flew off, but not before male tried to push her up with his antennae! Was she saying, 'No'?

HISTORICAL REVIEW:
Speckled Wood
Formerly: *Satyrus aegeria*
(as in Porritt 1883)

First named the **Enfield Eye** by Petiver (1704), who thought it uncommon. Wilkes (1747-49) called it the **Wood Argus** whilst Harris (1766) introduced **Speckled Wood**. Both names circulated into the early part of the 20th century. *Pararge* means 'close to the genus *Arge*'. *Aegeria* or Egeria is the name of a nymph known for telling prophecies in ancient Italy.

Before 1850, the butterfly was probably continuously distributed from S England to NW Scotland, and found widely in Yorkshire. Morris (1853) considered it, *'a common species in all parts of the country, from the extreme north to the extreme south'*. Porritt (1883) mentions: **VC62**-Scarborough, **VC63**-Doncaster, Huddersfield, Pontefract, Sheffield and Wakefield, and **VC64**-Bramham and York. Stainforth (1919) lists mid-19th century records from the Hull area (Birkhill Wood, Riplingham and Gilberdike, all VC61). A widespread but gradual decline set in around 1860 (a notably cold year) becoming more obvious towards the end of the century, probably in response to the 1879/1895 cold period. By the early 1900s, the bulk of the population appears to have become largely restricted to lowland Wales, SW England, Wiltshire, Dorset and W Sussex (Thomas & Lewington 1991), plus a significant but isolated remnant in NW Scotland and surviving patches (or temporary re-colonisations?) in N England [eg in Northumberland & Durham no records since before c1850 according to Robson (1902), but 7 sites around 1904, (which were not recorded later), are noted by Dunn & Parrack (1986)].

Porritt's 1883 list needs to be treated warily as he uses records collected over 40/50yrs but gives few dates. The earliest dated record is from the anonymous Wath-upon-Dearne (VC63) list of 1832 (Rimington 1992). Porritt notes an 1842 York area record reported by Robert Cook.

Rimington gives Adwick (VC63) in 1846 [JW Dunning]. Fryer & Lucas (2001) note early records for the Huddersfield (VC63) area: Honley (Hobkirk 1859,1868) and Almondbury [James Varley who recorded between c1855 and 1870]. Rimington notes that the species was still present at the Doncaster area (VC63) sites of Edlington Wood c1880, Maltby Wood c1884 and Roche Abbey c1896, whilst Wentbridge was the only known Yorkshire site to have carried on right through from the 19th century until 1970. Garland (1981) gives Sheffield area (VC63) records from Carlton-in-Lindrick in 1881 and Hemsworth (Barnsley) in 1882. Porritt (1904) adds his own record from Sledmere (VC61 c140m high in the N Wolds), presumably made between 1883 and 1904. His 1907 list continues to give sites dating back to 1842! It indicates the species was *'common'* at Sledmere. Further confusion is provided by Walsh (1956) whose Scarborough area summary notes: *'Very local; Scarborough, but not seen for many years; abundant in suitable seasons at Pickering'*. The Scarborough presence was actually recorded by Thomas Wilkinson prior to his death in 1876, and the Pickering comment was gleaned from an 1886 YNU excursion circular! Tetley (1915), who worked the Scarborough and Pickering areas from about c1902, specifically noted he had failed to find this species.

Nationally, the Speckled Wood recovery got underway around 1920, but evidence of any expansion in Yorkshire did not occur until the 1940s/50s when a period of warm years (1943/50) may have been the trigger. The species was noted in VC63 at Castleford (1946), Lindrick (1947) and regularly at Wentbridge. In the 1950s it showed clear signs of heading north again with VC64 records at Barwick in Elmet (nr Leeds) in 1957, Bishop Wood (nr Selby) in 1959, and East Rigton near Wetherby in 1960 (YNU 1967/70). Then came a temporary retraction in the early 1970s when the species was even lost from Wentbridge (VC63), but may have held on at nearby Owston Wood where it was discovered by P Seccombe in 1975 (Rimington 1992). Following a notably warm 1975 further increases were noted in VC63 (Sutton & Beaumont 1989), whilst the movement north through VC64 gathered momentum reaching Wetherby, Ripon Parks, Goldsborough and Ribstone Woods (nr Harrogate) in the early 1990s (Barnham *et al* 1993). Since then it has spread widely in this area and moved further north into the eastern edges of VC65.

The increase in range from 1976 is ascribed to climate warming despite a concurrent diminution in suitable habitat (Warren *et al* 2001, Hill *et al* 1999, 2002). Past observers have looked for reasons to explain the Speckled Wood's apparent preference for the Magnesian Limestone ridge in Yorkshire. An examination of the expansion maps covering the whole of the 20th century in Asher *et al* (2001) indicate a north-east facing frontal zone in 1970/82 with the bulk of the population SW of a line from the Thames to N Wales. Northward expansion on the western half of Britain has, therefore, been from a more developed population source than on the east where, until more recently, populations were very thinly spread. The butterfly also seems more likely to thrive in damper conditions of the kind found towards the west. This may relate to the fact that larvae continue to develop in winter when temperatures are above 6°C, but may suffer in the colder conditions more likely to be found in the east. Whatever the case, the situation is now changing with a steady build-up of populations on the eastern half of Britain.

Terry Whitaker

View W on new set-back Humber North Bank at Paull (nr Hull VC61). Thorngumbald lighthouses visible on old bank, now breached. Walls moved onto new bank when completed in 2003.

UK BAP Status: *Not listed.*
BC Priorities: National: *Low (to medium).*
N of Eng: *Low.* Yorkshire: *Low.*
European Status: *Not threatened.*

WORLD STATUS: Resident, 0-3000m: 2 or 3 generations depending on locality/ altitude/ weather, (April/Oct). Range: N Africa and Middle East to S Scotland, S Scandinavia (but not N Denmark), S Lithuania and S Latvia into Russia. Widespread throughout England and Wales, but absent or scarce in higher regions of Wales, Pennines and Lake District. Distribution becomes more coastal north of Yorkshire, with northern limit fluctuating considerably over the years. Very localised distribution in Ireland, mainly around coasts. Recent years have seen a marked decline in C & S England and N Ireland, coupled with slight increase in Yorkshire and N of England.

Wall

YORKSHIRE STATUS 1995/2003:

Resident: with a widespread but fairly localised distribution through much of the county, though apparently largely absent from high ground to the NW (the Dales) and on the N York Moors. It has a bias towards the southern half of Yorkshire, and towards coastal areas, but including a strong population in the Vale of York, extending northwards well north of York and eastward into the Hambleton and Howardian Hills. Annual numbers fluctuate considerably with recent years showing an extension of range into new areas of the Pennines VCs 63 & 64. It has successfully adapted to urban environments and can also be found along the field margins in areas of lowland arable agriculture. Although it has a definite preference for warm, dry habitats, it is increasingly being recorded from exposed sites at high altitudes in the west and north of the county, eg nr Holme (c300m VC63/SE10), Greenhow (c400m VC64/SE16) and Whitcliffe Scar, west of Richmond (290m VC65/NZ10).

There are normally two broods (May/June and Aug/Sept) and sometimes what appears to be a partial 3rd generation in Oct. Last sightings 1996/2003 (12/10, 19/10, 06/10, 28/10, 17/10, 02/10, 19/10, 12/11) suggest a regular trend in the direction of a 3rd generation. **Earlier than usual** first brood sightings have also been noted, including one on 18/04/1999 at Burton Leonard VC64 [Leonard Ratliffe]. The same year produced an exceptionally **late sighting** on 28/10 at Easby Abbey VC65 [Tim Helps] although not as late as in 2003 when one was seen at Cudworth (VC63) on 12/11 [Ralph Hibbert & Chris Parkin]. By contrast, in a poor spring, the Wall may not appear until June, as in 1955, when Pollard (1956) noted: *'In the Scarborough area, the late spring, marked as it was by recurring spells of cold and wet weather, had a marked effect on the successful spring emergence of insects and even our common species were remarkably scarce in early summer'* with the Wall *'not recorded until 01/06 and then only in small numbers.'* And more recently, in 1996, the earliest recorded sightings were from 02/06 in VCs 61 & 62 and 06/06 in VC63. Since 1995, maximum site counts have occurred in: **VC61**: **51** at Holme-on-Spalding Moor on 18/08/1996 [John Killingbeck], an estimated **200** daily from 15/08 to 21/08/2000 at Spurn NNR (which covers parts of 14x1km squares) [Barry Spence]. **VC62: c100** on 12/08/2000 at South Gare [Peter Waterton]. **VC63: 22** at Royston VC63 on 14/08/1999 [Roy Bedford], **73**

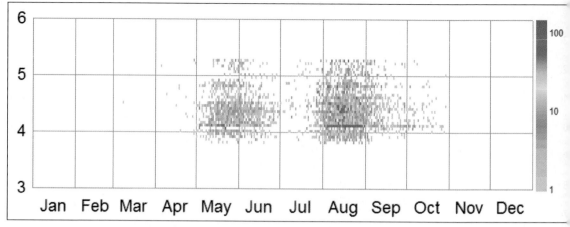

PHENOGRAM: Yorkshire 1995-2003. Clearly shows two broods and a hint of a partial third brood in Oct.

ID NOTES: An orange/brown butterfly with blackish/brown markings and white-pupilled eye-spots. Males have a dark brown band of scent scales on upper forewings; females slightly larger with more rounded wings. A very active species in sunshine: can superficially resemble a fritillary or a Comma but often with more of a darting, zig-zag flight. They are restless butterflies, which do not sit for long, but males usually remain within territories, which can be guarded aggressively. The writer recently observed a male driving off a much larger Peacock, which had intruded into its territory. To warm up, Walls bask on stone walls, pathways, banks and bare ground. By learning the type of places they favour in any given area you can predict where they are likely to be basking and find them when their presence is not altogether obvious. May be seen for 12 hours or more in the day when conditions favourable, having been noted on the wing in Yorkshire from as early as 08.10hrs, until well into the evening, when it can be seen with outspread wings on west-facing walls, absorbing the last rays of warmth. Over 40 variations described, affecting ground colour (golden brown to pale straw, white or even transparent), patterning, and eye-spots, which may be absent, altered in shape or multiplied.

nr Doncaster on 12/08/2000 [Ken Woolley]. **VC64: 20** at Rawdon on 13/08/1999 [Derek Parkinson]. **VC65: 10** near Bolton-on-Swale on 25/08/2000 [Arnold Robson].

Nick Lawman

Above: Wall aberration, Ellerburn VC62, 16/08/1992. Right: Wall resting on a clay bank at Spurn (VC61) 31/09/1982. Note attractive patterning which also serves as disguise.

CONSERVATION ISSUES: At the beginning of the 21st century, there is evidence to suggest that the Wall is extending its range in the county, and although its numbers fluctuate considerably from year to year and even from site to site, it does not seem to have suffered the marked decline that has occurred in parts of the south of England. The reasons behind its variable status are not entirely clear: the species deserves more study. Its continuing survival would seem to be linked to an ability to travel and to adapt to a wide variety of man-made habitats, as well as a need for suitable climatic conditions, which satisfy its love of dryness and warmth, but perhaps balanced with enough rain to promote good growth of suitable grasses. (The notably wet years of 2001 and 2002 were still quite good for this species.) Whilst the Wall doesn't currently appear to need our special help, conservation managers should remember the importance of sheltered, sun-facing, bare patches, stones, walls and rabbit grazing, in the life of this species. Between 2004 and 2006 Butterfly Conservation will be co-supervising an investigation into the ecological needs of this species.

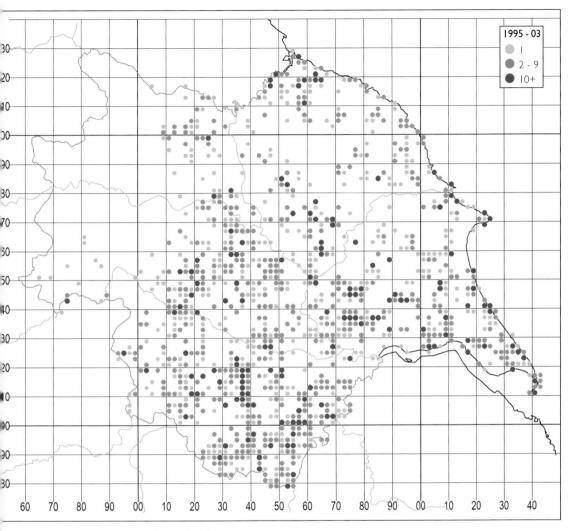

Wall: Yorkshire Tetrad map 1995-2003

Legend (top right of map):

1995 - 03
- 1
- 2 - 9
- 10+

MAP NOTES 1995-2003: Noted in 1084/3319 recorded tetrads (ie 32.7%), and out of 4120 tetrads in Yorkshire. Ranked 12ᵗʰ most widespread out of 36 breeding species in the county. Bearing in mind that this species has suffered a major crash over large parts of southern England in recent years, our own populations seem to be doing very well, with a 19% increase by 10km squares on the 1970-1982 Survey (Heath *et al* 1984). Populations are strongest in lowland areas with notable gaps in the NW Pennines (the Dales) and higher parts of the N York Moors. The 10km map is thought to give the better idea of the Wall's real distribution.

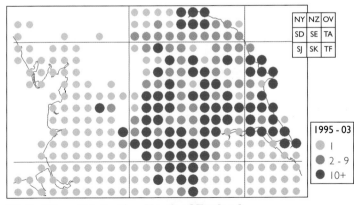

Wall: 10km distribution North of England

⬤ = 1 or more records out of county 1995-1999

Legend (right of map):

NY	NZ	OV
SD	SE	TA
SJ	SK	TF

1995 - 03
- 1
- 2 - 9
- 10+

LIFE STORY

HABITAT: Recent records have been received from gardens, allotments, cemeteries, field headlands, woodland clearings, moorland, commons, meadows, quarries, roadside verges, wasteland, a builder's yard, and the sides of ponds, rivers, canals and lakes. The butterfly shows a distinct preference for open, unimproved grassland, hedge banks and lanes, with rabbit holes, exposed stones and bare ground, particularly in coastal districts. It is one of the few butterflies which may also be found in small to medium numbers in prairie landscapes (eg in Holderness and the Vale of York VC61) where it utilises sheltered tractor 'tramways' for basking, whilst roadside verges and the growing number of conservation headlands provide potential egg-laying habitat. It is probable that the Wall's presence in arable farming areas is generally overlooked, as such habitats do not attract observers. Recent studies (Oates *et al* 2000) in Hampshire suggest larvae need an essential mix of fine grasses in early life and coarse grasses later.

Wall illustrating the reason for its name! This is Warren Cottage wall, part of Spurn Bird Observatory (VC61).

Light green eggs are attached, usually singly, to the leaf tips, stems and exposed roots of a variety of grasses including, Tor-grass *Brachypodium pinnatum*, False Brome *B.sylvaticum*, Sheep's Fescue *Festuca ovina*, Yorkshire Fog *Holcus lanatus*, Wavy Hair Grass *Deschampsia flexuosa*, Cocksfoot *Dactylis glomerata*, Annual Meadow Grass *Poa annua*, Common Bent *Agrostis capillaris*, and Black Bent *A gigantea*. Roots protruding through bank overhangs or rabbit holes are especially favoured by 2nd brood

females. The eggs become translucent after 2 to 3 days and hatch in about 10 days. On emergence, the hairy, yellow-brown larvae eat their eggshells then feed mainly at night. They turn green at the second instar, and bluish green with pale stripes at the 4th (and final) instar, when they also feed by day and may wander between plants. First brood larvae take about a month to develop whilst most of the second brood hibernate over the winter and commence feeding again in spring. Pupae vary from pale green to almost black and hang on, or nearby, typical foodplants. The pupal stage normally lasts 2 to 3 weeks, but it is thought that some second brood larvae pupate before winter and remain in this stage for 7 months. In mild winters some larvae may continue feeding during the winter, and pupate in March to produce the occasional early butterflies observed in April.

First generation butterflies more usually appear in May/June, with the second generation in Aug/Sept. In good years the second generation may begin in July and when this happens, it is more likely that, given suitable autumn weather, there will be a partial third generation in late Sept/Oct. Walls need warm, dry, habitats to help maintain a 25°/30°C body temperature, and are extremely vulnerable to weather. A proportion of Walls seem to be wanderers, giving them the ability to colonise new areas some distance from their areas of origin. Although not generally considered migratory, EB Ford (1975) draws attention to two records of their being seen on the Outer Dowsing Light Vessel, 30 miles off the Norfolk coast, perhaps having been blown that way accidentally. The Wall has also been known to 'hilltop', ie to gather on a prominent hillside in order to find a mate.

Wall using tractor tracks in open field situation.

HISTORICAL REVIEW:
Wall *Satyrus megaera* in Porritt (1883)

Illustrated by Mouffet in 1634, and described by Petiver (1699) as **'the golden marbled Butterfly with the black Eyes'**, and later (1717) as the **London Eye**. Other 18th century names included the **Great Argus Butterfly** (Berkenhout 1769), and the **Orange Argus** (Lewin 1795). Harris (1766) called it the **Wall** and most subsequent authors followed, except for Samouelle (1819), who (confusingly for us) called it the **Gatekeeper**, a name also used by Morris (1853). From Kirby (1896) onward it was generally accepted as the **Wall Brown**. The current Latin name *Lasiommata* means 'hairy eyes', and Megaera was one of the Furies who tormented people who had done wrong by following them hither and thither, the parallel being in the restless movement of the butterfly.

Prior to 1860 it is probable the species was fairly widespread although there are few records from this time. Duncan (1844) commented it was *'far from being a scarce species'* and was *'apparently found in all parts of the country'*. Rimington (1992) notes records from Wath-upon-Dearne (VC63/SE40) (Anon 1832), and Doncaster (VC63/SE50) in the mid-1830s (Morris 1853). Fryer & Lucas (2001) quote a reference from Hobkirk (1859): *'has occurred in Honley'* (Huddersfield area VC63/SE11). Robson (1902) noted it *'was until 1861 generally distributed throughout'* Northumberland and Durham. *'When I commenced to collect, it was much the most abundant butterfly of the district; but in 1861 the first brood never appeared; in the autumn I saw a solitary specimen, and since then I have never seen it hereabouts. The years 1861-2-3 were particularly disastrous seasons for Lepidoptera, and though this species appeared to survive in a few places for some years longer, I fear it has now totally disappeared.'* Up to 1860 it was probably also present as far north as Aberdeen on the E side of Britain. Then around 1860 it virtually disappeared north of Yorkshire and became locally quite scarce or absent from much of the county, especially in northern and western areas. Porritt (1883),

summarising some 50yrs, mentioned sites in **VC61:** Flamborough Head and Goole; **VC62:** Scarborough, Scalby Mills and Whitby; **VC63:** Doncaster, Sheffield, Wakefield, Pontefract, Huddersfield (*'formerly'*), Hunslet (Leeds) (*'rather scarce'*) and Gledhow (Leeds) (*'formerly'*); **VC64:** Bishop's Wood (nr Selby), and Pannal nr Harrogate. He also mentions an 1842 York record.

Filler & Smith (1979) note the Wall's absence from an 1879 list for Askham Bog (York VC64/SE54), whereas it does figure in the 1979 site list. However, the species was reported to *'frequent lanes, banks and walls in May and August'* at Great Ayton (VC62/NZ51) in the late 1800s (Lofthouse 1899), and by 1907 Porritt had revised his comment to: *'Widely distributed and in some places abundant'*. However, Stainforth (1919) makes no mention of the Wall from the Hull area, although Porritt (1922) is able to quote *'occasional'*, citing a record from Sutton Bank (Hull VC61/TA13). Rimington (1992) could find only one report for the Doncaster VC63 area between 1899 and 1928, namely from Wentbridge (SE41) in 1918. Fryer & Lucas (2001) noted an absence of more than 70yrs in the Huddersfield VC63 area, from a report at Hipperholme (SE12) in 1868 to a report from Elland (SE12) in 1944 followed by a spread in the late 1950s/1960s. Walsh (1952) suggests the species, though once 'abundant' at Pickering (SE78/88) in the earlier 1800s was not noted in Theakston's Guide (1871) and didn't reappear until May 1945, near Cayton (VC61/TA08). It seems likely that the Wall in Yorkshire crashed in the 1860s, was further affected by the 1879/1895 cold period, but began to recover in some areas in the early 1900s before falling back again until the 1940s.

In 1947 it was recorded from Pilmoor nr York (VC62/SE47) as late as 26/10 [Joyce Payne & J P Utley], and in 1951 was described as *'plentiful'* at Spurn (Michaelis 1951). Hewson (1958) stated it was common west of Hull (VC61) in 1957 and *'is found all round the Knaresborough* [VC64] *district, but only in ones and twos'*. It was also *'fairly common at Wakefield'* with further reports from Selby, and Pannal (nr Harrogate) both VC64. By 1959 the species was stated to be *'prolific'* at Wath-upon-Dearne (VC63/SE40), with *'a partial 3rd brood in Sept'*, and also *'quite common'* on Cliffe Common (east of Selby) (VC61/SE63) on 10/10/1959. Records indicate that during the 1960s, the Wall increased in abundance in contrast to a reported decline for most other species. The YNU Lepidoptera Report for 1960 (Hewson 1961), stated: *'The majority of our butterflies have been noticeably fewer, two species only, Wall and Red Admiral, appear to have been abundant'*. Joyce Payne noted, *'The Wall was the butterfly most in evidence'* on a YNU excursion to Fairburn Ings (VC64/SE42) on 13/08/1960. Smith (1966) re the Teesmouth area VC62, stated: *'The Wall has had the rare distinction of becoming more abundant in recent years than it used to be: most other species of butterfly have declined in numbers'*. The YNU 1967/70 Report noted: *'This species has shown a marked increase in recent years, its present localities being too numerous to mention. In the environs of large cities and towns of the West Riding it occurs regularly. Within the Bradford boundary it was recently observed at 1,100ft, an unprecedented occurrence'*.

During the remaining decades of the 20th century, the Wall population seemed to be constantly fluctuating with marked variations from year to year and even from site to site in the same year. 1982 and 1984 were good years whilst summers from 1985 to 1988 were poor and seem to have contributed to a major population crash in the S of England. There are few records from VC65, although sightings of 6 in Clapgate Gill, near Marske (VC65/NZ10) on 21/08/1989, and 3 near Downholme (VC65/SE19) on 01/09/1991, raise questions as to whether they indicate under-recording or range expansion. During the 1990s the Wall was regarded as a common species over much of the county.

Arnold Robson

1620 MARBLED WHITE *Melanargia galathea* (Linnaeus 1758)
Family: Nymphalidae, sub-group Satyrinae ('the Browns').

Kiplingcotes Quarry YWT NR, May 2003.

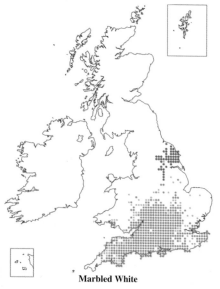

Marbled Whites: mating pair, Cowlam (VC61) 2004.

Marbled White

UK BAP: Status: *Not listed.*
BC Priorities: National: *Low.*
N of England: *Low.* Yorkshire: *Uncertain.*

YORKSHIRE STATUS 1995/2003:

Fairly localised, currently expanding, resident: one generation (June-Aug); mainly, (but not exclusively) associated with flower-rich chalk and limestone grasslands, particularly on the Wolds (VC61) where it was recorded in well over 70 tetrads (in 14x10km squares) during the 1995/2003 Survey Period. This represents a considerable increase on the 1970/82 Survey, which found the species in only 3x10km Wolds squares, and a 1982 survey reported in Rafe & Jefferson (1983) which discovered a presence in five N Wolds 10km squares covering three areas: Thixendale/Wharram, Cowlam/Cottam and Langtoft/Crakedale. In addition, recent sightings on the N York Moors suggest low-density colonisation in two 10km squares and wanderers or marginal colonisation in 6 others. The most northerly record in our Survey was from the Goathland area (VC62/NZ80) some 10km further north than any previous records.

In addition, a number of private re-introduction projects have successfully re-established the species to Magnesian Limestone sites in S Yorkshire, where it died out in the late 1800s. Regular records seem to indicate core populations in 7 tetrads, with sightings in many others presumed to represent wanders or casual releases. A wide scatter of sightings along the Magnesian Limestone ridge (approximately following the route of the A1) as far north as the Harrogate area is thought to have resulted from further releases, although the possibility of some 'natural' northward spread from

WORLD STATUS: Resident: one brood (Jun/Aug). Range: N Spain to N Britain and eastward through central and southern Europe into temperate Asia. Also present in NW Africa, but not Scandinavia, although in recent times it has apparently spread into the Baltic States as far north as Estonia. British race (subspecies *serena* Verity 1913) concentrated in SW Britain, and extends to central areas, with Yorkshire Wolds and N Yorks Moors forming separated outliers at northern edge of range. Recent experimental releases of Yorkshire stock into Co Durham as part of a joint Leeds & Durham Universities project investigating the effects of global warming on butterfly species have resulted in at least one colony surviving in Co Durham from 1999 until 2004. In SW Britain it uses suitable habitats on all soils except acid. Further east and north it shows increasing preference for chalk and limestone.

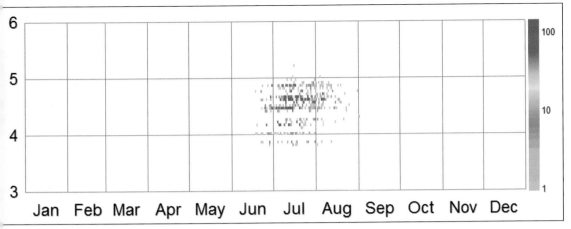

ID NOTES: A very distinctive black butterfly with white spots. Unlikely to be confused with any other species. Male and female similar but latter usually larger with yellowish tinge showing in closed-wing view. Flies in a very leisurely way. A very variable butterfly with some 70 described aberrations ranging from all white to all black.

PHENOGRAM: Yorkshire 1995-2003. Shows the scattered nature of observations and the strength of the population on the Yorkshire Wolds.

colonies now established in S Yorkshire cannot be ruled out. The A1 might provide suitable habitat along its wide grassy verges. On the one hand, evidence from introduced colonies seems to indicate they remain very sedentary and take many years to spread, even to suitable adjacent sites (Rimington 1994). On the other, the species is clearly spreading northwards and eastwards from its core populations in S/SW England with a 66% increase in 10km squares recorded between the two national surveys. Therefore, once established, there is every reason to expect a spread from S Yorkshire as well, given that global warming continues to push up temperatures. One of the specimens released in a private introduction project in Withernsea left the site but got lost when it flew into the local Woolworth's store c700m away!

Typical maximum site counts since 1995 have been in the range **10** to **200+** on the Wolds (VC61); **1** to **25** on the N Yorks Moors (VC62) and **10** to **125** in S Yorks (VC63). Most VC64 records are of singles with the exception of Barlow Common, nr Selby, (SE62) where up to 5 have been reported [Pat & Jim Bone]. The **earliest and latest** dates recorded in the Survey period were both for the Wolds (VC61) in 2000: 17/06 at Fordon in the north [David Woodmansey] and 24/08 on the Hudson Way in the south [John

CONSERVATION: The species seems to be holding its own in the county, but in its strongholds is dependent on the maintenance of suitable grasslands, some of which have been planted with trees in recent times and others which are steadily scrubbing over. The growth of rabbit populations during the 1995/2003 Survey period could be an eventual threat if it continues at the current pace. Specific management might involve scrub control, rabbit control and very light grazing to maintain a suitable mix of fine and coarse grasses up to about 0.5m. Fortunately, a number of Countryside Stewardship schemes are underway to improve N Wolds grasslands and these are already benefiting the Marbled White in clearing back the scrub invasion on some sites. The East Riding of Yorkshire BAP includes Marbled White.

Killingbeck]. Based on casual observations reported by Survey participants, emergence in S Yorkshire tends to be about a week earlier than on the Wolds but with the flight season up to two weeks shorter. The longest flight season reported in S Yorkshire was in 2002 with emergence on 18/06 [Bill Smyllie] and last sighting on 14/08 [Ralph Hibbert and Chris Parkin], both records from Brockadale YWT NR.

Marbled White: male (no yellow tinge).

Lawrie King

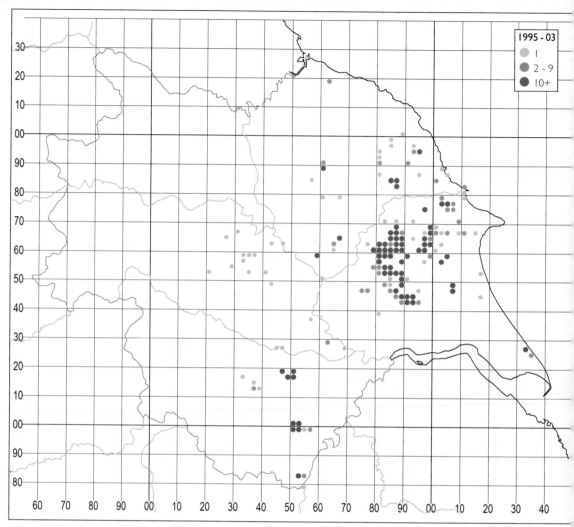

Marbled White: Yorkshire Tetrad map 1995-2003

MAP NOTES 1995-2003: Noted in 161/3319 recorded tetrads (ie 4.9%), and out of 4120 tetrads in Yorkshire. **Ranked 25th most widespread** out of 36 breeding species in the county. Wolds populations have expanded in recent years and appear to have spread northwards to occupy a number of areas on the N York Moors. The tetrad map shows that colonies on the Magnesian Limestone ridge are more isolated than appears from the 10km map. Yellow dots to the north appear to result from casual (and probably ephemeral) introductions. Red 10km dot N of Spurn indicates an unofficial introduction in Withernsea area.

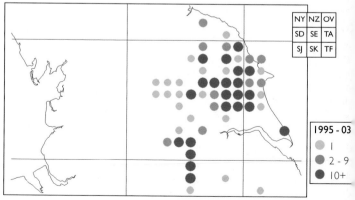

Marbled White: 10km distribution North of England

● = 1 or more records out of county 1995-1999

LIFE STORY

HABITAT: Usually unimproved, lightly grazed, chalk and limestone grasslands with a mix of fine and coarse grasses up to 0.5m high on a site with shelter and/or a generally southerly aspect. The species can also utilise non-calcareous grassland, woodland rides, road and rail verges and quite small areas of suitably rough grassland. Over 70 sites recorded on the Wolds (VC61) in 1995/2003. Typical habitats are found towards the heads of steep valleys especially in the N Wolds eg around Warter Wold, Millington and Bishop Wilton Wold (all SE85); along disued railway tracks, eg Beverley-Market Weighton, (now the Hudson Way Leisure Trail); the former Driffield-Malton railway track around Wharram Percy (SE86) and in disused quarries like Kiplingcotes and Wharram (both YWT reserves), and even on the north-facing escarpment at Flixton Quarry, towards Filey (TA07). The still-open Filey to Bridlington line is reported to have a small colony on the trackside near Bempton (pers comm. Neville Stead 2000). The species is increasingly encountered on roadside verges in the Wolds.

Adults are at their peak in July and early August although first emergence may occur as early as mid-June (see above). Mating occurs freely in the open, and females appear to lay their eggs at random into the depths of suitably grassy areas. They perch briefly on a stem or flower head, vibrate their abdomens, then take off and eject a green egg, which quickly turns white when exposed to the air. Brown or green larvae hatch after about 20 days, eat their eggshells and go into hibernation. They usually awake in spring when weather is mild enough, but in mild winters, (usually in south of England), this could be as early as January. They continue to feed on and off until about 3 weeks before emerging as a butterfly in June or July. Bright red spots can often be seen on the butterflies' bodies, which are the larval stages of red mites belonging to the Erythraedidae and Trombidiidae families. In dull or wet periods or at night these butterflies can easily be spotted, at rest with folded wings on grass stems or flower heads. Marbled Whites often feed communally, with a preference for purple nectar plants. Rafe and Jefferson (1983)

Marbled Whites: mating pair (female L – yellowish) Cowlam (VC61) 2004.

noted Woolly Thistle *Cirsium eriophorum*, Creeping Thistle *Cirsium arvense*, Black Knapweed *Centuarea nigra* and Field Scabious *Knautia arvensis* as particularly favoured on the Wolds.

INTRODUCTIONS: This species has proved a popular subject for private introductions/re-introductions, particularly in S Yorkshire. Such projects appear to have been undertaken with very variable degrees of scientific rigour and in some cases without any monitoring or reporting, an approach which many feel does harm to the idea of re-introducing species. Lockwood (2002) draws attention to three S Yorkshire areas where apparently successful introductions have taken place. The most southerly is the Anston Stones/Lindrick Common area (SK59), close to Yorkshire's border with Derbyshire and Nottinghamshire. This was introduced in the mid-1980s without any details reported. Numbers observed since suggest the colony is still in existence but is very small. There was also an introduction at Letwell in 1978 in the same area. Further north, the species is more widespread in the Conisbrough/Sprotborough area (inc Cadeby Rattles, Earth Centre and Denaby Ings NR) in adjacent 10km squares SK59/SE50. The origins of this population date back to 1985 when 10 Yorkshire Wolds females were introduced. The project was fully reported in Rimington (1994). The third, and seemingly most successful area, is around Brockadale YWT NR, Went Hills/ Smeaton Craggs area (SE51) where site counts up to 125 represent the highest outside the Yorkshire Wolds and a natural spread to Pot Hills Marsh, Upton (SE41), appears to have taken place. Full details of the Went Hills/Brockadale introductions were published in the Annual Reports of Castleford Naturalists (1989/1992). Rimington (1994) indicates that behavioural observations of introduced Marbled Whites in the Sprotborough area suggest that the species is very sedentary and slow to extend its range even when apparently suitable sites exist nearby. It seems likely, therefore, that the sightings along or near the Magnesian Limestone ridge to the north of the above three areas [Wintersett (SE31), Fairburn Ings RSPB NR (SE42) and the Harrogate (SE35 etc) areas] indicate casual introductions (of which we have had some specific reports) rather than an expansion from S Yorkshire sites, although both could be occurring side by side. There have also been small scale, unreported introductions in Holderness (VC61) on a meadow in Withernsea c1988 (TA32) and a small strip of grassland to the west of Hornsea c2001? (TA14). We have been informed that the Withernsea colony was made up of stock from Dover (in Kent) and Fordon on the Yorkshire Wolds.

Petiver (1695) called it the **Half Mourner**, after the way a widow would have a period of mourning in black, followed by a period of 'half-mourning' in black and white. Wilkes (1741-42) used **Marmoris,** and Harris (1766) called it the **Marmoress** (from marmoreal = 'like marble') or the **Marbled White**. Berkenhout (1769) used **Marble Butterfly** whilst Lewin (1795) used **Marbled Argus**. Many other similar names were tried before Marbled White finally became more widely accepted in the 1800s.

Duncan (1844) noted that the Marbled White was *'abundant near York'*. Morris (1853) gave: *'Marr, near Doncaster, and on Buttercrambe Moor near Stamford Bridge'* as well as *'Werst Hill near Pontefract'*. Rimington (1992) listed many early VC63 records including: Wath-upon-Dearne (SE40) 1832; Marr (SE50) 1830s; Smeaton (SE51) 1842; Adwick (SE50) 1846; and Went Hill (SE41) c.1870. But by 1883 Porritt had to write, *'At one time a well-known Yorkshire butterfly, but now probably extinct'*. He looked back to earlier records: 1842 (a quarry near Tadcaster (VC64/SE44); 1858, 80 counted in Maltby Wood (VC63/SK59); 1860 Marr nr Doncaster; and *'many years ago'* (stated in 1883) a record made by WH Taylor at Bramham Park (VC64/SE44) (just south of Wetherby). Porritt also mentions Buttercrambe Moor (VC62/SE75) and York, adding sightings (singles?) from the Beverley area (VC61/TA03?) and Scarborough (TA08). This seems to indicate that most known sites at the time were on the Magnesian Limestone between Maltby (VC63) and Tadcaster (VC64).

Thomas Stather of Hull (b1812-d1878) recorded the species around Riplingham (VC61/SE92) and Cottingham, (just W of Hull, TA03) during his lifetime (Stainforth 1919). Yet reports in *The Naturalist* from 1884 onward indicate the butterfly was thought to be extinct in the county from about 1870, following a series of cold, wet and gloomy summers in the 1860s, and in the case of Melton (VC63/SE50), the ploughing up of the site! Then in 1891 a live specimen was taken by William Hewitt at Sledmere (Wolds VC61/SE96) on a YNU excursion. Wolds colonies were largely unknown to 19th century lepidopterists. In 1919 Thomas Stainforth of Hull Naturalists', referring to several species of butterfly including Marbled White, complained that areas of the Wolds near Hull were not visited often enough to *'prove the capabilities of a locality'*. GB Walsh (Scarborough Field Naturalists') commented as late as 1956 that *'due to inaccessibility very little collecting has been done...on the Wolds'*.

Porritt (1904) revised his entry: *'This species has evidently occurred a Sledmere for many years.'* He also added a number of previously unknown sites: 1901, Raincliffe Wood (Scarborough VC62/SE98) [HW Head]; 1901 Sleightholmdale (NW of Kirkbymoorside, VC62/SE68/69) [Rev Hubert F Drew]; 1902 *'around Hull'* (VC61) [Reginald H Barker]; 1902 (between 05/08 and 08/09!) three localities *'within easy distance of York'*, [Harold J Burkhill], (over 60 counted on one of these sites). Porritt (1907) added *'This species may still be taken regularly and freely in several places in the Sledmere district.'* Tetley (1915) noted the species *'really abundant in 1914 near Cowlam on the Wolds. I turned it up there in 1902; this must be, I think, its most northerly habitat in the British Isles.'* However, EB Ford (1945/1975) noted that the species had long ceased to occur in Yorkshire. This incorrect statement probably hearkened back to Porritt's 1883 list! Walsh (1956) described the species as *'locally common on the Wolds'* and noted VC62 records for Cayton Bay in 1929, and more recent specimens in Falsgrave Park (Scarborough) and nearby Raincliffe Woods (1945) (all TA08). The *Naturalist* also records sightings on the Wolds (1946), and at Keld Head, nr Pickering (VC62/SE88) in 1948. By 1963 Wold's (VC61) colonies were known in Burdale (SE86), Cowlam and Sledmere (SE96), Fridaythorpe (SE85), High Fordon (TA07), Langtoft (TA06), and Weaverthorpe (SE97), and in 1970 the YNU Lepidoptera Report reported a *'new'* colony discovered in 1968 at Warrendale (nr Pocklington, VC61/SE84) well to the west of other known colonies.

It has been suggested that the advent of myxomatosis, in the early 1950s, could have triggered the current expansion in allowing more growth of the taller grasses favoured by this species. In 1958 the Malton to Driffield railway route (passing through Wharram, Burdale and Sledmere) was closed. As it reverted to the wild it would have provided an ideal corridor to other sites. The species still uses current remnants of the line. The Driffield-Market Weighton-Selby line closed in 1963 and the Beverley-Market Weighton link (passing Kiplingcotes Quarry) followed in 1965. This has been retained as the Hudson Way Leisure route and now marks the southern boundary for the Marbled White on the Wolds.

The N York Moors populations are more problematical. They appear to have been present on and off for a long period of time along the southern limestone escarpment, but being at the very northern limit of the range they are probably the first to disappear in poorer years and are then presumably re-colonised from the Wolds. There is also a suspicion that some unofficial introductions may have been made in recent times. The 1990s have been exceptionally warm and Marbled Whites have become resident in forest clearings around Pexton and Ellerburn, as well as in Wilton Heights Quarry (all VC62).

The first-ever VC64 record at Hetchell Crags nr Bardsey (between Leeds and Wetherby SE34) in 1947 is difficult to explain except in terms of an introduction, or just possibly as a hitchhiker. A trainload of quarried chalk from Wharram might conceivably have moved off with resting Marbled Whites on board! However, in July 1988 several specimens were released in Hetchell Wood by K Bradbury. Mike Barnham recorded a female at Allerton Mauleverer (nr Knaresborough VC64/SE34) on 16/07/1985 and argues that this could have been the offspring of a wandering female from the previous year (Barnham & Foggitt 1987). Whilst this is possible, an introduction seems more likely.

Howard M Frost & John Killingbeck

Tees Marshalling Yard, Middlesbrough (VC62).

UK BAP Status: *Not listed.*
BC Priorities: National: *Low.*
N of England: *High.* Yorkshire: *High.*
European Status: *Not threatened.*

North Wolds chalk grassland specimen (2000).

Grayling

YORKSHIRE STATUS 1995/2003:

Rare, very localised resident. Appears sedentary yet has colonised offshore islands such as Holy Island and the Farnes in Northumberland implying an ability to be mobile on occasion. (Notable expansion in 1950s also suggests ability to become highly mobile in right conditions.) Single brood (Jul/Aug). In 1995 only known on a single N Wolds chalk grassland site, hence its *High Priority* status in Yorkshire. However, following a series of determined searches by BC members, other important sites have been discovered linked to railways and brownfield areas. In 2001 the species was unexpectedly found on various sites through the industrial centre of Middlesbrough (VCs 62/66), mainly alongside the river over c10 miles from the Tees Barrage to South Gare and including Corus Steelworks. The biggest colony is on the Yorkshire side of the river, centred on the large and active Tees Marshalling Yard, where railway wagons are scrapped. As no entry is permitted, observations have been made from the edges of the site, using binoculars. **55** Grayling were counted in 2002, but it is likely the population is much bigger. Amazingly, the butterfly can be seen patrolling under the busy A19 viaduct, one of the last places anyone would have thought worth visiting in search of one of Yorkshire's rarest species! The Maze Park, a linear Tees Valley Wildlife Trust Nature Reserve, lies between the Marshalling Yard and the River Tees and is used as a marginal breeding and nectaring area. Following a meeting between Butterfly Conservation and representatives of landowners and interested bodies, Dave Wainwright was employed by Northumbrian Water to survey the area in 2002 and to come up with management proposals (Wainwright 2002). By 2003 these were already being put into operation and the butterfly given a high profile in the area, with a special display board.

In 2002 a quarry colony was discovered near Wakefield (VC63) and

WORLD STATUS: Resident: 0-2000m, 1 brood (Jun/Sept). Range: Europe from the Mediterranean to Lat 63°N and eastward into W Asia then increasingly uncertain due to confusions with related species. In northern part of range (inc British Isles) tends to be a coastal species though largely absent from east coast between Norfolk and Northumberland. Declines in many countries, inc British Isles, probably due to changes in land-use, forestry and farming and reduction in rabbit grazing after the myxomatosis outbreak (1950s). Regional variations distinguished by race names: *anglorum* in England, Wales and southern Scotland (but with a dwarf race *thyone* on Great Ormes Head, N Wales); *scota* in N Scotland; *hibernica* in Ireland, where a second race *clarensis* is found on the Burren limestone.

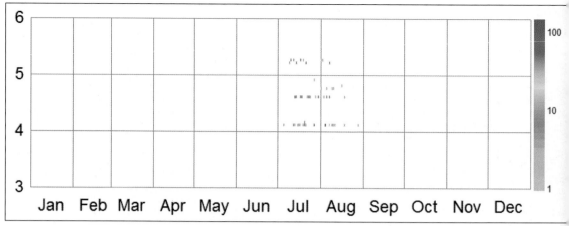

	Jan	Feb	Mar	Apr	May	Jun	Jul	Aug	Sep	Oct	Nov	Dec

PHENOGRAM: Yorkshire 1995-2003. The well-separated lines highlight the isolation of colonies in S Yorks (bottom), the Wolds (middle) and Middlesbrough (top).

ID NOTES: Brownish butterfly, easily confused with Meadow Brown. Grayling often a shade larger, but sizes overlap and both species lean over on the ground. Diagnostic feature is the double eyespot visible on both sides of the upper wing, although these are not readily revealed, as the butterfly invariably perches with wings closed or only very slightly apart, and the upper wings retracted. Seen close to, the lower underwing is distinctively mottled in brown with a paler, broken, zig-zagging bar from top to bottom. A nervous butterfly will flick its upper wings upwards and briefly reveal one or both 'eyes'. In flight, the Grayling looks large and distinctively buoyant; with the pale bands of the lower underwings often visible as a pale rump on the disappearing butterfly. It is extremely well-camouflaged, especially on broken ground, and can melt away before your eyes, often walking short distances after landing. On a well-occupied site, in good weather, mid-air territorial tussles between males occur fairly frequently. Graylings vary in shade, colour and sometimes size, between regions and even between colonies. Chalk and limestone colonies produce lighter shades, heath and woodland areas, darker. Howarth (1973) indicates 33 known variations.

monitored throughout the flight season by members of the Wintersett Wildlife Group, with up to 15 butterflies counted between 12/07 [Richard Bell] and 27/08 [Peter Smith]. In 2003 a much larger rail-based site was found in the same area with at least 70 butterflies counted [David & Stuart Wise].

The chalk grassland site on the N Wolds (at 150-170m and on private property not open to the public) has been monitored by Butterfly Conservation on a weekly basis in each flight season since 1999, although it appears to have been known since at least 1991 and is probably fairly recent as its occupies the site of a felled wood. The flight period usually runs from the 2nd week in Jul to mid Aug with the **earliest** record on 28/06/2003 [Howard & Christine Frost] and **latest** on 18//08/2000 [David Woodmansey]. Peak counts are usually fairly small, in the 12 to 20 range, except for one early peak of 49 on 12/07/1999. A single sighting was made on a second N Wolds site in 2003 [Mike Lockwood].

A number of unconfirmed reports may indicate other colonies yet to be discovered eg 2001: Filey Brigg (VC61) [Filey Brigg Ornithological Group] and Wombwell (VC63) [Dean Stables]; 2002: Deepdale (N York Moors VC62) [Gwenda Wadsworth], although, there are concerns that unofficial introductions may also be taking place especially in the Wakefield area. There appears to be scope to find more colonies on industrial and rail-based sites around the county especially in VC63, as well as along the coastal strip between Scarborough and Middlesbrough, but it would be a shame if this possibility was muddled by thoughtless introductions.

CONSERVATION ISSUES: The discovery of new colonies has not changed the threatened status of this species. There are medium to long-term possibilities that marshalling yards such as at Middlesbrough may be sold off for development land. Graylings mainly thrive where ground conditions keep changing to maintain a balance between bare ground and clumps of suitable grasses: active quarrying, active mining with spoil heaps, active railways with lineside management, active forestry with felling and replanting work, active grazing on thin stony soils, active rabbit disturbance, or blowing sand-dunes etc. Unsprayed railway sidings are ideal in that they develop a light plant cover, but ballast and sleepers provide permanent bare patches. Once activity stops, vegetation increases, succession to shrubs and trees develops, and the butterfly declines, but probably over such a long period that the reason may no longer be obvious. Yorkshire Graylings appear to have suffered through conifer afforestation (shading out rides and clearings), changes in agriculture (fertilisation and overgrazing), myxomatosis in the 1950s (reducing active rabbit disturbance), the greening over of disused Wolds quarries like Kiplingcotes, and the closing of branch lines in the 1950s and 1960s, (resulting in the tracks becoming overgrown and unsuitable). The Tees Valley Wildlife Trust has created ballast filled scrapes on The Maze NR to encourage the species. The Yorkshire Wildlife Trust has cleared shrubs and trees at Wharram Quarry NR in the hope that the species might expand there. A re-introduction project has been mooted but not yet thought practical, until more is learned about the species' needs.

Left: Showing the attraction of railway sleepers or bare ground basking. Above right: In the Maze Park NR (Tees Valley Wildlife Trust) adjacent to the Tees Marshalling Yard, the Grayling has become a flagship species. Lower right: Grayling, showing diagnostic double eyespot, Teesaurus Park Middlesbrough.

Paul W Forster

MAP NOTES 1995-2003: Noted in just **9/3319** recorded tetrads (ie 0.3%), and out of 4120 tetrads in Yorkshire. **Ranked 34th most widespread** out of 36 regular breeding species in the county. Tends to occur on or near coasts and estuaries with the single Wolds colony being unusually on a chalk grassland site. Other colonies recently discovered have a railway or brownfield site connection. The yellow dots, marking single sightings, are thought to be unofficial introductions. The Grayling is normally very sedentary and only likely to expand over very short distances.

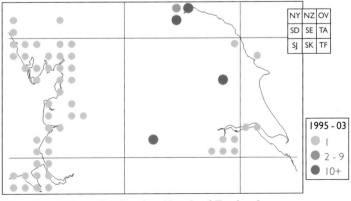

NY	NZ	OV
SD	SE	TA
SJ	SK	TF

1995 - 03
1
2 - 9
10+

Grayling: 10km distribution North of England

= 1 or more records out of county 1995-1999

LIFE STORY

HABITAT: Yorkshire Wolds Graylings use one of the many steep-sided valleys where soils are thin and the presence of sheep, slipping and sliding on the steep slopes causes open scars and screes, which provide the butterfly with the bare hot-spots it needs. Conditions are often blustery and extreme, as most of these valleys run east/west, and funnel winds from both directions. Dust devils may develop on the hottest days! In Middlesbrough, brownfield sites on both sides of the River Tees are used, including large railway sidings and a sewage works. Butterflies have been noted crossing the fairly wide River Tees. Bare ballast and sleepers provide the sheltered hot-spots, whilst patches of suitable grasses for egg-laying are found all over the sidings. Stationary wagons may add shelter. In the Coatham Sands/S Gare area, east of Middlesbrough the butterfly appears to be using sand dunes.

Lays white oval eggs, which turn dull yellow before hatching after 10 to 20 days. Eggs tend to be deposited individually on clumps of grass surrounded by bare ground. Many grass species used, including Sheep's Fescue *Festuca ovina*, Red Fescue *F. rubra* and Marram Grass *Ammophila arenaria* (on coastal sites). Joy (1996b) shows that on disused Shropshire lead mine sites, the species selects *Festuca* clumps with high ratios of brown to green stems, presumably so that the brown, yellow and white stripes of the larvae serve as better camouflage. Larvae progress through five instars and feed only at night in the first three, hiding at

Grayling mating pair, Ossett (VC63), July 2004.

the base of a grass tussock by day. During the third instar they move into winter hibernation, often below ground level and sometimes under stones. They may still emerge to feed at night during milder spells. Pupation takes place around early June in a silk-lined cell excavated about 1cm under the ground.

Past Yorkshire records suggest the species probably emerged in mid to late July and flew well into August, whilst recent monitoring suggests this may have become earlier in recent years. The species is very easy to overlook and our observations on the Wolds suggest that maximum activity, when almost the whole of the colony may take to the air at once, is short-lived. Although the species is not reputed to nectar very much, this is quite often observed on the Wolds. The 'Brown' group of butterflies, often lean at an angle when on the ground. The Grayling is particularly noted for this. But is it done to minimise shadow so as not to be spotted by predators, or is it done to regulate body temperature? Findlay *et al* (1983) argue for the latter. Their survey showed that in sunny conditions, Graylings present a maximum wing area to the sun in lower temperatures, and a minimal area in higher temperatures. In the hottest conditions they may seek shade by hiding in grass clumps, or they may avoid ground heat by 'stilting' (stretching up on 'tip-toes'). In cooler conditions they may lay with wings together but flattened to the ground to absorb ground heat, or they may 'shiver' like some moths and raise body temperatures through wing vibration (observed several times on the Wolds). Mobility on the Wolds site is very limited with most individuals keeping to one side of the valley and close to the driest, stoniest parts of the area. Individual flights mostly range from 5m to 10m and only rarely up to 20m.

This Grayling in Hoge Veluwe National Park (the Netherlands) was attracted to the bonnet of the Editor's car and made several dipping flights touching the surface as though it might have been water, before landing and resting.

Petiver (1699) called it **'the black-eyed marble Butterfly'**. In 1703 he used **Brown Tunbridge Grayling** for the male, and **Tunbridge Grayling** for the female. Wilkes (1741) christened it the **Rock Underwing**, whilst Harris used **Grailing** in 1766 and **Grayline** in 1775. Berkenhout (1769) returned to Petiver's **Black-eyed Marbled Butterfly** whilst Lewin (1795) introduced **The Great Argus**. Haworth (1803-1828) used **Grayling** and was followed by most subsequent authors, although Morris (1853) tried **Rock-eyed Underwing**, but this never really caught on. The Latin names are derived from Hipparchus, a Greek astronomer, and Semele, the beautiful mother of Dionysius.

Rimington (1992) gives an early Doncaster (VC63) area presence: Wath-upon-Dearne (Anon 1832) and Thorne Moors (Heppenstall 1842). Morris (1853) wrote: '*I have seen this interesting insect in the parish of Nafferton, Yorkshire*' [VC61] '*on the scanty remains of the heath on the road to the hamlet of Pockthorpe.*' He also gives: *York; on the railway near Burnby* VC61/SE84 – railway opened 1847]; *at Drewton nr Market Weighton* [actually nr S Cave VC61/SE93], *and Scarborough*'. Porritt (1883) also mentions Scarborough ('*abundant on Castle Hill*') as a personal undated record. It is also included in the Thomas Wilkinson/Peter Inchbald list in *Theakston's Guide to Scarborough* (1871) which notes: '*Grayling: Abundant on Castle Hill in July and August*'. Tetley (1915) then records it '*used to be taken on Castle Hill*'. Rimington comments that there were few Doncaster area records, and none between 1842 and 1947. Garland (1981) includes an undated 19th century record from Maltby VC63/SE59). Porritt (1883) only gives 2 sites besides Scarborough: Great Almes Cliff (presumably Almscliff Crags nr Harrogate VC64/SE24), and Nafferton. In 1904 he adds Grassington in Wharfedale (VC64) (1896 and 1905 in YNU Card File) and Kirkbymoorside (VC62), but with no more additions in 1907. Tetley (1915) notes: '*on the Wolds and near Pickering*'. Stainforth (1919) refers to a 19th century

presence at Riplingham (VC61/TA93) and Houghton Moor (VC61/TA83), both in the SW corner of the Wolds west of Hull and near Morris's Drewton site.

Few records have come to light from the first half of the 20th century. Re the Scarborough District, Walsh (1952) writes, '*it occurs all over the district in dry localities on the edge of the moors and wolds and is quite commonly seen sunning itself whilst lying on its side on stony paths. It is plentiful at Pickering, Hutton-le-Hole and Kirkbymoorside* [all VC62], *though not so common in 1950 and 1951*'. Walsh (1956) reports an increase from 1947. The YNU 1967/70 Report (amplified by details from the YNU Card File and other sources) also indicates an apparent increase in the 1950s and notes: **VC61:** Speeton Cliffs 1954 [H Henson], Kiplingcotes Quarry c1956 [D Wade]; also recorded on the old railway track at Burdale 30/07/1967 [Adrian Norris via J Dickinson]; **VC62:** Pickering 1933, Hutton-le-Hole 1940, Paxton Common (YNU 02/08/1941, presumed misprint for Pexton), Seamer Moor nr Scarborough 1946, Harwood Dale 1946 [E Dearing], Haugh Rigg nr Pickering 1955 [E Ramsden], Burniston 04/08/1955 [Scarboro' Field Nats Soc]. Thornton-le-Dale 21/07/1959 [RS Pollard], Kirkbymoorside [GB Walsh]; **VC64:** several localities in the Selby area inc Barlow 1956/1957 [SM Jackson]; Rimington (1992) also notes an increase around Doncaster (VC63) between 1947 and the 1960s with records from Blaxton, Finningley, and Bull Moor. The cooler, wetter 1960s appeared to cause a retraction, although with hints of some expansion from 1975 onward, eg a single noted on Thorne Moors on 11/07/1976 [Brian Eversham]. Several N Wolds sites were known in the 1980s including one near Sledmere and another near Fridaythorpe [pers comm. Tom Upton], the latter becoming unsuitable due to fertilisation and overgrazing. However, by 1989, Sutton & Beaumont were noting, '*a decline in recent years. One was recorded in 1980 on the Wolds, and several seen at the same site in 1981, but the site has not been re-visited*'. They concluded that the '*species now appears to be in a precarious state in the county and is probably our most endangered butterfly*'.

Morris's observation of the species on the railway at Burnby lends weight to the possibility that as industry spread in the 19th century and new farming methods removed old pastures, the butterfly found suitable habitat opening up along railway routes and around the spoil heaps of industry. It is difficult to spot at the best of times and could easily have been overlooked on such sites. By 1996 it appeared we had only one Wolds site still active. However, evidence from Scotland (Saville 1996) indicated Graylings were being discovered along railway cuttings and embankments. Once alerted to the possibility, Yorkshire observers were soon uncovering similar sites, and raising questions about railway connections to past sites. Kiplingcotes Quarry on the former Driffield-Market Weighton line was developed in conjunction with the line opened in 1865 and not far from Burnby. Photographs of Wolds' rail routes in the 1930s/50s (Burton 1997, Mason 1990) reveal an open, close-cropped landscape with few lineside shrubs or trees and chalky screes on embankments. Lineside fires caused by passing steam engines would have provided regular bare patches. Ideal Grayling habitat! A Grayling once landed on the bonnet of the writer's (HMF) stationary car and rather than fly off as the car began to move it stayed on board, aligning itself with the direction of movement so as to reduce resistance. It only flew when the speed exceeded 20mph. High sided rail wagons waiting to leave quarries would enclose warm and sheltered micro-climates, and might well have enabled butterflies to hitch-hike around the rail network, establishing colonies as they went. There may yet be many more inland sites to find, although in more recent times many railway verges have become overgrown.

Howard M Frost & John Killingbeck

Roger Mitchell

Potteric Carr YWT NR from the air. Big counts of Gatekeeper have been made along the railway embankments.

UK BAP Status: *Not listed.*
BC Priorities: National: *Low.*
N of England: *Low.* Yorkshire: *Low.*
European Status: *Not threatened.*

WORLD STATUS: Resident, 0-1700m. 1 brood (Jul/early Sept). Range: N Mediterranean coast (plus Morocco but not S Italy) northward to S Ireland, N England, Netherlands and eastward to Asia Minor and the Caucasus. Distribution uneven within these boundaries with some declines and also expansions towards the northern edge of range (Britain, Netherlands, NE France). Limit of British range lies across central Yorkshire, roughly from Flamborough Head to the southern lake District, but with a scatter of records to the north of this line.

YORKSHIRE STATUS 1995/2003:

Expanding resident: 1 brood (usually Jul/Aug). However, this species appears to be extending its flight season, with an increasing number of sightings in Jun and Sept, and even the suggestion of a previously unheard of partial second generation in 2001 and 2003. First and last records in the Survey period have been: **1996:** 08/07 to 01/09, **1997:** 07/07 to 12/09, **1998:** 06/07 to 08/09, **1999:** 29/06 to 10/09, **2000:** 28/06 to 04/09, **2001:** 30/05 to 12/10 (!), **2002:** 19/06 to 20/09, **2003:** 14/06 to 02/10 (!). The earliest record on 30/05/2001 involved 2 butterflies at Firsby (VC63) [Bill Ely/P Leonard] and was an isolated report in a very warm spell with unusually high night temperatures. The general emergence that year was still in early Jul. However, there were 3 remarkably late records in 2001: 30/09 – 1 at Bolton Percy (VC64) [Joyce Payne]; 12/10 - 2 at Clifton (York, VC62) [B Skerritt], and 12/10 - 2 at Garforth (VC64) [Mary Palmer].

This is a species which can produce very large numbers in quite small areas, therefore counts in the multiple hundreds are not uncommon, although currently these are confined to the southern half of the county and do not occur every year. Fairburn Ings RSPB NR (VC64) recorded **840** on 27/07/1996 [Robin Horner]. Spurn NNR (VC61) had an estimated **1000** on 08/08/2000 [Barry Spence]. **622** were counted at Potteric Carr NR (VC63) on 28/07/2002 [Potteric Carr Recording Group] and there were **769** at York Cemetery NR (VC62) on 20/07/2003 [Pat & Jim Bone]. VC64 has seen a considerable expansion during the Survey period and the species has been recorded up to 260m. However, in VC65 it appears to be very much on the edge of its range with a Richmond area site producing **30** on 11/07/1997; and Nutwith & Roomer Common **30** on 20/07/1997 and **25** on 25/07/1999 [all Arnold Robson], but most other records in ones and twos. In VC62, the butterfly has yet to colonise much of the forested southern edges of the N York Moors but has already appeared in the Middlesbrough area, perhaps having spread unnoticed along the VC62 coastline. In the 1995/2003 period the species was also recorded in 9x10km squares in Co Durham although with no certain records since 2000 (Hunter & Norman 2003).

Gatekeeper

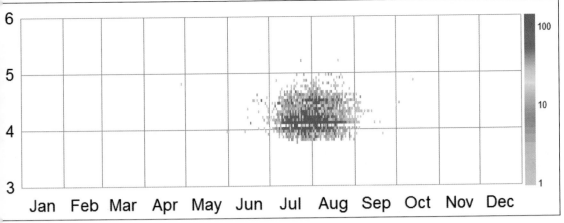

PHENOGRAM: Yorkshire 1995-2003. Not only shows later peaks as you move north, but also the lack of sightings in the N of the county.

ID NOTES: Similar to Meadow Brown (which shares same habitats) but smaller and brighter, with central parts of upperwings strongly orange. Male smaller than female, with broad, dark sex brands across centre of upper forewings. Note two white dots in black eyespots (upperwings and underwings) compared to Meadow Brown usually with one, (although two sometimes seen in Scottish Meadow Brown specimens). Also look for pattern of white dots on lower wing in closed-wing view. Meadow Brown is generally darker and more drab. A very variable species with over 60 described aberrations, many of which involve variations in the style and number of eyespots eg ab *excessa* Tutt with I to 5 extra spots on upper forewing, and ab *posttriexcessa* Leeds, with up to 3 extra spots on the upperside of the hindwing.

Since 1995 distribution has become steadily more widespread in the southern half of the county, although some of this apparent increase may also reflect growing recorder effort. Between 1998 and 2003 the butterfly's 10km square coverage increased by about 65%, whilst tetrad coverage more than doubled in the same period.

Male showing typically well marked sex brands.

Female.

CONSERVATION ISSUES: Suitable habitat for this species is readily available throughout the county. The maintenance of the general policy of only cutting Im strips along roadside verges may be quite important in providing routes along which the species can spread. Areas of uncut grass are vital for this butterfly's success, as are wildflower nectar sources, particularly sheltered banks of bramble. The current trend to reinstate hedgerows could also benefit this butterfly. However, the most important issues regarding the further consolidation and expansion of this species will relate to climatic trends and the actual weather experienced from year to year.

Worn specimen.

Seen York Cemetery NR 18/08/2002. Initially thought to be a strange aberration. Now seems more likely to be a marked and released specimen, as tool marks can be detected in each yellow patch.

Roy Bedford

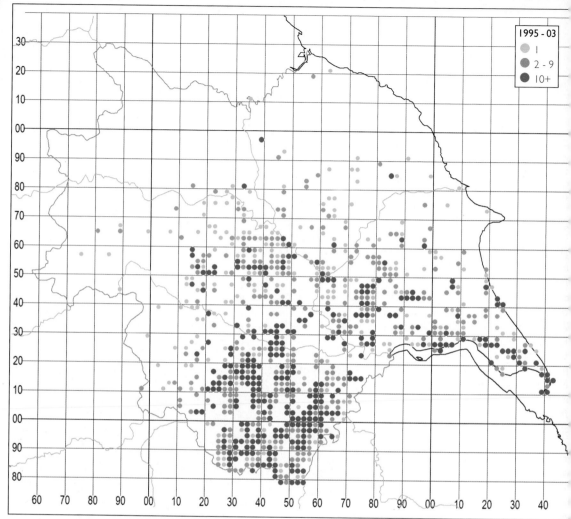

Gatekeeper: Yorkshire Tetrad map 1995-2003

MAP NOTES 1995-2003: Noted in **843/3319** recorded tetrads (ie 25.4%), and out of 4120 tetrads in Yorkshire. **Ranked 15th most widespread** out of 36 regular breeding species in the county. Formerly found only in S and SE of the county, now expanding steadily, if rather slowly, northward, with northern edge of distribution currently across centre of county, roughly in line with Flamborough Head. A northward salient extends beyond this in the Vale of York, with a scatter of records suggestive of colonisers in northern parts of 100km squares SE and TA. As yet only a handful of vagrants have forged ahead into Co Durham.

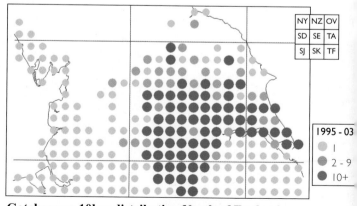

NY	NZ	OV
SD	SE	TA
SJ	SK	TF

1995 - 03
● 1
● 2 - 9
● 10+

Gatekeeper: 10km distribution North of England
● = 1 or more records out of county 1995-1999

LIFE STORY

HABITAT: Found in rough grassy areas in sunny spots, especially in the shelter of hedges and scrub, or along woodland edges, including wide rides and sunny clearings. Also found in unimproved pastures and meadows as well as sand dunes (as at Spurn) and heathland. It is quite common along the uncut parts of suitable roadside verges and disused railway tracks. It is often seen nectaring on bramble flowers in sheltered but sunny corners. Where colonies exist not far from built up areas, individuals may sometimes stray into gardens and nectar on buddleia.

The eggs, which become mottled and darker with time, are laid singly on tallish grasses, sheltered by hedges, shrubs etc in sunny places. Quite a wide range of grasses are used, including: Couch Grass *Elytrigia repens*, the bents *Agrostis* spp, the fescues *Festuca* spp, and meadow grasses *Poa* spp. Eggs also sometimes ejected in flight or attached to the bark of nearby shrubs. They hatch after c3 weeks and hibernate as larvae, usually in Oct after first moult. Night feeding commences around Mar/Apr. Larvae have two colour forms in final instar: greenish-grey, or dingy grey-brown, both with darker stripes and fine spotting. Pupation usually takes place in early Jun, the pupa being a rather striking brown with cream streaks when seen in isolation, but well disguised when suspended in the vegetation. Adults emerge after about 3 weeks and the timing of this is usually more synchronised across the population than with the other Browns. Males often spend several days in one small area,

Gatekeepers: mating pair, Wentworth (VC63), 2004.

Dean Stables

frequently perching and keeping a lookout for females and rival males. Then they may move on to a further territory up to 150m away (Brakefield 1979). Butterflies are thought to live for about a week. It has been noticed that the flight period is more closely synchronised in northern populations than in those to the south, suggesting that temperatures may become more critical towards the northern edge of the species range (Brakefield 1987). However, the recent period of extremely warm years appears to have initiated a breakdown in synchronisation, resulting in greater variability, and greater length in the flight period. The pattern of expansion suggests that most Gatekeepers move only short distances, whilst a few (perhaps mated females) make quite big journeys in attempts to colonise further north. At the edge of its range, the species is likely to get further north along milder coastal areas than inland.

Left: Gatekeeper with extra dot on wing. Right: male attracted to Privet blossom at Spurn (VC61) 03/08/1982.

HISTORICAL REVIEW:
Gatekeeper
Satyrus tithonus (in Porritt 1883)

Described by Merrett in 1666, and given many names including the **Orange Field Butterfly** (Wilkes 1741/42) and the **Small Meadow Brown** (Samouelle 1819). Harris (1766) was first to use **Gatekeeper** (Gate Keeper or Gate-keeper). Many 19th century authors used **Large Heath** to describe the Gatekeeper, whilst some (including Morris) used Gatekeeper to describe the Wall, which is not only confusing, but means we must be wary when investigating historical records! Newman & Leeds (1913) introduced **Hedge Brown**, favoured by a number of other 20th century authors, and leading to the current situation of two names still in regular use. The Latin name *Pyronia* = 'fiery-eyed', whilst Tithonus was a Trojan youth granted immortality but without eternal youth, a story celebrated in a poem of the same name by Tennyson.

Duncan (1844) sums up the then national situation: *'The butterfly appears in June, and is of frequent occurrence in England, and many places in the south of Scotland'*. Morris (1853) comments similarly, *'This is a very common British species, and is widely distributed occurring in lanes and meadows'*. Neither author felt the need to give specific sites. Rimington (1992) provides our earliest Yorkshire records (all VC63): Wath-upon-Dearne (Anon 1832) and Thorne Moors (Heppenstall 1842). He also notes Barnsley, 1871 [J Goodyear]; *'scarce at Hemsworth'* around 1880 (Brady 1884), and a lack of records around Doncaster suggesting a gradual decline by 1880. Robson (1902), summing up for Durham and Northumberland noted it was, *'widely distributed throughout both counties, though scarcely as plentiful as it was twenty or thirty years ago'*. Robson implies a presence at Hesleden Dene and elsewhere (presumably c1899 or earlier), but only two 20th century Durham & Northumberland sightings (1918 and 1925) are listed in Dunn & Parrack (1986). It would appear the species largely disappeared north of Yorkshire between c1870 and 1900. Thomson (1980) suggests that any 19th century Scottish presence was probably marginal, leading to extinction in

the 1870s. Rimington also points to a severe 19th century decline in Derbyshire and Nottinghamshire, although not Lincolnshire, whilst Fryer & Lucas (200?) could find no 19th century records for the Huddersfield area. Theakstone *Guide to Scarborough* (1871) carries a butterfly list compiled by Pe Inchbald, which gives the Gatekeeper as *'usually abundant'*. Walsh (195? notes it was taken by DW Bevan on Seamer Carrs (nr Scarborough VC62) the 1870s, but adds, *'There is no recent record, however, and it seems to ha disappeared locally'*. Tetley (1915) doesn't mention it, indicati disappearance from the Scarborough area before 1902 when he beg recording there.

Porritt (1883), looking back over 50yrs, gives the impression the Gatekeep was quite widespread although he does comment: *'Very common in the lan etc, on the east coast, but **less plentiful** in other districts'*. He lists: VC6 Bridlington, Filey, **VC62:** Raskelf (N of York), Redcar, Scarborough a Whitby, **VC63:** Hunslet and Methley (both Leeds area), Sheffield a Wakefield, **VC64:** Askham Bog, Bishop Wood, Bramham and Thorner (Leeds). Porritt (1904) adds **VC61:** Everingham (inc Market Weighto VC63: Thorne and Wheatley Wood, and, rather surprisingly, VC6 Grassington. Limbert (1975) casts doubt on this latter record suggesting it w more likely a Wall reported as a 'Gatekeeper'. Porritt's 1907 comme virtually repeats what he wrote in 1883, and cannot be depended upon as up-to-date statement. In similar fashion, his 1922 update of Boult's 1899 H area List repeats Boult's comments: *'Occasional, Sutton Bank'* (ie the H VC61 Sutton Bank).

The Gatekeeper is critically dependent on warm conditions, and would ha been badly affected by the cold years 1860/1863 and 1879/1895. (See p2 Towards the end of the 19th century, the northern edge of the Gatekeepe range slipped south and probably came to rest along the S Yorkshire border. the first half of the 20th century, records were scarce, even around Doncast but with occasional better years such as 1935 when it was reported *'abunda* on Crowle Moors. It was first recorded at Kilnsea (Spurn) in 1910 (Spen 1991) and has probably been present there continuously ever since, even in t 1960s when it suffered further in several cool, wet summers, leading S Jackson (YNU Lepidoptera Recorder) to comment in 1965 that the speci was, *'just about holding on in Yorkshire'*. However, early hints of the drama change to come can be picked up in the YNU 1967/70 Report, which not the species seen at Market Weighton (VC61) *'in fair numbers in 196* Spence (1991) recorded it particularly abundant at Spurn in 1970. Rimingt (1992) reports it doing well in 1970, and charts the subsequent spread in t Doncaster area.

For the Sheffield area (VC63) Garland (1981) detected a spread in Rotherham in the 1970s but only recorded 9 tetrads, all to the east of Sheffie between 1971 and 1980. By 1992 over 100 additional tetrads had been adde although still largely to the east (Whiteley 1992). Fryer & Lucas (2001) rep the first-ever record in the Huddersfield area (VC64) c1960 [MD Bridge p BD Cain], followed by the beginnings of real colonisation in 1983, wi sightings in the Hall Dike Valley (YNU Card File). The species was first not near Knaresborough (VC64) in 1978 (Barnham & Foggitt 1991) and fro 1983 was seen on several other sites SE of the Harrogate district. Limbe (1975), Jackson (1983), Barnham & Foggitt (1987), Barnham *et al* (199? and Fryer & Lucas (2001) add further detail to the earlier part of th expansion, which has developed steadily yet relatively slowly, with occasion set-backs in poorer summers. Rimington notes a crash on Thorne Moo (1986/1990), and Spence records poor years at Spurn in the cold, wet summe between 1986 and 1988. Although populations have recovered since, the records remind us that the Gatekeeper is still very much on the edge of i range in Yorkshire and liable to suffer further retractions in future poorer yea

Terry Whitak

1626 MEADOW BROWN *Maniola jurtina* (Linnaeus 1758)
Family: Nymphalidae (sub-group Satyrinae, 'the Browns').

View N from N end of Wolds (VC61) across the Howardian Hills to the N York Moors (VC62), July 2003.

UK BAP Status: *Not listed.*
BC Priorities: National: *Low.* N of England: *Low.* Yorkshire: *Low.*
European Status: *Not threatened.*

WORLD STATUS: Resident, 0-2500m. I brood (May/Sept with period of summer hibernation possible in S, and shorter flight period in N). Range: N Africa to N Scotland, S Norway, and eastward across Europe & Asia to W Siberia, Asia Minor and Iran. Some authorities distinguish 4 sub-species in British Isles: *iernes* in SW Ireland and nearby offshore islands; *cassiteridium* in the Isles of Scilly; *splendida* in Scotland north of the Great Glen, inc Hebrides and Orkneys; and *insularis* in the rest of Britain. A number of European countries such as Sweden, Finland and Luxembourg have reported declines, whilst the Netherlands and Romania have seen increases.

Meadow Brown

YORKSHIRE STATUS 1995/2003:

Resident: 0-430m. Widespread and common, with 1 brood (mainly Jun/Aug but with increasing numbers of May and Sept records). **Earliest:** 10/05/2002 South Gare (nr Middlesbrough VC62) [AP Kirk]. **Latest:** 30/09/2003 Wensley (VC65) [Jennie White]. Generally widespread in lowland areas, especially along roadside verges. Together with the 'Cabbage Whites', it is probably the most widely distributed butterfly in urban areas such as Leeds, Rotherham and Sheffield. It is absent, however, from much of the highest ground to the north and west, and even in some of the Pennine valleys it is very local. This may be due to the nature of livestock farming in this area, which leaves few corners that are not intensively managed and heavily grazed. Site counts across the county are variable, with figures in the 10 to 30 range fairly typical, whilst multiple hundreds may be seen in favourable situations such as at North Dale, Fordon, on the Yorkshire Wolds (VC61) where **485** were counted on 20/07/1996 [John Killingbeck]. Numbers vary quite considerably from year to year with 1999 the best in the Survey period: over **1000** were estimated at Spurn NNR (VC61) on 09/07 and 10/07 [Barry Spence], **845** counted at Thorpe Marsh (VC63) on 20/07 [J Wozencroft], and **798** noted in and around a cliff top hay meadow at Speeton on 07/07 [Howard Frost].

Although less common in the higher Pennines, recent observations suggest it is colonising higher levels than previously recorded, with sightings now common on moorland edges up to 250m to the west of Sheffield (VC63), and reports from Marsden, Meltham Moor and Holme Moss (all VC63) at heights above 300m. Since 1995 reports have come from significantly higher rough grassland sites up to 300m, including Menwith Hill (Harrogate area VC64). In Swaledale, Wensleydale and Arkengarthdale, and on the south side of the Middle Tees (VC65) small numbers are found up to the high moor edges at 300m. In 2002, it was recorded in VC64 at Gayle Ings (408m), and between Locker Tarn (345m) and Gooseberry Nab (400m) [Terry Whitaker]. The species was also noted at Duck St Quarry (VC64, 426m) in 2001 [Mike Barnham] and at High Folds Scar, Malham Tarn (VC64, 430m) where it is now considered a resident, although not recorded at all in the 1954/58 YNU study of the area (Michaelis 1963).

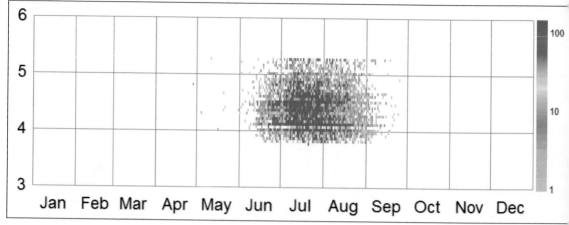

	Jan	Feb	Mar	Apr	May	Jun	Jul	Aug	Sep	Oct	Nov	Dec

(Graph y-axis values: 6, 5, 4, 3; scale legend: 100, 10, 1)

ID NOTES: Medium to large, drab brown butterfly. Male upperwings overall brown with an eyespot on each forewing, usually containing single white dot on black circle (compared to 2 white dots in Gatekeeper). When freshly emerged, adult male is rich glossy, chocolate brown, soon fading to a dull sooty shade, becoming steadily paler with age. Females usually larger (sometimes much larger) and brown with orange patches in central part of upper forewing. In closed wing view, forewings often retracted, but occasionally flicked upwards to reveal eyespot – an attempt to frighten or confuse potential predators. Although strongly associated with meadows it is also a woodland butterfly and may be seen flying quite high around trees. Can be confused with Gatekeeper, Grayling or Ringlet, but all have distinct differences in patterning, which can be studied in ID books. Meadow Browns are very variable with around 100 aberrations described. Specimens with varying degrees of paler shading on upperside hindwings are not uncommon and are grouped into ab *partimtransformis* (see photo). The upperside of ab *excessa*, with additional eyespots circled in orange, could be mistaken for a Scotch Argus.

PHENOGRAM: Yorkshire 1995-2003. Shows a single brood peaking in Jul and Aug, and also an interesting scatter of records into Sept, which could be a result of recent warmer summers.

Meadow Browns: mating pair.

CONSERVATION ISSUES: The Meadow Brown could have a problem in being taken for granted! Being dependent on wild grassy areas which some people see as useless 'wasteland', it has suffered from the general cleaning up of the countryside in the name of agricultural improvement, and is now also suffering from the reclamation and landscaping of brownfield sites in industrial areas. Many disused railway tracks have evolved from routes with open grassy verges (ideal for this species), to overgrown, shrubby woodlands, which are no longer reservoirs for this or many of our other butterflies. Over assiduous grass cutting in urban areas and along roadside verges can also spell trouble. Cemeteries often hold populations, but only when grassy areas are allowed to grow without too much control. Many woodlands lack conservation management and rides have become too shady. Nature Reserves often hold important colonies without anyone realising how important such a reservoir is to maintaining the species' presence within an area. In meadows, the timing of cutting grass could be important. Larvae need to be hatched and able to drop into the litter. The development of conservation headlands around fields could be of great value although initial problems of too much growth due to fertiliser-rich soils can militate against the presence of the suitable fine grasses and wild flowers needed by this species.

David Howson

Meadow Brown, male ab *transformis* Leeds, Ilkley (VC64) 08/08/2000.

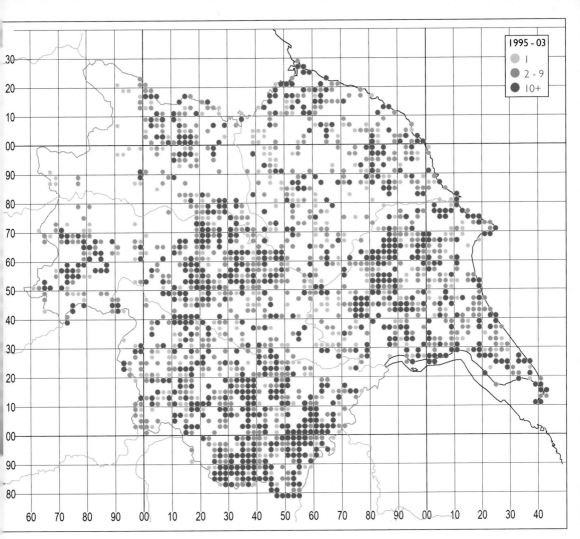

Meadow Brown: Yorkshire Tetrad map 1995-2003

MAP NOTES 1995-2003: Noted in **1760/3319** recorded tetrads (ie 53%), and out of 4120 tetrads in Yorkshire. **Ranked 6th most widespread** out of 36 regular breeding species in the county. One of our most common butterflies, although populations thin out towards the NW (the Dales).

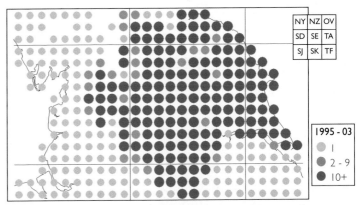

Meadow Brown: 10km distribution North of England

= 1 or more records out of county 1995-1999

HABITAT: Anywhere with patches of rough, uncut grassland up to c50cm height. The typical butterfly of old-fashioned hay meadows. A wide variety of grass species are used as foodplants with a preference for medium to fine-leaved species such as bents *Agrostis* spp., the ryegrasses *Lolium* spp., and meadow grasses *Poa* spp. Common along roadside verges, used and disused railway tracks and sidings, and the sides of ditches and river banks. Also found on brownfield sites, along woodland rides and edges, in parks and cemeteries, sheltered moorland areas, coastal cliffs and sand dunes, and occasionally in gardens.

Females usually mate on first day of emergence, courtship being short, with few preliminaries. In the process, the male surrounds its partner with a scent, which to humans may be reminiscent of musty hay or dirty socks! (Thomas & Lewington 1991) Pale eggs are laid singly on grasses or ejected into the litter layer. Several eggs may be left in the same neighbourhood. Brown larvae hatch after about two weeks, and eat their eggshells. They turn green soon after starting to eat grass. Larvae are not thought to hibernate in the full sense of the word, remaining active, and feeding by day throughout the winter whenever it

is mild enough. In colder spells they shelter in grass tussocks. By Mar, usually in the 3rd instar, they switch to night-time feeding to avoid predation by nesting birds. Pupation usually takes place by early Jun, with the pupa suspended on a grass stem or leaf blade. The green and black pupal colours vary from pale to dark according to the amount of light, warmth and humidity available on chosen site, which may be near ground level or up to c20cm high. This stage may last up to a month, but can be much shorter in warmer conditions.

Emergence is weather dependent, usually earlier in the warmer parts of VCs 61,63 & 64, although it has been reported as early as mid-May in all areas on occasion. Individual butterflies live from around 5 to 21 days. Main emergence often around 2nd week of Jun and fairly synchronous across all Yorkshire VCs, except for VC65 which may be up to 2 weeks later. Numbers usually peak in Jul with a few individuals lingering on through Sept. Whilst many authors agree with Emmett & Heath (1989) and say it is, *'Strictly univoltine'*, some, like Russwurm (1978), are uncertain: *'Although reputed to be single brooded it seems certain that when conditions are right a second brood occurs'*. In parts of the Mediterranean area, where summer heat regularly browns the grass growth, mated females hide away in the woodland understorey in a state of hibernation referred to as aestivation. They re-emerge in late summer, usually after thunderstorms have promoted grass re-growth, and proceed to lay their eggs. Although this is described as a Mediterranean feature, Howard & Christine Frost (pers comm.) noted aestivating Meadow Browns in woodland undergrowth as far north as Lat 48°N near Langres (France), in the hot summer of 2003. It raises the question as to whether it could also happen further north and be an explanation of some late appearances in hotter drier years.

Being a brown butterfly, the Meadow Brown is good at absorbing heat, which is a useful adaptation in a northern climate. As a result it may still fly when it is cloudy and even slightly damp. In cool sunny conditions it may lean over on a patch of bare ground to present a closed-wing view to the sun to absorb its heat. The Grayling does likewise, which sometimes leads to mistaken identities. When the Meadow Brown is hot enough it will face the sun with wings closed to reduce absorption.

This species is a much-studied insect, with detailed investigations into its genetic make-up in relation to the reasons behind its variability (eg Ford 1975, Dowdeswell 1981, Brakefield 1984 and Brakefield & van Noordwijk 1985). In particular, the tiny dots visible on the lower wing, in closed-wing view, are variable in number, and although so small, different numbers of dots appear to confer specific advantages on different sites. It is possible that potential predators may be able to see more in these dots than is perceived by the human eye, as seemingly dull colours in butterflies and moths can sometimes fluoresce in light wavelengths beyond human sight, making a dull eye pattern much more life-like.

During our Survey period the flight period appears to have been extending, due it is presumed, to an increase of temperatures and suitable flying weather, although increased encouragement to observers to take note of early and late records may have been an added influence: **1996:** 04/06 to 01/09; **1997:** 08/06 to 13/09; **1998:** 17/06 to 13/09; **1999:** 15/05 to 21/09; **2000:** 19/05 to 23/09; **2001:** 23/05 to 16/09; **2002:** 10/05 to 20/09; **2003:** 01/06 to 30/09.

Meadow Brown, ab cinerea Cosmovici, Tophill Low Reservoirs (VC61), 2003.

HISTORICAL REVIEW:
Meadow Brown

Initially, there was confusion about the sexes and Petiver (1699) gave male and female separate names, **the brown Meadow, ey'd Butterfly** (male) and **the golden Meadow, ey'd Butterfly** (female). He actually thought the drabber male was the female. Albin (1720) introduced **Meadow Brown** and most authors followed suit, although Morris (1853) used **Large Meadow Brown** to distinguish it from his Small Meadow Brown (ie the Gatekeeper). The Latin *Maniola* links the butterfly's brown colouration to the souls of the departed in the dusky nether regions! *Jurtina* was probably a typographical error for 'Jurturna', a nymph associated with a Roman fountain.

Yorkshire's earliest records are found in the Wath-upon-Dearne (VC63) list (Anon 1832), in Heppenstall (1842) re Thorne Moors, and in a report from Adwick in 1846 [JW Dunning] (all Rimington 1992). It was not a well-reported species in the 19th century, presumably because it was so common. Duncan (1844) summed up the national picture: *'next to the white Cabbage species, may be regarded as the most common insect of its tribe'*. He goes on to quote from a Mr Kapp in the *Journal of a Naturalist*: *'In that arid summer of 1826, the abundance of these creatures was so obvious as to be remarked by very indifferent persons'*. Morris (1853) made a

similar comment: *'It is one of our most plentiful species and occurs in all parts of the country. I well remember the extraordinary numbers in which it appeared in the unusually hot and dry summer of the year 1826'*.

Porritt (1883) considered it *'generally distributed; abundant in the East Riding, but less common in the West Riding'*. He went on: *'At Huddersfield it seems to be extinct, for although I saw it in abundance in a field at Almondbury many years ago, I have never seen a specimen there since'*. Rimington (1992) also points to a decline in N Derbyshire (late 19th century) and parts of N Nottinghamshire (*'by 1900'*), but no noted fluctuations in Lincolnshire. Fryer & Lucas (2001) investigate the situation around Huddersfield in considerable depth, noting that Hobkirk (1859, 1868) considered it *'common in meadows'* in the 1850s and 1860s. However, the rather vague evidence currently available indicates that sometime around 1870 it largely disappeared, or became so localised, that it was rarely seen around the Huddersfield and Barnsley areas. Much hinges on Porritt's 1883 comment. Just how long ago was *'many years ago'*? The severe weather years (1879/1895) started with one of the ten coldest summers on record. They were also preceded by several cooler years (1876 onward) during which the species may have retracted. On top of that we have the growing industrialisation of the West Riding, especially around Huddersfield. Fryer & Lucas (2001) put forward a cogent case for smoke and soot pollution playing a major role in reducing sunshine levels in this area. It seems likely that the Meadow Brown was hit by both weather and pollution. Rimington (1992) notes that the Meadow Brown was inconsistently recorded in the Doncaster area during the 19th century with only 4 records up 1887, which he puts down to familiarity with the species. However, the 'selected' records he gives are mainly post 1896 when observers also specifically noted large numbers, as though in reaction to a previous scarcity. It seems likely that Meadow Brown numbers went down over much of the county between 1879 and 1895, but as the species didn't completely disappear no-one paid any great notice. In spite of *'immense numbers'* in the Doncaster area in 1901 it took until 1932 before it began to reappear around Huddersfield and 1940 before it returned to Barnsley. Thereafter it spread steadily with sightings implying a westward movement towards the Pennines.

Over the Pennine watershed, Alan Brindle (1939) considered it a very rare visitor to the Pendle Hill area (VC64) in the 1930s. However, the butterfly appears to have remained common in many rural areas, although with annual fluctuations due to the weather. Populations were probably boosted by the warmer 1940s, although local declines were reported in the Doncaster area during the cooler, wetter 1960s, only to be followed by new expansions soon after. The YNU 1967/70 Report noted it: *'widely distributed and abundant in many areas. In recent years it has become commoner in the industrial regions of the West Riding'*. Sutton & Beaumont (1989) considered it *'generally common on lower, uncultivated ground in all five vice-counties'*, as well as probably *'the most widely distributed butterfly in urban areas such as Leeds'*, but still *'absent from the higher ground to the north and west, even in the valleys'*. In fact, it was found *'only as far west as Pateley Bridge (VC64) (Barnham & Foggitt 1987)'*. The exceptionally warm 1990s appear to have encouraged further colonisation in the Pennines, reaching higher levels than previously recorded. The species remains common and widespread throughout the county, but probably less so than 200yrs ago.

Meadow Brown: another ab *transformis* variation, Moorends (Thorne VC63) 14/08/1996.

Terry Whitaker

1627 SMALL HEATH *Coenonympha pamphilus* (Linnaeus 1758)
Family: Nymphalidae, sub-group Satyrinae ('the Browns').

Fleet Moss, 550m+ (VC64/65 border). This site is drier than it appears and home to Small Heaths rather than Large. The white drifts are cotton grass.

UK BAP Status: *Not listed.*
BC Priorities: National: *Low.*
N of England: *Low.* Yorkshire: *Low.*
European Status: *Not threatened.*

WORLD STATUS: Resident: 0-2700m. 1 to 3 overlapping broods (Feb/Nov) according to height and latitude. Range: N Africa to N Norway and eastward across Europe into Asia as far as S Siberia and Mongolia. Widespread in British Isles up to 750m, although populations thinner in Ireland and N Scotland (and absent from Orkney and Shetland). Subspecies *rhoumensis* Harrison 1948 found on Isle of Rhum in Scotland, although this status is considered doubtful by some authorities.

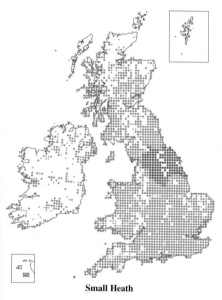

Small Heath

YORKSHIRE STATUS 1995/2003:

Resident: 0-700m. 1 or 2 overlapping broods according to height & weather, with perhaps a small partial 3rd in good years. **Earliest:** 06/05/2000, **2** in Newton Dale (VC62) [John Hume]. **Latest:** 07/10/2002, Spurn NNR (VC61) [Barry Spence]. The species is widely distributed in suitable habitats throughout all five VCs, with the densest populations in warmer, lower areas, such as Spurn NNR, valley grasslands and quarries in the Wolds (VC61), Strensall Common and South Gare in VC62, and on various sand and gravel sites to the east of Doncaster (VC63). It is also thinly but widely, distributed over large regions of upland in VCs 62, 64, and 65, with small concentrations in areas where there are warm, dry sites, with limited grazing (eg Beldi Hill VC65, Scar Close NNR and Buckhaw Brow VC64). Rough acid grassland at around 300m on the moorland edges around the Yorkshire Dales provides typical upland habitat, and although it is rare to see two individuals together, many dozens may be observed on a long walk. This is a situation which appears to be unchanged from that indicated by Michaelis (1963), referring to grassland around the lower slopes of Fountains Fell.

Most reports are of 1 to 10 butterflies on any given site. Counts in excess of 50 are uncommon and those over 100 unusual, except on particularly favoured sites. Highest counts in the Survey period have been: **1996: 245** at Cottam (Wolds VC61) on 17/06 [John Killingbeck], **100+** in Settle area (VC64) on 17/07 [Brian Shorrock]. **1997: 120** at Cottondale (Wolds VC61) 21/07 [John Killingbeck], **70** at Spurn NNR (VC61) 08/07 [Barry Spence]; **50** at Wath-upon-Dearne (VC63) on 29/05 [Roy Bedford]. **1998: 121** at Heath (VC63) on 10/07 [Roy Bedford]. **1999: 665** at Wharram Quarry YWT NR (Wolds VC61) on 08/07 [Howard Frost]. **2003: 227** at Burdale (Wolds VC61) on 12/07 [Ralph Hibbert]; **150** at South Gare (Middlesbrough VC62) on 20/07 [Paul Forster & Derrick Wood].

During the Survey the first and last dates indicate a slight lengthening of the flight period: **1996:** 25/05 to 17/09; **1997:** 14/05 to 29/09; **1998:** 17/06 to 13/09; **1999:** 09/05 to 23/09; **2000:** 06/05 to 01/10; **2001:** 21/05 to 06/09; **2002:** 11/05 to 07/10; **2003:** 07/05 to 25/09. All these sightings were made in lower areas and mainly in the southern half of the county. Flight seasons on higher ground to the north and west are much shorter and

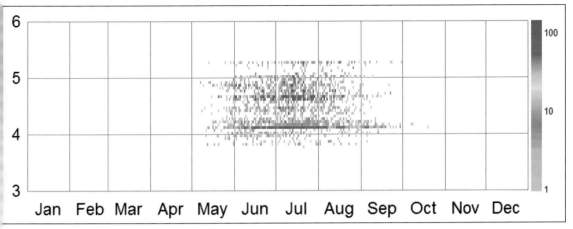

Jan Feb Mar Apr May Jun Jul Aug Sep Oct Nov Dec

ID NOTES: Small, brown and orange butterfly about same size as Common Blue or Small Copper. Always perches with wings closed, therefore orange upperwings only seen in flight, when both bright and drab specimens may be distinguished. Perched, it looks rather like a mini-Meadow Brown, with drab lower wing, and small but prominent eyespot on upperwing set against an orange brown background. On landing it usually retracts the upperwing and becomes well disguised in a grassy backcloth. Can be separated from the usually somewhat larger Large Heath by the latter's greyer appearance in flight, and multiple eyespots in closed-wing view. Some ID books suggest you can also use habitat to separate the latter two species. Whilst only the Large Heath is likely to be seen at Thorne and Crowle Moors near Doncaster (VC63), both species may be seen flying together on the N York Moors especially at Fen Bog YWT NR, one of the main Large Heath sites.

PHENOGRAM: Yorkshire 1995-2003. No clear generation breaks can be seen except possibly on the strong line on the bottom (ie to the south), which appears to relate mainly to observations at Spurn NNR. Individual sites may show clearer distinctions.

more likely to involve just one brood rather than two or more. Hints of local declines have also been received during the Survey period. Cain & Baggaley (1997, 1998) noted reductions around Halifax, and Fryer & Lucas (2001) suspect possible losses around Huddersfield. These are almost certainly associated with habitat loss and degradation caused by intensive agriculture which has previously been at its most destructive on land below 300m where most of the strongest colonies are found.

Small Heath, Strensall Common (VC62).

Lawrie King

CONSERVATION ISSUES: Being a rather drab butterfly, which doesn't show itself with wings open, its importance on any given site is easily overlooked. It is particularly vulnerable to the 'tidying up' of landscapes by amenity grass mowing and also by 'conservation' tree planting on what some people view as grassy 'wastelands'. It has also moved in to brownfield sites, which are now subject to increasing development and the subsequent landscaping of what were previously suitable habitats. The species has lost out on intensively farmed grasslands where a fertilised or re-sown sward destroys the fine grasses it requires. Although the butterfly remains fairly widespread it is often in very low numbers and therefore much more likely to be affected by adverse conditions. It could be under greater threat than seems apparent especially as it does not normally appear to fly very far, putting its populations at increasing risk through isolation. Butterfly Conservation is currently studying these problems.

Roosting Small Heath. Easily missed! (Wharram VC61).

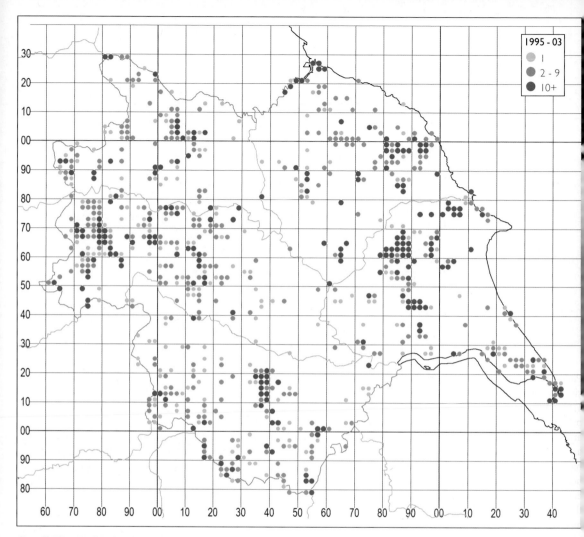

Small Heath: Yorkshire Tetrad map 1995-2003

MAP NOTES 1995-2003: Noted in **753/3319** recorded tetrads (ie 22.7%), and out of 4120 tetrads in Yorkshire. **Ranked 17th most widespread** out of 36 regular breeding species in the county. Appears less common in the N/S band down the centre of the county (Vale of York), and in some parts of the east (eg Holderness), probably a result of disliking damper areas, plus the lack of suitable habitat where prairie agriculture prevails. Red dots indicate a preference for higher regions (Pennines, Wolds and Moors) and in the south of the county where disused rail tracks and brownfield sites are common.

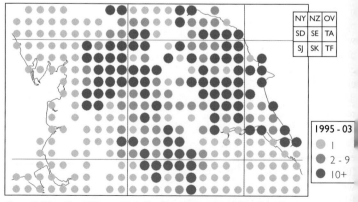

Small Heath: 10km distribution North of England

◉ = 1 or more records out of county 1995-1999

LIFE STORY

Pale green, barrel-shaped eggs are placed singly on grass blades. After laying around 100 eggs females then produce a smaller pale yellow version, the reasons for which are unknown. Eggs become paler with time and develop darker patches, then just before hatching (after about two weeks), they become almost transparent, with the young caterpillar visible inside. Larvae live low in the grass sward and when young, mainly emerge at night to nibble the tips of grass blades. They are green with narrow pale and dark stripes, which provide excellent camouflage in grassy situations.

Growth patterns are complex with 2 broods in the south of Britain (plus an occasional partial third), and only one in the north, with Yorkshire seeing a transitional zone between the two. The situation is further complicated by the fact that a proportion of each brood stay as larvae, becoming well-developed by the end of the summer, and ready to pupate early the following year. They overwinter as larvae and may continue feeding throughout winter when mild enough. The first of the attractive pupae (usually with purple-brown stripes edged with white on the wing cases) are formed by late April, hanging beneath grass stems. The first batch of adults emerges after about 3 weeks, often during May. These are usually overlapped by adults from the later developing larvae which were offspring of the previous year's 2nd and 3rd broods, leading to a peak of butterflies in Jun/Jul which is further boosted by offspring of the year. Annual and local climatic variations will influence exactly when this might occur. In good years adults are often on the wing continuously from May to Sept making it difficult to distinguish between generations, and individuals from the previous year, which have simply developed at different rates (Blakeley 1997,1998; Whitaker 2001).

Warm temperatures experienced in early spring appear to promote advanced larval and pupal development and

Small Heath: mating pair.

Shirley King

early emergence. Cold wet Junes can delay development of any later brood and lead to low numbers the following spring (Blakeley 1999). The species appears to produce 2 broods on most Yorkshire sites, except on higher ground in cooler years. In poor years that 2nd brood may be only partial, whilst in warm years a scatter of late Sept/early Oct sightings appears to indicate a small partial 3rd brood sometimes occurs in the south of the county.

Wickman (1985a, 1985b, 1986) provides the main source of information about this species. The flight stage of individual Small Heaths lasts around 7 days. Males spend most of their time searching for mates. Each establishes a territory near a prominent vegetative feature and perches or patrols the nearby area, occasionally straying more widely. Such territories are defended against other males and spiralling combat flights are commonly seen before one of the participants (often the one with shorter wings!) leaves the territory. Virgin females show extensive solicitation flights, flying back and forth about 1m off the ground. If they enter a territory it is usually to mate. Females will land on the ground whilst the male approaches with fluttering wings and head butts her. Once mated, females then avoid males and set off in search of suitable open, grassy areas in which to lay their eggs.

HISTORICAL REVIEW:
Small Heath
Chortobius Pamphilus L. in Porritt

Merrett (1666) was first to describe this species, although it was left to Petiver (1699) to give it its first name, **Small Heath**. However, in 1717 he decided that the bright and dark specimens were actually two species, which he re-named **the golden Heath Eye**, and **the selvedg'd Heath Eye**. Subsequent writers introduced further new names including **Little** or **Small Gatekeeper** (Harris 1766) and **Small Argus** (Lewin 1795). Berkenhout (1769) reverted to Small Heath and this eventually became more widely accepted, although Morris (1853) introduced **Least Meadow Brown**. *Pyronia* means *fiery eyed*, whilst Tithonus was a Trojan youth granted immortality but without eternal youth, a story celebrated in a poem of the same name by Tennyson.

Like the common Whites, this species has been very much taken for granted over the years being considered so common that it was often not listed at all. Duncan (1844) summed up the national picture: *'This pretty little butterfly is very common in all parts of the country, on heaths and upland pastures. It appears in the beginning of June and there is a second flight in September.'* Morris (1853) made similar comments: *'This is one of our commonest species, being abundant in almost all parts of the country...It is frequent on heaths, as also in meadows and various other situations'.* Rimington (1992) provides the county's earliest known records from VC63 at Wath-upon-Dearne (Anon 1832) and at Thorne Moors (Heppenstall 1842b). Then, perhaps surprisingly, there are no further Donaster area records until 1923! Rimington puts this down to *'poor levels of recording in eastern sites'.*

Shirley King

However, the investigations of Fryer & Lucas (2001) reveal that in the Huddersfield area (VC63) the species suffered a definite population crash in the late 19th century. Hobkirk (1859, 1868) noted it was common on dry banks in the Huddersfield area, but by 1883, Mosley was unable to give a single currently occupied site. Records from the Halifax Scientific Society indicate a report from Luddenden in 1866, then nothing more until 1942! The *'Naturalists' Column'* in the *Bradford Weekly Telegraph* of 31/05/1890 noted *'The Small Heath is abundant on Baildon Moor'* and recorded its continuing presence in 1885 and 1886. Butterfield (1906) in an article on *'Vanishing local plants and animals'* reported it had almost disappeared from the neighbourhood of Bradford, except on Baildon Moor and Newsholme Dean, and by 1911 he was reporting a further decrease. However, by 1925 a note in the YNU Card File indicates it was *'Now considered well established in the Bradford area'.* Porritt (1883) described it as, *'Distributed all over the county, but rare in some parts of the West Riding'.* His 1907 comment was similar although he did indicate that by this later date it was, *'**Abundant** in most districts'*, which could be an indication of a recovery after a leaner time. Fryer & Lucas note a presence recorded in Morley's manuscript list for 1896/1908 in the Skelmanthorpe area at Gunthwaite and Langsett, and then they chart a slow but steady improvement as numbers apparently built up again in the 1920s/1930s, with re-colonisation appearing to progress from east to west. The species spread through the Halifax area in the 1940s, and by the 1960s had become *'strongly established'* (Collinson 1969), a situation which has continued to the present day albeit with some slight local declines noted during the 1995/2003 Survey period.

Elsewhere in the county there are no hints of population extinctions, although there could well have been declines which were simply not noted. All butterfly numbers tend to fluctuate for many reasons, and a decline in such a common species could easily have been overlooked. For the Sheffield area Garland (1981) thought the Small Heath was one of the few species which had remained reasonably constant in range and number throughout the 19th and 20th centuries. Stainforth (1919) referring to the mid-19th century Hull area (VC61) mentions its presence at Riplingham and Cottingham, whilst Boult's 1899 Hull list noted it was (as today) common on the Humber Bank

For the Scarborough area, Tetley (1915) included it in the general comment *'I have not mentioned species of general distribution...'.* Walsh (1952) considered it, *'Common all over the district, wolds, moors, lanes and carrs'.* The YNU 1967/70 Report noted it, *'Well distributed and common throughout the county'.* Sutton & Beaumont (1989) thought it, *'One of the most widespread butterflies in Yorkshire...it vies with the Small Tortoiseshell as the butterfly breeding at the highest altitude'.* They also noted it much less abundant in lower areas like the Vale of York where intensive farming has left few suitable corners for this butterfly.

Fryer & Lucas (2001), assume that the 19th century disappearance of this species was part of a pattern of losses localised to the West Riding and therefore probably caused by industrial pollution, although they admit that more than 100yrs after the event it is no longer possible to prove such a theory. Studies of the severe weather in the late 19th century (summarised in earlier chapters) also suggest another potential cause. In fact it is probable that the two factors combined to produce extremely low sunshine levels due to smoke and fog, made worse for butterflies by a period of notably cool summers, exacerbated by volcanic dust in the atmosphere. In less polluted areas the species may well have declined sharply, but by managing to hold on and later rebuild its populations, any such fluctuations failed to produce lasting comment.

Terry Whitaker

Thorne Moors (VC63): part of the 3300 hectare NNR, 2003.

UK BAP Status: *Species of Conservation Concern* **BC Priorities:** National: *Medium.* N of England: *Medium.* Yorkshire: *Medium.* **European Status:** *Vulnerable.* **Protected in Great Britain for sale only.**

WORLD STATUS: Resident: 1 brood, 0-1200m (June/early Aug). Northern British Isles, and in a broad band from NE France to Scandinavia, and eastward across temperate Asia to N America (where 1 to 3 broods may occur). Very variable throughout range and within individual colonies. In northernmost areas c 5% of larvae may take 2 years to mature. Declining in Europe. In British Isles traditionally divided into 3 subspecies or forms: *davus* (with larger eyespots) in lowland sites in Shropshire and NW England; *polydama* in Ireland, Wales, N England (inc Yorkshire) and S Scotland; and *scotia* (a less variable form), north of a line from Glasgow to Aberdeen.

Large Heath

YORKSHIRE STATUS 1995/2003:

Sedentary resident: 1 brood (June to early/mid-Aug). Currently, found only on lowland peat moors near Doncaster (VC63), and on mires, wet heaths and marshy grasslands on the N York Moors (VC62). BC *Medium* priority given due to declining numbers and loss of sites (eg now extinct on Goole Moors and Hatfield Moors VC63/SE70/71). The species is on the **southern** edge of its range in the county, the line of which runs south-westwards from southern Yorkshire into central Wales.

Populations at Thorne Moors (VC63/SE71), and adjacent Crowle Moors (straddling the traditional county border with Lincs (VCs63/54/SE71), have been monitored by English Nature in most years since 1987 using single species transects. Rimington (1992) reported casual counts as high as **186** and **140** in two separate parts of the area in 1987, whilst transect count results for 1995 (Plant 1995) give some idea of the relatively small and then apparently shrinking size of these colonies: Thorne: 25/06 (**5**); 04/07 (**19**); 12/07 (**87**); 21/07 (**74**); 03/08 (**29**); Crowle: 24/06 (**0**); 03/07 (**19**); 11/07 (**37**); 20/07 (**24**); 02/08 (**9**). More detailed surveying at Crowle in 1999 (Pickett 1999) indicated a somewhat higher population than in 1995, with peak counts on two transects up to **58+11**, which could be a positive result of conservation management techniques. However, with peat cutting finally ended in Sept 2004, and the transfer of the land to English Nature for management as part of the Humberhead Peatlands NNR, the butterfly seems to have been saved at Thorne Moors. Restoration of the peat bog is already taking place with cotton-grasses increasing and Large Heath numbers going up: eg **210** counted at Thorne Moors on 14/06/2003 [Ralph Hibbert & Chris Parkin].

For the N York Moors, a month-long BC survey by Dave Wainwright in 2004 indicated a larger presence than previously realised (or shown on our maps) with records from 40x1km squares in up to 6 adjacent 10km squares. 58 occupied habitat patches were distinguished in and to the E of Newton Dale, ranging from c0.5ha to >50ha in size. Whole season population estimates (excluding the large Fen Bog colony) indicate 32 patches were *small* (<100 adults), 24 were *medium* (100-1000) and one was *large* (1000+). Adult Large Heaths live c3days, with fresh butterflies emerging regularly through the season producing much larger populations than a single day's count might suggest. However, some observers still feel such estimates may err on the high side. Populations appear to be grouped into 4 or 5 networks based around

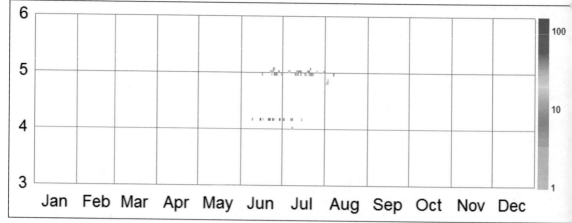

Goathland, Newton Dale, Fylingdales and Wheeldale/Murk Mire Moors. **Earliest reports:** 21/06/2004, already present on 8 sites [Dave Wainwright]. **Latest:** 06/08/2000, May Moss [Len & Norma Auckland]. Highest counts: **20** Jugger Howe 10/07/1998 [Peter Waterton], **48** Fen Bog 24/06/2003 [Howard Frost], **26** Maybecks 21/06/2004 [Dave Wainwright]. Historical records from the area to the west of Newton Dale suggest there may yet be other sites to discover.

The Humberhead Levels NNR: Although peat digging has been established at Thorne and Hatfield Moors for centuries, it was low key until the introduction of mechanised extraction in 1962, which then resulted in large-scale drainage and complete removal of vegetation to exploit the underlying peat reserves for horticultural purposes. The effect was catastrophic. Rimington (1992)

PHENOGRAM: Yorkshire 1995-2003. Indicates the later flight season on higher N York Moors sites (upper area) compared to lowland colonies of Thorne/Crowle Moors (bottom).

notes that in the early 1980s counts of **40/50** Large Heaths were possible at Hatfield. This dropped steadily to the point of extinction by 1995. Plant (1995) suggests the last record was probably that of Brian Eversham in 1994. Populations at Thorne dropped in similar fashion with the last high count of **235** in 1989. By the early 1990s, growing interest in gardening and potted plants encouraged even larger scale mechanised digging, capable of removing peat from hundreds of acres per season. But then the resulting destruction provoked a notable campaign to save the Moors complex, backed by local and national groups as well as the *Yorkshire Post*. After some success in 1994, resulting in a part buy-out of the sites, the campaigners from both voluntary and statutory nature conservation sectors eventually won the day, when in 2002 the Government bought out the peat extraction rights, and English Nature was charged with the ownership, restoration and future management of most of the Moors. Large-scale peat-mining finished in Sept 2004 with a two-year restoration project beginning immediately. The process of raising water levels actually began in 1992, through small-scale management improvements at Crowle, and in the relatively small refugium nature reserve at Thorne. Large Heath numbers at Crowle responded quickly as the hare's-tail cotton-grass recovered. The prospects for restoring huge areas of peatbog now look very good with large-scale re-wetting underway, and cotton-grass already re-colonising large areas of both Thorne and Hatfield, signalling better times ahead for one of Yorkshire's rarest butterfly species.

ID NOTES: Medium-sized brown butterfly, with slow erratic flight. Nominally *polydama* in Yorkshire but so variable that examples close to any form may be found. Similar to the **smaller** Small Heath but usually separated by habitat: dry for Small and wet for Large. However, both fly together on Fen Bog (VC62). Large Heath appears **greyer** and more moth-like in flight. Both species always perch with wings closed and also tilt wings to absorb warmth. In closed-wing position, Large Heath usually has distinctive cream band below forewing eyespot, and a line of 'Ringlet' type spots towards the edge of the hindwing. Small Heath is similar but plainer and less strongly marked, with only a hint of hindwing spots. Over 20 aberrations have been described, inc ab *thornensis* (Pilleau 1952), described from a Thorne Moors specimen which lacked spots and cream band.

CONSERVATION ISSUES: More work is needed to establish exact ecological requirements for the Large Heath. Butterfly Conservation has produced a national Large Heath Species Action Plan (Bourne & Warren 1997), which stresses the need for care in restoring or conserving mire habitats. Sites need to be wet, but not too wet. Water levels should not be allowed to totally submerge tussocks of Hare's-tail Cotton-Grass for more than a few days at a time. Recent studies suggest larvae may drown if underwater for more than about 7 days (Joy & Pullin 1997). Drier winter refuge areas for larvae, appear to be an essential habitat constituent. Sites can easily be degraded: a) by drying out in drought years or through drainage; b) by scrub encroachment, eg Birch; c) by burning, or d) by overgrazing. These issues are being addressed at Thorne & Hatfield through the NNR Management Plan. Consideration is also being given to the potential for re-introduction of the Large Heath to Hatfield from the increasingly strong Thorne populations. Detailed surveying of N York Moors populations took place in 2004 with a view to producing specific management guidelines.

Top left: Fen Bog YWT NR lies at the head of Newton Dale and provides a mix of mire, wet heath and moorland, where Small Heaths and Large Heaths fly together (2004). Lower left: a scene from Thorne Moors with cotton grass growing in marshy land, ideal for Large Heath (2003). Lower right: Large Heath, Jugger Howe (VC62).

Peter Waterton

MAP NOTES 1995-2003: Noted in just **20/3319** recorded tetrads (ie 0.6%), and out of 4120 tetrads in Yorkshire. **Ranked 32nd most widespread** out of 36 regular breeding species in the county. Clearly one of our rarer species, restricted to suitable damp, boggy areas on the N York Moors and the lowland bogs of the Humberhead Levels. However, information collected by Dave Wainwright in 2004 indicates a much greater N York Moors presence than previously realised (see notes above).

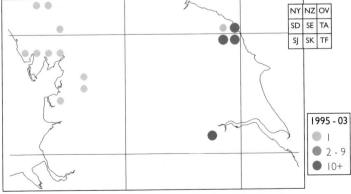

NY	NZ	OV
SD	SE	TA
SJ	SK	TF

1995 - 03
- 1
- 2 - 9
- 10+

Large Heath: 10km distribution North of England

◉ = 1 or more records out of county 1995-1999

LIFE STORY

Pale yellow eggs are laid singly, usually (but not always) low down in tussocks of Hare's-tail Cotton-grass. David Wainwright (pers comm.) writes: *'Literature frequently states that eggs are laid on tussocks. This is by no means the case where my research was carried out,'* (in Northumberland). *'Roughly one quarter of ovipositions I observed were on tussocks, but by far the commonest situation was in sparse, dead vegetation*

Large Heath, Fen Bog, 15/06/2003.

close to the ground. Post-diapause larvae were almost invariably found in tussocks (often small ones), which may account for the widely held assumption that the butterfly selects tussocks on which to oviposit. The best habitat was found where small (often unhealthy looking) tussocks were present and where vegetation was sufficiently sparse and short to enable ground layers of mosses to be seen easily.'

On hatching, after about 15 days, the pale-striped green larvae feed by day (and in warm, humid conditions also by night) until late Sept, when, in the 3rd instar, they hibernate deep in the base of a Cotton-grass tussock. In this position it appears they can survive being underwater or even encased in ice, but probably only for short periods. British colonies can exist up to about 500m; those on the N York Moors reach 150/200m, so they have to be pretty hardy insects. Larvae typically awake in March, continue feeding, and finally pupate in late May/early June in their fifth instar. The species flies from early to mid-June, into early Aug, with stragglers possible to mid-Aug. 1999 transect information from Crowle indicates a season running from around 09/06 to 23/07 (Pickett 1999).

In 1995/2002 only casual records were made on the N York Moors, suggesting a later season in these higher areas, with the earliest record being 25/06/2000 and the latest 06/08/2000 (both May Moss, Len & Norma Auckland). A few British colonies are very large, with populations up to 15,000, which emphasises the small size of those in Yorkshire. Fortunately, the species can exist at very low densities, although that makes it easy to overlook. Mobility is generally low, with lifetime distances covered, often no more than 450m, although, on the wide, open expanse of Thorne Moors, the species is subject to wind-blow. Cawdell (2002) refers to *'high winds blowing them up and over trees northwards'*. It also appears that populations exist in networks, with occasional interchange between adjacent colonies, but natural colonisation/re-colonisation seems likely to be slow.

Large Heath, Nectaring on Crowle Moor (1984).

HISTORICAL REVIEW:
Large Heath
Chortobius davus (in Porritt 1883)

Early naming suffered from confusions with other species and the describing of the three or more forms as separate species. It was first put on the British list by William Lewin in 1795 as the **Manchester Argus** and later the **Manchester Ringlet**. Donovan (1797) called it the **Scarce Meadow Brown**, whilst Haworth (1803) used 3 separate species names: **Marsh Ringlet** (*polydama*), **Scarce** or **Large Heath** (*tiphon*), and **Small Ringlet** (*davus*). Rennie (1832) used **July Ringlet** and **Silver-bordered Ringlet**. Duncan (1844) and others used Large Heath to describe the Gatekeeper! Confusion continued well into the 1900s. **American dimension:** Large Heaths in America are called 'Ringlets' and according to Pyle 1981) some American lepidopterists think that all five described species of the *Coenonympha* genus are 'forms' of the Eurasian Large Heath, namely: Kodiak Ringlet *Coenonympha Kodiak*; Prairie Ringlet *C. inornata*; Ochre Ringlet *C.ochracea*; Northwest Ringlet *C.ampelos* and California Ringlet *C. californica*. In the current Latin name *Coenonympha* has the sense of 'sharing with a nymph', and *tullia* is derived from the Roman name Tullius.

More widely distributed in past than today, especially in the Humberhead Levels (VCs54/63), the Valley of the River Hull (VC61), the N Yorkshire Moors (VC62) and the Pennines (VC64/65). The species was first discovered in Denmark in 1764 by OF Müller and later documented existing in Britain by William Lewin in 1795. Haworth (1803) referred to its presence *'in the county of York'*, whilst Stephens (1828) indicated this presence was at Beverley (VC61) from where he had been sent two specimens by Peter Watson. Stainforth (1919) writes that the Beverley site was actually near Cottingham probably in TA0432t) in a marshy area called Stainton Bogs. By 1919 Stainforth notes: *'Only a small area of this now exists, void of any special interest and serving only as a convenient tipping place for garden refuse, but in the middle of the century past, the Marsh Ringlet was common there.'* Newman (1860) visited the site and was struck by the fact that it was *different from Thorne Moor which is*

mossy or spongy, but the Cottingham locality is rather like those spots where I have taken Davus in Scotland'. Boult (1899) indicates that it was probably last recorded at Cottingham by James C Dale who died in 1872. Prior to the first Holderness Drainage Acts in 1763 and 1765, the Hull Valley was a huge marsh, mainly too wet to be farmed. Drainage around Cottingham began c1766 and continued to the end of the century, although it was well into the 1800s before the Hull Valley water levels were anything like under control. The Humberhead Levels cover the floodplain associated with the rivers which run into the Humber nr Goole (VC63) (inc the Trent, Ouse, Aire and Derwent, draining around one-sixth of England). This was formerly a huge marshland and lowland raised bog, lying mainly in Yorkshire, but including part of Lincolnshire near the Trent. (The traditional county boundary runs through Crowle Moor, with the Yorkshire section sometimes called 'the Yorkshire Triangle'.) In the 1700s the Large Heath would have been found over a wide area of the floodplain. Stephens (1828) seems to have been first to write up a Thorne Moors record, noting it had been seen there by James Backhouse. (NB 'Thorne Moors' or 'Thorne Waste', occasionally misprinted as 'Shorne Moors' in old books, is often used as a generalisation to include the adjacent Crowle and Goole Moors and in the past probably referred to an even wider area. References to Hatfield Moor just south of Thorne come somewhat later, with Newman (1860) recording that Edwin Birchall had seen the species there. Stainforth (1919) refers to a mid-nineteenth century presence on Whitgift Moors (to the east of Goole Moors VC63/SE82), today an area of prairie farming on reclaimed marshland almost devoid of butterflies. Rimington (1992) notes: an 1879 reference to a presence at 'Black Carr' which could have been at Potteric Carr or Rossington Bridge (both VC63/SE60); and a late 1800s reference to it being taken near Rotherham.

Parts of Crowle Moor are managed as a nature reserve by the Lincolnshire Wildlife Trust, but the greater part of the Thorne/Goole/Crowle peatlands and Hatfield Moors are now owned and managed by English Nature as the Humberhead Peatlands National Nature Reserve (3318ha/8201acres). Past records on the Lincolnshire side of the boundary at Manton Common (VC54/SE90) in 1953, and Epworth Turbary (VC54/SE70) up to 1967, indicate the wider area formerly occupied by this species. In 1883 Porritt was able to note the Large Heath was *'abundant nearly every year'* at Thorne. Similar generalised comments have been made since then by many recorders right up to the 1980s.

The Large Heath also occupies moorland mire sites in higher regions. In Porritt's day it was found on the Pennines near Hawes, Wensleydale (VC65/SD88?) and in Langstrothdale (VC64/SD97?). In a note in *Naturalist* (9:53) the Rev Trevor Basil Woodd of Oughtershaw Hall (VC64/SD88) wrote: *'I have also taken Chortobius Davus in this district'*, although no sites were indicated. Specimens were sent to Porritt and he thought them *'very curious'*. W E Clarke took a specimen on Adel Moor near Leeds c1870 (VC64/SE24?). There were three reported sightings from the Combe Scar, Dentdale area (VC65/SD68) as recently as 1974. It has been assumed that the species is now extinct in the Yorkshire Pennines but it could be being overlooked due to the difficulties of reaching and searching potential areas. Porritt's 1883 list did not mention any N York Moors sites, but his 1904 *Supplement* refers to one in Glaisdale VC62/NZ70, and another at 'Pickering' VC62/SE88/89, which was probably Fen Bog. In 1904 A S Tetley (of Scarborough) discovered sites near the Falcon Inn (VC62/SE97/98) where the former moorland is now covered in the trees of Harwood Dale Forest and the site probably lost, and near the Flask Inn a few miles further north. Walsh (1952) notes that the May Moss and Robin Hood's Bay (Fylingdales?) sites were discovered in the earlier part of the 20th century. Walsh (1956) also refers to sites at Murk Mire and Upper Langdale, the latter place probably lost to the extension of Langdale Forest (but now being opened up again by the Forestry Commission in the interests of conservation). There is scope to find more colonies, although the search area is limited by the military presence on Fylingdale Moors and further complications may arise from announcements in 2002 that the area is to become a major link in the American 'Star Wars' programme.

Peter Waterton

Pocklington Canal Aug 2004 (VC61). Ringlets tend to favour damper areas.

UK BAP Status: *Not listed.*
BC Priorities: National: *Low.*
N of England: *Low.* Yorkshire: *Low.*
European Status: *Not threatened.*

WORLD STATUS: Expanding resident, 0-1800m, 1 brood (Jun/Aug). Range: N Spain to N Greece (not Italy) and northward to S Scotland, C Scandinavia and E through Europe and Asia to NE China and Japan. (Specimens often larger in S of range.) Stable in Europe with expansion on N edge of range and contraction in south. Lafranchis (2000) notes a decline in 7 *départements* along N half of French W coast. Dramatic expansion in Britain since 1970 (and in Yorkshire). Present in Britain as far north as S Scotland, but with notable gaps in distribution, probably a legacy of late 19th century range contraction.

Ringlet

YORKSHIRE STATUS 1995/2003:

Expanding resident: 0-300+m. One brood (mid-Jun/mid-Aug) Widespread in eastern two-thirds of county, and extending its ran northward and westward. Prior to c1970 it was largely confined to the and E of the county within 100km square TA and the eastern half of S Now widespread in SE, except for the Pennine edges to the west and sou west. It has also colonised the Yorkshire part of NZ and moved rapidly into Durham and Northumberland where 40 new tetrads were recorded 2003 alone (Hunter & Norman 2003).

The **earliest** record in the Survey period was 05/06/1999 from Cotta (Wolds VC61) [John Killingbeck], and the **latest** was on 14/09/2002 wh 2 were seen at Malham (VC64) [Dave Howson]. During the recordi period, emergence was generally in mid-June with most records tailing in mid-Aug. The Sept record quoted was exceptional, coming from t Pennines, and may represent a later emergence associated with height. T only other Sept record came from the south of the county at Whitley (Goole VC63) on 01/09/2001 [John Wint].

Ringlets favour damp, sheltered places where grass is lush. They often appe in quite large numbers and site counts in the hundreds are not uncommon e **VC61: 126** at Sledmere on 16/07/2001 [Joan McCagney]; **VC62: 2000+** York Cemetery NR on 07/07/2002 [Pat & Jim Bone]; **VC63: 436** Brockadale YWT NR on 05/07/2003 [Ralph Hibbert & Chris Parkin]; **VC6** **435** at Stainburn Forest on 20/07/2001 [Dave & Rosemary Howson]; **VC6** **270** at Foxglove Covert, Catterick on 26/06/2003 [Sam Ellis].

During the 1990s the species has been noted penetrating westward along t valleys of the Pennine Dales (as yet mainly towards the north in and arou the Dales National Park, leaving an empty space still to be filled to the S of Sheffield). In the mid-Wensleydale area (VC64), it has been noted clo to Ballow Fields (nr Redmire) in 1997, at Castle (nr High Fremington) 1999, and from Hurst and Cogden Gill in Swaledale and into Arkengarthda in 2000. By 1998 it was also established further north in mid-Teesda (VC65) at Boldron, Barningham Moor and to the west of Hunderthwaite.

Not only is this butterfly becoming established in the Dales, but it is al being found at unexpectedly high levels. Asher *et al* (2001) indicate it normally found no higher than 200/300m in Scotland. Yorkshire sightin

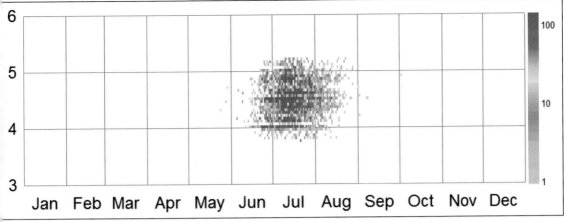

PHENOGRAM: Yorkshire 1995-2003. Indicates a single brood, flying mainly in Jul with slightly later peaks as you move north.

ID NOTES: Around Small White size but almost black when fresh, fading to brown with wear. Upperwings plain black-brown with variable number of small white-pupilled black circles highlighted by yellow or orange rings (eyespots or ocelli). Similar, but usually larger and more strongly marked ocelli can be seen in closed-wing view and are a key feature to separate from Meadow Brown. Very variable with 35 recognised aberrations, mainly associated with the number, size and shape of the ocelli. In ab *arête* Müller, the rings are missing, leaving white pupils on a small black spot, whilst ab *obsoleta* Tutt lacks even the white pupils. One of the most striking variations is ab *lanceolata* Shipp where the ocelli are teardrop shaped. In ab *caeca* Fuchs the underside spots are restricted to the hindwings and reduced to white specks. In ab *pallens* the upperside is a pale yellowish brown. All these varieties have been recorded in Yorkshire. The Ringlet is one of the few butterflies which can be seen flying in cloudy conditions and occasionally even in rain.

at around 300m are not uncommon eg at Menwith Hill (VC64) and along rides in the Stang Forest (VC65). In 2001 it was reported from Duck St Quarry, Greenhow (VC64) at 385m (1263ft), whilst a colony persisted for several years nr Rise Hill, Dentdale (VC65) at 340 to 380m. In 2003 the writer observed two individuals which had reached Malham Tarn Mosses at 390m (1280ft).

As eggs are simply ejected into grassy areas, often whilst the female is flying, it is difficult to track down the range of grass species used by the larvae, although this is thought to be quite restricted. Thomas & Lewington (1991) note Cock's-foot *Dactylis glomerata* and Wood False Brome *Brachypodium sylvaticum* as favourites, whilst Emmet & Heath (1989) give Tufted Hair-grass *Deschampsia cespitosa* as frequently used, and Creeping Bent *Agrostis stolonifera* as less commonly used. A wider range of grasses has been accepted in captivity.

Sutton & Beaumont (1989) include a report suggesting that the practice of mowing a metre strip along roadside verges may have provided an ideal habitat in its mix of long and short grasses, although the presence of a hedgerow may have been more important. However, whilst surveying Wolds verges (2000/2002) Howard & Christine Frost (pers comm.) noted that verges without hedgerows were mostly devoid of Ringlets, whilst those with hedgerows usually had good populations. Ringlets also avoided busy main roads where the frequent turbulence of fast-moving traffic caused constant and considerable movement amongst the roadside grasses and plants.

CONSERVATION ISSUES: Requires damp, sheltered places with lush grassland which is relatively undisturbed by cutting or grazing. Removing scrub from a site can lead to local extinction. However, the species is usually so widespread that scrub clearance to help another species would generally take precedence over retaining the Ringlet on a given site. Roadside verges are a key habitat in Yorkshire and the practice of not cutting more than a metre strip (except on corners) is important to the maintenance of these core colonies.

Ringlet ab *lanceolata* Shipp, Marton-cum-Grafton, 02/08/2001.

Ringlet ab *arete*, Knaresborough (VC64), July 2002.

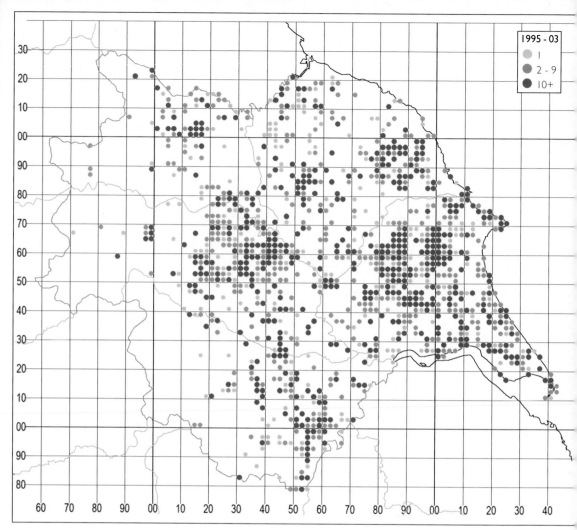

Ringlet: Yorkshire Tetrad map 1995-2003

MAP NOTES 1995-2003: Noted in **1128/3319** recorded tetrads (ie 34%), and out of 4120 tetrads in Yorkshire. **Ranked 10th most widespread** out of 36 regular breeding species in the county. It has expanded considerably in recent years and is now found in all parts of the county except in the higher Pennines. Notably this expansion is taking place to the east of the Pennines but not as yet to the west, except in Cheshire where the first record for 50yrs occurred in 1997 (pers comm. Barry Shaw).

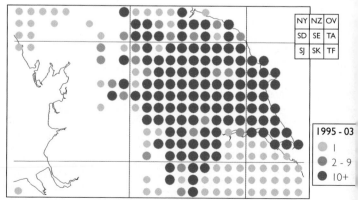

Ringlet: 10km distribution North of England

● = 1 or more records out of county 1995-1999

LIFE STORY

HABITAT: The Ringlet is a creature of moist and sheltered grasslands where it can flutter around a dappled jungle of tall plants in air which is damp and still. It can be found on wastelands, in rough pastures, conservation headlands and old-fashioned meadows. It also haunts the edges of rivers and streams and is common along the verges of road and rail routes as well as being found along woodland edges and rides, and in clearings. Wanderers may also turn up in gardens. It can occur in drier areas such as along the sand dunes of Spurn NNR or on the chalk pastures of the higher Wolds, although numbers are usually lower on such sites. In the Wolds, many of the valleys run east/west and the Ringlet usually occupies the cooler north-facing slopes, which are thick in mosses, whilst all the other species are found on the drier, hotter south-facing sides, which have a completely different flora. The butterfly is particularly prone to suffer from drought conditions, especially where this shrivels up grass growth when larvae are active. The 1976 drought caused a crash in numbers whilst the notably hot year of 2003 was also very wet and therefore a good one for the Ringlet.

Ringlet: mating pair, Thixendale, July 1999.

Non-adhesive eggs are dropped in flight or ejected whilst females sit on grass heads. Initially, each dome-shaped egg is a pale primrose yellow and the shell glossy and transparent. Larvae can be seen though the shell prior to hatching after about 18 days. Once hatched, they feed until about late Oct then partially hibernate after the 3rd instar. Feeding continues whenever conditions are mild,

although growth is slow. Later stage larvae are easiest to find by torchlight at night. They reach about 2cm in length by June and then pupate at the base of grass tussocks, emerging after about a fortnight. Butterflies live in colonies ranging from a few dozen to several thousand. Within one area there may be many small colonies, which can emerge at different times, fly for a couple of weeks and then disappear after mating and egg-laying. The succession of emergences gives the impression of butterflies flying for a long period of time rather than of a series of short-lived colonies. Emergence in higher areas tends to be a week or two later than on lowland sites. Little is known about the Ringlet's mobility although its steady expansion indicates that it must be able to fly considerable distances on occasion.

Ringlets show much variation in spot patterns. Courtesy WE Rimington collection.

Ringlet, female.

The first vernacular name, as opposed to an abbreviated description, was introduced by Petiver (1717) as **the Brown and Eyes**. He also deduced a second species from the Ringlet which he called **the Brown seven Eyes**. Harris (1766) introduced **Ringlet**, subsequently accepted by most authors, although **Brown-eyed Butterfly**, **Brown Argus** and **Wood Ringlet** were also used occasionally. The Latin name is derived from a satyr and Hyperanthus (now written *hyperantus*) was one of the 50 sons of Aegyptus.

In the first half of the 19th century, the species appears to have been common and widespread throughout much of Britain as far north as central Scotland. Duncan (1844) noted it: *'pretty abundant in all parts of Britain'*, a comment reiterated by Morris (1853), *'This insect is plentiful throughout the country generally'*. Porritt (1883) looking back over 30+ years noted reports from: **VC62:** Raskelf and Scarborough; **VC63:** Edlington Wood (Doncaster), Huddersfield (formerly), Maltby Woods (nr Sheffield), Pontefract and Wakefield; **VC64:** Bishop's Wood (Selby), Bramham (nr Wetherby) and Ledsham (E of Leeds); **VC65:** Richmond. Stainforth (1919) fills in Porritt's lack of VC61 records with mid-19th century references to Riplingham and Gilberdike (both W of Hull). Yorkshire's earliest record is noted in the Wath-upon-Dearne list (Anon 1832 in Rimington 1992).

By the end of the 19th century, the Ringlet had disappeared from areas around London, large parts of the Midlands and the western half of N England, as well as Northumberland and Durham and parts of central Scotland, which isolated Scottish populations into two areas. Robson (1902) noted for Durham and Northumberland that it had been considered abundant up to 1858, *'but became exceedingly scarce shortly after that date, and has now almost if not entirely disappeared from its old haunts'*. The years 1860/1862 were notably cold (summer and winter) and may have been implicated in this loss. The decline left a strangely discontinuous population pattern, still present in the 1970/82 Survey maps (Heath *et al* 1984), and also discernible

today, even though the gaps are steadily narrowing. Heath *et al* draw attention to *'speculation'* that the species could have suffered from the growing atmospheric pollution of the industrial age. The areas from which Ringlets disappeared largely correspond to Britain's main industrial regions and match the disappearance of lichens affected by sulphur dioxide pollution. It is possible that larvae feeding on polluted grasses could have been poisoned although Fryer & Lucas (2001) in their in-depth examination of 19th century pollution in relation to Huddersfield area butterflies, suggest that smoke and soot may have been worse pollutants, whilst Thomas & Lewington (1991) suspect drainage and the disappearance of moist grasslands in favour of housing and industry may also have been contributory factors. It seems likely that the Ringlet (and many of the other species which suffered towards the end of the 19th century) could have been affected by a combination of factors although the rather scant evidence available also suggests that the Ringlet began to decline much earlier than many other species.

For Sheffield (VC63) Garland (1981) notes that after being locally common, it declined sharply sometime before 1900. Around Huddersfield (VC63) Mosley (1883) was already referring to it as *'formerly occurring'* (Fryer & Lucas 2001). In the Doncaster (VC63) area it was recorded up to 1888 (the last at Wadworth Wood - AE Hall Diaries in Rimington 1992) then nothing until 1917. Boult (1899) and Porritt (1922) failed to note it for the Hull area. Theakston (1871) reported it, *'Met with commonly along the coast'*, around Scarborough, whilst Walsh (1952) noted it not seen for a long time after a last record in 1886. However, Tetley (1915) indicated it *'locally abundant'*, but Walsh implies that Tetley's comment referred to observations at Sledmere (Wolds VC61), which some might consider outside the Scarborough area.

There were other isolated survivals (or periodic re-colonisations?) in the far south of the county in the first half of the 20th century, particularly around Doncaster (eg Hatfield, Crowle, Wroot and Martin Beck), as well as odd sightings of probable wanderers, as at Elland (nr Huddersfield) in 1934 [H Spencer] (YNU Card File). Expansion from outposts in the E and SE probably got underway in the warmer 1940s. By 1952 Walsh was able to report it common once again in the Scarborough area (VC62). The YNU 1967/70 Report noted the species widely distributed and common in VCs61 & 62 as well as the eastern margins of 63 and 64, though still absent from most of the western half of the county. The first hints of an expansion into the Huddersfield area came with sightings around Bretton in 1983 and 1984 (Fryer & Lucas 2001). By 1989, Sutton & Beaumont were reporting the species as far west as Rotherham (VC63), Ripon (VC64) and Bedale (VC65), and Whiteley (1992) was noting the beginnings of expansion into the Sheffield area. Roy Bedford observed first arrivals in the Wakefield area (VC63) in 1992 with several colonies established by 1996. Rather surprisingly the species spread more quickly and more successfully further north around Harrogate (VC64) after becoming established at High Batts NR (beside the R. Ure NW of Ripon) in the early 1970s. By the 1980s it was appearing along the eastern edges of the Harrogate Naturalists recording area, quickly spreading westward to Knaresborough, Harrogate and Masham, by 1985 (Barnham & Foggitt 1987, 1991, Barnham *et al* 1993). In the early 1980s, small numbers of specimens obtained in Lincolnshire were released over two years nr Ledsham (E of Leeds VC64) resulting in a colony being established in Newfield Wood, but by c1985 this had been overlapped by natural colonisation. Details were recorded by Castleford & District Naturalists' Society (pers comm. Mike Lockwood) In the late 1980s the species had reached as far as Lofthouse in Nidderdale and the general movement northward and westward continues today.

Terry Whitaker

A late evening view of Spurn from the middle of the Humber Estuary looking N. This is the mid-point of a 5 mile stretch of water which Essex Skippers and others have to cross to move between Lincolnshire and Yorkshire.

UK BAP Status: *Not listed.*
BC Priorities: National: *Low.*
N of Eng: *Not yet listed.* Yorkshire: *Not yet listed.*
European status: *Not threatened.*

WORLD STATUS: Resident, 1 brood (May/Aug, Jun/late Aug in England) 0-2300m. Range: N Africa northward through Europe to SE Britain and S Scandinavia, and eastward across Asia to Siberia. Accidentally introduced to N America (London, Ontario) in 1910 from where it spread dramatically through Canada and USA to reach 'pest' proportions. Known as the **European Skipper** in N America. Expanding on northern edge of range in Europe, including Britain where it is found mainly to the SE of a line from the Humber to the Severn.

YORKSHIRE STATUS 1995/2003:

New resident species not previously recorded in the county, expanding on edge of range. Recorded as **new to Yorkshire in 1996** with up to **3** seen between 22/07 and 30/07 at Wintersett Reservoir, (Wakefield VC63/SE31) [Mark Thompson *et al* Wintersett Wildlife Group] but the species was not found on the same site in subsequent years.

Further unconfirmed sightings of single butterflies came from Anston Stones Wood, Rotherham (VC63/SK58) in 2001, and The Muddies, Maltby (VC63/SK59) in 2002 [Paul Townsend]. In 2003, singles were again recorded at Anston Stones on 01/08, and Maltby 14/08 [Paul Townsend], and also at Old Moor Wetlands (nr Barnsley VC63/SE40) on 08/07 [Martin Greenland], and at Ellis Laithe (nr Wintersett VC63/SE31) on 06/07 [Wintersett Wildlife Group].

The butterfly has been building up populations on the Lincolnshire side of the Humber Estuary and by 1999 records had come from Donna Nook (opp Spurn), Barton (on the motorway interchange roundabout opposite the Humber Bridge) and Crowle. So the first-ever VC61 sighting at Spurn NNR in 2003 was not unexpected, as the tip of Spurn is only c5 miles from Donna Nook, albeit 5 miles of mudflat and open water. This arrival suggests that the Humber Estuary (9 miles wide in the east, tapering to about 1mile some 40 miles upstream nr Goole) will not be an insuperable barrier to the Essex Skipper. The first Spurn sighting [Barry Spence *et al*] was on 16/07/2003, after which up to **7** were seen daily until 05/08/2003, suggesting a female may have laid eggs here in 2002.

It looks as though the Essex Skipper could be on the threshold of a major expansion into Yorkshire and is likely to become a regular resident in southern areas of the county in the near future. Unfortunately, the possibility that this species may have been privately (and unnecessarily) introduced to some sites cannot be ruled out. It is also easily misidentified.

Essex Skipper

ID NOTES: Often confused with Small Skipper although readily separable with practice. A pair of close-focusing binoculars (to 2m/6ft or less) makes this process far easier. In particular, look for a sharply defined, glossy **black** tip to the **underside** of each antenna. It is as though the antennae tips have been dipped into black ink, leaving a stain on the undersides, but not the uppersides. However, the antennae are often held with the undersides facing one another sideways, which makes them more visible (see photo). The antennae are often bright orange-brown above and paler underneath, with the black tip forming a sharp contrast. They can also be darker with an orange-brown patch adjoining the black tips. Small Skipper underside antennae tips are rather variable, from orange brown to dark brown and can look as though they also have black tips, but with less sharply defined edges and the darkness extending above and below the tips. Male Essex Skippers can also be picked out by their shorter, straighter sex brands, which are parallel to the forewing edge (compared to Small Skipper's longer brand being at an angle). Both male and female Essex also tend to have slightly thicker black edges to the wings than Small Skipper, but variability within both species can make this feature unreliable. (See panel on p66.)

CONSERVATION ISSUES: The foodplants and preferred habitats of this species are widespread in the county, therefore a further spread seems feasible. The trigger for such an expansion is unclear, but probably climatic as a similar spread is taking place across its northern distribution edge from Scandinavia to Russia. Roadside verges (especially motorway verges) and hay movements could facilitate this spread. The species may already have benefited from reductions in rabbit grazing, as well as reductions in the maintenance of road and rail verges. There will be a future need to examine in more detail how the Essex Skipper adapts to Yorkshire habitats.

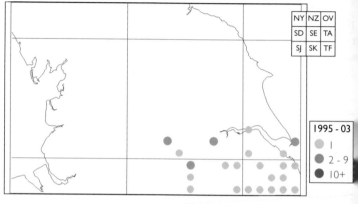

Essex Skipper: 10km distribution North of England
⬤ = 1 or more records out of county 1995-1999

Male Essex Skipper at Spurn NNR (VC61) 18/07/2003.

MAP NOTES: Noted in 5/3319 recorded tetrads (ie 0.2%) and out of 4120 tetrads in Yorkshire. Ranked 35th most widespread out of 36 breeding species in the county. The Essex Skipper appears to be on the threshold of a major expansion into the county, and although currently our second rarest breeding species, it has the potential to become more common and quite widespread in the lowland areas of southern Yorkshire, over a fairly short period of time.

LIFE STORY

Pale eggs are laid in small groups, typically on Cock's-foot *Dactylis glomerata*, or Creeping Soft-grass *Holcus*

HISTORICAL REVIEW:
Essex Skipper

This species was not recognised as a separate species in Europe until 1808 when it was first written up by German entomologist and actor, F Ochsenheimer. Its presence in Britain was not noticed until 1889 when FW Hawes discovered it at St Osyth in Essex. Initially it was called the **Scarce Small Skipper** (Kirby 1896) or the **Lineola Skipper** (Coleman 1897). South introduced **Essex Skipper** in 1906, whilst in 1959 Heslop attempted to introduce **New Small Skipper**. However, this unimaginative attempt fell on deaf ears and failed to catch on! In the Latin: *Thymelicus* derives from dancers in the Greek chorus (therefore dancing butterflies) and *lineola* means *small line* being a reference to the small size of the male's sex brand.

As a result of such a late discovery, we now little about this species' past distribution. Today it occupies the SE segment of England, with a north-west facing frontal zone between the Rivers Severn and Humber. It seems possible that the butterfly has long occupied a similar area, perhaps retracting south-eastward in older times and edging north-westward again in clusters of warmer years. Garland 1981) draws attention to an intriguing 880 record from Clumber Park (Notts VC56), discovered in Barrett (1893), and identified retrospectively from a

mollis, as well as a whole range of other grass species. Larvae develop inside tough eggshells in which they remain through hibernation until the following April. These eggs are well adapted to a life in fens and saltmarshes and can withstand the prolonged immersion of winter flooding. As the butterfly is also a typical species of hayfields, and the eggs are not easily destroyed, they can be transported with the hay to other sites. It is thought this is how the species spread so successfully in N America. After five instars larvae pupate in a silken cocoon spun inside a cluster of leaf blades at the bottom of a tussock. Essex Skippers form colonies, sometimes very small and sometimes extremely large. Although they spend the daytime in isolation from one another, in the late afternoon they come together to bask and later to roost communally. Adults fly from late Jun to the end of Aug and even into Sept. Although they overlap with the Small Skipper, they tend to peak much later, in late Aug. Therefore, any skippers still flying beyond mid-Aug deserve close scrutiny to ascertain the species.

Lawrie King

Male Essex Skipper (Barnack Hills and Holes, Northants). Note obvious black antennae tips and position of sex brand.

specimen. Clumber lies only about 6 miles south of the Yorkshire border, indicating the possibility that the current arrival of this species in the county may not have been the first! The 1879/1895 cold period appears to have affected the Essex Skipper, and by the early 20th century it had become largely restricted to coastal and marshland areas in Kent and Essex, with outliers as far north as Cambridgeshire. Duddington & Johnson (1983) note that the Lincolnshire Naturalists' Union reported it as, *'spreading fast in the Boston area* [in S Lincs VC53] *in 1960'*. By 1979 it had reached the centre of Lincolnshire around Chambers Wood (just east of Lincoln VC54), and by 1993 records had been gathered from 17x10km Lincolnshire squares, mainly in the southern half of the county (Tyszka 1994). By 1999, the Lincolnshire presence had spread to over 50x10km squares and the butterfly was being found right up to the South Bank of the Humber (the Lincolnshire side). Interestingly, if you extend the current frontal zone line from the Severn to the Humber north-eastward into Europe, you pick up the frontal zone for this species right through Norway to Finland. In other words, the Essex Skipper is found further to the north as you move eastward, and the British distribution is part of the same pattern, a probable result of the species' preference for warm, dry habitats.

Howard M Frost

UK BAP Status: *Priority species.*
BC Priority: *High.*
Protected in GB for sale only.
European Status: *Not threatened.*

WORLD STATUS: Resident: I brood, 0-2800m (late Jun/mid-Sept but late Jul/early Sept in England). Range: N Spain to S Scandinavia (with outliers in N Africa, N Norway and Sweden) and eastward across temperate Asia to China and Japan. Also found in N America, where it *'occupies one of the most extensive ranges of any N American butterfly'* from British Columbia to Quebec and south to Baja California, N Mexico and Florida (Pyle 1981). Declined in 19th and 20th centuries in England and neighbouring continental countries, but has partially re-expanded in the 1980s.

Silver-spotted Skippers. (Parc Naturel Regional du Vercours, France Aug 1999). Note how silver spots stand out.

ID NOTES: Similar to Large Skipper, but with more obvious yellow spots on upperwings and **silvery white** spots on underwings.

YORKSHIRE STATUS 1995/2003:

Extinct former resident. Last known dated record: 1874 at Ryhill Pits, Barnsley (VC63).

HABITAT: Thomas & Lewington (1991) describe the ideal habitat for this species as warm, south-facing downland with thin soils and a sparse sward. About 40% of the surface should be bare, 45% covered with Sheep's Fescue *Festuca ovina* and the rest occupied by wild flowers. Grazing by rabbits, cattle or sheep is clearly important in the creation of such a habitat, and the 1950s myxomatosis outbreak in rabbits resulted in the loss of many colonies in southern England. Silver-spotted Skippers remain inactive in cloudy weather and only begin flying when temperatures are 20°C or higher. Therefore aspect is very important.

HISTORICAL REVIEW:
Silver-spotted Skipper

In the past the species appears to have been confused with other skippers, particularly the Large Skipper. Harris (1775) was the first to describe and report it correctly, calling it the **Pearl Skipper**. Haworth (1803) was the first to use **Silver-spotted Skipper**, but Pearl Skipper remained the preferred name throughout much of the 19th century. In the Latin, 'Hesperia' was one of a group of nymphs called the Hesperides who guarded the golden apples of Hera, whilst *comma* refers to the shape of the male's sex brand (ie the dark mark on each upper forewing).

Emmet & Heath (1989) deduce that the early lack of awareness of the species may indicate that it was very rare in the 18th century, but became more widespread in the 19th. It is a species which is on the northern edge of its range in England, and which requires some of the hottest and driest grasslands available. The cooling effect of the Little Ice Age (1300/1850) would undoubtedly have had some effect on it, and the 1690s and the 1810s were two of the coldest decades in this long cool period. As the weather warmed in the early 19th century, an expansion may well have occurred. However, the dramatic cooling in the last 20 years of the 19th century, may have sealed the fate of this heat-seeking butterfly in Yorkshire. Morris (1853) mentioned that, *'Mr Dale records the neighbourhood of Hull as another locality for it'*. In addition, he mentions Brough (also in the neighbourhood of Hull, so they could refer to the same site). Both Porritt (1904) and Stainforth (1919) refer to the existence of specimens in Thomas Stather's collection, captured at Brantinghamthorpe (VC61/SE9429) which is part of the *'Riplingham'* area, near the southern edge of the Yorkshire Wolds and probably covered parts of two 10km squares, SE92 and SE93. This is just to the west of Hull **and** near Brough so could be duplicating Morris's references. Stainforth noted that the species was *'plentiful at Riplingham'* before Stather died in 1878. Unfortunately, although Stather's collection ended up in Hull Museum, it was destroyed during the bombing of World War Two.

All other known records seem to refer to a period around the 1860s and 1870s, with the latest dated record being in 1874. Garland (1981) cites 4 specimens recorded at Ryhill Pits, Barnsley (VC63/SE30), between 1872 and 1874, and mentions the existence of a specimen in the Sheldon Collection (Sheffield Museum), which was reportedly taken at Maltby (VC63/SE59).

Porritt (1883) comments that the species was *'not common'*. He mentions John Grassham's undated record from Bishop Wood (Selby VC64/SE53), and also quotes Newman (1860/1871) who mentions records from *'York and Scarborough'* made by Edwin Birchall. A *'York'* record is difficult to place, but is most likely to come either from the nearby Wolds to the east (perhaps in the Buttercrambe Moor/Bishop Wilton area VC61/SE75/85), or from the Magnesian Limestone to the west, near Tadcaster/Bramham in (VC64/SE44).

The *'Scarborough'* VC61 record could be anywhere within a day's trip of the town by horse and cart: Pickering (SE78/88) perhaps, or even on the town's famous Castle Hill (TA08), which in the days before it was planted with trees for the tourists must have been quite a butterfly hotspot. Walsh (1952) points out that there are no other references to Silver-spotted Skipper records in the Scarborough area other than from Newman's mention of Edwin Birchall's sighting, which is perhaps a little surprising considering the number of people actively recording in the area. Although Yorkshire records are few, and the evidence scant, it appears likely that the Silver-spotted Skipper was once more widespread in the county than these few reports suggest. It probably occurred more widely on the Wolds and possibly in the grazed grasslands and organised rabbit warrens along the limestone edge of the N Yorkshire Moors between York and Scarborough.

Howard M Frost

1534 GRIZZLED SKIPPER *Pyrgus malvae* (Linnaeus 1758)
Family: Hesperiidae, ('the Skippers').

BAP Status: *Not listed.*
BC Priorities: National: *Medium.*
N of England: *High.* Yorkshire: *High.*
European status: *Not threatened.*

WORLD STATUS: Resident, 0-2300m. One or two broods (May/July) or (April/June, Jul/Aug) according to latitude and height. Univoltine in Britain with possible partial second brood in good years. Recent information (Asher *et al* 2001) suggests there may be more of a partial second generation in Britain than previously realised because it overlaps the first generation from June onward. Range: N Mediterranean coast to central Norway and eastward through temperate Asia to Mongolia, N China and Korea. Replaced by subspecies *malvoides* in Spain, Portugal and other parts of southern range. The species has declined in a number of W European countries including Belgium, the Netherlands, and Britain. Discounting private releases, the northern edge of its natural British range now appears to be roughly in the same latitude as the Wash. This represents a retraction from a line previously running across N Yorkshire to Cumbria in the 1950s. Present day records from Cumbria are thought to result from private releases.

YORKSHIRE STATUS 1995/2003:

Probably extinct. Formerly a rare, rather localised resident, apparently on the northern edge of its range in Yorkshire and presumed to have one generation. Now either extinct, or close to extinction. The last reported observation of a butterfly, which might have been present by natural means, was at Holbrook Marsh nr Sheffield (VC63/SK48) on 29/05/1990 [Bill Shaw in Whiteley (1992)].

Bill Ely reported the species re-discovered in VC63/SK58 in 1993, but it appears that any records in this 10km square (Lindrick Common, Deep Carrs Quarry etc) are likely to have been part of an unauthorised private project to re-introduce the species to South Yorkshire, North Lincolnshire and Nottinghamshire. It is thought to have spanned c20yrs and appears to have been carried out without any proper reporting or scientific monitoring. Such introductions have cast doubt on the real status of this species in Yorkshire and neighbouring counties. (See p51 for further discussion on introductions.)

Although the species can exist in small and isolated colonies, giving rise to the possibility of a hidden presence still to be discovered, it is more likely that there are no longer any naturally occurring Grizzled Skippers in Yorkshire. In addition, the lack of any regular reports from South Yorkshire (VC63), where specimens have been released, seems to cast doubt on the success of such releases.

ID NOTES: A small, unobtrusive, moth-like butterfly, which appears basically black with a variable pattern of small, white flecks. The wings are distinctively fringed in black and white. An agile and rapid flier, capable of such spectacular manoeuvring that it can readily defeat the eye and disappear. Can be confused with several day-flying moths, including the common Latticed Heath *Semionthisa clathrata*, which is found throughout the county. Although the Latticed Heath is usually more of a brown on yellow-brown insect, it does produce relatively common variations similar in looks to the Grizzled Skipper. Observers should be particularly wary of ab *alboguttata* Fettig a melanic form of the Latticed Heath which can look very similar to the skipper. Always check antennae first: clubbed for butterfly, unclubbed for moth.

Lawrie King

Grizzled Skippers. (Twyford Wood, Lincolnshire).

LIFE STORY

HABITAT: Uses sunny, open spaces and rides in woodlands; unimproved calcareous grassland; brownfield sites, inc spoil heaps, railway track verges and cuttings; and less commonly, may be found in heathland, damp grassland and dunes. Uses a fairly wide range of foodplants from the Rosaceae family, particularly Wild Strawberry *Fragaria vesca*. Typical habitat needs a mosaic of short vegetation (less than 10cm high) containing foodplants, with taller patches up to 50cm and scrub or woodland edge nearby. Rabbit grazing may help to provide the right kind of habitat mix.

Eggs (translucent green turning to opaque grey) laid singly on the underside of foodplants (typically Wild Strawberry *Fragaria vesca*, Creeping Cinquefoil *Potentilla reptans*, Silverweed *P. anserina*, and Tormentil *P. erecta*). Hatches after about 10 days. Larvae construct a silken web on the upper part of a leaf and graze underneath, leaving distinctively blotchy patterns. They then progress to other leaves, building new shelters as required and develop through 5 instars over a period of about two months. Winter is spent in the pupal stage wrapped in a silken cocoon near ground level. It is probable that when the butterfly emerges, small adjacent colonies function as a larger metapopulation. The success of the species may depend on this population structure.

CONSERVATION ISSUES: There is interest in the possibility of an 'official' re-introduction of this species to Yorkshire. However, re-introduction would only be viable if the factors which caused the extinction could be assessed and reversed. Simply throwing the species at every apparently suitable habitat in the hope that some will stick is not a good recipe for sustainable recovery and could well be a waste of valuable resources. Areas needing further study include: habitat requirements; ongoing site management requirements needed to maintain the right habitat; metapopulation requirements - re-introduction might only succeed as a landscape level project involving several sites and built-in site links; an appraisal of current weather conditions and their suitability for the species; and a study of potential disease and predation problems. The last increase in the population in Yorkshire appears to have been in the 1940s. Interestingly, this coincided with a notable series of warm springs (1943 to 1950). From 1950 to 1961 there were 7 further relatively good springs, and Grizzled Skipper sightings continued fairly regularly up to 1958. Then 1962 was persistently cool, 1963 was one of the 10 coldest winters of the century, and from then until 1975 the weather tended to be cool or average, and often wet. There are strong indications that cool springs and frequent wet weather militate against the success of this species.

The 1950s also saw the advent of myxomatosis in rabbits, which removed one of the main sources of grazing capable of creating the right conditions for this butterfly. In the 1960s, the end of steam on most of Britain's railway system, coupled with the widespread closure of branch lines, brought an end to managed (and accidentally burned) rail verges, which quickly became overgrown and scrubby, and began to revert to woodland. More recently we have seen a huge reduction in coal mining and attendant industries, followed by the reclamation of spoil heaps and old industrial sites. Reclamation has often meant creating parkland, which has sometimes destroyed the natural habitats which might have retained this species. Over the same period agriculture has cleaned up much of the countryside, reclaiming any last fragments of suitable habitat. Forestry has moved away from coppicing, reduced the frequency of rides and planted shade-producing conifers. The Grizzled Skipper may well have been driven towards extinction in the county by a 'multiple whammy' effect! In Essex a recent attempt to re-introduce the species to a woodland site by releasing butterflies, resulted in immediate predation and virtual annihilation by Wood Ants *Formica rufa* (Corke 1997), an indication that re-introductions may be far from easy! The future of conservation work is moving towards landscape level biodiversity management. If Grizzled Skipper requirements could be added into some of the forthcoming schemes being planned by English Nature, there might be a future for this species in Yorkshire. Butterfly Conservation has produced a Species Action Plan (SAP) for the Grizzled Skipper which can be consulted on its website.

HISTORICAL REVIEW:

Grizzled Skipper
Formerly: *Syricthus alveolus*
(in Porritt 1883)

First recorded in Britain by Petiver, who caught one on Hampstead Heath on 11/05/1696 (date adjusted to the Gregorian Calendar). He later christened it **Our Marsh Fritillary** in 1699. Wilkes called it **the Grizzled Butterfly** in 1747. Harris and others used **the Grizzle** or **the Gristle** from 1766 onward, whilst Berkenhout favoured **the Brown March Fritillary** (1769). Lewin introduced **the Spotted Skipper** in 1795, Donovan called it **the Mallow** in 1813 and finally, Jermyn introduced **the Grizzled Skipper** in 1824. In the Latin, *Pyrgus* appears to be derived from the word for the kind of tower you find on castle walls (perhaps a reference to the chequered wing pattern), whilst the species name *malvae*, 'mallow' is an incorrect reference to a supposed foodplant, an error made by Linnaeus.

The earliest Yorkshire records date from around 1858 from Roche Abbey (VC63/SK58), WH Smith (1858) and Maltby (VC63/SE59), Batty (1858), both in Rimington (1992). Stainforth (1919), deducing information from Thomas Stather's collection made prior to 1878, noted that the species was then *'plentiful'* near Hull at Newbald (VC61/SE93) and Brantingham (VC61/SE92). Porritt (1883) added VC63 sites at Pontefract (SE24), Sheffield (SK38), and Wakefield (SE32); and VC64 sites at Ledston (SE43) (N of Castleford), Selby (SE64) and Bramham Park (SE44) (nr Wetherby). He also mentions a site near York (SE65?), which could be in any of 3 VCs. Porritt's later Lepidoptera lists (1904 and 1907) add no further sites but include the note: *'not common'*. It seems probable that the species would have suffered in the severe weather of the last 20yrs of the 19th century. It was noted to be particularly scarce in parts of Lincolnshire in 1901 (Duddington & Johnson 1983). Lincs numbers improved around 1925, were poor in the 1930s and improved again in 1943. It is notable that 1925 and 1943 both

had exceptionally mild winters. Yorkshire produced few Grizzled Skipper records in the first half of the 20th century. Rimington (1992) notes a report by G E Hyde that it was *'very scarce and local'* on Bull Moor (nr Hatfield Woodhouse VC63/SE60) between 1920 and 1960. This suggests that the species can hang on and survive over long periods of time even though in very small numbers.

From about 1940, reports began to increase. Rimington (1992) notes: 1940/49 Hirst Priory (VC63/SE71) [JH Seago]; 1951 Brockadale (VC63/SE51) Hewson (1952); 1953 Stapleton Park (VC63/SE51) and 1956 Went Hill (VC63/SE41) [both JH Seago]. The YNU 1967/70 Report gives: 1947 Lindrick Common (nr Woodsetts VC63/SK58); 1951 and 1953 at Wentbridge (VC63/SE41), (Rimington adds 1954 for Wentbridge, picked up from the LGF Waddington collection); 1958 Barnsley area (VC63/SE30?); and 1958 Doncaster area (VC63/SE50?). The YNU Report goes on to mention records for 'the Hull area' (VC61) in 1954 and at South Cave (nr Hull SE93) on 31/05/1966 and again in 1967. The Report also gives a previously unrecorded set of sightings in the north-east of VC62 with records at Sandsend on 28/05/1955, and at Mulgrave Wood and Runswick Bay on 29/05/1955, all in NZ81. It is strange that these are the only records ever made in this area. Rimington (1992), notes 3 specimens seen at Thorne Colliery (VC63/SE71) [AH Wright], and one seen at Crowle Moor (VC54/SE71) [REM Pilcher] in 1971. Sutton & Beaumont (1989) note Brancliffe Lime Works (VC63/SK58) as a site recorded via Bill Ely in 1976, which might have been the last naturally occurring record before introductions began to muddle the situation, although the 1990 Holbrook Marsh report noted above may possibly be natural.

The past national distribution of the Grizzled Skipper is both curious and challenging. In the 19th century, there was a thin scatter of records up the east coast, through Northumberland and Durham into southern Scotland, with a single isolated report from N Scotland (Sutherland) as well as a more recent (unconfirmed) 20th century report from the same county (Thomson 1980). Could this be a remnant of a wider past distribution? Or has the species the ability to react to favourable conditions by jumping long distances northwards and establishing temporary colonisations in new territory? Many existing records seem to be 'one-offs'. Subsequent visits fail to confirm any presence. However, in captivity, it has been shown that the winter hibernation of pupae can actually extend over two seasons. One would expect this to be more readily triggered in response to the inclemency of a northern climate. Could the species be playing tricks on us by sometimes appearing biennially?

The Grizzled Skipper is not known to be a migrant, yet the scatter of east coast records would fit such a scenario, especially as the continental distribution of the species extends as far north as central Norway. There is also a very similar-looking Northern Grizzled Skipper *P. centaureae* found from central Norway northward, which inhabits marshes, bogs and damp heaths. Its foodplant is Cloudberry *Rubus chamaemorus*. Could this species once have inhabited northern England and Scotland, unnoticed, perhaps already dying out, as lepidopterists first came on the scene and wrongly identified it? Could it even still exist unnoticed in Scotland because no-one has looked for it at the right times in the right places with eyes to see? Of course, it is always possible, and certainly more likely, that these northern records were simply misidentifications and the species has never existed much further north than Yorkshire. Thomson (1980) indicates that there are no known cabinet specimens available to double check.

However, the fact that the Grizzled Skipper's continental distribution extends into Norway suggests it should also be able to survive as far north as Scotland unless, of course, northern Britain is just a bit too wet for it.

Another possibility is a rail link. Shepperson (1998) draws attention to the butterfly's liking for sheltered cuttings, sun-baked ballast, and railway verges, which in the past (in the days of steam), were both deliberately and accidentally burned. This management provided a constant re-creating of the right habitat conditions, whereas today, with minimal management, rail verges are becoming increasingly overgrown and are reverting to linear woodland. Many disused lines are also losing their former value to butterflies as they become more scrubby and covered with trees. Up to the 1960s large numbers of slow moving goods trains still linked urban and rural areas. Many wagons were open-topped with sides, which would have provided shelter and mini hot-spot habitats. Wagons parked in sidings could easily become part of a butterfly's regular habitat. Could this have led to hitch hiking butterflies? It might explain the odd colony outliers as at Sandsend and Runswick Bay, both rail linked, as well as nearby Mulgrave Woods to which the hitch-hikers could have spread. Rail might even explain some of the Scottish records. It is possible that Graylings and Dingy Skippers also spread around the rail network in this way.

Howard M Frost

UK BAP Status: *Species of Conservation Concern.*
BC Priority: *Medium.*
European Status: *Not threatened.*
Fully protected in Britain:
No collecting allowed. An RDB species.

SPECIAL NOTE: It is possible to see two sub-species of this butterfly in Britain: the resident and generally sedentary British race mainly restricted to Norfolk and called *Papilio machaon britannicus* Seitz 1907; and the migratory continental race *P. m. gorganus* Fruhstorfer 1922 (although formerly called *P. m. bigeneratus* Verity 1947). The term 'Swallowtail' can be used to describe a large, worldwide group of butterflies with 'tails' or streamers on the lower part of their hindwings. Within this larger grouping are the 'true' Swallowtails belonging to the family group Papilio being considered here.

WORLD STATUS: Resident and partial migrant, 0-3000m (probably only as a migrant above c1000m). Ssp *gorganus* has 1 to 3 broods according to latitude, height, weather (Feb/Oct) and tends to be very mobile and capable of flying long distances. It is a fairly regular immigrant to southern areas of Britain and has occasionally established a breeding presence lasting several years. *Britannicus* is relatively sedentary, and confined to the Norfolk Broads usually with 1 brood (May/Jul) although a partial 2nd is possible in good years (Aug). Range: circumpolar, NW Africa to N Norway and eastward across Asia to Japan and N America (where it is known as the **Old World Swallowtail**).

Beverley and Cottingham Marshes no longer exist, but this view from Beverley Bypass looking SW across to Cottingham shows a hint of the past in a temporary set-aside field in 2003.

YORKSHIRE STATUS 1995/2003:

Extinct former resident, possible vagrant. Available evidence strongly suggests that colonies of *britannicus* occurred on Beverley marshes (VC61/TA03/04/05?) prior to final drainage around 1800, a fact accepted by Porritt (1883). Almost certainly, any other Yorkshire sightings, historical or recent, are due to private releases, escapees from butterfly houses, or in the case of *gorganus* to vagrants, and of *britannicus* possibly due to the transportation of pupae in reed thatch. Yorkshire's only 20th century records (both unconfirmed) are: a single specimen at Spurn (VC61) on 21/08/1991 [Richard Bolton *et al*]. Spurn is c65 miles by sea from the nearest *britannicus* colony in Norfolk, but only c8 miles from a butterfly house at Cleethorpes (Lincolnshire) where foreign Swallowtails, similar in looks to *machaon* were flying and could have escaped; 2 seen in an allotment in Sothall Green (VC63/SK58) on 02/08/1999 [K Dutheridge] were assumed to be escapees from a butterfly house.

D NOTES: Unmistakeable in appearance even to the most casual observer, being large, tailed and strikingly coloured in yellow and black. Both subspecies are very similar, with *gorganus* usually slightly larger and paler (the black colouration on the wing being rather less pronounced). The sexes are closely similar but with males having visible claspers on their bodies, like dragonflies. Although not known to produce regular aberrations, around 90 variations have been described, some of which are quite spectacular, and might appear to be tropical escapees.

Continental Swallowtail nectaring on lavender in a French garden (Neuilly l'Eveque, France 1996)

LIFE STORY

HABITAT: Ssp *britannicus* is found in the established fenlands associated with the Norfolk Broads where its larval foodplant Milk Parsley *Peucedanum palustre* grows freely. The butterfly's sedentary nature is well documented and was confirmed by ML Hall (pers comm.) during release experiments at Wicken Fen in 1975. By comparison, *gorganus* uses a wide range of umbelliferous plants including carrots and fennels. As a result, it can adapt to many kinds of habitat and is not uncommon as a garden or allotment butterfly on the continent.

...mooth, pale-coloured, globular-shaped ...ggs are laid on young leaflets in June and ...uly and hatch after about 10 days. Larvae ...re large, bright green and adorned with ...lack orange-spotted bands. Pupation ...ccurs around the base of reed stems at ...bout 30 days. When alarmed the ...aterpillar has the ability to raise an ...osmeterium, a forked appendage situated ...ear to the head, which exudes an acrid ...mell often described as reminiscent of ...otting pineapples. Adults may emerge ...rom mid to late May and there is often a ...mall second brood in Aug, the pupae of ...vhich hibernate along with those of the ...irst brood. The early stages of the two ...ub-species are indistinguishable. ...lowever, *gorganus* is fully double ...rooded and in unfavourable British ...utumns the second brood may not ...urvive to the pupal stage leading to the ...xtinction of any colonies. Warren (1951) ...onsidered this to be the main reason for ...he temporary status of *gorganus* as a ...British resident.

HISTORICAL REVIEW:
Swallowtail
Included in Porritt (1883)

An illustration of the Swallowtail (without a name) was included in Mouffet (1634). Petiver (1699) called it **the Royal William**, a name apparently used until Harris (1766) introduced **Swallowtail**. Rennie (1832) tried to introduce **the Queen**, but Swallowtail remained the most widely accepted name. In the Latin *Papilio* simply means 'butterfly'; Machaon (=lancet) was a surgeon who served with the Greeks in the Trojan War; *britannicus* = British; *gorganus* is thought to be taken from Gorgan, the name of an Iranian town, whilst the older sub-species name *bigeneratus* means 'two generations'.

Though now confined to the Norfolk Broads *britannicus* may well have colonised other marshlands where its foodplant Milk Parsley flourished, from the Somerset Levels, through the Thames Valley and northwards through Essex and Lincolnshire to Yorkshire. There are references to *machaon* from: *'the osier beds by Battersea Fields* [larvae]*'* (Austin 1856); from the Lincolnshire fens, *'Mainly from that cause* [drainage of the Lincs fens] *have disappeared...the Great Copper and the Swallowtail butterflies'* (Cordeaux 1866), and of course from Beverley. With the exception of Battersea, the larval foodplant Milk Parsley is recorded in all these areas (Perring & Walters 1962).

The vast majority of the many genuine non-marshland *machaon* records undoubtedly refer to vagrants or temporarily established colonies of *gorganus* in the S of England. It is accepted that consistent records of double-brooded *machaon* in Dorset in the early 19th century (which disappeared following climatic deterioration around 1816) represented such a colony

Continental Swallowtail larva found on a roadside verge (Haute Marne, France 1984).

(Bretherton 1951), and similar establishments have been documented since 1850 in Kent, Hampshire, Dorset and possibly Sussex in suitable climate spells, the most recent being in Kent during the 1940s. More recently, the species has been observed regularly on Jersey over the last 5yrs, with circumstantial evidence suggesting the possibility of overwintering (pers comm. Nina Hall). In view of the current increase in British annual temperatures it is important to be aware of the habits of, and possible re-colonisations by, *gorganus*, not only in the southern counties, but also in more northerly areas such as Yorkshire, where any Swallowtail record must now assume new significance.

There are two historic records of *machaon* from Yorkshire. The first is a specimen which resides in the Ben Morley collection at the Tolson Memorial Museum, Huddersfield and bears the data, *'supposed to have been captured somewhere about Horbury Bridge* [VC63/SE21] *about 1840'*. This specimen, said to resemble *britannicus*, is almost certainly a bred vagrant since it is known that hundreds were released in Derbyshire about this time (Garland 1981); moreover neither Lees (1888) nor Perring & Walters (1962) give records of the foodplant remotely near to Horbury Bridge.

The Beverley records (Haworth 1803) refer to the period c1775 to 1803 and were accepted (perhaps too uncritically) by Porritt (1883) and others, until their outright rejection by the highly influential (if delightfully romantic) author, PBM Allan (1958). The status of these records has, however, been restored following recent research by Rimington (1987). Haworth's account ran thus: *'An ingenious and practical Aurelian friend has informed me that he took two sorts of swallow-tailed Papilios near Beverley in Yorkshire five and twenty years ago but no specimen of them are now extant, a fire which unhappily destroyed a great part of his property having consumed them likewise. Now, as we have only two swallow-tailed species in great Britain, one of the above in all probability was Podalirius* [ie the Scarce Swallowtail]. *I know machaon (the common swallow-tailed Papilio) breeds*

near Beverley yet; and my brother in law R. Scales of Walworth ne[a]r London possesses a specimen of it which was taken there about seven yea[rs] since'. Rylands (1839) identified Haworth's 'friend' as John Rippon of Yo[rk] (and first recorder of the cranefly species *Ctenophora flaveolata* Fabrici[us] in Britain).

The case for *machaon* at Beverley is conveniently made while considerin[g] Allan's objections, which run briefly thus: 1) 'Podalirius' was neither northerly species nor was it a migrant, therefore by implication Rippo[n's] testimony was unreliable; 2) Since Scales' collection was unlikely to ha[ve] been labelled, his recollections were unreliable; 3) Haworth's only eviden[ce] that *'machaon breeds near Beverley yet'* was Scales single specime[n] whereas his friend Peter Watson, then living in Hull, could have told him [of] any butterfly in the district around 1803 'by return of post'. (Haworth live[d] in Little Chelsea, London, from around 1793 to 1812.)

The key personalities involved and documented appear to be Hawort[h,] Scales, Watson, Rippon and the noted botanist Robert Teesdale. It [is] important to note the high level of competence and close relationships [of] this superb group of naturalists. Haworth and Watson were lifelong friend[s,] natives of Hull, and together with Scales and Rippon, were founde[r] members of the third Aurelian Society in London in 1801. Teesdale, wh[o] published the first record of Milk Parsley at Beverley (made by Christophe[r] Machell in 1796), noted the plant *'abundant at Beverley'* (Teesdale 1800[).] He visited the marshes on several occasions in the 1790s, and also live[d] near to Haworth in Little Chelsea.

Allan's dismissal of Rippon's evidence is unreasonable because th[e] 'assumption' made by Haworth is in regard to the Scarce Swallowtail, n[ot] *machaon*. Rippon may well have seen an eye-catching variant of *machao[n]* that became another 'sort'. The written or reported word is a dangerou[s] medium, especially after 200 years!

The comment concerning labelling is similarly unreasonable, for Scale[s] lived near Beverley around 1795 and could have taken the specime[n] himself. Indeed, Haworth may even have seen it. Also, would Scales [–] Allan's *'fine* [and then young] *entomologist'* – forget such a recent novelt[y] as a Beverley *machaon* unlabelled or not? Allan's third point is confuse[d] for the record reads: *'...it breeds near Beverley yet; **and my brother i[n] law...'* (our emphasis), thus strongly implying receipt of furthe[r] information of sightings, possibly also of the distinctive larvae. Moreove[r,] Watson very probably **was** this source; we know he corresponded wit[h]

Display from the Ben Morley collection, Tolson Memorial Museum, Huddersfield (See text). Photo: courtesy Tolson Memorial Museum, Huddersfield.

aworth around 1800, supplying him with local specimens of Large Heath and Mazarine Blue. Neither is the paucity of historic Beverley records surprising, for the popular entomological journal and the motorcar had not yet arrived, and 'fenman's ague' (malaria) rendered remaining Yorkshire swamps inhospitable and dangerous until the 1840s (pers comm. Martin Limbert). The same applied to the Norfolk fens where *machaon* was certainly commonplace around 1760 and well known to Norwich naturalist William Arderon (Whalley 1971) but scarcely gained a national mention until the early 1800s.

With Milk Parsley *'abundant'* at Beverley (Teesdale 1800) and *'common in south Lincolnshire and Yorkshire swamps at the turn of the [18th] century'* (Lees 1888), there can be little doubt that these extensive swamps then provided suitable habitats for *britannicus*. By 1800,

however, progressive drainage had reduced the Beverley marshes to a few northern meres, notably Tickton and Leven (Sheppard 1957, 1958) and the butterfly must have disappeared shortly after this. It is intriguing that Morris (1853) who was much closer to these records than Porritt (being born in 1810) wrote: *'it has been met with in Yorkshire, near Beverley **and** Cottingham…'* (our emphasis) which suggests he might have been in possession of more specific information than has been published in other sources. (Cottingham marshes (VC61/TA03) and Beverley marshes (VC61/TA04) were adjacent, and part of a much bigger wetland covering the lower reaches of the valley of the River Hull.)

It can be said that Scales, Rippon and any other informant, including Watson and Teesdale, though in ignorance of the exacting habitat and foodplant requirements of subspecies *britannicus*, and indeed even of the presence of the larval foodplant at Beverley, concentrated their focus on precisely its appropriate habitat. The above evidence taken together with the almost complete lack of documented historic Yorkshire records for *machaon* and our knowledge of the habits and historic distribution of ssp *gorganus* and *britannicus* indicate that these historic Beverley records do not, as has been suggested, represent strays, but the dwindling remnants of a relict population which once colonised the formerly extensive marshlands of Yorkshire and Lincolnshire.

Ted Rimington

1540 SCARCE SWALLOWTAIL *Iphiclides podalirius* (Linnaeus 1758)
Family: Papilionidae, sub-group Papilioninae ('the Swallowtails').

WORLD STATUS: Resident, 0-2700m, 1 to 3 broods according to latitude/height (Mar/Oct) (One generation in N France, May/June, with occasional partial second in Aug.) Range: N Africa to N France and the Benelux countries and eastward through temperate Asia to China. Thought to be weakly migratory on northern edge of range. Generally widespread and common, especially in the south of its range. Less common in N France and Benelux and only rarely reported as reaching the Channel Coast (Lafranchis 2000). Rarely recorded in Britain, but a persistent scatter of very occasional reports over the last 250yrs suggests it may possibly be a very occasional vagrant. However, both historical and present-day records are clouded by a background of both deliberate and accidental introduction (eg with the importation of fruit trees). Larvae feed on a wide range of wild and cultivated fruit trees and shrubs of the *Prunus* family (including plum, cherry, peach, apricot etc), and occasionally on other species including Hawthorn *Crataegus monogyna*.

YORKSHIRE STATUS 1995/2003:

Potentially an extremely rare vagrant from the continent. There is one unlikely and much debated historical record dating from around 1778 when a Mr John Rippon of York may have taken a specimen from the Beverley Marshes (VC61/TA04&05).

Scarce Swallowtail caught in flight (Brenne, France c1969).

Scarce Swallowtail on buddleia (motorway services between Mâcon & Annecy, France 1992).

The first record of *podalirius* as a British species is by Ray (1710). Later, Berkenhout (1769) refers to it as being *'rare in woods'*. Since then there have been at least a dozen records of larvae and adults mainly from southern England, with the most recent in 1987. However, between 1807 and 1828 the species appears to have been established in the Netley area (Shropshire), the most northerly location definitely recorded. The Netley concentration stimulated a long 19th century controversy over the British status of the Scarce Swallowtail, which for years has fascinated investigative entomologists. Was it a rare British breeding species or not? Stephens (1828) rejected the claims outright, Curtis (1836) and Morris (1853) as vehemently accepted them, whilst Newman (1871) declined even to discuss the issue. Allan (1980) examined the Netley records and considered that the Rev FW Hope and a local lady, a Mrs Plymley, who bred and painted butterflies, including *podalirius*, whilst of unimpeachable honesty, could have been the unwitting vectors of records arising

from the imported early stages of the butterfly, which, over a 20yr peri[od] may have been bred and released and also supplied to Mrs Plymley f[or] material gain.

Commonsense dictates that with the general availability of its larv[al] foodplants, a species so very rarely seen in southern England would b[e] unlikely to establish itself in grand isolation for some 20yrs as far north a[s] Netley. The persistent 'capture' of larvae and adults in this area appears [to] indicate a temporary and artificially maintained colony.

The reference to a Yorkshire specimen is found in Haworth (1803) a[nd] repeated in Morris (1853). Haworth wrote: *'An ingenious and practic[al] Aurelian friend* [John Rippon] *has informed me that he took two sorts [of] swallow-tailed Papilios near Beverley in Yorkshire five and twenty yea[rs] ago.'* He goes on to explain that the actual specimens had since been lost [in] a fire, but that *'as we have only two swallow-tailed species in Gre[at] Britain, one of the above in all probability was Podalirius'*. However, Jo[hn] Rippon himself never claimed to have captured a Scarce Swallowta[il.] Haworth simply made an assumption. It is far more likely that Rippon[s] second type of *'swallow-tailed Papilio'* was a variant of the norm[al] Swallowtail, a species which **was** most likely found near Beverley at th[e] time. Emmet & Heath (1989) mapped Scarce Swallowtail records reporte[d] between 1803 and 1988 and included the Beverley record. Salmon *et [al]* (2000) provide a useful summary and discussion of Scarce Swallowta[il] records, but don't include Beverley.

Environmental conditions change and improbable records should not b[e] lightly discarded, but *podalirius* records were always very rare an[d] southerly. The possibility of a Beverley **colony** cannot be entertained. If [in] the unlikely event that Rippon's capture **was** *podalirius*, it is evident that [it] must have been a vagrant arising either from the release of livestock, or ju[st] possibly, from genuine migration. Unfortunately, these events occurred to[o] long ago for any confirmation to be possible.

Ted Rimington

UK BAP status: *Species of Conservation Concern.*
BC Priority: *Medium.*
Protected in Great Britain for sale only.

YORKSHIRE STATUS 1995/2003:

Extinct former resident. Last known record in the Huddersfield (VC63) area in the 1850s. The species has been privately introduced to Whitwell Wood, Derbyshire (VC57/SE57) which adjoins the border with Yorkshire and could mean that specimens occasionally stray into our county.

SPECIAL NOTE: In 2001 it was recognised that we have **two** species o[f] Wood White in the British Isles. They are so similar that at the moment the[y] can only be certainly separated by examination of the genitalia. The 'new' species is **Réal's Wood White** *Leptidea reali*, which is known on th[e] continent, but has only recently discovered in Ireland where it turns ou[t] to be the commoner of the two Wood White species. Its distribution takes [it] into Northern Ireland in approximately the same latitude as the Scottis[h] border. It remains to be discovered if Réal's Wood White also exists in Britai[n.]

WORLD STATUS: 1 brood, 0-2300m, (June/Aug) in north, two (May/June, July/Aug) in central Europe, and three in south (Mar/Sept). Range: Mediterranean to Arctic Circle and eastward to W Siberia and the Caucasus. In British Isles, found mainly in S England and the Burren area of Ireland (usually one generation May/July but a second partial generation possible in good years July/Aug). Also mainly absent from the Netherlands, N Germany, and Denmark (where it has decreased by 75% in the last 25yrs). English distribution now mainly restricted to 4 areas: Hereford/Worcestershire, Northampton/Buckinghamshire, W Somerset/Devon, and a small presence in Surrey. Recent isolated occurrences (sometimes in large numbers) in Derbyshire, Cumbria and Lincolnshire are reported to result from private introductions.

Wood White male (left) and female (right) reproduced from woodcuts in Morris (1853): (illustrated by Frank Lydon, printed by Benjamin Fawcett).

HISTORICAL REVIEW:
Wood White
Formerly: *Leucophasia sinapis*
(in Porritt 1883).

First recognised as a British species by Merrett in 1666 and called the **small white Butterfly** by Petiver in 1699. It fell to Harris (1766) to give the present name, **Wood White**, which has been accepted and used by most writers since then. In the Latin *Leptidea* meaning thin or delicate, relates to the abdomen, whilst *sinapis* incorrectly links the larvae to feeding on cruciferous plants.

t does not seem to have been particularly common anywhere in Britain. Duncan 1844) notes, *'Although an abundant species in most parts of Europe, it is rather scarce in Britain'.* He goes on to mention sites in Essex, Surrey, Kent, Devon and *'near Carlisle, the most northern locality hitherto ascertained.'* It was recorded in Yorkshire in the first half of the 19th century, but only rarely, and only from three areas, around Doncaster, Sheffield and Huddersfield, which suggests it may have been on the edge of its range at the time. Morris (1853) provides the earliest dated record. He wrote, *'I have once taken this interesting insect in the year 1837 in the Sandall Beat Wood near Doncaster,'* (VC63/SE60). Rimington (1992) surmises that in the very early years of the 19th century, it may well have been found more widely in the local woodlands of the area.

However, Garland (1981) is of the opinion that the handful of early records, *'are almost certainly introductions or escapes'*, and that the species *'may never have been truly established in our area during the last two centuries'.* Garland includes a single undated record from the Sheffield area, which was also included in Porritt (1883). The record was reported by A Doncaster and is usually ascribed to VC63/SK38. Emmet & Heath (1989) and others also map another old record in VC57/SK37 (Derbyshire) indicating a possible source for a vagrant Sheffield sighting immediately to the south.

Porritt (1883) also included an undated 19th century Huddersfield record reported by Peter Inchbald, which Fryer & Lucas (2001) suggest must have been post 1846, as the observer only arrived in the district in that year. Mosley (1883) gives the location as Storthes Hall *'many years ago'.* Hobkirk (1859) listed the species as, *'very local'* in the Huddersfield area and knew of only one site at South Crossland. Mosley (1883) also mentions an undated report from Alan Godward, who recorded the species at Almondbury. Fryer & Lucas point out that all three sites (in VC63/SE11), just to the south of Huddersfield, are fairly close together, Storthes Hall being about 3km from Almondbury and both situated about 6-7km from South Crossland.

The Wood White appears to have been declining steadily in the 19th century, a fact put down **a)** to the reduction of woodland coppicing, which constantly renewed the ideal conditions for this species, and **b)** to the severe weather conditions at the end of the 19th century. Fryer & Lucas (2001) also suggest industrialisation and its consequent pollution, devastated insect populations in parts of Yorkshire and quote evidence indicating that at least 10 species disappeared in the Huddersfield area between 1865 and 1870. The Wood White probably disappeared in the 1850s but may have been one of the first to suffer not only from changes to woodland management, but also from the growth of the textile industry and its attendant population, all burning coal, producing smoke and reducing sunshine. Only one 20th century sighting appears to have been logged and that was in Worral VC63/SK39. A specimen was caught here around 1951 but thought to be privately introduced (Garland 1981). The discovery of a second Wood White species present in the British Isles raises some intriguing questions about the possibility of its further discovery in Britain. Could it be an explanation of the rather odd distribution pattern in England, with colonies in the south, and just a scatter of past colonies in the north? Could the northern colonies have been Réal's Wood White? The continental distribution of Wood White extends into Norway and up to the Arctic Circle. If the species is so hardy, why wasn't it even more common in northern Britain in the past? There is yet more to learn about these two species!

Howard M Frost

1543 PALE CLOUDED YELLOW *Colias hyale* (Linnaeus 1758)
Family: Pieridae, sub-group Coliadinae ('the Yellows').

[1544 BERGER'S CLOUDED YELLOW *Colias alfacariensis* **Berger 1948]**

SPECIAL NOTE: Whilst Yorkshire has a handful of historical records of the Pale Clouded Yellow, the very similar Berger's Clouded Yellow has never been recorded in the county. However, Berger's was only separated from Pale Clouded as a new species in the 1940s, and, therefore, it could have been overlooked in the past. That said, since its separation, Berger's has only been identified as a rare or occasional visitor to England, south of a line from the Severn to the Thames. It may never have strayed further than this. Pre-1940's records of Berger's have been deduced from the study of collections, but no Yorkshire specimens appear to have been discovered in this way, at least not as yet. The notes below refer to Pale Clouded Yellow except where specifically stated otherwise.

WORLD STATUS: Resident & migrant, 0-1800m. Two or three broods (May/Oct) according to latitude/height. Also occasional migrant on northern edge of range. Range: from Pyrenees to N France and eastward through central Asia to China. Largely absent from Mediterranean area, including much of Italy. Northern edge of resident range faces NW, running from Brittany to the Baltic States. A narrow migratory range runs in parallel, with its northern edge extending roughly from SW England to central Finland. Yorkshire lies at the very edge of the migratory range. (The distribution of Berger's is similar, but extends to the Mediterranean coast in the south, whilst its northern edge runs east/west in the latitude of northern France.) The Pale Clouded Yellow does not appear to be as strongly migratory as the Clouded Yellow. When it does reach Britain, it is thought to come mainly from N France, and perhaps occasionally from central Europe.

Identified as the likely remains of a Pale Clouded Yellow on the basis of pointed wings, and straight leading and outer edges to forewing. Colour distinctively different to normal Clouded Yellow. However, not enough of the wings are visible to confirm an ID, as it is the upperside hindwing features which are most important. (Auberive, France 1986).

YORKSHIRE STATUS 1995/2003:

Very rare migrant, odd specimens of which seem most likely to turn up as part of a major invasion of Clouded Yellows. The last Yorkshire records were probably in 1947 (see historical review), since when there have been no further reports (except for the specimen discussed in the accompanying photo), although the species continues to turn up occasionally in southern England. Unfortunately, there are major problems with identification, and confusion possible with other Clouded Yellows as well as with yellow forms of the Small White.

ID NOTES: The three Clouded Yellow species able to reach Britain, mainly perch with wings closed, in which position they are pretty well identical! Unless the butterfly can be caught for closer examination, the upperwing colours and wing-tip patterns have to be noted in flight, which is not always easy. Sometimes these can be partially observed through the closed wings. Unfortunately, the ID issues surrounding the Pale Clouded Yellow are far from simple, and beyond the scope of this book to tackle in any detail. Clouded Yellow colours can usually be picked up in flight: rich mustard yellow in the male, and orange-yellow in the female. But then around 10% of all Clouded Yellow females are of the *helice* form, which still has the yellow underwing, but is white or grey above. The combination of upperwing and underwing colours in flight can appear

pale yellow, quite similar in looks to the Pale Clouded Yellow. The most important ID features are on the upperside of the lower wings where the Clouded Yellow has continuous strong black wing edges compared to the Pale Clouded Yellow's thinner and more broken dark edge and **pale** orange discal spot. To add to the complications, both species may vary in their shades of yellow, whilst female Pale Clouded, and Berger's are generally white above (just like the Clouded Yellow *helice*). Further confusion is created by the fact that a proportion of females in both species can also occur in variable yellow forms instead of the white. Perched Pale Clouded Yellows often show rather more pointed wings than those of Berger's, and this is considered an important ID feature, although one which is not easy to use in the field without a fair bit of practice, and not one which

helps distinguish it from Clouded Yellow.

A Pale Clouded Yellow suspect seen in Yorkshire is one of the few species we would suggest is best captured, and temporarily retained alive for confirmation and photography. However, it should be noted that, even with a dead specimen, it is not always possible to separate these species! It might also be possible either to take a rapid series of pictures of such a butterfly in flight at a thousandth of a second to stop movement and catch an open wing picture, or to film it and look at individual frames. Around 100, mainly minor, variations have been described for the Clouded Yellow, and a further 70 odd for the Pale Clouded Yellow, which don't make the problems any easier! It is also necessary to be wary of very yellow specimens of Small White, which can appear quite similar in flight.

The Butterflies of Yorkshire

LIFE STORY

HABITAT: On migration, Pale Clouded or Berger's could turn up anywhere. The Pale Clouded Yellow will be looking for habitats containing its foodplants, the clovers *Trifolium* spp or Lucerne *Medicargo sativa*. Berger's is more restricted, as its foodplants are chalk-based Horseshoe Vetch *Hippocrepis comosa* and (occasionally) Crown Vetch *Coronilla varia*. These limit Berger's non-migratory distribution to suitable dry habitats on calcareous soils.

Eggs are laid singly on leguminous species. Larvae appear after 7/10 days and develop through 6 instars. The species winters in the larval stage, and in France may appear as early as April, with successive generations flying until late Oct and even early Nov. Numbers often build up considerably in late summer. The species has occasionally bred successfully in S England through two or more generations. On rare occasions, larvae have even survived winter hibernation and produced a spring generation the following year. This last happened in the winters of 1947/48 (in Kent) and 1948/49 (in Essex).

CONSERVATION ISSUES: Whilst this species is too rare for any thought of conservation action in Yorkshire, it does illustrate the growing need for us to be aware of the situation in Europe. The way other countries are dealing with agriculture and conservation issues is likely to have an increasing effect on what happens to our butterfly immigrants. The most likely reason for the virtual disappearance of this species as an immigrant to Britain is the changing agricultural scene on the continent, and particularly in France. Since 1963 French farming life has altered dramatically, with the old strip farming ownerships progressively re-organised into larger units. The mosaic of small plots, periodically 'rested' in clover or Lucerne, provided an ideal breeding ground for many butterflies including the Pale Clouded Yellow. Not only have the farming units grown in size but the development of the European Community has encouraged the ploughing out of old meadows in favour of subsidised crops like maize and rape. In the few places where this hasn't happened, old meadows have often become disused and are rapidly scrubbing over and reverting to woodland. However, unlike their British counterparts, many intensive grain farmers in France still use clover and lucerne as break crops, even on the prairie lands of the Paris Basin. But unfortunately for the Pale Clouded Yellow (and the Clouded Yellow), these are usually cut for cattle feed two or three times a year, and it is very much hit and miss as to whether or not the butterfly can fit its breeding cycle into such a regime. Some authorities suggest that the irregular pattern of migration, with some long gaps over the years, must indicate that the weather plays a significant part in creating the ideal conditions which trigger an eruption, and that such conditions may yet recur and produce a major resurgence of the species as a migrant to Britain. In view of the situation in France, this seems increasingly unlikely, unless the reported decrease (Lafranchis 2000) has more to do with a lack of recording coverage than an actual reduction.

Photo taken at South Gare (VC62) on 04/10/1984 illustrating the problems of identifying this species. If a Clouded Yellow, the dot just visible on the black wing tip indicates female. However, the upperwing colour lacks the rich orange of the normal colour form of the Clouded Yellow and appears closer to the more acidic yellow found on the Pale Clouded Yellow. If the latter, it would be a male. However, it is possible that the flash used in the photography may have distorted the colour, or more likely, that this is one of the many variant forms of the Clouded Yellow. The pointed wings, and straight leading edge to the upper forewing rule out Berger's Clouded Yellow. Unfortunately, it appears impossible to confirm, but a Pale Clouded Yellow cannot be ruled out.

Peter Waterton

HISTORICAL REVIEW:
Pale Clouded Yellow
Berger's Clouded Yellow

The history of this species is riddled with confusion and even Linnaeus failed to realise that his 'Clouded Yellow' included more than one species. As a name, **Pale Clouded Yellow** was introduced by Harris in 1775, whilst the distinction between the Clouded Yellow and Pale Clouded Yellow was finally clarified by Humphreys & Westwood in 1841. **Berger's Clouded Yellow** was not distinguished as a species new to science until 1945, and its scientific name *alfacariensis* was not published until 1948. Even now, the scientific name is not fully accepted, and the alternatives *australis* and *calida* appear in some publications. In the Latin *hyale* is derived from the name of one of the daughters of Danaus, whilst *alfacariensis* refers to Alfacar in southern Spain, the place where the first, or 'type' specimens were obtained.

The Pale Clouded Yellow was much more common as an immigrant in the past, probably a reflection of the widespread small scale farming found on the continent, which provided a huge acreage of suitable habitat. Nationally notable years for Pale Clouded Yellows in Britain were: **1821**, **1828**, **1835**, **1842**, **1868**, **1872**, **1900** (with 2200 specimens reported!), **1945** (318), **1947** (870), **1948** (310), and **1949** (450). Although the species has been reported from southern England in most years since then, numbers have been very low. During the same period the butterfly has also disappeared from some 20 *départements* in the western half of France, particularly those nearest the Channel Coast.

For Yorkshire, the earliest reference appears to be that in Morris (1853): '*It has been captured or seen in Heslington Fields near York in 1842*'. Today's Heslington Common is in VC61/SE6348k. Porritt (1883) noted that the Pale Clouded Yellow was, '*Very rare, but there was an invasion of the species in 1842*' when it was recorded around '*Horningsea*' (presumably Hornsea, VC61/TA24), Selby (VC63/64 SE63) and York (presumably Morris's record). In his 1904 *Supplement* Porritt mentions the 1900 invasion: '*Along with C. edusa* [Clouded Yellow] *there was apparently an invasion of this species in 1900: the localities included Beverley (JR Lowther)* [VC61/TA03]*, Bridlington (HH Corbett)* [VC61/TA16]*, and Hull (C Couldwell)* [VC61/TA03/13]*'*. Garland (1981) notes a 1947 record from Worral (nr Sheffield, VC63/SK39), whilst Sutton & Beaumont (1989) mention 1947 records from the Harrogate area (VC64) and from the north of VC62 but without evidence that would prove they were not simply *helice* Clouded Yellows misidentified.

Howard M Frost

[1547 CLEOPATRA] *Gonepteryx cleopatra* (Linnaeus 1767)
Family: Pieridae, sub-group Coliadinae ('the Yellows').

WORLD STATUS: Widespread and common hibernating resident within its range. Emerges from hibernation Jan/Apr, and produces one brood May/Nov, 0-1600m (up to 2100m as a vagrant). May go into diapause in hottest part of summer. Regular wide-ranging vagrant to the north of its range perhaps extending several hundred miles. Range: NW Africa, Spain and eastward around the Mediterranean area to Turkey and the Middle East. Resident in the southern third of France and a regular vagrant to the middle third as far north as *Département 44, Loire-Atlantique*, centred on Nantes, just to the south of Brittany (and approx 200 miles south of the English coast). The French distribution map of this species in Lafranchis (2000) indicates a tendency for it to go further north on the west side of France than on the east, which lends weight to the possibility of occasional arrivals on the south coast of England, particularly in more recent times.

YORKSHIRE STATUS 1995/2003:

Potentially, an exceptionally rare vagrant, with one claimed sighting in 1860 near Rotherham, and a specimen in Doncaster Museum bearing the label: *Collected by E A Schofield Doncaster 1911*.

Left: Cleopatra specimen bearing the data, 'Collected by EA Schofield, Doncaster Aug 1911' and right, a specimen for comparison obtained in Italy. Both from the LGF Waddington Collection, courtesy Doncaster Museum Collection, Doncaster Metropolitan Borough Council.

Two specimens from southern Europe showing the way the orange flush stands out in male Cleopatras.

Similar to Brimstone. It hibernates in winter, typically in dry woodlands (with females sometimes already mated). Appears from Jan onward, to Jun, as weather and temperature dictates. Main generation flies from late May to Nov, but often aestivates during the hottest part of the summer. Lafranchis (2000) reports that a partial second generation may fly in late Aug/Sept although other writers suggest this is a confusion with re-emergence after summer diapause. Like the Brimstone, therefore, it can be seen in every month of the year. It uses a range of buckthorns as foodplants, particularly, the Mediterranean Buckthorn *Rhamnus alaternus*.

ID NOTES: Related to, and very similar to, the Brimstone, but slightly larger. Male upper forewings each show a large patch of orange red, which fades away through shades of yellow towards the wing edges leaving a variable band of very pale yellow around the patch. So although the patch lacks a sharp edge, the reddish blush looks fairly well defined. The female is pale, but more suffused with pale yellow than the female Brimstone. Any observers of a potential Cleopatra in the British Isles should be aware that there are some rare aberrations of the Brimstone which also have red or brown patches, and sometimes the orange spots on the Brimstone's upperwings may be enlarged sufficiently to cause confusion. The problems are well illustrated by the fact that even a well-known entomologist of the calibre of Frohawk could become confused. He identified two specimens from collections as aberrant forms of the Brimstone (ab *aureus* Frowhawk), but later examination in the London Natural History Museum has shown them to be Cleopatras. A typical Brimstone ab *aureus* Frohawk has only a very pale suffusion of reddish-orange scales, which hardly amounts to a patch.

HISTORICAL REVIEW:
Cleopatra
Included in Porritt (1883)

Linnaeus named this butterfly in 1767 and it has remained unchanged. In the Latin *Gonepteryx* refers to the angular shape of the wing and 'Cleopatra' was the wife of Meleager who was associated with a famous wild boar hunt in Calydon, a story in Greek mythology.

Yorkshire's first possible record of this species was reported in an 1860 edition of the *Entomologist's Weekly Intelligencer* by the Rev H A Pickard, of Christ Church, Oxford. His note was headed *'Singular, considering the Season!'* a reference, no doubt, to the fact that 1860 was a notably poor year with a very cold summer. He wrote: *'I have to announce an important capture—that of the Cleopatra variety of Gonepteryx rhamni (the Brimstone). It was taken by my uncle, John Fullerton Esq, in his grounds at Thrybergh Park near Rotherham on June 27th 1860'.* Thrybergh

Park is in VC63/SK49 (now a country park with visitor centre and nature trail). In 1861, HT Stainton commented on the capture, in the *Entomologist's Annual* for that year:' *The forewings are much more suffused with orange than those of the specimen which Mr Curtis figured could have been, and the specimen resembles exactly the Italian specimen of Cleopatra in Mr Hope's collection.'*

It should be noted that at this time it was not generally realised that butterflies could migrate, hence the idea, seemingly more reasonable, that this was a *variety* of the Brimstone. It was even suggested that such a red-flushed variety, though rare in Britain, occurred more frequently as one moved south. In fact, this strong flier, is now known to be a regular vagrant in France, being seen not infrequently up to 200 miles north of its regular Mediterranean breeding range. A further 200 miles would take it to the south coast of England, not such a huge distance in favourable weather conditions.

The Thrybergh sighting was the first of a series of scattered reports of Cleopatras in Britain: 1870 Isle of Wight; 1873 Isle of Wight; 1882 or 1887 Forfar, Scotland (probably introduced); 1896 Suffolk; 1911 Doncaster; 1916 Kent (judged to be escapees); 1957 Cornwall (at Feock, close to the River Fal where surplus merchant ships are laid up); 1981 Kent; 1984 Scilly Isles; 1986 Jersey. The Thrybergh and Forfar records are often discounted together, as being just too far north for this species to reach unaided. Salmon (2000) discusses them both in some detail, and regarding the Thrybergh report concludes, that in view of the place of capture, it was very likely to have been an extremely rare aberration of the Brimstone, with a similar reddish suffusion on the forewings.

South coast records are generally accepted as probable natural vagrants, although there are always concerns about captive raised specimens having been introduced or escaped. The Kent record in July 1981 is thought more likely to have hitched a lift on a lorry or other vehicle (Philp 1993) than to have reached England by its own means. The fact that the Cleopatra often aestivates (ie goes into temporary summer hibernation) in the hottest part of summer means that it is not impossible for it to choose to hide away in a sheltered corner of a lorry, or even inside a container just before it is about to be hauled away on a long journey. RF Bretherton (in Emmet & Heath 1989) accepts the possibilities of Cleopatras flying to Britain unassisted from France and even from Spain. A further possibility, not previously suggested, is that the Thrybergh specimen could have flown to the south coast of England in 1859 (a year with a much warmer spring and summer) and then successfully hibernated in Britain before heading further north the following year.

Some observers have wondered if the Cleopatra has sometimes hitched lifts from the Mediterranean area by boat. This would seem as likely a possibility as travelling on road vehicles. At first sight Thrybergh would seem to have little to do with boats, but it turns out to be adjacent to the River Don with its parallel canal system linking to the Humber. There was a thriving wood trade in the area, importing continental timber, which made neighbouring Rawmarsh a known site for hitchhiking Camberwell Beauties. The possibility of a Cleopatra arriving by this same route cannot be ruled out.

Garland (1981) suggests that the Thrybergh Cleopatra was a variety of the Brimstone described as ab *decora* Oberthür, but Rimington (1992) thinks that such an identification was made *'without sufficient justification'.* Certainly, the lack of a specimen to study means we can only draw on the scant descriptive comments quoted above. Stainton's observation that the Thrybergh specimen, *'resembles exactly the Italian specimen of Cleopatra',* is the nearest we shall ever have to a confirmation that this was indeed a Cleopatra.

The LGF Waddington Collection in the Doncaster Museum contains a worn male Cleopatra specimen labelled: *'Collected by EA Schofield, Doncaster 1911'.* (See photo.) Nothing appears to be known about the history of this specimen, although Rimington argues, from evidence within the display in which it is found, that this Cleopatra was re-set and re-pinned when the other Brimstones in the same display were mounted in 1944. He goes on to suggest that it would seem more likely that this is the original Thrybergh specimen, than that it could have been a second Cleopatra caught in the same area. One would certainly have expected a second Cleopatra to have been more widely reported. Rimington's theory assumes that at some point data cards were muddled. However, this can only remain a theory. It is equally possible that if one Cleopatra could come in via wood imports, another could do the same some 50yrs later! This remains an intriguing and unsolved mystery, and one in which we cannot rule out the possibility that Yorkshire has had two Cleopatra records, even though strong doubts have been expressed about both records. The Cleopatra is a species that might shift its range northward under the influence of global warming. We may yet get other county records!

Howard M Frost

[1548 BLACK-VEINED WHITE] *Aporia crataegi* (Linnaeus 1758)
Family: Pieridae, sub-group Pierinae ('the Whites').

WORLD STATUS: Resident 0-2200m+ with suspected 'dispersive/migratory tendency' (Tolman 1997). 1 brood (Apr/Aug, earliest in S; later in north). Range: N Africa to S Norway (but not British Isles where it became extinct in 1920s) and eastward across temperate Asia to Japan. (In 2000 the editor noted it as common along verges of trans-Siberian Railway, inc disused railway sidings: from St Petersburg to Irkutsk.) Still relatively common in suitable habitats in W Europe, but numbers fluctuate a great deal from year to year. Decreasing in N France and Benelux, especially in intensively farmed areas. Lafranchis (2000) draws attention to the huge loss of hedgerows (and therefore foodplants) in France between 1960 and 1990, amounting to an area of 440,000 hectares!

YORKSHIRE STATUS 1995/2003:

Probable former resident and/or immigrant, now extinct. Early references suggest it was probably once a marginal resident, or dispersive immigrant from counties to the immediate south. It has been extinct in Yorkshire since around the 1880s, which may indicate that any precarious hold it had in this period came to an end as a result of the notable cold period between 1879 and 1895.

ID NOTES: A very large white butterfly (larger than a Large White) with strong, yet floppy or bouncy flight. It often glides with wings held upwards in a V-shape. The veins only become apparent in a closer view. Male has black veins, female brown veins. Female also semi-transparent with fewer white scales on the wing than the male.

Detail from a James Bolton painting 1796 (see text). *Courtesy: National Museums & Galleries Merseyside.*

LIFE STORY

Eggs laid in batches of 50-200 on the undersides of foodplant leaves and hatch after 2-3 weeks. Larvae live communally in a web, emerging a group at a time, to feed up, return to the safety of the web, and be replaced by the next group. A stronger web is spun in autumn and the colony goes into diapause from Oct to Mar. On re-awakening, they feed on buds and tender new leaves. When fully grown they become more independent and their hairs can cause a rash if touched. They also give off an unpleasant smell, which invades the whole nesting area. Pupae are patterned in green, black and yellow and are usually attached to the stem or branch of a typical foodplant for 2-3 weeks. The butterfly then flies for about 3 weeks, may roost communally, and may disperse some distance from its birthplace.

HISTORICAL REVIEW:
Black-veined White
Not listed in Porritt (1883)

First illustrated by Mouffet in 1634 it was originally called **the White Butterfly with black Veins**. Harris (1766) changed it to **Blacked-veined White**, a name accepted by most authors since, although Rennie (1832) tried unsuccessfully to make it **the Hawthorn**. In the Latin, the meaning of *Aporia* is uncertain but may be linked through various ideas to its fluctuating numbers, whilst the species name *crataegi* = hawthorn.

There are three positive records for Yorkshire and the tantalising possibility of an earlier occurrence. Among the paintings of butterflies that Halifax naturalist James Bolton (1735?/1799) added to the bird portraits of Vol. 2 of his

Black-veined Whites: mating pair being investigated by another male. (Haute Marne, France, June 2002).

Harmonia Ruralis (1796) is an excellent illustration of the Black-veined White. Unfortunately, he does not record the provenance of this, or indeed of any of the eight butterflies illustrated this way. Most of them, which receive brief comments, were probably painted from locally collected individuals, as was the damselfly *Pyrrhosoma nymphula*, which he records as being common by the River Calder, near Halifax.

Morris (1853) reported: '*It has been taken, I am told, at Bishop's Wood, Cawood, Yorkshire*' (VC64/SE15). His comment is on the authority of an un-named informant and whilst probably valid, is unsubstantiated. It was also seen in plenty '*in a rough place close to*' Stockton Forest (VC62/SE65), a woodland which no longer exists (in the region of Stockton on the Forest, between York, Strensall and Stamford Bridge) by John T Carrington (Weir 1888). Whether he saw it there in more than one season is not clear, but his remark that, following a very severe winter in 1878 or 1879, both it and the Marbled White, which occurred with it in abundance, were no longer to be found, suggests that he may have done so. It is probable that the severe winter referred to was that of 1879.

The Black-veined White's presence at Sewerby Hall, Bridlington (VC61/TA26) (by a typographical error given as Sewerby, Hull) in 1885, is well substantiated (Rockett 1892). Adults were reared from two larvae and six pupae collected there on a '*species of thorn*'. However, as the food plants may have been recently planted stock imported from the continent, eggs or small larvae could have been brought in with them, putting the indigenous nature of the insects in doubt. Details of these records are elaborated by Fryer (2000).

Geoffrey Fryer

UK BAP Status: *Species of Conservation Concern.*
BC Priority: *Medium.*
European status: *Not threatened.*
Protected from sale in GB.

WORLD STATUS: Localised, sedentary resident, 0-700m. One brood (mid-Jun/late Jul - earlier further east). Range: Franco-Spanish border, north-eastward to S Sweden and S Finland, and east through Europe and Asia to Japan. Stable over much of Europe, but declining in Austria, Belgium, Denmark, Lithuania, N & W France and Slovakia. Current British population comprises 40-50 colonies restricted to Midland localities between Oxford and Peterborough.

LIFE STORY

HABITAT: Favours sunny sheltered rides, woodland edges, hedgerows or scrubby areas on heavy clay soils, where dense patches of the main larval foodplant, Blackthorn *Prunus spinosa* can develop to maturity. It may occasionally use other *Prunus* species for egg-laying, and field maple and ash for honeydew feeding.

Eggs laid singly, usually from 1.5m to 5m from ground, mainly on older specimens of blackthorn (20 to 60yrs old), but sometimes lower down on fresh sucker growth. Although blue-green when laid, they become yellowish brown, and fade to grey by winter. Larvae develop inside the egg but do not emerge until the following spring. Pupae are attached to nearby leaves or twigs and look like bird droppings. The butterflies have a very short flight season and are difficult to find as they spend much time in the woodland canopy feeding on honeydew. Very occasionally they may be seen nectaring nearer the ground on privet, bramble, thistles etc. The sedentary nature of *pruni* inhibits the colonisation of new areas.

SPECIAL NOTE: This species is included here because there are historical references to a past Yorkshire presence which require clarification. For brevity, Latin names are used in the text: *pruni* for Black Hairstreak and *w-album* for White-letter Hairstreak.

YORKSHIRE STATUS 1995/2003:

Uncertain. Possible past resident in S Yorkshire area, but historical references to a past presence should be treated with great caution.

Above left: Black Hairstreak closed wing view. Above right: female. Right: male. Illustrations from Morris (1853) where the orange brown has remained yellow, probably due to a missed tint! These were not the most helpful of ID pictures!

ID NOTES: Closely similar to, and historically mistaken for, the White-letter Hairstreak, as both have a white 'W' pattern in closed-wing view (although usually less distinct letter shape in *pruni*). Both species always perch with wings closed, therefore the upperwing difference, where *pruni* has orange lunules towards wing margins (similar to Brown Argus), and *w-album* has featureless dark wings (save for the hint of an orange spot near the tails), is of little use in the field. Both species also have similar orange bands visible in closed-wing view but in *pruni* this includes a distinct (and diagnostic) row of black dots lined in white on one side. As this butterfly spends most of its life high up in trees, binoculars are an essential aid to seeing this key feature.

HISTORICAL REVIEW:
Black Hairstreak
Not listed in Porritt (1883)

The Black Hairstreak remained undiscovered in Britain until 1828. Up to that time the closely similar White-letter Hairstreak was called the **Black Hairstreak** or **Dark Hairstreak** and given the Latin name *Thecla pruni*. Curtis (1829) transferred these older names to the newly discovered species, leaving the White-letter Hairstreak to be re-named by others. However, many entomologists went on using Black Hairstreak to describe the species we now know as the White-letter Hairstreak. For the rest of the 1800s Black Hairstreak was often used to describe either species, leaving considerable potential for confusion in the historical record. Kirby (1882) and South (1906) finally clarified the situation and left us with the names we use today. In the Latin, the family name *Satyrium* refers to the mythical creatures known as satyrs, whilst the species name *pruni* links it to its foodplant, in effect meaning 'the Blackthorn' butterfly.

Investigations into the early history of this species in Yorkshire are complicated by fraudulence as well as nomenclatural confusion. In 1828 an Ipswich dealer in natural history objects named Seaman, without realising the identity (or the financial worth) of his capture, obtained specimens of the true Black Hairstreak, correctly giving Monk's Wood, Huntingdonshire, as the locality. One purchaser of some of this stock, believing he had bought what we now know as White-letter Hairstreaks, shared specimens with fellow members of the Entomological Club, including the distinguished entomologist Edward Newman, who identified them as the 'continental' Black Hairstreak, and therefore new to Britain.

Newman (1870) graphically recalls the event and points out that as soon as Seaman became aware that he had stumbled on a new species, 'then the locality became a mine of gold; and Mr Seaman very judiciously concluded to remove the mine to a greater distance, even to the ultima thule of his geographical knowledge, Yorkshire; and Mr Curtis who published the insect under its correct name shortly afterwards, gave Yorkshire as the locality where it had been found'. Curtis (1829) called it the Black Hairstreak *Thecla pruni*, the same name as used then for today's White-letter Hairstreak, and until the end of the century, confusion reigned, as new names

were introduced for *w-album* but old names continued to be used as well. Where the new names such as **White-letter Hairstreak**, **W Hairstreak**, **White-w** and *w-album* were used, they were used correctly. Unfortunately, some authors continued to use Dark Hairstreak and Black Hairstreak almost interchangeably for both species, as well as *Thecla pruni* when referring to White-letter Hairstreak.

There remains a further twist to this complicated history. In the catalogue of the Dale collection (Hope Dept, University of Oxford) is an entry for 17/07/1837, recording the capture of the Black Hairstreak, 'Th pruni', by the Rev W Guenee at Doncaster. In a separate article, JC Dale (1838) quoted Hugh Reid and a Mr Simmonds as saying that 'T. pruni' was 'common' at Doncaster. Later, in his 1846 annotations, JW Dunning (Rimington & Beaumont 1996) noted, 'Thecla pruni – Taken some years ago in great plenty in Yorkshire. Feeds on blackthorn'. However, Dunning's reference to blackthorn should not be regarded as significant for the White-letter Hairstreak had for many years previously, often, but erroneously, been said to feed on blackthorn.

A final and curious reference is made by none other than JC Dale's son CW Dale as recently as 1890 (Dale 1890) in which, after discussing the fraudulent history of the butterfly and making it quite clear that he refers to the true Black Hairstreak, 'Thecla (=Satyrium) pruni', goes on to record: 'In 1832 several were taken by Mr Henderson in Melton Wood near Doncaster' and adds 'found in the extreme south of Yorkshire'. There are points of particular interest in CW Dale's evidence. Firstly, JC Dale – a highly respected entomologist – is known to have visited Doncaster in the 1830s and 1840s in the company of his friend FO Morris who resided in Doncaster for some years and it is inconceivable that father and son would not have discussed such a matter, and secondly the confident reference to 'the extreme south of Yorkshire', made 60yrs after Newman's revelation.

These points lie together uneasily and will not now be clarified. However, it is hardly credible that such an entomological coup as the discovery of the true Black Hairstreak S. pruni at Doncaster would have escaped the notice of local lepidopterists of the calibre of Reid, Hawley, Morris and Warren, to say nothing of Heppenstall, Evans, Gascoyne, d'Arcy Preston, Wragg and others; also the later attention of Hall, Porritt and Corbett, none of whom appear to have been at all interested in this matter.

While truth is often discarded for lack of hard evidence, and it is known that an introduced colony of S. pruni survived for many years in a locality away from its normal Midland stations (Thomas & Lewington 1991), by far the most reasonable explanation for all references to *Thecla pruni*, or the 'Black and Dark Hairstreaks' at Doncaster or in Yorkshire, is that these have always referred to the White-letter Hairstreak, and that any other interpretation is unlikely to be other than the result of deception, confusion and misunderstanding.

Ted Rimington

UK BAP Status: *Species of Conservation Concern.*
BC Priorities: National: *Medium.*
N of England: *Not listed.* Yorkshire: *Not listed.*
European Status: *Not threatened.*
Protected from sale in GB.
Fully protected in N Ireland.

WORLD STATUS: Localised resident, 0-2800m. One (Apr/Jul) or two broods (Apr/Jun, Jul/Sept) according to latitude/height. Range: N Spain to N Scotland and eastward across Europe and Asia to Mongolia; mainly absent from Scandinavia (except Norway). Has declined across NW Europe, and throughout British range, where colonies are becoming increasingly scattered and isolated. Still survives along coasts of eastern Scotland and still present in Derbyshire, where it is known on two sites but could well be under-recorded (pers comm. Ken Orpe).

SPECIAL NOTE: Also known as the **Little Blue** (Thomas 1991, Tolman 1997).

YORKSHIRE STATUS 1995/2003:

Former resident now probably extinct. Last confirmed record in 1908 at Buckden in Wharfedale (VC64). (However, see historical review for discussion on later reports.) This is a species which is very easy to miss, as it has a short flight season and can be localised to one small corner of a suitable site. The possibility that there are overlooked colonies in the county cannot be ruled out.

ID NOTES: Very small, easily overlooked butterfly with dark black/brown upperwings, and pale grey-blue underwings with black dots (similar to Holly Blue). Male has a dusting of blue scales towards the centre of the upperwings. Both sexes show weak, fluttery flight. Readily confused with Chimney Sweeper moth *Odezia atrata*, which is locally common throughout Yorkshire in similar habitats to those where Small Blue might be expected. In flight, might also be confused with Brown Argus, although at rest, the latter's orange lunules (on the upperwings), and the more colourful, patterned underwings, are distinctive.

LIFE STORY

HABITAT: Requires dry, sheltered grasslands with Kidney Vetch *Anthyllis vulneraria* (its only known caterpillar foodplant). Typically, this habitat is often found on chalk and limestone (eg in the past, along the Magnesian Limestone outcrop, which runs north/south through the middle of the county), although suitable habitats can also be found elsewhere, particularly in quarries, along road and railway embankments, and on cliff tops and coastal dunes. Kidney vetch is a colonising plant and needs a continuing element of erosion, or wear and tear, on the habitat, to help maintain its presence. The butterfly can manage to survive in extremely small areas *'often not straying further than the size of an average room'* (Murray & Souter 1998). Hence the ease with which colonies can be overlooked.

Small Blues: mating pair (Workington, Cumbria).

Normally single brooded (mid-May/late Jun), but a partial 2nd generation is possible in S England (late Jul/Aug) in good years. Eggs usually laid singly on kidney vetch flower heads. Where two or more larvae end up on the same plant, the strongest is likely to fight and eat any weaker brethren. Larvae hibernate through winter, hidden in the soil surface. They have the possibility of remaining in diapause (a state of inactivity) for 15 months. Pupation takes place in Apr/May. Butterflies are often very sedentary, rarely moving more than about 40 metres in a lifetime, although occasional longer movement up to 17km have been recorded (Asher *et al* 2001), and natural colonisation of newly created man-made sites, such as road cuttings, has been observed. Colonies are usually very small, numbering less than 30 butterflies in total.

First recognised as a British butterfly by Lewin in 1795, who called it the **Small Blue** *Cupido alsus*. Others referred to it as the **Bedford Blue** after the county in which it was first discovered, and Morris (1853) introduced **Little Blue**, a name that has been revived in more recent times. However, most authors (inc South 1906) have used **Small Blue**. In the Latin *Cupido* comes from Cupid, the God of Love, and *minimus* means smallest'.

Duncan (1844) assessing the national situation, noted that the species, *'seems to occur, but not in great abundance, in most parts of the kingdom. Numerous localities, scattered over the southern parts of England, have been cited for it. Mr Wailes informs us that it is common on the magnesian limestone district near Newcastle: it is also found in woods near Durham...'* Morris (1853) notes: *'In Yorkshire, it has been met with at Wadsworth* [presumably Wadworth VC63/SK59] *and Brodsworth* [VC63/SE50] *near Doncaster, Langton Wold* [nr Malton VC61/SE86], *Londesborough* [VC61/SE84], *by myself, and in other parts'*. Porritt (1883) quotes a report published in 1842, referring to the species 10 miles from York. Rimington (1992) notes an 1860's record from Balby Doncaster VC63/SE50. Porritt mentions several other sites including Boston Spa (VC64/SE44), Bramham (VC64/SE44) [J Smith], Scarborough (VC62/TA08/09?) [Thomas Wilkinson], Sheffield (VC63) *'in an old list'* [A Doncaster], Sutton-under-Whitestonecliffe (VC62/SE48) [John Grassham], and Wakefield (VC63/SE31/32?) [W Talbot]. Garland (1981) mentions two seen at Ryhill Pits, near Barnsley (VC63/SE30) in 1871. Walsh (1952) notes that Thomas Wilkinson considered it plentiful at Pickering (VC62/SE78/88) in the 1880s, and very abundant on the coast at

Scarborough'. Stainforth (1919) writes that Thomas Stather referred to it as being, *'plentiful at Riplingham, the only East Riding record'*. This comment refers to the period prior to Stather's death in 1878. Stainforth also notes that 'Riplingham' *'refers to the Wolds area around Weedley and Brantinghamdale'* (VC61/SE92/93). Porritt (1904) adds East Keswick [Samuel Walker], and the Wetherby district [BB Thompson 1901], both in the same area (VC64/SE34). The last accepted YNU record comes from Buckden (Wharfedale VC64/SD97) on 13/07/1908.

By 1910, the Small Blue was considered extinct in Yorkshire, although still present in the Derbyshire Dales. However, James Dickenson has tracked down an interesting reference in *The Boys and the Butterflies* (Birdsall 1988), which indicates the likelihood that a Yorkshire colony still existed in 1949, close to Sedburgh School (VC65/SD69). The author, James Birdsall, discovered it along the LMS railway line near the school, during a cross-country run! Maps of the cross-country route kindly provided by the Sedburgh School archivist, indicate the most likely site to have been along a series of railway cuttings/embankments, just inside the county border. Unfortunately, with the railway route now disused, the cuttings appear to have become very overgrown and as far as can be seen, no longer hold suitable habitats for this species. EB Ford (1975) said of the Small Blue: *'It exists in Yorkshire, and in several places, chiefly* **railway cuttings**, *in Cumberland'* (our emphasis). Ford originally composed his comments for the first edition of his work in 1945, still in the days of steam when railway verges were generally kept as periodically burned grasslands, to reduce the risk of accidental line-side fires. However, his observation provides an indicator as to the kinds of places a surviving Small Blue colony could yet be found. A 1970s 'hearsay' record from Kiplingcotes Quarry (YWT NR VC61), mentioned in Sutton & Beaumont (1989) was never reported officially, and is generally thought to have been a mis-identification. A 1990's larval report from an east coast site has not been ruled out, but has not been confirmed in spite of searches.

The reasons for the Small Blue's disappearance from Yorkshire are unclear. The severe weather towards the end of the 19th century may have played a part, perhaps coupled with the huge changes in agriculture associated with enclosing the land, followed by the increasingly intensified use of farmland in the 20th century. The few historical records which do exist suggest that this butterfly may never have been common in the county, although it was almost certainly overlooked in the past when travel was difficult for most lepidopterists.

Howard M Frost

CONSERVATION ISSUES: As the species is probably extinct in the county such issues do not currently arise. But if a surviving colony were to be found, the habitat reasons for survival should be carefully studied, with a view to ensuring their continuation, and if possible their spread. A 'whole landscape' approach to management may well be preferable to attempting to maintain a single site, with the emphasis on creating and maintaining a mosaic of kidney vetch patches within a mixture of short and tall plant growth and patches of bare ground, which can be colonised by the vetch. (See Asher *et al* for further discussion on suitable management by grazing etc.)

1571 SILVER-STUDDED BLUE *Plebejus argus* (Linnaeus 1758)
Family: Lycaenidae, sub-group Polyommatinae ('the Blues').

UK BAP Status: *Priority species.*
BC Priority: *Medium.*
Protected in GB for sale only.
European status: *Not threatened.*

WORLD STATUS: A very sedentary resident, 0-1500m. One brood (June/Aug) or two (May/June and July/Aug) according to height/latitude. Local but widespread from Mediterranean to central Norway, Sweden and Finland, and eastward through temperate Asia to N China and Japan. Considered fairly stable in Europe, but with some declines in west balanced by expansions in east. In Britain largely confined to heathlands south of a line from the Thames to the Severn, with a presence in East Anglia, Shropshire and Wales. Successful introductions have been made in Suffolk and on the Wirral.

ID NOTES: A very variable species with around 120 described aberrations and many subspecies or racial forms across Europe and the rest of its range. Easily confused with the very similar Common Blue, although flight is more fluttery and the butterfly usually keeps close to the ground. Male upperwings are more strongly edged in black, than in the Common Blue but have a similar white fringe. Females of the nominate race/subspecies *argus* are usually brown with orange lunules on the upperwings similar to Brown Argus. Both sexes show blue/green spots in the middle of some of the black spots found inside the orange lunules of the underwings (visible when the butterfly is viewed with closed wings). These blue/green spots are the 'silver' studs, which give the species its name. The extinct north-western race *masseyi* (which may possibly have been found in Yorkshire) was distinguished in the male by more pronounced black lunules on the blue upperwing than is usually found in *argus* and rather thinner black margins on the upper forewings, whilst the females had a proportion of blue on the brown upperwings, rather similar in looks to blue female Common Blues.

SPECIAL NOTE: Four subspecies are recognised in the British Is[l] although their validity is questioned, and some authors prefer to class the variations as racial forms rather than distinct sub-species. The ma[in] subspecies is *argus* Linn 1758 thought to have occurred throughout [the] species' British range; with *cretaceous* Tutt 1909 found in Dorset and n[ow] very rare; *caernensis* Thompson 1937 (a Red Data Book endem[ic] subspecies) found in N Wales (Caerns, Great Ormes Head and Anglese[y]) and *masseyi* Tutt 1909, now extinct, and formerly found on the mosses [of] NW England in Lancashire and Westmorland where it last disappear[ed] from Witherslack (VC69) in the 1940s following a fire in 1941. It [is] unclear as to whether *masseyi* could have been a more widespread form [in] northern England and Scotland as some sources assume.

YORKSHIRE STATUS 1995/2003:

Extinct former resident, which probably disappeared towards the end [of] the 19th century. Shortly before going to print, Ben Keywood recorded 2[?] males and 18 females *'in a scraped field'* near Lindrick Comm[on] (VC63/SK58) on 25/06/04, undoubtedly the result of a private a[nd] unreported release.

Ben Keywood

Ben Keywood

Silver-studded Blue: male above, female bottom (Lindrick Common area VC63 June 2004).

CONSERVATION ISSUES: The natural habitat for this species in Yorkshire was probably lowland heath, but lowland heath which was disturbed by man's activities such as turf cutting, and small scale grazing. Asher *et al* (2001) suggest that this is a difficult species to conserve as its requirement for thinly vegetated soils (as caused by the small scale burning of heathland or by the erosion of soils) is not easy to replicate on a regular and long-term basis. Recent experience has shown that any effort to conserve the Silver-studded Blue requires *'considerable resources and a concerted strategic approach'*. Any serious re-introduction project would need similar or greater resources.

LIFE STORY

HABITAT: Typically a species of lowland heaths, but also sometimes found on chalk grasslands and in areas of sand dunes. Strongly favours warm, south-facing slopes on sheltered sites. Uses quite a wide range of foodplants including heathers, heaths and gorses as well as Bird's-foot Trefoil *Lotus corniculatus*. In the past the species appears to have thrived in areas where small-scale controlled burning of heaths was undertaken to re-juvenate growth. Now suffers from overgrown heathlands.

Eggs laid singly on foodplant stems in areas of sparse vegetation, but they do not hatch until the following spring. Larvae are strongly associated with ants and usually pupate close to, or inside, ants' nests. Butterflies are on the wing for only four or five days. Colonies vary considerably in size from very small to very large, some with several thousand specimens flying together. Typically, individual butterflies rarely stray more than 20 metres from their point of emergence so natural colonisation is slow, requiring a continuation of suitable habitat. In N Wales, where the species was helped to spread to the Dulas Valley, colonisation was at the rate of about 1km in 10 years (Thomas & Lewington 1991).

HISTORICAL REVIEW:
Silver-studded Blue
Formerly: *Lycaena aegon*
(in Porritt 1883)

Early lepidopterists confused this species with other blues. Its similarity to the Common Blue means it is still easy to overlook. The **Silver-studded Blue** was not distinguished for certain, until the appearance of *The Aurelian's Pocket Companion*, by Moses Harris, in 1775. Most authors have kept the name he proposed, although Rennie (1832) called it the **Lead Blue**. The Latin *Plebejus* is related to plebeian, referring to the common folk in Roman times. So this butterfly is one of the 'plebs'! Its species name *argus* connects it to the Greek story of Argus with the hundred eyes, thus highlighting its key feature in the silver studs.

Ben Keywood

Silver-studded Blue (nr Lindrick Common VC63, June 2004). Note 'silver' studs in hindwing lunules as indicated.

Duncan (1844) noted that the species was *'found as far north as York where it is not rare. It must be very scarce, however, northwards of that city, and it probably does not occur at all in Scotland'*. In fact, there are a number of historical records scattered across Scotland (see Thompson 1980 for detailed discussion). If these Scottish records were correct identifications (which is no longer easy to judge), their spread would seem to hint at a wider distribution across northern Britain in the past. This is not really surprising considering that the species extends further north than Scotland on the continent. Even more intriguing is the possibility of overlooked colonies in Scotland (or elsewhere?). The last known Scottish record is supported by a male specimen taken in 1936, which suggests that the Scottish form was close in looks to *masseyi*. The species' similarity to Common Blue and its apparent ability to exist in small and very localised colonies, means it could quite easily be overlooked.

Brief mentions by a number of past authors indicate a thinly scattered historic Yorkshire population, which stretched from the Humberhead Levels northward through the Vale of York, as far north as Darlington, and eastward through the Vale of Pickering to Scarborough. Unfortunately, there are few dated records or site details, but the general inference seems to be that the species had largely disappeared from the county by the end of the 19th century. Drainage, land enclosure, industrialisation, the severe period of weather in the last 20 years of the 19th century, and perhaps most of all, the reclamation of lowland heaths, probably all took a toll. However, the widely scattered nature of records in northern Britain is puzzling for a species which has such great difficulty in colonising new areas. It seems probable that the few remaining 19th century records represented a relict population which was once much more widespread (perhaps prior to the 1300/1850 Little Ice Age), but became so depleted that it was all the more readily driven to extinction by adverse conditions.

In 1883 Porritt already assessed the species as *'rather scarce'* and found only in: Selby (VC61/64/SE63) by R Hebson and Thomas Foster; York

(VC61/2/4/SE55/56) by W Prest; and Scarborough (VC62/TA08) by Thomas Wilkinson. Unfortunately, no site details are given. Walsh (1952) notes that it was recorded as *'scarce near* Scarborough' by Thomas Wilkinson, but *'plentiful at Pickering'* according to a YNU circular (no date given). He goes on to report that more recent searches (prior to 1952) had failed to find the species in the Scarborough area. Morris (1853) gives *'Langwith near York'* which appears to be the area now occupied by Elvington Airfield (VC61/SE64). Porritt also notes a past presence in the Sheffield area evidenced from its inclusion in *'an old list'* in the name of A Doncaster. By 1907 Porritt's entry in the *Victoria County History* adds *'Scarce, and has apparently disappeared from some of its old recorded localities'*. Unfortunately, he doesn't say which, but simply repeats Selby, York and Scarborough as known sites, which could easily be based on information 50yrs old.

Stainforth (1919) commenting on the Thomas Stather collection (lost in the bombing of Hull in 1943), points to Stather (b1812/d1878) having taken a specimen on *'Whiggift Moor'* (ie Whitgift Moor between Eastoft and the Humber in

VC63/SE71/81, now a reclaimed and intensively farmed area). The adjacent Crowle/Thorne/Goole Moors area must have held this species in the past with the population stretching across the border into Lincolnshire. It was still found just across the border in the Laughton Common and Owston Ferry areas (VC54/SK89) up to 1945 (Duddington & Johnson 1983). Sutton & Beaumont (1989) suggest that the Whitgift Moor specimen may have dated from around 1860, whilst Rimington (1992) suggests it could have been taken earlier than 1827, the date of the enclosure of Whitgift Moor.

Garland (1981) refers to two specimens in the Sheldon Collection *'reputedly from Maltby',* (VC63/SK59) which *'appear to be of the northern subspecies masseyi'*. Garland also draws attention to the presence of the species in Sherwood Forest and Clumber Park just to the south of the Yorkshire border. Rimington (1992) highlights an 1866 newspaper report (in the *Doncaster, Nottingham and Lincoln Gazette*) featuring a talk by John Riley Hawley to the Doncaster Philosophical Society. In this is a reference to *Polyommatus Agou* being seen in Melton Wood (Doncaster VC63/SE50). At the time *Polyommatus aegon* was the scientific name for the Silver-studded Blue. *Agou* is almost certainly a misprint, perhaps resulting from the lead type-piece for the 'n' being placed upside down! A further record is referred to in Newman (1871) who noted that John Sang considered the species *'very common at Darlington',* (VC65/66/NZ21/31). Although Darlington is in County Durham, it is close to the border with Yorkshire and both its 10km squares include parts of the traditional area of Yorkshire. John Sang was known to collect in the Richmond and Redcar areas. The fact that Robson (1902) doesn't include this species for Durham & Northumberland, in spite of knowing John Sang personally, suggests that Sang's Silver-studded Blue records came from Yorkshire, but where exactly is unclear!

Howard M Frost

[1575 CHALK HILL BLUE] *Lysandra coridon* (Poda 1761)
Family: Lycaenidae, sub-group Polyommatinae ('the Blues').

UK BAP Status: *Species of Conservation Concern.*
BC Priority: *Low.*
European Status: *Not threatened.*
Protected in GB for sale only.

WORLD STATUS: Resident, 0-2000m. One brood (mid-Jul/mid-Sept). Range: found on calcareous soils across S and C Europe, through W Russia and the Ukraine to S Urals. In Europe: from N Spain, S France and parts of Italy and Greece to NW France, Benelux, N Germany and Lithuania. Also populations in S England south of a line from Severn to Wash, with the most northerly colonies near Cambridge and Stamford. Formerly found as far north as S Lincs (Ancaster) where it was last seen in 1974 (and unsuccessfully reintroduced in the 1990s). Very variable, leading to confusions over species/sub-species status in Europe.

YORKSHIRE STATUS 1995/2003:

Possibly a former resident up to the mid-1800s, but **now extinct**. There is a single reference to this species occurring in the Settle area (VC64/SD76/86) c1865. Whilst of questionable authenticity, and not listed by Porritt, the record merits serious scrutiny.

ID NOTES: Larger than Common Blue, but with similar underwing pattern. Male upperwings distinctive in pale silver-blue; female is brown (sometimes with variable amounts of silver-blue) and has wing edge spots with orange lunules. Characteristically, uppersides and undersides of both sexes have dark veins extending visibly into the white wing margin. Very variable indeed, with around 450 aberrations described!

Underside view of Chalk Hill Blue: specimen labelled *'Witherslack 1913'*. The only known specimen from the NW of England, although provenance cannot be guaranteed.

LIFE STORY

HABITAT: Unimproved and unfertilised chalk/limestone grasslands with Horseshoe Vetch *Hippocrepis comosa* and a preferred sward height no higher than 10cm. Occasionally, temporary colonies are found away from chalk/limestone areas where larvae will use other species of vetch and clover including Birds-foot Trefoil *Lotus corniculatus*. However, the lack of Horseshoe Vetch appears to cause such colonies to fail after a few seasons. The current national map showing distribution of Horseshoe Vetch shows the plant's presence on the Yorkshire Wolds and in a region stretching from the Yorkshire Dales into Cumbria, indicating these areas were likely to have held suitable habitat in the past.

White disc-shaped eggs are laid singly on stalks, litter and leaves on or near the foodplant. Larvae overwinter inside their eggs and emerge in spring to feed up over a 9-10-week period. They are woodlouse-like in shape, and bright green, with two segmented yellow bands along the back and a matching double stripe low down round the sides, which can give a yellow-edged appearance. Pupae may be found lying loosely in earth. Larvae and pupae are usually attended by ants. Adults emerge after about 20 days. Males are sometimes quite mobile and have been recorded 10 to 20km away from colonies (Asher *et al* 2001).

HISTORICAL REVIEW:
Chalk Hill Blue
Not listed in Porritt (1883)

Petiver (1704) referred to it as **the pale blue Argus**. Harris (1775) changed it to **Chalkhill Blue** and so it has remained, except for minor variations in writing Chalkhill (eg Chalk Hill and Chalk-hill). In the Latin, Lysandra was an Egyptian princess and daughter of Ptolemy, whilst Corydon was a shepherd in Virgil's *Eclogues*.

The Settle record is documented in the *Naturalist* by the respected entomologist B Hodgkinson (1885). The relevant passage reads, *'Some twenty years ago a*

man from Settle had at an inn here (Preston) a museum in which he had pictures [presumably a decorative display] *made of the Chalk-hill Blue (L. coridon). He told me that they were in profusion about or near Settle* [Yorkshire] *and Beetham* [formerly Westmoreland now Cumbria] *some twenty miles from Lancaster'*. Of Hodgkinson's acquaintance we know nothing and the Settle record was rightly declared *'not proven'* by the exacting Yorkshire recorder of the time, George Porritt.

In considering this record, it is essential that it be seen not in isolation, but in the context of a number of contemporaneous records for *coridon* in nearby north-western stations in Lancashire and Westmoreland (now Cumbria).

The earliest public notice of *coridon* in NW England was given by the eminent naturalist CS Gregson (1859) who stated that a fellow naturalist, Anthony Mason, had shown him a *'great lot'* of *coridon* taken at Grange (N coast of Morecambe Bay), the year being unspecified, but presumably recently. Mason had added that *coridon* was then the *'commonest blue he took by far'*. Gregson expressed surprise at the captures since Grange is on limestone: *'...P. corydon should be a chalk insect and Grange is a limestone district ...'*. This comment reflected Gregson's assumption that *coridon* was rarely if ever found on limestone, but not that he doubted Mason's integrity. Indeed, later (1862), Gregson again refers to the record without questioning its validity or Mason's integrity. Within a few years of Mason's disclosure *coridon* was reportedly recorded from the nearby localities of Beetham (Hodgkinson 1885), Grisedale by Saddleback: *'This butterfly (coridon) used to occur at the foot of Saddleback in Cumberland. I have seen specimens taken there by Mr Hope of Penrith.'* (Hodgkinson 1888), [There being no Grisedale in the vicinity of the *'foot of Saddleback'*, Hodgkinson probably refers here to nearby Mungrisdale], Milnthorpe (Newman 1871), Silverdale (Goss 1885), Arnside and Warton (Forsythe 1905), Witherslack (Wright 1940), and of course, Settle; all of which are on limestone except for Mungrisdale. Collectors were purported to have taken series of butterflies from four of these sites. The Grange district records quickly gained credence and were reported by popular and major authors from Coleman (1860) to Frohawk (1934) and as recently as Howarth (1973). But for the work of AE Wright (1940) it is possible that these records would still stand today.

Wright's suspicions as to the validity of Mason's disclosures, and all subsequent north-western records, were aroused by an exchange notice placed in the *Entomologist's Weekly Intelligencer* by Mason (1857), in which specimens of *coridon* were requested in exchange for other species; the point being that Mason would hardly request in 1857, a butterfly that was, in 1859, *'the commonest blue he took'*, and the *'great lot'* of *coridon* shown to Gregson, were those specimens supposed by Wright to have been obtained through exchange. After examination of all Grange district records, Wright could find no evidence of any extant labelled specimens from the district, nor that any recorder apart from Mason had personally seen or captured *coridon* there. Reference was also made to HH Massey (Tutt 1910) who had worked the area for 25yrs (since c1885) and who considered all Grange records to be *'suspect'*; also to the diaries of J Davis Ward, an experienced local entomologist, who regarded all such records as *'very doubtful'*. Wright's conclusion was that, though the Grange district, *'apart from latitude and other factors'*, seemed suitable, all *coridon* records were due to reiteration of

Mason's original *'false'* claim, and without substantiation should be *'ruled out'*. Wright clearly considered Mason to be at best a 'romancer'.

Rimington (1988) considered that whilst Wright's views were balanced, he had: a) overlooked important points, b) on occasion misrepresented others, and c) judged Mason (whose statements are pivotal to the matter) subjectively. If indeed Mason was a 'romancer', he was both unashamed and convincing, for in later years he repeated his claim for the Grange district as a locality for *coridon* (Goss 1885). Goss had apparently been informed by Mason that *coridon* had *'appeared in abundance at Silverdale in 1869 or 1870 and had as suddenly disappeared'*. If these dates were a transcription error for 1859 or 1860, they do not appear to have been corrected subsequently; moreover, Goss states that his *'old correspondent'*, James Murton of Silverdale, had sent him specimens of *coridon* in 1870, the locality, while not specified by Goss, plainly being Silverdale. Interestingly, in the *Entomologist's Weekly Intelligencer*, Murton (1861) also offered *coridon* for exchange. In respect of Mason's 1857 request notice for *coridon* it is noteworthy that he also requested *'P Artaxerxes'*- a butterfly common enough at Arnside to this day. Mason may have simply been requesting examples of both species from other geographical areas.

Any assumption that the Grange or Settle districts were adequately worked entomologically, around and even much later than 1860 (and particularly prior to the establishment of the rail network) is scarcely justified. HH Massey (T... 1910), speaking of Arnside, says, *'...twenty-five years ago* [c1885] *ve... little worked entomologically...'* whilst JB Hodgkinson (1885) referring the country to the east of the main Preston/Tebay railway route, whi... includes Settle, says, *'...many miles of which have never been looked up ... entomologists...'*. Also, Hodgkinson, though a resident of Preston, had ... his own admission not collected at Grange prior to 1877. For the Sett... area, excursion circulars of the YNU make the position clear: *'...th... district provides a fine field for original work ...in entomology...and w... repay investigation'*, (Fourth Meeting for 1878) and *'...nothing appears ... be on record as to insects...'* (96th Meeting in 1892).

Horseshoe Vetch, the only long-term natural foodplant of *coridon* larva... occurs as outposts about the limestone of NW England right on the edge ... its northern range. Also, and significantly, every recorded north-weste... *coridon* station, including Settle, but with the sole exception of Grisedal... occurs in a *comosa* vicinity. Mungrisdale is however, within c2km or 3k... west of the limestone, though the nearest *comosa* records appear to be so... 15km to the south-east and the immediate locality is said to be unsuitab... for *coridon*. Hodgkinson's 'Mr Hope' was most probably a local taxidermi... whose son later (1901) became curator of the Tullie House Museum ... Carlisle and who would certainly, therefore, have had contact with lat... naturalists (pers comm. Stephen Hewitt). Whilst history has a habit ... distorting truth, it is perhaps significant that more information regarding ... Hope's specimens has not come down to us. Certainly however, for a tim... when the close relationship between *comosa* and *coridon* was not proper... understood, Mason may be said to have chosen his localities well.

It is true that the lack of labelled specimens casts doubt on all north... western records. However it is also true that a century of entomologic... litter bins carry the remains of many thousands of unlabelled and mit... infested Victorian specimens. Rimington (1988) revealed that he possesse... a specimen of *coridon* still extant and bearing the following data: C ... *Johnson, 2nd August, 1913, Witherslack*. This specimen must be seen in th... context of a series said to have been taken by 'Mallinson' at Witherslack ... 1910, but dismissed by Wright as due to release. Rimington's specime... remains a mystery, for Johnson and Wright were respected entomologis... and colleagues in the Manchester Entomological Society. Possibly the da... label is in error, or maybe Johnson chose not to disclose his information. ... is however known that Johnson did visit Witherslack in 1913.

The Chalk Hill Blue occurs on the continent at latitudes somewhat mo... northerly than Grange and Settle, and in England occurred formerly as f... north as Lincolnshire. Around Grange it would have been both isolated an... at the edge of its British range and therefore unusually sensitive to th... environmental fluctuations that undoubtedly accompanied the rang... retractions of a number of northern lepidoptera in the second half of the 1... century. Interestingly, the only notably hot summers between 1847 an... 1875 were 'Mason's years', 1857, 1859, 1868 and 1870.

The Grange district and Settle records must stand or fall together. Wheth... or not later records were indeed due to reiteration, it is possible that th... early records were genuine and that Anthony Mason witnessed the passin... of a relict population of the Chalk Hill Blue in the NW of England.

Chalk Hill Blue (Kent 1983).

Ted Rimingto...

[1576 ADONIS BLUE] *Lysandra bellargus* (Rottemburg 1775)
Family: Lycaenidae, sub-group Lycaeninae ('the Blues').

WORLD STATUS: Resident. Mediterranean to S England and east across Europe into Russia. Two broods (May/Jun, Jul/Sept). Confined to calcareous soils where its foodplant Horseshoe Vetch *Hippocrepis comosa* is found. In England, historical and current distribution lies on or south of a line from the Severn to the Wash. A scarce butterfly in England today.

YORKSHIRE STATUS 1995/2003:

An introduced species no longer present. It was regularly reported from the Bradfield/Worral area (VC63/SK29/39) between 1945 and 1955 (Garland 1981). It is thought that specimens were released by a local breeder, even though the habitat in this area does not appear to have been suitable.

[1578 MAZARINE BLUE] *Cyaniris semiargus* (Rottemburg 1775)
Family: Lycaenidae, sub-group Polyommatinae ('the Blues').

WORLD STATUS: Resident and possible vagrant, 0-2700m. 1 to 3 broods (3rd partial) according to latitude/height (May/Aug or April/June and July/Sept-Oct). Range: N Spain to central Scandinavia and eastward through central Europe to N China and Korea, with outliers in S Spain and NW Africa (Morocco). Formerly present in England as far north as W Lincs (where it probably survived until c1900) and possibly E Yorkshire. Not thought to be threatened in Europe, but recent decreases widespread, especially in the Benelux countries, due to steady loss of flower meadows in favour of intensive farming.

ID NOTES: Similar in size to the Common Blue but with undersides closer in looks to Holly Blue. Male is a deep blue glossed with violet. Continental specimens observed in France are often a drab blue, which may result from wear and tear. The female is brown. Undersides are spotted with black dots ringed in white against a variable grey to brown background. Experience in France suggests that very worn specimens are more common than in many other butterflies, perhaps indicating a tough species which battles on to the last.

HABITAT: Commonly meadows and roadside verges with clovers up to 2200m or more, but can also be found in heathland, woodland and wet areas. Red Clover *Trifolium pratense* is the main foodplant on the continent, although other clovers are also used. The foodplant in Britain is assumed to have been the same.

YORKSHIRE STATUS 1995/2003:

Probable former resident now extinct. Recorded as a Yorkshire species c1800, but without any specified sites or sources.

Mazarine Blue (Haute Marne, France, Aug 2003).

CONSERVATION ISSUES: This species is considered by some as a potential candidate for a national re-introduction project, using hardy N European stock. Its habitat and foodplant requirements would seem to be fairly straightforward and could probably be satisfied on many nature reserves. As the West European population appears to be declining it would seem sensible to attempt to balance that loss with some gains in Britain. However, it would be advisable to take note of any existing studies of the species on the continent, or to instigate such studies, before embarking on such a project, in order to be certain that no key factors in its requirements have been overlooked.

Nationally, the earliest references to this species were probably in 1710, but they are not very clear, and could refer to other species. William Lewin appears to have been the first person to make a definite reference to the Mazarine Blue, but he called it the **Dark Blue** *Papilio cimon*, and considered it very rare (Lewin 1795). The name **Mazarine Blue** was first used to describe the Large Blue *Maculinea arion*, by Donovan in 1797, but in 1803 Haworth began using it to describe the present species, and the name has been accepted ever since. In the Latin *Cyan* = dark blue, and *iris* is a reference to 'rainbow'. The species name *semiargus* means with fewer spots on the underwings than in the *argus* (the Silver-studded Blue).

The known British records of this species came from at least 24 English and Welsh vice-counties, and were mapped for the 1970/82 Biological Records Centre Survey by John Heath and his team. They have since been used in a number of publications, including the Millennium Atlas (Asher *et al* 2001), and show a sparse and patchy distribution, which probably says more about the distribution of lepidopterists than actual butterflies. Known populations were centred around Dorset, and in an area stretching from the Severn Estuary (Glamorgan and Gloucestershire) to Herefordshire, with some smaller patches in eastern England from Kent through Norfolk to Northamptonshire. Two isolated dots indicate a past presence in Lincolnshire, very close to the south Yorkshire border, and apparently, around York, although this may be a nominal placing to indicate 'somewhere in Yorkshire'. One of the problems about mapping this species is that from around 1860 onward there was a considerable trade in specimens as a growing number of enthusiasts tried to complete collections. Unscrupulous dealers were known to pass off continental caught specimens as British. As a result, even data labels on old specimens cannot necessarily be believed.

Unfortunately, the evidence regarding this species' past presence in Yorkshire is somewhat vague and lacking in detail. Garland (1981) mentions that several old lists from the Sheffield region include the species as present in the *'South Yorkshire Area'* a long time ago. Porritt (1883) was unaware of any presence. He writes, *'This rare species, although it has never yet been found in Yorkshire, has occurred so near the county boundary that it deserves mention here.'* He goes on to highlight the Lincolnshire site. The York site appears to originate from a reference in Tutt (1908) to a reference in Haworth (1803/28) regarding Peter Watson (b1761/d1830) having supplied various specimens *'taken in the county of York'* to help with the illustrations. Rimington (1992) points out that these included Mazarine Blues. Haworth and Watson were friends who both lived in Hull, Watson for the whole of his life and Haworth until 1793 when he went to live in London. It is assumed therefore that the specimens were sent between 1793 and 1803, when Haworth's first volume was published. Watson was the most likely person to have given Haworth information about Swallowtails in the Beverley Marshes. He also provided specimens of the Large Heath, which came from the same area. It would seem more likely that the Mazarine Blues came from Watson's home area rather than from York, and the chalk grasslands at the southern edge of the Wolds around Riplingham (VC61/SE 92/93) would seem a reasonable possibility for the site.

Duncan (1844) noted that the Mazarine Blue was, *'Rather a scarce species which was usually found to frequent chalky districts. 'It has occurred in Norfolk, Dorset and Yorkshire'*. After a spate of records well to the south of Yorkshire in the early part of the 19th century, the species seems to have become steadily less common and finally began to disappear from sites completely between 1841 and the 1870s. Different sources give different last dates but a site near Cardiff, with records up to 1877, is often quoted as the last site on which this species was seen before extinction as a resident in Britain. However, it appears that the Lincolnshire site is a stronger contender for this doubtful privilege. The exact site was, perhaps wisely, never revealed although it was known to be near Epworth (VC54/SE70), and could well have been just two or three miles from the Yorkshire border. The source of this information is Samuel Hudson (1860) who lived in Epworth and who reported the presence in *The Entomologist's Weekly Intelligencer* noting, *'On Monday last I took a female of the above species in fine condition in the same field where my brother took one last season'*. In 1864 Hudson had a letter published in the *Zoologist* apparently in answer to some query about the Mazarine Blue. *'I find it in meadows (grass) at Epworth between the 10th and 25th July, but they are large in extent; and the insect appearing just before the grass is ready for the mower, prevents a proper search being made for it'*. Rimington (1992) draws attention to two of Hudson's specimens, which apparently still exist in private collections and are dated 1876 (or1878) and 1902. Porritt (1907) reports that Samuel Hudson *'stated only three years ago that he believed it could still be found there'* (ie at Epworth). This comment appears to be derived from a note in the *Naturalist* (1904 p224), and the fact that it was in a Yorkshire based journal, and mentioned by the Yorkshire recorder George Porritt in his 1907 list of Yorkshire species, seems to have led researchers to overlook that Epworth is in Lincolnshire. Even Lewin (2003) perpetuates the myth of 20th century Mazarines in Yorkshire!

Since its extinction as a resident in Britain the butterfly has continued to be reported from coastal sites in S and SE England, although only very occasionally, and with the last record in 1958. It is assumed that these were genuine vagrants. The species is sometimes bred from continental stock and may occasionally escape or is deliberately released, so any inland records are treated as unlikely to be natural. As the species is declining in Europe especially on the French coasts visible from southern England, vagrants and strays would seem to be less and less likely to reach our shores. It is strange that the species can exist as far north as the Arctic Circle on the continent, yet only managed to reach Yorkshire or its borders when it lived in Britain.

Howard M Frost

1584 WHITE ADMIRAL *Limenitis camilla* (Linnaeus 1764)
Family: Nymphalidae, sub-group Limenitinae ('the White Admirals').

WORLD STATUS: Fairly mobile resident, 0-1500m. I brood (mid-Jun/mid-Aug, but late Jun/mid-Aug in Britain). A small partial 2nd brood can occur in good years. Range: Pyrenees to SE England and east across central Europe and Asia to Japan. In Britain found mainly along, or to the SE of, a line from the Severn to the Humber. Recent years have seen expansion on the N edge of its range in both Britain and Europe, although some declines also noted in the Benelux, Austria and Germany.

ID NOTES: Similar in size to a Small Tortoiseshell, but black (or dark) with prominent white bands on the upperwings. These also show on the underwings, which are more colourfully patterned in grey, black and orange-brown. The White Admiral is a skilled glider.

LIFE STORY

HABITAT: Woodlands with sunny rides and clearings, coupled with dappled shade and plenty of Honeysuckle *Lonicera periclenum*, which is the foodplant in Britain.

Olive-green eggs are laid singly, close to the upper part of a leaf. Larvae then eat the leaf, but leave the midrib, which provides a clue to the butterfly's presence. Larvae have 5 instars and winter inside a hibernaculum, becoming active again in April. They usually pupate on honeysuckle, and emerge after 2/3 weeks. Adults may nectar on brambles, but also feed on animal dung and aphid honeydew. Populations are often small and isolated, and it is unusual to see more than one or two at a time.

This photo indicates a further Yorkshire sighting, made by Kristofer Swain in his Wakefield garden on 22/07/2004. The long distance from any natural colonies raises queries about introductions.

YORKSHIRE STATUS 1995/2003:

Recorded as a vagrant, new to Yorkshire, on 09/07/1994, in a small woodland in the village of Hollym, just south of Withernsea (VC61/TA32). Identified and reported by the owner of the wood, John Carmichael (a local farmer and naturalist), and confirmed by the then local society recorders for South Holderness, Howard & Christine Frost. This record represents the furthest north the White Admiral has yet been observed in Britain.

White Admiral. A woodland butterfly which thrives in dappled shade (Haute Marne, France 1984).

HISTORICAL REVIEW:
White Admiral
Formerly: *Ladoga camilla*

The first-ever report of this species in Britain dates from 1695, when it was discovered in Essex. In 1703, Petiver called it the **White Leghorn Admiral** because he had obtained a specimen from Italy. Later he shortened the name to **White Admiral**, a name which has been accepted ever since, although Rennie unsuccessfully tried to re-christen it **the Honeysuckle** in 1832. In the Latin, *Limenitis* is linked to the idea of gods who protected harbours, whilst Camilla was a princess in Virgil's *Aenid*.

The population of this species has waxed and waned considerably over the years. The weather in June seems to be a key factor in the butterfly's success, due to birds eating both larvae and pupae. Poor weather slows larval and pupal development and gives birds a longer period to find and eat them. By contrast, good weather has the opposite effect, leading to fewer specimens lost to predation. Garland (1981) highlights a reference to the species in Sterland (1875), which refers to it having been seen sparingly in Sherwood Forest, Notts, in the early 18th century. This seems to suggest an earlier expansion. Duncan (1844) notes that: *'Some of the south-eastern counties formerly produced it in tolerable plenty, but of late years it has been nowhere abundant although it has been noticed in a considerable* number of places...It does not appear to inhabit the north of England nor Scotland'.

As the decade starting 1810 was extremely cold, a contraction would have been expected around that time, but better weather followed, and by the 1840s it was probably expanding again. Then it appears that the cold period covering the last 20 years of the 19th century, caused devastation to the White Admiral and it retracted to a small part of southern England centred on Hampshire. Around 1920 it began expanding again, and re-colonised many of its old haunts in southern England. Between 1930 and 1942, this expansion gathered momentum and took the species as far north as southern and central Lincolnshire. Then the cool, wet years of the 1960s caused a further retraction 'with the species

disappearing from most haunts' in Lincolnshire (Duddington & Johnson 1983), only to begin reappearing in the 1970s, and to spread further in the 1980s and 1990s, until around a dozen Lincolnshire 10km squares were occupied by the turn of the century.

Nationally, the Millennium Atlas Survey (1995/1999) showed a 56% increase in occupied 10km squares compared to the 1970/82 Survey. So a Yorkshire record has not exactly been unexpected, although a first appearance in the east of East Yorkshire (VC61), which must have involved a River Humber crossing of at least 3 miles width, is something of a surprise. However, the record occurred in a year in which visible expansion of the species was being noted in Lincolnshire (pers comm. Mark Tyszka) and on a warm, sunny day when a light SW wind was blowing directly from Bardney Forest (probably the nearest stronghold) to Hollym, a straight line distance of about 35mls. Of course, the butterfly may not have arrived on the day it was spotted. The species is usually noted expanding in smaller steps of 2 or 3 miles, although bigger journeys are not unknown. Unfortunately, the possibility of a private and unreported release cannot be ruled out, although, in this case, the surrounding circumstantial evidence seems to point to a genuine record. The details are more fully discussed in Frost (1995).

Howard M Frost

[1585 PURPLE EMPEROR] Apatura iris (Linnaeus 1758)
Family: Nymphalidae, sub-group Apaturinae.

UK BAP Status: *Species of Conservation Concern.*
BC Priority: National: *Medium.*
Protected from sale in GB.

WORLD STATUS: Resident: 1 brood (mid-June/mid-Aug). Range: N Portugal/N Spain to Denmark and southern edges of Scandinavia, then eastward through central Europe and across temperate Asia to China, Japan and Korea. Has declined in Austria, Belgium, Croatia, Luxembourg and Netherlands, but is spreading northward on northern edge of range in Denmark, Finland and NW Russia. In Britain: largely confined to central southern areas of England with northernmost colonies in Northamptonshire and sightings (and probable private releases) in Nottinghamshire. It was once found widely in England as far north as Yorkshire's southern borders (eg Sherwood Forest in Nottinghamshire), and close to the Humber shores opposite Spurn. Declined in the earlier part of the 20th century, but began to expand again in the 1980s. In the 1995/1999 National Survey it was recorded in about 33% more 10km squares than in the 1970/82 Survey.

YORKSHIRE STATUS 1995/2003:

Probable rare resident, now extinct, and possible vagrant. Literature references suggest this species was a rare resident in the Doncaster area (VC63) in the early 1800s where it would have been on the northern edge of its range. The lack of later records suggests it may have been discovered either as a short-lived presence, or towards the end of a longer period of colonisation. Only two isolated records have been reported since then: in 1941 and 1997. For clarity these are dealt with together in the historical review.

Female Purple Emperors feeding from mud in same forest, left 1992, right 1996 (Haute Marne, France).

ID NOTES: Very large butterfly with white bars on upper wings on dark background. Male is slightly smaller and has a purple sheen but this only shows up at certain angles to the light. Female is brown-black. The species is very elusive and easily overlooked, especially as it can apparently exist at very low levels of population and spends much of its time hidden away in the upper parts of the woodland canopy.

Male Purple Emperor feeding on mud (Fermyn Woods Northants).

Lawrie King

LIFE STORY

HABITAT: The Purple Emperor is a butterfly of large deciduous woodlands, which contain the larval foodplants Goat Willow (Sallow) *Salix caprea*, Grey Willow *Salix cinerea*, or occasionally Crack Willow *Salix fragilis* and other willows species. The butterfly can also utilise regions which have lots of smaller woodlands within sight of one another. Males and females may occasionally be seen at ground level, usually singly. Males are often drawn to feed on animal excreta or corpses. Purple Emperors don't visit flowers but instead feed on honeydew (from aphids), as well as sap bleeding from damaged branches. They are especially fond of oak sap, but don't necessarily live in oak woodlands. Males are also reported to feed in muddy areas, probing to suck out vital salts. It is often said that females don't do this, although the writer has twice observed females visiting muddy patches in a forest in France.

Eggs are laid on the upper surfaces of various species of willow (as listed above). Green larvae striped with thin yellow lines hatch out after about 10 days. They develop horns after the first moult and go into hibernation in early Nov, turning brown to match the bare wood, and attaching themselves to forked twigs with the aid of silken pads. Activity is resumed in late May/early Jun when they turn back to green. Pupae hang from twigs looking remarkably like Sallow leaves. Adult butterflies hatch after about 2 weeks appearing from late June and flying until mid to late Aug.

CONSERVATION ISSUES: If global warming encourages the Purple Emperor to expand further north than it has ever been before (in recorded butterfly history), it is uncertain if we have enough suitably large deciduous woodlands in Yorkshire to satisfy the needs of this species. Most of our bigger forests are still predominantly of conifers, and many of our smaller deciduous woodlands lack the suitable willows. Managers of woodlands should be encouraged to include Oak and Goat Willow in any future plantings. Colonies also appear to depend on having a 'master tree', usually a notably tall specimen (of any species), which is on a rise or hilltop, and which becomes the meeting place for males and females. Retention of such a tree may be important in maintaining a viable colony, although if a master tree is felled, Purple Emperors will usually transfer their interest to another tree. Unfortunately, that tree might be in another woodland!

HISTORICAL REVIEW:
Purple Emperor
Not listed in Porritt.

First called **Mr Dale's Purple Eye** by Petiver in 1704, as it was 'discovered' in the collection of a Mr Dale. It was later known as the **Purple Highflier**, the **Emperor of the Woods** and the **Purple Shades** but it was Harris's name proposed in 1766, which eventually stood the test of time. In the Latin, the derivation of *Apatura* is uncertain but probably connected to the idea of 'deception', whilst 'Iris' was a messenger of the gods and linked to the rainbow, with both names connected to the variable iridescence seen in the male.

Humphreys & Westwood (1841), discussing various sites within its British range, include a quote from a manuscript provided by the Rev William T Bree, which notes that the Purple Emperor was *'occasionally though rarely seen in Warwickshire, **near Doncaster** and in the Isle of Wight'*. The implication is that these were sites known to Bree himself. He appears to have been a highly respected lepidopterist, and regular contributor to entomological journals in the period 1820/1860. Salmon (2000) describes how the Rev FO Morris (author of *A History of British Butterflies* 1853) met the Rev Bree when the latter was a curate at Polebrook (Northants). Bree introduced Morris to Purple Emperors in Ashton Wood, nr Oundle, Northants. In the list of Purple Emperor localities in his book, Morris includes, *'the neighbourhood of Doncaster, Yorkshire; but'*, he adds, *'I must confess that I never saw it there'*. Morris lived in Doncaster between 1835 and 1837 and was presumably repeating Bree's record because he considered it a reputable report from a fellow cleric who had shown him how to observe and catch the species. Ted Rimington (pers comm.), an expert on the historical records of the Doncaster area, thinks this record has all the hallmarks of a genuine observation. After all, at this time (and up to about 1895), the species was known in Sherwood Forest (Notts) which is only a few miles from Yorkshire's southern border. He thinks the most likely site would have been Edlington Wood (VC63/SK59) which in the early 1800s was much bigger than today.

The two 20th century records are difficult to explain in natural terms and are easily dismissed as misidentifications, unofficial releases, or escapees from private collections or butterfly houses. However, little is known about the dispersal abilities of this species except that it is a strong flier and may occasionally be seen crossing open countryside. Oates *et al* (2000) note that *'individuals can turn up almost anywhere'* and draw attention to some intriguing Hampshire reports. In 1916 a specimen was seen on Bournemouth Pier, which might have been a freshly arrived immigrant from the continent. In 1919, another Purple Emperor was spotted two miles out to sea, flying in from the direction of France! Yet many authors suggest the species is not a vagrant. However, whenever the butterfly attempts to expand its range it must run the risk of getting stranded by fatigue or changes in the weather in the wrong kind of habitat. Oates *et al* give a number of such occurrences for Hampshire including one, of a specimen turning up in a branch of Boots the Chemist in Petersfield!

JP Utley (1941) reported a solitary male at Ewden Head, NW of Sheffield

Male Purple Emperor feeding on mud (Fermyn Woods Northants).

VC63/SK29 seen on 22/09/1941. The late date immediately raised suspicions and Garland (1981) suggests it was *'probably a released specimen, though its origin, if otherwise, is mysterious'*. However, 194[?] produced a notably cold winter and spring, an average summer and a warm autumn, just the conditions that might be expected to produce a late emergence in many species. This is about a month later than expected last sightings in the S of England, but it is probable that few people bother to look for such an elusive species towards the end of its flight period, when with fewer butterflies flying, the chances of seeing one are not very great. Therefore, genuine last dates are very much more difficult to elucidate than for many other species. One might also expect at least a slight shift toward a later flight period in a more northerly site. Utley was on wartime reconnaissance duty at the time. He writes: *'I was waiting at the edge of glade in a large area covered with scattered Oak trees on the side of th[e] valley at Ewden Head. The day was sunny and warm.... Suddenly, ther[e] appeared to drop out of the sky a large butterfly of arresting appearance. settled on a bracken frond, and I cautiously got nearer, being careful t[o] avoid casting a shadow over it. Hastily, I wrote down notes of its colouring etc'*. He goes on to give a clear description of what could only have been male Purple Emperor. *'After a period of rest during which it kept opening and closing its wings, it flew off, mounting rapidly high in the air.... Th[e] point where the observations were made is four and a half miles within th[e] Yorkshire boundary,'* (probably in SK2396k). This record is puzzling from many points of view. There was a national decline in the first half of the 20th century leading to losses in eastern and central England by the 1940[s] (Asher *et al* 2001). So if it was a genuine wild record could it have been long-distance vagrant or might it even indicate an overlooked colony? A[s] we think the species is no longer present in Yorkshire, we don't go looking for it. Perhaps we should!

The second record is equally puzzling. Another (presumed) male dropped down into the York VC61 garden of Pat and Jim Bone on 08/08/1997. Th[is] report is unconfirmed and unexplained. It is presumed to be a release o[r] escapee. Whatever its status, it serves as a second reminder that we ought to be identifying suitable Purple Emperor sites and keeping a watch!

Howard M Frost

[1592 AMERICAN PAINTED LADY] *Cynthia virginiensis* (Drury 1773)
Family: Nymphalidae, sub-group Nymphalinae (the 'Nymphalids' or 'Vanessids').

WORLD STATUS: N American species with a somewhat uncertain status in its home region. Appears to be both resident and partial migrant with a thinly dispersed northward migration in spring, but no recorded return in the autumn. 2 broods in north, 3 or 4 in south. Pyle (1981) suggests it can tolerate cold conditions and hibernate as a butterfly or a pupa, but Opler (1992) indicates this is not yet clearly documented. The species ranges from Cuba, Central America, Colombia and the Galapagos Islands, northward through the entire USA to S Canada, with populations stronger on the eastern side than the west. Pyle indicates that the species does not appear to emigrate in the same impressive numbers as the Painted Lady, which is also found in N America.

The butterfly is also a rare vagrant to Europe, inc British Isles, and has become established in the Canary Isles, S Spain and Portugal. In Tenerife it has been described as 'polyvoltine' whilst in Portugal, 2 broods seem to be the norm. Some authors suggest the species could well be more common in the British Isles and in Europe, but is overlooked due to its similarity to Painted Lady.

ID TIPS: Easily mistaken for Painted lady, but differs in having **two large, black-ringed blue eyespots** on the underside of the hindwing (ie visible in closed-wing view). Painted Ladies have 5 much smaller eyespots in the same position. However, the eyespots are only really evident on close inspection. The features likely to impress as being different are the triangular shape of a perched butterfly and the striped appearance of the forewings (pers comm. Nick Bowles). American Painted Ladies are often a shade smaller and have less strongly pointed wings. The upperwing view is brighter, and at a distance can appear vertically banded in shades of yellow-orange and darker orange brown. By contrast, Painted Ladies appear darker and duller. Worn specimens of the two species look very similar. Summer generations of the American Painted Lady are larger and more brightly coloured than those produced in winter months, which are smaller and paler, with reduced black markings (Opler & Krizek 1984). *Atropos* 16 (April 2002) carries two valuable articles on this little known species with a detailed examination

YORKSHIRE STATUS 1995/2003:

Potentially, an extremely rare vagrant. An article by Peter May in the Feb 2004 edition of the Amateur Entomologists' Society *Bulletin* drew attention to that author's recent discovery of an American Painted Lady specimen in an old collection which carried the data label: **Caught in Ilkley Yorkshire 1868**. This raises the tantalising possibility of an overlooked Yorkshire species, with the specimen representing the first and sole record for the county. However, as Peter May points out, there is no known history or corroboration behind this record. Many fraudulent specimens were sold to unsuspecting collectors in the 19th century and this could easily be one of them. In addition, it is not unknown for data labels to get accidentally muddled. It is equally possible that the specimen was caught as a Painted Lady, in which case the original owner would not have recognised its rarity value, so wouldn't have reported it anyway. The fact that the species name is not included on the label lends weight to such a thesis. Without further details this record must remain uncertain, but possible. There were only five other 19th century reports of this species occurring in the British Isles.

American Painted Lady. Upperside of specimen found in an old collection and labelled, *'Caught Ilkley, Yorkshire 1868'.* (Ilkley is in VC64.)

Peter May

of ID and 'jizz' (charactistic distinguishing features, especially in flight style and habits). The larva is rather striking, being large, green, and banded with thin pale yellow stripes interspersed with hairy bands made up of black, white and deep brown oval nodules and a lateral band in pale yellow.

HABITAT: In N America it is reported to use a wide range of open habitats such as meadows, flood plains, waste ground and dunes. It will also visit gardens. Foodplants used, tend to be from a comparatively limited range belonging to the 'everlasting' tribe of the Compositae family, including Sweet Everlasting *Gnaphalium obtusifolium*, Pearly Everlasting *Anaphalis margaritacea* and Plantain-leaved Pussytoes *Antennaria plantaginifolia*. Species of burdock, *Arctium* spp, wormwood *Artemesia* spp and ironweed *Vernonia* spp are also mentioned (Opler & Krizek 1984, Scott 1986). In Europe, larvae have been noted on Jersey Cudweed *Gnaphalium luteoalbum* on La Gomera (Canaries) and in Portugal. Emmet & Heath (1989) give thistles *Carduus* spp as a foodplant used in Portugal.

American Painted Lady.
Underside of Ilkley specimen.

Caught Ilkley
Yorkshire
1868

HISTORICAL REVIEW:
Formerly *Vanessa huntera*.
Not listed in Porritt (1883).

Petiver (1704) was first to describe this butterfly from an American specimen and called it **Virginiana**. Morris (1853) used **Scarce Painted Lady** or **Hunter's Cynthia**, whilst Newman (1860) referred to it as **the Beautiful Painted Lady**. It is also known as **Hunter's Butterfly, Hunter's Painted lady** and **the Scarce Lady**. In the USA it is sometimes called **the American Lady, the Virginia Lady** or **Hunter's Butterfly**. The Latin name links the species to Virginia, USA because that is where Petiver's specimen came from.

The species appears to have been a long-standing resident in the Canary Islands, having been recorded there since 1805 (on Tenerife, la Gomera and La Palma). In recent times its presence has diminished, almost to the point of extinction, although Crolla *et al* (2002) indicate a single sighting on Tenerife in 1992, and the discovery of larvae on La Gomera in 1999. The status of any presence in the Canary Isles is uncertain. They could have been introduced via the shipping trade or come as wind blown immigrants. The population may depend on periodic immigration to keep it going. The species has also been a rare vagrant to Madeira (1870) and the Azores (1996).

19 sightings have been noted in the British Isles, **all in coastal situations**. Jul/Aug 1828 (Pembrokeshire), c1840 (Wales), Aug 1876 (Hampshire), Sept 1876 (Cornwall), Jul 1886 (Kent), 1901 (Co Cork), Aug 1905 (Isle of Wight), Sept c1911 (Dorset), Aug 1929 (Co Cork), Aug 1930 (Co Kerry), Sept 1942 (Devon), late summer c1943 (Lancashire), Aug 1944 (Glamorgan), Jul c1956 (East Sussex), Aug 1956 (Isle of Wight), Aug 1970 (N Devon), Sept 1970 (S Devon), Oct 1972 (S Devon). Sept 1980 (Glamorgan). For fuller details see Emmett & Heath (1989) and Crolla *et al* (2002). One additional 1871 record turned out to be a Brazilian Painted Lady *Vanessa braziliensis* and is thought to have been imported. This very similar species (also known as *Cynthia braziliensis*) is found in S America and sometimes considered a race of the American Painted Lady. The range of these two species may overlap leaving an open question as to whether or not Brazilian Painted Ladies could reach Britain unassisted. A sole German record of an American Painted Lady (Frankfurt am Main 1974) has turned out to be the Brazilian species, leaving its provenance uncertain. Accidental import? Deliberate release? Or an implication that Europe is within the extreme range of both American and Brazilian Painted Ladies? Re-examination of American Painted Lady specimens at a museum in Munich which were probably taken in the Canary Isles in the 19th century, has revealed 3 further Brazilian specimens. This background is given to stress the unusual nature of an Ilkley (VC64) record, which would also be the only inland British Isles record, and one of only two from the N of England.

The American Painted Lady has also become established in S Spain and Portugal since c1948 and is now found in around a dozen regions of Portugal. Since 1959 it has been seen with greater frequency in Spain where it is thought to have become a regular immigrant from Portugal. It is also interesting that of 9 French records since 1936, six were in the year 2000 and all six were May sightings. In 2001 an early June sighting was made in the Rhone Valley in Switzerland. If this species becomes more widely established in southern Europe, the next Yorkshire record may not be as far away as the 1868 specimen might suggest!

Howard M Frost

1594 LARGE TORTOISESHELL Nymphalis polychloros (Linnaeus 1758)
Family: Nymphalidae, sub-group Nymphalinae (the 'Nymphalids' or 'Vanessids').

WORLD STATUS: Mobile resident up to 2600m. Migratory status uncertain. 1 brood (June/Aug). Very occasionally aestivates and re-appears Sept/Oct or later. Otherwise hibernates and awakens Feb/May. Range: N Africa to N France and eastward to S Urals and Himalayas. Appears to be migratory on N edge of range, occasionally reaching Britain, Denmark, S Norway and S Finland. Has declined in W Europe over last 50 years, especially in Netherlands, Belgium and N France. Reasons not clear. Status in Britain uncertain, but probably extinct as a resident with occasional sightings explained by immigration and deliberate or accidental release.

ID NOTES: Looks very similar to a Small Tortoiseshell, **but much larger**, and lacking the black or dark central area of the upperwings which is replaced with orange-brown. Male and female alike.

LIFE STORY

HABITAT: A woodland butterfly found in woods and along tree-lined roads and tracks where there is a mixture of one of its foodplants and Sallow *Salix* spp or Blackthorn *Prunus spinosa* (for nectaring in early spring). The main foodplant is thought to be Wych Elm *Ulmus glabra* but many other tree species may be used including: other elms and willows, poplars, birches, wild cherry, pear etc.

Eggs laid April/May in batches of 100/200 close together, forming a sleeve around an outer twig anywhere from about 3m in height to the top of a tree. Spiny larvae feed together in the protection of a distinctive communal web. After about 4 weeks they usually drop to the ground in the 5th instar and seek out trunks, twigs and even fence posts on which to change into cryptically coloured pupae, a stage lasting about 14 days. Emergence is usually in July with adults often going into hibernation shortly after hatching. A few may only aestivate and re-appear for a while in autumn. Hibernation sites are similar in range to other Vanessids and include garden sheds and derelict buildings. Numbers of this species fluctuate considerably, possibly as a result of parasitic attack at the larval stage.

YORKSHIRE STATUS 1995/2003:

Former resident, now extinct. Possible vagrant. One unconfirmed report during the survey period made by Paul Forster in Guisborough VC62/NZ61 on 11/07/2002. This occurred in a year in which one other was seen in Essex, and Camberwell Beauties arrived from the SE in fair numbers with at least 10 individuals recorded in Yorkshire.

Large Tortoiseshell: specimen caught by Dennis Wade at Wawne (nr Hull, VC61) 25/04/1948. Photo courtesy Barry Spence collection.

HISTORICAL REVIEW:
Large Tortoiseshell
Formerly: *Vanessa polychloros* (in Porritt 1883).

The scientific name *polychloros* dates back further than most other butterfly names. It was given by an Italian naturalist, Ulysses Aldrovandi, in 1602, and later adopted by Linnaeus in his *Systema Naturae* of 1758. Petiver introduced its English name as the **Greater Tortoiseshell** in 1699. Later authors tried to introduce **the Elm**, or **the Elm Tortoiseshell**, but **Large Tortoiseshell** eventually prevailed. In the Latin *Nymphalis* relates the butterfly to a 'nymph', whilst the intended meaning of *polychloros* appears to be 'many coloured'.

Throughout its known history in Britain, its populations have been erratic. Duncan (1844) summed it up as follows, *'Although abundant in most parts of the continent of Europe, the Great Tortoise-Shell (or Elm Butterfly, as it is sometimes called) cannot be ranked amongst the most common of our day-flying Lepidoptera; at least, it is scarce in many districts and appears in plenty in others, only in certain years'.* Porritt (1883) wrote *'Not uncommon, but not often taken in numbers'.* Brady (1884) (quoted in Fryer & Lucas 2001) commented in reference to the Barnsley area (VC63), that it was *'of erratic occurrence and less common than formerly'*. Stainforth (1919), looking back over the previous 50 yrs or so, noted, *'This species is decidedly uncommon in the East Riding in spite of an abundance of the foodplant. Boult refers to the capture of two at Bilton in Holderness (VC61/TA13), while Porritt does not give a single East Riding locality'*.

The species appears to have been much more common in Britain in the 19th century than in the 20th, but it still showed in very variable numbers. 19th century populations were concentrated in the SE with a salient stretching up through the Midlands to VC63 in Yorkshire. North of this, it appeared only to be a very rare vagrant, although with a scatter of records stretching right up into Scotland, indicating its ability to wander great distances. In the 20th century, there were population peaks in 1901/02 and then it largely disappeared except in a few local areas until 1944/48, when a series of warm summers appeared to boost the population considerably and around 370 butterflies were reported. But then it crashed again in 1949/50 and over the next 50 years only about 130 Large Tortoiseshells were recorded nationwide, which would put it in the category of a very rare vagrant, rarer even than the Camberwell Beauty and the Monarch! Very little evidence of breeding has been noted.

Various theories have been put forward to explain this rather odd situation. The most convincing suggests that the species is in fact a regular migrant from the continent, but usually only in small numbers. Occasionally it arrives in sufficiently large numbers to set up temporary breeding populations, which may then last several years before crashing and disappearing. For a species on the northern edge of its range such a theory rings true (although yet to be fully proven) and may well be weather related. However, the Large Tortoiseshell is also prone to attacks by parasites during the larval stage, and it is possible that, like the Holly Blue, its population is cyclical for the same reason. Major arrivals in Britain may depend on a year of low parasitism corresponding with a specific set of ideal weather conditions.

Emmet & Heath (1989) discuss distribution issues in great detail, accompanied by historical distribution maps covering the last 200 yrs. All the maps indicate a similar pattern with largest numbers in the SE of England, tailing off to the NW. In the 19th century, this spread was largely contained south of a NW-facing line from the Mersey to Scarborough. In the 1940s the line still faced NW but ran from the Severn to the Wash, and the scatter of records since then falls into a similar area. It may be that if breeding is successful in the SE of England, a proportion of the succeeding generations of the butterfly move further to the north-west if weather conditions permit.

VC63 records for the 19th century suggest the species was quite widespread in the 1850s, 1860s and perhaps the 1870s. No dated records appear to come from the cold period between 1879/1895, which decimated many of Yorkshire's species at the time. Then, when there was a national upsurge of the species in 1901/02, Porritt (1904) added only one further record, from Helmsley VC62 in 1901, suggesting few specimens reached Yorkshire in this peak. In Porritt's day, recorders tended to assume that if a species had been seen on a site in the past (even 20 to 50 years previously), it would still be there. This can be particularly misleading in the case of a species like the Large Tortoiseshell where the sighting of a vagrant would be taken to mean that the species was breeding! In the 19th century few observers had any idea that butterflies could migrate.

One particularly intriguing aspect of this species in Yorkshire is the apparent continuation of a breeding population in the Huddersfield area. Fryer & Lucas (2001) have unearthed a wealth of important records in their study of the butterflies of this area. The species was certainly a resident between the 1850s and possibly the early 1880s (based on an 1883 report referring to *'occasional specimens'* having been seen, but without any indication of timescale). Records of the species seen around 1920, 1934 and 1935 as well as again in 1949 seem to suggest the possibility of a continuous colonisation over quite a long period of time. The 1910 sighting at Keighley (YNU 1970) could also be related, as it is only 18 miles away (and to the NW of known Huddersfield sites!). If there has been no continuous colonisation, the area must either be on a regularly used line of migration (which seems a little unlikely), or have been subject to repeated introductions (which is not impossible). On top of that we have a 1984 report (Sutton & Beaumont 1989) that several adults were released in nearby Halifax in 1984. This was followed by subsequent reports from the same area of singles at: Norton Tower in 1989, Sowerby Bridge in 1991, Cromwell Bottom on 11/06/1992 and Well Head on 26/07/1992. There is a strong suspicion that these are all the result of released specimens but without any details reported. All known records are listed in the adjacent panel together with sources.

A question mark remains over the future of this species in Yorkshire. A long-lasting remnant population seems extremely unlikely, but cannot be ruled out. The possibility of a fresh invasion of the species from the continent seems to be a diminishing likelihood in view of the way the species has also retracted its range in the Benelux countries and northern France, areas from which our past immigrants are most likely to have come. Even so, an unexpected invasion cannot be ruled out, especially if temperatures continue to rise. The possibility of occasional vagrants reaching the county must remain, so if one comes your way, do try to get a photo, write a description and get someone to confirm the sighting!

LARGE TORTOISESHELL RECORDS:

All known Yorkshire references are listed indicating literature source, observer (if known) and 10km OS map reference. These should be treated as generalised rather than exact, because literature sources usually gave the starting place for a day trip rather than the site of the observation. Some authors gave the home area of the observer irrespective of where they were observing! In a few cases (like Leeds and York) we have given two 10km squares even though this does not indicate two distinct records. It is simply because these places are evenly spread across two squares and we have no means of knowing in which area the observation was made. It is possible that other Yorkshire records are hidden away in Society archives etc. We would be pleased to learn of any additions.

VC61: Porritt's 1883 reference to **York** (SE55/65) could have been in VC61. Boult (1899) refers to 2 caught at **Bilton** (nr Hull TA13) in 1878; Barry Spence holds a specimen obtained in 'P Wood' (Paradise Wood?), **Wawne** (nr Hull TA03) by Dennis Wade on 25/04/1948; Sutton & Beaumont (1989) note 3 seen at **Allerthorpe Common** (SE74) by D Ormston on 16/05/1948.

VC62: Morris (1853) notes: *'I have seen this insect in the parishes of **Bossall** and **Huttons Ambo**, Yorkshire'*, (both VC62/SE76). Porritt (1883) gives **Scarborough** (TA08) [Thomas Wilkinson d1876]. Walsh (1952) adds detail to this,

pointing out that Wilkinson found it on Seamer Moor (which no longer exists) around the 1850s. Walsh (1956) thought it *rare* in the Scarborough area and referred to another Thomas Wilkinson record from **Pickering** (SE78). Porritt (1904) adds **Helmsley** (SE68), 1901 [Arthur Angel]. Porritt (1883) also gives **York** (SE55/65), which could have been in VC62.

VC63: Porritt (1883) gives **Barnsley** (SE30) [John Harrison]. Brady (1884) said it was, *'of erratic occurrence and less common than formerly'* in the Barnsley area, giving **Wath-upon-Dearne** and **Clayton** (both SE40), and **Brierley** (SE41). Porritt (1883) gives **Bradford** (SE13), *'rare'* [JW Carter]; **Leeds** (SE23/SE24) [John Grassham]; **Halifax** (SE02/12), which he picked up from Newman (1871), whilst Fryer & Lucas (2001) give recent 20th century records which are noted in the adjoining text. Porritt (1883) also gives **Huddersfield** (SE11) and Fryer & Lucas add site details: South Crosland (Hobkirk 1859); Birkby in 1859; Farnley *'occasional specimens'* (Mosley 1883); Penny Spring Wood (Mosley 1883); Newsome c1920 and in 1934, 1935 and 1949 (2 on 04/08/1949, and 3 on 15/10/1949, an exceptionally late date!), also 1 at Lower Castle Hill on 04/08/1949. Porritt (1883) also recorded it himself at **Horbury** (SE21/31) and Brady (1884) mentions a report by J Firth from nearby **Clayton West** (SE21). Porritt (1883) gives **Doncaster** (SE50) [JR Hawley c1875?], whilst Rimington (1992) adds 1857 and 1872 (from Potts 1873) and Campsall Park from Lankester (1842), the latter being the earliest Yorkshire record we have of this species. Rimington also gives **Edlington Wood** (before 1879) and **Maltby Wood** (before 1884), both **Doncaster area** (SK59). Porritt (1883) also lists: **Sheffield** (SK38) [A Doncaster] and **Wakefield** (SE32) [W Talbot]. The YNU 1967/1970 Report gives **Keighley** (SE04) in 1910.

VC64: The only certain VC64 record is in Porritt (1883) from **Bishop's Wood nr Selby** (SE53), although records listed above for Leeds, York and Keighley could all have been in VC64. Emmet & Heath's (1989) national map of 1980/88 records, lists one Yorkshire report, and that in VC64. We have no trace of such a record and can only assume it is a misplaced dot referring to the 1984 VC63 Halifax releases.

VC65: No known records.

Howard M Frost

1596 CAMBERWELL BEAUTY *Nymphalis antiopa* (Linnaeus 1758)
Family: Nymphalidae, sub-group Nymphalinae (the 'Nymphalids' or 'Vanessids').

Hull Docks 09/2001, once reputed to be a source of imported Camberwell Beauties. Today the wood comes ready dried and plastic wrapped as can be glimpsed inside this store shed.

World STATUS: Resident and migrant: I brood 0-2000m: June/July in S Europe; Aug/Sept in Scandinavia. Hibernates and re-appears from March to June according to latitude/height/weather. Range: resident from N Spain to S Sweden & S Finland, and eastward through temperate Asia, to N America, but its regular distribution stops short of the Channel and N Sea coasts. The species then periodically ventures north-westward from this line and can turn up anywhere in the British Isles, Norway or N Finland.

A few immigrants may successfully overwinter and re-appear in spring. However, it has never been recorded breeding in British Isles perhaps because successful hibernators are too isolated. It is probable that the line of demarcation between resident and immigrant populations on the continent is quite variable according to annual swings of weather, with milder, damper winters being a key factor militating against the butterfly.

Although the overall European residential range appears stable, declines have been reported from many countries including N & W France, Belgium and Luxembourg. In the British Isles it is a rare immigrant from Scandinavia, or other parts of Europe, which arrives almost annually in very small numbers, and periodically in larger invasions.

Camberwell Beauty resting at ground level (Haute Marne, France 29/07/1996).

ID NOTES: Very large, apparently black butterfly with broad white, cream or lemon-yellow bands edging the wings. Close view should reveal a line of blue spots inside the pale bands, and a brown-burgundy gloss to the dark areas. May fly high around trees with the light wing bands not especially evident and can be confused with the similarly dark (but usually smaller) Peacock.

YORKSHIRE STATUS 1995/2003:

A rare but regular immigrant which can turn up anywhere and is invariably seen singly, usually between June and Sept, but occasionally in spring. Immigration to Yorkshire is often assumed to be from Scandinavia, but it can also be from central or southern Europe as indicated by the consistently higher number of reports from south-eastern England than from Yorkshire. June/July sightings are more likely to be from the latter area (as the southern flight period is earlier), whilst Aug/Sept records are more likely to emanate from Scandinavia, but this is not a golden rule, and weather conditions in any one year may cause variations and overlaps.

Of some 350 sightings recorded nationally in **1995** around 25 came from Yorkshire, although some of these were never formally recorded, but gleaned from newspaper reports. In **1996** there was only one report Ravenscar (VC62/NZ90) on 18/08 [Carol Robinson]; in **1997** two reports Rotherham (VC63/SE49) on 10/03 [Alan Cawthrow *et al*], and 08/0 Ashberry Woods (VC62/SE58) [Brian Mallison]; in **1998** one probable record on 20/08 from Richmond (VC65/SE09) [via Tim Helps]; **1999** three reports: on 04/04 from Paull Holme (nr Hull Docks VC61/TA12 [Raymond Chapman]; on 01/06 from Quarry Moor NR nr Ripon (VC64/65/SE36) [Robert Adams], and on 29/08 Easington (nr Spurn VC61/TA31) [John Wozencroft *et al*]. There were no records in **2000** and **2001**, then no fewer than 15 reports in Aug and Sept **2002** covering four VCs (See *Argus* **43:** 48 for details), but none in **2003**.

HABITAT: Typically a woodland butterfly, laying eggs on Sallows *Salix* spp., Poplars *Populus* spp., Elms *Ulmus* spp., and Birches *Betula* spp. It will also use other habitats which contain its foodplants or suitable sources of nectar, including gardens and orchards.

Adult emerges from hibernation and lays clusters of eggs on the twigs of the above tree species, usually in March or April. May be seen nectaring on *Salix* blossom (eg 'Pussy Willow'). It is thought that butterflies fresh from hibernation do not migrate. Hence the general assumption that spring sightings in the British Isles are of individuals which arrived the previous year and successfully hibernated in this country. Larvae feed together protected by a silken web, but then disperse long distances after about 50 days. After a period on the wing adults go into hibernation using a wide range of hiding places, from tree hollows to drainage pipes and garden sheds. As with all our hibernating butterflies, disturbance or a warm spell in winter may cause an early emergence. As a result, the butterfly can be seen in any month of the year, even in the British Isles. It may feed on garden flowers or rotting fruit. It is thought that British winters are usually too mild for this species, and although a few immigrants from one year may survive into the following spring, it is spring when they mate and too few individuals survive to ensure any males and females meet up to breed.

Camberwell Beauty (Ingleby Greenhow (VC62) 06/08/2002).

Peter Waterton

HISTORICAL REVIEW:
Camberwell Beauty
Formerly: *Vanessa antiopa* in Porritt 1883.

The first recorded sightings of this species in Britain were around the 1750s when it was variously referred to as the **Willow Butterfly**, **the Grand Surprise** or **the Camberwell Beauty**, the latter name referring to the second-ever sighting, which was of two butterflies seen in what was then the village of Camberwell (now a district of London). It was also called **the White Border** and **the White Petticoat(s)**, whilst in N. America it became **the Mourning Cloak**. In the Latin, *Nymphalis* refers to a bride or a nymph, whilst *antiopa* is derived from Antiope who gave birth to twin sons via Zeus.

Early on it was erroneously thought that the white edged form of the Camberwell Beauty was a resident British butterfly, whilst the yellow-edged varieties were continental. As a result, the rarer 'British' variety was much sought after by collectors, and forgeries were attempted! In fact, yellow edges are the norm and white edges are produced either as a result of scale defects in fresh specimens, or as a result of hibernation in older specimens.

There are one or two records of this species in Britain almost every year, with periodic 'good' years when there may be 10 to 20 reports. Over longer periods of time there are occasional exceptional years, the so called **'antiopa years'**. Being something of a rarity there are many historical records noted in the various sources of Yorkshire records indicating that the species has been of regular if sporadic occurrence over the years. The actual recorded numbers in antiopa years must bear a strong correlation to the number of observers able to recognise the species, so may only give a rough indication of the size of the immigration. Nationally, only 8 years stand out in over 200: 1789, 1793, 1819, 1846, 1872 (with 472 records nationally), 1947 (with 50), 1976 (with 300+), and 1995 (with 350+). 'Antiopa years',

Camberwell Beauty (Outer Head, Flamborough VC61) 14/08/2002).

and sometimes, 'good' years, can give rise to a scatter of spring records in the following year. The Camberwell Beauty is also a species which is sometimes kept in butterfly houses or which is bred by enthusiasts, therefore escapees and private releases are possible.

Many 19th century entomologists not understanding or believing in migration, were highly puzzled at the erratic occurrence of this butterfly. Morris (1853) wrote: *'The wide uncertainty of the periodical appearance of this very fine butterfly in our country is extremely remarkable, and 'wither away?' between the dates of its visits is a question we cannot answer. About eighty years ago it appeared in immense numbers. Again in 1819, it was observed in abundance in all parts of the kingdom: comparatively few have been seen since, but latterly, within the last few years, more have been met with, probably from having been better looked after'.* Porritt (1883) noted: *'This fine and rare species has at different times been taken in almost every part of the county. In 1872 it occurred in numbers all over England, and in our own county was almost common, being observed or taken in the following places: Barnsley, six specimens (John Harrison); Beverley, in numbers (F Boyes); Bradford (JW Carter); Cleckheaton (J Firth); Driffield (WH Jennings); Helmsley, two (F Raine); Hornsea (F Boyes); Huddersfield, several (GT Porritt & SL Mosley); Hull; Keighley*

(JT Calvert); Leeds, several (John Grassham); Malton, seven (William Prest); Richmond (GP Harris); Saltburn; Scarborough, two (JF Rowntree), York, four (William Prest); Wakefield (W Talbot); and in many other places.'

As this is a strong-flying immigrant, subject to the vagaries of the weather it can turn up anywhere in the county. That said, observations are rather more likely along the east coast and around the Humber Estuary. The link to the coastline is obvious enough, as a newly arrived immigrant will be likely to land there to feed and rest after a North Sea crossing. Robson (1902) refers to an arrival in Co Durham, close to the Yorkshire border just north of South Gare, Middlesbrough: *'The earliest record I have…is in the notes of the late William Backhouse, who, 'about the year 1820* [presumably 1819] *found it in vast numbers on the sands at Seaton Carew washing up by the tide. Many were dead, but some were still living'.* There is probably also a strong human element in the preponderance of coastal records, especially in more recent times, when many observers are drawn to the coast to birdwatch and record the natural world at such places as South Gare (VC62), Filey Brigg, Flamborough and Spurn, (all VC61). Camberwell Beauties reaching the coastline are likely to be spotted, but once *en route* inland they are less likely to be noticed. In *'good years'* the one or two Yorkshire sightings probably only represent the tip of an iceberg.

The environs of the Humber, and particularly the Port of Hull, have long been associated with Camberwell Beauty sightings. Newman (1955) suggested that the butterfly was not a natural immigrant, but came in with timber ships delivering pit props from Finland. This idea was popularised in the *AA Illustrated Guide to Britain* (1971). Garland (1981) draws attention to the fact that Scandinavian wood shipments were carried far up the River Humber and its tributaries, as far as Rawmarsh in Rotherham (VC63/SE49), and the presence of a wood import company there could explain the comment made by Morris (1853): *'The neighbourhood of Rawmarsh, near Rotherham, Yorkshire, is one of the most uniform localities for this rare insect that I am aware of'.*

It seems quite possible that wood imports **have** accounted for a small proportion of past records. Whole trees were often imported and left to dry out in dockside wood yards. It is possible that larvae, pupae or even hibernating butterflies may have been imported with these supplies. Today the Port of Hull is seeing a growing trade in wood supplies from Finland, but the product now usually arrives in kiln dried, ready-cut, plastic wrapped stacks which are stored under cover in dock-side sheds. It is still possible that the odd individual manages to hitch a lift on board one of the wood boats, and this may account for some of the periodic sightings which still occur in the Hull area. However, there is little doubt today that most Camberwell Beauties which manage to reach Yorkshire have flown across the North Sea using their own efforts coupled with favourable winds and weather conditions.

Rex Bradshaw

Camberwell Beauty feeding on rotting fruit: Spofforth (VC64) 02/08/1995

Howard M Frost

WORLD STATUS: Resident and migrant to c2500m. Up to 3 broods (Mar/Oct) according to latitude/height. Range: N Africa to S Norway and eastward through central Asia to N India, Mongolia and Japan. On the continent migrates as far north as central Norway and Finland.

ID NOTES: Strong, fast flier. Can be mistaken for a Wall in flight. Closed-wing view shows a pattern of large silver-white patches, on the underside of the hindwing, which can shine dramatically when seen at an angle to the light. Female larger than male, with an area of darker, green-tinged colouring on the upperwings, where the wings join the body.

Queen of Spain Fritillary showing 'pearls' (Auberive, France Sept 1996).

YORKSHIRE STATUS 1995/2003:

Extremely rare vagrant, with records in York and Scarborough in 1868; possible records in Doncaster and near Penistone in 1945, and a further possible record at Spurn in 1995, all detailed in the historical review below.

Queen of Spain Fritillary (Haute Marne, France Aug 2003).

LIFE STORY

HABITAT: As a migrant, it can turn up anywhere. Uses a wide range of breeding habitats wherever pansies *Viola* spp. occur. In N Europe usually uses Wild Pansy *Viola tricolor* and Field Pansy *V. arvensis* as foodplants. Occasionally chooses Lucerne *Medicago sativa*, and Borage *Borago officinalis* on the continent, and other species of viola in S Europe.

Has a very adaptable lifestyle being able to survive winter as a larva, pupa or fully-grown butterfly. Although circumstantial evidence suggests that the Queen of Spain bred in England in 1945 (Cornwall) and in 1995/1997 (Suffolk), no larvae or pupae were found, and indeed, it appears that none have ever been found in England. The larvae are grey to black and spiny, with a pale line above and a pattern of black rectangles, orange brown white-centred circles, plain orange brown circles and tiny black dots with white centres. Pupae are similarly dark-coloured and patterned, but with the addition of white splodges which appear to help them be disguised as bird droppings.

HISTORICAL REVIEW:
Queen of Spain Fritillary
Formerly: *Argynnis lathonia*
(in Porritt 1883)

The species was first caught in England around 1704, and called the **Silver-spotted Fritillary**, or **Riga Fritillary** (the latter name given because the first specimen to be described in England, a few years earlier, was obtained in Latvia). In 1775, the species was first described as the **Queen of Spain Fritillary**, in *The Aurelian's Pocket Companion* by Moses Harris. The reason for this choice is not known, but a majority of later authors have since, accepted it. In the Latin *lathonia* comes from Latona (= Queen Lat) the mother of Apollo and Artemis in Greek mythology.

The butterfly has a history of very occasional 'invasions' reaching the south coast of England, with the odd one or two specimens recorded in the years in between. Except for 1872 all of these years correspond to the warmer years of the last 200 years. The figures are gleaned from Williams (1958), with the totals recorded, where known, bracketed after the year: **1818**; **1857** (17); **1868** (46); **1872** (50); **1882** (25); **1943** (5); **1944** (2); **1945** (37); **1946** (2); **1947** (6); **1948** (2); **1949** (7) and **1950** (1). A few specimens were recorded annually between 1857 and 1885, but none between 1886 and 1892 (inclusive), which marks one of the coldest periods in the 19th century. In all there have been somewhere around 500 Queen of Spain Fritillaries recorded in the British Isles over the last 200 years with rising numbers towards the end of the 20th century. Very few were recorded in the first half of the 20th century until the 1940s 'invasions'. The numbers were not huge, but then there were few people around actively recording, so many must have been missed. There followed another long gap with very few reports until 1995. Up to that time most records were mainly confined to the south coast as far west as Cornwall, which suggested immigrants from France or Spain coming in over the sea. By contrast, the 1995 invasion was centred on Suffolk and seems

to have resulted from a big build-up of the species in N France, the Netherlands and Belgium. Stewart (2001) gives Suffolk numbers as: **199** (6); **1996** (11); **1997** (28); **1998** (1), and **1999** (1). Although no egg-laying was noted, mating was observed, and there appears every indication that the build-up from 6 to 28 observations resulted from local breeding. In the same period Norfolk only registered one record and that in 1996.

The 1868 invasion led to two observations as far north as Yorkshire and even one in Scotland. Newman (1871) records that JH Rowntree found one on the west side of Oliver's Mount in Scarborough (VC62/TA08) in Sep 1868, whilst Edwin Birchall saw the other at an unnamed site in the York area. No confirmed Yorkshire records occurred in the 1940s, but both Garland (1981) and Rimington (1992) mention a now lost local newspaper report about one having been seen in the Doncaster area (VC63/SE50), by persons unknown, probably in 1945. A 1961 YNU circular written by JR Seago, noted that the species *'has been reported'* from Gunthwaite Hall (just north of Penistone, VC63/SE20). If correct, this would presumably also have been in 1945, or at least in the 1940s. However, no other trace of this report has been found, so it must remain somewhat doubtful, but certainly not impossible.

In Sept 1995, a visitor to Spurn reported having seen a 'fritillary' at the tip of the peninsula. Unfortunately, it disappeared before confirmation of identification could be made, and like most uncertain records it was not even officially logged. After all, fritillaries are not, and never have been recorded at Spurn, therefore a mistaken identity appeared to be the most likely explanation. However, much later on, it was learned that, at about the same time, no fewer than two Queen of Spains were recorded on the Lincolnshire side of the Humber Estuary at Donna Nook (VC54/SE49) on 24/09/1995 (*Argus* 27) by Paul Troake and the record was confirmed by Mark Tyszka, the then BC Lincolnshire County Recorder. The tip of Spurn is about 7 miles from Donna Nook, or about 4 miles from the nearest point of land on the opposite bank, no distance at all for a roving Queen of Spain.

FUTURE TREND: This could well be a species we might see more of in the future, if global warming continues, although the relative scarcity of its foodplants in the prairie landscapes of the eastern half of the county may be an inhibiting factor. On the other hand the growth in the commercial production of borage, especially in East Yorkshire, could just possibly provide an unexpected bonus! Keen observers should remember that this is a challenging and easily overlooked species. All observations need confirming either with video, photographs, or if practical, by catching and temporarily holding the species until it can be viewed by an expert. Keen gardeners might like to keep a display of wild pansy relatives just on the off-chance that they might one day attract a Queen of Spain! The odds might be rather long, but the species does visit gardens on the continent!

Howard M Frost

UK BAP Status: *Priority species.*
BC Priority: National: *High.*
A Red Data Book species.
Fully protected in GB.
European Status: *Not threatened.*

WORLD STATUS: Resident to 2100m. 1 brood (May/Aug), (June/July to Aug/Sept in Britain). Range: N Africa to central Norway and eastward across temperate Asia to Japan. Has declined in parts of Europe, and especially in Britain where 77% of recorded 10km squares have been lost since 1970/82 (Asher *et al* 2001). Formerly fairly widespread in England and Wales from Cumbria and N Yorkshire southward, although somewhat thinly spread on the eastern side of Britain. Now restricted to a few sites on the western side of Britain from Cornwall to Cumbria. Butterfly Conservation is co-ordinating a national conservation programme to halt its decline and restore suitable habitats within its range. British population belongs to subspecies *vulgoadippe* Verity, 1929.

YORKSHIRE STATUS 1995/2003:

Extinct former resident and very rare vagrant. Probably died out in Yorkshire in the 1870s. Ten or eleven 20th century county records are known, all of which appear to represent wanderers. The last was at Nutwith and Roomer Common (VC65/SE27) in 1983 [Helga and Arnold Robson].

Helga Robson was out riding in this extensive woodland area on 31/07/1983 when she spotted a fritillary at SE222778. She reported it to her father, Arnold Robson, and they returned later in the day to search for it, but without success. Arnold continued the search the following day 01/08/1983 and found a High Brown Fritillary about 1km west of his daughter's sighting, in SE213780. The species was found basking on a bracken frond and was temporarily netted and photographed before release. Two of the photos are reproduced here.

The nearest known colony of this species is in Cumbria about 65 miles to the west of Nutwith and Roomer Common. In the light of the theories suggested in the historical review below, it is interesting to note that this species appeared to be heading NW.

ID NOTES: About same size as a Small Tortoiseshell, or slightly bigger. Can be confused with similar-sized Dark Green Fritillary or the golden *hutchinsoni* form of the Comma. The most distinctive feature in an upperwing view is the shape of the outer edge of the forewings (ie the side edges), which are straight or even concave, in the High Brown, but curved outwards in the Dark Green. Resting males with wings open can be separated by checking the long, thin (and not very noticeable) scent marks which are found on the first two veins (counting from the bottom) in the Dark Green, and on veins two and three in the High Brown. A closed wing view reveals that the High Brown has an additional (and diagnostic) row of spots between the row of half moons near the outer edge and the main row of white spots towards the centre of the wings. These extra spots are white, with some highlighted in black, and all **ringed with orange-brown**. In addition, the Dark Green usually has a greater area of the underwings suffused with dull green, but this feature is variable. Both these fritillaries can differ from the typical specimens illustrated in ID books, with over 20 described aberrations in the High Brown, and almost 100 noted for the Dark Green.

CONSERVATION ISSUES: Butterfly Conservation co-ordinates a national conservation programme for this species, and although it remains vulnerable, the rapid decline seen in recent years appears to have been more or less halted. Work in the Morecambe Bay area has been particularly successful. In the future, it is hoped to restore additional habitats in order to encourage a natural spread of the species.

High Brown Fritillary (Nutwith & Roomer Common, VC65, 01/08/1983)

LIFE STORY

Cone-shaped eggs are laid on stones or leaf litter near the foodplant, typically Common Dog Violet *Viola riviniana*, although other species of violet may also be used. Larvae are fully formed after about 3 weeks, but spend winter inside the egg, usually emerging in April and developing through 5 further instars, making 6 in all, a process taking about 9 weeks. They spend much time basking on dense bracken litter. The pupa hangs inside a tent of leaves secured with silk and hatches after 2-3 weeks depending on weather conditions. Butterflies usually fly Jul/Aug but may be earlier or later according to the season. They are particularly attracted to brambles, thistles and ragworts for nectaring, and may even turn up in gardens to feed on buddleia.

HISTORICAL REVIEW:
High Brown Fritillary
Formerly: *Argynnis cydippe*
(in Walsh 1952/1956).

The first-ever record of this species in Britain was noted in Leicestershire in 1699 and Petiver named it **the greater silver-spotted Fritillary**. Wilkes (1741/42) introduced the name **High Brown Fritillary**, (where 'high' equates with 'richly coloured'). However, it was not generally adopted until used by Haworth in 1803. In the Latin *Argynnis* is derived from Argynnus, a lady for whom Agammemnon built a temple after her death, which linked her name to Aphrodite or Venus. The original species name *cydippe* meant a sea-nymph but this more properly belonged to another species and *adippe* appears to be an artificial construction without specific meaning, which was invented by Linnaeus to replace it with a similar sounding name.

Deducing the Yorkshire status and distribution of this species is problematic as few historical records give any idea of numbers and we are dealing with a species which appears to be able to wander far away from its source colony. Past observers didn't understand this, and assumed that if they saw one butterfly, it meant it was breeding where they saw it, or close by. It seems probable that in the mid-19th century there were colonies in S Yorkshire, the Vale of York and around the southern edges of the N Yorkshire Moors. The only indication of anything more than an odd sighting comes in Walsh (1952) (picked up from the archives of the Scarborough Field Naturalists' Society) that Thomas Wilkinson considered the species *'common at Pickering'* in the 1860s. But Walsh (1956) uses the same phrase *'common at Pickering'* as though it applied to the 1950s rather than to a period a century before, which is a little misleading!

Until the 1950s, the species was still fairly widespread nationally, although much thinner on the ground on the eastern side of the country, and almost certainly absent as a breeding species in Yorkshire during the 20th century, when only ten county records were logged between 1901 and 1983 inclusive. As far as is known, all reports referred to singles, with the possible exception of Grass Wood (Wharfedale VC64) where the report rather vaguely refers to *one or two*, which could easily have been a couple of sightings of one butterfly.

Conventional wisdom suggests that this is a resident butterfly, which may sometimes wander from its home colonies. Yet the rather odd scatter of records in Yorkshire, Lincolnshire and other eastern areas would also fit a pattern of sporadic, small-scale immigration from the continent, with a predominant movement from SE to NW. This might be comparable to movements of Camberwell Beauties or Large Tortoiseshells and would probably place Yorkshire and other northern counties close to the northern extreme of such flights. Is it possible that in the past, British populations of both High Brown Fritillary and Large Tortoiseshell might have depended in some degree on the arrival of new stock from the continent? The availability of suitable habitat is clearly important, but could there also have been climatic or other factors militating against the continued presence of the species in some parts of Britain or on some sites? There appear to be no Yorkshire records between 1876 and 1901, which was one of the coldest periods in several centuries. But as the weather began to improve, 4 or 5 scattered records seem to indicate an attempted comeback in 1901. It has been assumed that these butterflies probably came from remnant colonies in Nottinghamshire, although in the case of the Birdwell (Penistone) sighting, it was suggested at the time that the specimen had probably hitched a lift on a train!

A suspected presence of High Brown in the Grass Wood area in 1936 would seem more likely to be connected to wanderers from Cumbria, although such a site would also be on a SE/NW track from SE England. The two 1945 records at Shipley Glen and Allerthorpe Common, occurred in an exceptional year for migrants to Britain, not only for the regular ones (including Clouded Yellows and Pale Clouded Yellows), but also for Bath Whites (650 records!), Queen of Spain Fritillaries (37 records) and Longailed Blues (31 records)! The last Yorkshire record at Nutwith and Roomer Common in 1983 also occurred in a notable Clouded Yellow year, indicating favourable travel weather from the continent. It is intriguing to note that over the two days this specimen was recorded, it moved about a kilometre to the north-west, a fact which does not seem to suggest it was heading away from Cumbria!

High Browns have also been disappearing from the near continent (N and W France, Belgium and Luxembourg) in recent years, which might in part explain the reduction of sightings in eastern England if this was indeed a more regular migrant than was generally realised. Lafranchis (2000) draws attention to sporadic wanderers seen in western Belgium since the 1980s, suggesting an effort to re-colonise lost ground. Was it one of these 'sporadic wanderers' that reached Nutwith and Roomer in 1983? As the very similar Dark Green Fritillary is much more common than the High Brown, there is a general expectancy in Yorkshire that any such medium-sized fritillary will be a Dark Green. As a result, could we be overlooking a sporadic trickle of immigrant High Browns because we are not looking closely enough at each Dark Green seen? Such thoughts may simply raise false hopes, but unless we are alive to the possibility, we might all too easily overlook making some important discoveries!

Howard M Frost

HIGH BROWN RECORDS:

VC61: Morris (1853) gave **Sutton-on-Derwent Wood** (SE74). The *Naturalist* **71:** 40-41 gives 1 seen at **Allerthorpe Common** (SE74) on 07/07/1945 [Robert Procter]. Walsh (1956) refers to *'one record from the Wolds'* without giving any details.

VC62: Morris (1853) recorded it on **Buttercrambe Moor** (SE75). Walsh (1952) gives **Pickering** (SE78/88), common in 1860s [Thomas Wilkinson]; Newman (1871) gives **Yedmandale** (SE98) and **Cloughton Moors** (SE99?) on the authority of JH Rowntree. It is probable that Porritt's (1883) ref to Thomas Wilkinson's 'Scarborough' record in fact refers to Yedmandale or Pickering. Porritt (1883), on the authority of Robert Cook and *Stainton's Manual* (1857/59), gives **York** (SE65) (which could also be VCs 61 or 64 and several other 10km squares). Porritt (1904) refers to a record from **Great Ayton** (NZ51) reported by W Hewett. Emmet & Heath (1989) note on their map for this species, a record from NZ81 just north of Whitby, but this has been checked and found incorrect (pers comm. Paul Harding).

VC63: Porritt (1883) refers to **Sheffield** (SK38) [A Doncaster]; and **Pontefract** (SE42) [B Hartley]. Porritt (1904) gives singles seen in 1901 at: **Birdwell, near Penistone** (SE20), (Mr Dyson, of Hoyland); **New Park Spring Wood, Cudworth, (Barnsley** SE30) (A Whitaker); and **Wadworth Wood, Doncaster'** (SK59) [LS Brady]. Corbett (1901) refers to records in **Edlington Wood (Doncaster** SK59) in 1876 and 1901. Wadworth Wood and Edlington Wood are adjacent and were connected (although divided by the M18 today), so it is possible, if not probable, that Porritt and Corbett are referring to the same 1901 butterfly. *The Entomologist's Record* Vol **69** 1957 p250 records a note by George E Hyde regarding a July 1917 record from **Martin Beck (nr Bawtry** SK69) when a worn male vagrant was seen by himself and HH Corbett. The YNU Card File has a 1945 record from **Shipley (SE13)**. Bradford Naturalists' Recorder F Hewson wrote the following note in the Card File on 12/05/1952: *'In August 1946 a young soldier named Alan Wheeler brought me a specimen of this species, saying that he had taken it at Shipley Glen on July 22nd 1945. I did not record it at the time, for there was no confirmation and for various reasons I thought it may have been a joke. In answer to a query from Mr CR Haxby, he now assures me that the capture was a genuine one and that in view of its rarity he intends to record it in 'The Entomologist'. He is (and was even then) an experienced lepidopterist and I think that we may now accept the record'.* AS Wheeler published the following note in The Entomologist Vol **85** June 1952 p142: *'Argynnis cydippe in Yorkshire. It has recently been brought to my notice that a specimen I caught on July 22nd 1945, at Shipley near Bradford, is the only one known by the Bradford Natural History Society to have been taken in the neighbourhood since that Society's records of lepidoptera commenced in 1875. In view of diverse opinions which appear to have existed in the past as to the origin of this specimen, I would like to put it on record that to the best of my knowledge this was a genuine capture, though the insect offered little resistance when approached. It must not therefore be discounted that this specimen might have gained its freedom from a local collector'.*

VC64: Porritt (1883) infers the species was known in **Bishop's Wood (nr Selby SE53),** whilst the YNU Card File picks up a reference in the YNU Annual Report for 1936 (*Naturalist* **62:** 47-48): referring to the work of RG Warren in recording lepidoptera in **Grass Wood (Wharfedale** SD96) Rosse Butterfield noted, *'Some Lepidoptera have become rare, or have disappeared from the wood since the latter end of the 19th century....on the other hand Argynnis adippe, a rare species in the north, has been seen on one or two occasions recently'.*

VC65: The only VC65 record comes from Nutwith & Roomer Common in 1983 and is detailed above under 'Yorkshire Status'.

1608 SILVER-WASHED FRITILLARY *Argynnis paphia* (Linnaeus 1758)
Family: Nymphalidae, sub-group Argynninae ('the Fritillaries).

UK BAP Status: *Species of Conservation Concern*
BC Priority: *Low.*
European Status: *Not threatened.*

WORLD STATUS: Localised resident, 0-1800m. 1 brood (May-Sept), (but usually mid-Jun/late Aug in Britain). Range: N Spain to Ireland, SW England, S Norway, and S Finland and east across C Europe and Asia to China and Japan. (In 2000, the writer travelled for 9 days along the trans-Siberian Railway from St Petersburg to Irkutsk and found the species one of the commonest lineside butterflies along the 5000km route.) In Britain it is locally common in the SW, bounded by a line from the Mersey to the Thames and has shown recent signs of range expansion (hence BC's *Low* priority). The natural spread of the species has been clouded by recent unofficial releases, which may have affected Warwickshire, Bedfordshire, Northamptonshire and Cumbria. In Europe: declines in Austria, Belgium, the Netherlands and Latvia, but appears to be expanding on the northern edge of its range in Sweden and Finland.

YORKSHIRE STATUS 1995/2003:

Former resident, now extinct, except for very occasional wanderers which may come from populations well to the south, or from Cumbria. In addition, the species is sometimes bred by enthusiasts and may be released without reporting the details. This complicates the study of natural expansion. Graham Foggitt saw a lone male on 21/08/1996 in his garden at Pannal, (near Harrogate VC64/SE35), nectaring on buddleia. It was the first reported in the county since 1941. The nearest colonies at the time were in Cumbria (c75km to NE), Warwickshire (c150km to S), and possibly Lincolnshire (c125km to the SE), all of which are thought to have arisen from private introductions, so the nearest natural populations were even further to the south.

ID NOTES: Very large (as large as Red Admiral or larger), rich orange-brown butterfly, dotted and blotched with black. Males have 4 prominent sex brands on each of the upper forewings. These appear as parallel black bars along 4 of the wing veins on each forewing. In closed-wing view both sexes are greenish, stippled with silvery bars, giving the 'silver wash' effect after which it is named. In some populations, up to 15% of females have a dusky grey-green background colour replacing the orange-brown on the upperwings, and a delicate pink wash on the lighter parts of the lower underwings. This variation, known as *valesina* appears to be more common in some years than others. Males don't seem very keen on these dark females, but they are better able to absorb heat and fly in dull conditions. Many other varieties occur with some 50 aberrations described.

LIFE STORY

HABITAT: A butterfly of open, broad-leaved woodland, and sheltered wooded lanes. Where the species is fairly common, it will sometimes visit gardens and nectar on buddleia. It particularly favours oak woodlands. Requires violets of any species as its larval foodplant.

Silver-washed Fritillary: typical male. Note bold parallel sex brands (Brenne region, France Aug 1996).

Silver-washed Fritillary: closed wing view (Haute Marne, France 1994).

Eggs laid on tree trunks up to 2m off the ground and occasionally up to 6m. Larvae hatch after 2/3 weeks and go into hibernation almost immediately, hiding away in the bark. Larvae become active again in Mar/Apr, descending to the ground in search of violets, and developing through 5 instars. Pupation takes place in late May, lasting 2-3 weeks according to the prevailing weather. Adults are strong fliers, feeding high up on honeydew, and at ground level on various plants such as brambles and thistles. The writer observed some unusual behaviour at a large woodland barbecue near Irkutsk (eastern Russia) in July 2000, where a hundred guests were each welcomed with a glass of vodka, and much to their astonishment, Silver-washed Fritillaries were landing on the glasses to sip at the alcohol! They were also investigating some of the sweeter foodstuffs prepared for the guests.

HISTORICAL REVIEW:
Silver-washed Fritillary

Petiver (1699) called it the **Greater Silver-streaked Fritillary**. Other authors used similar names, often with the addition of '**Orange**' or '**Golden**' in front of Fritillary. Harris (1766) was first to use **Silver-washed Fretillaria** and later (1775) **Silver Wash Fritillary,** whilst others used **Silver Streak Fritillary** or **Silver Stripe Fritillary**. Most 19th century authors from Haworth (1803) onward adopted **Silver-washed Fritillary**. In the Latin, *Argynnis* appears to be derived from Argynnus a lady whose name was linked to Aphrodite or Venus. Aphrodite had connections with Paphos, a coastal town in Cyprus where she was worshipped, hence she is sometimes called Paphia, or referred to as the Paphian goddess.

Silver-washed Fritillary: well-disguised mating pair about 5m above ground in thick forest (Haute Marne, France 31/07/1996).

Duncan (1844) summed up the national distribution of the time as, *'The adult is not uncommon in nearly all parts of England and is also found in Scotland, but much less frequently'*. In fact, even at this time it seems to have been of fairly rare occurrence north of Cumbria and Yorkshire. Robson (1902) commenting on the situation in Durham and Northumberland wrote: *'This beautiful species has occurred in our district, but I know of no recent records'*. Amongst a handful of isolated and undated reports he mentions John Sang's 1853 record (see VC65 records) and the fact that he had seen specimens taken from Castle Eden Dene in 1855.

Yorkshire records and comments suggest the butterfly was not uncommon in the eastern half of the county in the earlier years of the 19th century (probably as far north as the southern edges of the N York Moors), but then became progressively less common in the later part of the 19th century, and finally disappeared in the first half of the 20th century. It is often assumed that sightings indicated permanent colonies of what was thought to be a sedentary species, but it is also possible that as the national range retracted, Yorkshire remained close to the northern edge of the butterfly's range and in good breeding years vagrants spread into the county and sometimes established temporary colonies.

The national range reduction is usually put down to changes in woodland management, which abandoned coppicing and allowed close growing conifers to shade out the growth of violets. The species is extremely hardy and able to survive the coldest winters, even in Siberia, so at first sight, weather conditions should not be a problem. However, there is a hint in a comment by HH Corbett (1901) that the severe weather period from 1879 to 1895 may have caused problems, perhaps more for the way it affected weather in summer than in winter. He points out that the 1901 sighting of a Silver-washed Fritillary in Edlington Wood, near Doncaster, was the first in that wood for 25yrs. Nationally, 20th century expansions were recorded around 1901, in the 1930s/40s, in 1975/76 and in the 1990s. Most 20th century Yorkshire sightings correspond to these years suggesting that this butterfly may be able to wander greater distances than is generally appreciated.

Most authors imply that the species is mainly sedentary with little interchange between neighbouring colonies. However, Thomson (1980) highlights an intriguing observation made c1910 and reported in the *Scottish Naturalist* (1948 p224) when an immigration of butterflies was spotted flying in from the south-east on a strong SE wind near the Kincardineshire coast. They were followed (by bike!) for 12 miles inland and noted to include a Silver-washed Fritillary and a Common Blue. Assuming the report to be accurate, it suggests the possibility of long-distance or even continental immigration. More recently the species is reported to have disappeared as a resident from much of western Belgium, but wanderers continue to be seen, perhaps flying in from France. If odd ones continued across the Channel or the N Sea would they be noticed, and could mated females make such journeys?

In that respect, George Hyde's experience is intriguing, as recorded in the YNU Card File: *'I caught a single female in a small area of woodland near Crowle, North Lincolnshire, in 1953, and obtained fertile eggs from her. This is the only A. paphia I ever saw in N Lincolnshire.'* Duddington & Johnson (1983) note that the species was *'classed as a locally common*

butterfly around the Market Rasen area particularly, but the population seemed to decline around 1950'. (The species disappeared from Lincolnshire around 1960.) Market Rasen is situated c30 miles to the SE of Crowle and seems the most likely source of this sighting, and perhaps an indication of this butterfly's flight capabilities. It also suggests that wandering females may have the ability to lay eggs far from their home colony, which could account for the sporadic nature of 20th century Yorkshire sightings.

Howard M Frost

Silver-washed Fritillary: As you go east across Europe into Asia, the frequency of the darker form *valesina* increases. This picture was taken in a garden near Lake Baikal, Russia where, of some 40 nectaring on shrubs, about half were *valesina*.

HISTORICAL RECORDS: In this section we give all the Silver-washed Fritillary records and references for Yorkshire that we have been able to find. Porritt (1883 & 1907) made a general comment for the county: *'Distributed, but not by any means common.'* This appears to cover records from the 1840s to the turn of the century.

VC61: Morris (1853) gives **Sutton-on-Derwent** and **Allerthorpe** (both SE74). Stainforth (1919) notes **Raywell** (SE9930k) and **Birkhill Wood** (TA0335k), both near Hull, where specimens were taken in the lifetime of Thomas Stather (b1812/d1878). EB Ford (1945/1975) maps a presence on the N Wolds at approx SE97 Ganton. We have been unable to confirm this from any other source and it may be that the dot was intended to be placed one step up on the N York Moors.

VC62: Morris (1853) gives **Buttercrambe Moor** (SE75), **Stockton** (ie Stockton on the Forest) and **Sand Hutton** (both SE65). Porritt (1883) gives **York** (probably one of the preceding sites) [Robert Cook prior to 1842], and **Scarborough** (TA08) probably in the 1870s/80s [JH Rowntree b1850/d1937]. Walsh (1952) notes a YNU circular (2 viii 1886), which reports the species as, *'common at* **Pickering***'* (SE78/88). A YNU excursion list for 22/06/1901 records the species from **Wykeham** (SE98). Porritt (1904) adds, *'common at Helmsley'* (SE68) [Samuel Walker]; and recorded at **Great Ayton** (NZ51), but Tetley (1915) makes no mention of the species being present in the Scarborough

area. The CEH/BRC database holds an 1887 record gleaned from an edition of *The Transactions of Cleveland Naturalists* for **Whitby** (NZ81) [B Lockyer]. The YNU 1967/70 Report includes a record from **Hovingham** (SE67) dated 03/08/1935.

VC63: Lankester (1842) gives **Sutton Plantation** (nr Doncaster SE51). Porritt (1883) includes: **Edlington Wood** (SK59) [John Harrison c1875]; **Huddersfield** (SE11) *'very rare'* [Peter Inchbald]; **Maltby, Sheffield** (SK59) [A Doncaster c1875]; **Pontefract** (SE42) [B Hartley]; and **Wakefield** (SE32), *'rare'* [W Talbot]. Porritt (1904) adds a specific Edlington Wood record for 1901 [Herbert H Corbett]. Rimington (1992) gives further Edlington Wood records: c1876 [HH Corbett], 1901 [A Whitaker & HH Corbett], and 1906 [W Hewett]. The YNU 1967/70 Report notes an Edlington Wood record for 08/1907. Rimington also gives **New Park Spring Wood** (SE30) in 1901, and two borderline VC54/Lincs records from: **Hirst Priory** (SE7718k) when *'a worn male was seen by LGF Waddington'* in 1940, and **Crowle** (SE71) where *'a fertile female'* was captured by George Hyde (reported as 1953 although a specimen in his collection suggests 1949). Fryer & Lucas (2001) researched past reports for the **Huddersfield area** (SE11) in some detail, and found records for **Storthes Hall** (SE1812k) in 1847 [JW Dunning]. Mosley (1883) noted, on the authority of Peter Inchbald, *'Formerly at Storthes Hall, but very rare'*. (A similar comment also included by Porritt in 1883.) Fryer & Lucas put a convincing case for re-instating a record turned down by the YNU. Herbert Spencer (b1884/d1949) reported a boyhood recollection of seeing the species regularly in **Elland Park Woods** (SE12), presumably around the turn of the century. Halifax Scientific Society also holds an unconfirmed, but probable record of the species at **Elland** in 1927. Ben Morley recorded 2 specimens in **Bank Wood, Skelmanthorpe** (SE2613k), in 1918. In his notebook (quoted from the YNU Card File) he wrote: *'I saw a fine male in the old garden of the ruined keeper's house in Bank Wood on Aug 10th 1918. Mr J Hooper caught a female on the same ground the following day'*. (These records were publicly reported as being made at Bankhall Wood or Deffer Wood, probably as a ruse to confuse collectors.) Fryer & Lucas give further records from **Broken Cross, Almondbury** (SE11), when 3 specimens were seen by WE Wattam in 1929; and **Emley Park** (SE2411k) in July 1941 [W Buckley].

VC64: Stainforth (1919) includes a Thomas Stather record from **Cowick Wood** (nr Goole SE62) (probably in the 1830/60 period). Porritt (1883) gives **Bishop's Wood** (nr Selby SE53) [John Grassham], whilst the YNU Card File notes that it was included in a 1920s lepidoptera list for Grass and Bastow Woods in Wharfedale compiled by Rosse Butterfield (Crowther 1930) although it is not known what timescale this list covered.

VC65: There is just one record ascribed by Porritt to VC65, namely **Richmond** (NZ10) [John Sang]. Although no details are given, there appears to be corroborative evidence in Robson (1902). John Sang lived in Darlington, Co Durham (VC66/NZ21), not far from the Yorkshire border. A Silver-washed Fritillary record is listed in Stainton's Manual (1857) under Sang's name and 'Da' for Darlington. Stainton invariably referred to the observer's home area rather than the site of the observation. As a result 'Da' has led to a dot on the national historical record maps, which is probably incorrect. Robson searched Sang's diaries for information about this site for his own book, but could only find one Silver-washed reference re the species being found at *'Hartford on 21/08/1853'*. There do not appear to be any Hartfords in Yorkshire or Durham, but just north of Richmond is a small village called **Hartforth**, with Hartforth Wood close by. It is known that Sang was a regular visitor to the Richmond area, and a handwritten 'Hartforth' might easily be mis-read as Hartford. **Hartforth Wood** (NZ1606k) in Yorkshire seems a likely candidate for this record.

1610 MARSH FRITILLARY *Euphydryas aurinia* (Rottemburg 1775)
Family: Nymphalidae, sub-group Argynninae ('the Fritillaries')

UK BAP Status: *Priority Species.*
BC Priority: *High.*
Fully protected in GB and N Ireland.
European status: *Vulnerable.*

WORLD STATUS: Resident up to 2500m: 1 brood (mid-April/mid-July according to height and latitude, usually mid-May/mid-Jul in Britain). Very occasionally, a partial 2nd generation has been noted in France in Aug/Sept (Lafranchis 2000). Range: N Africa to W Scotland and eastward across Europe and temperate Asia to Korea. Extinct in E Britain (except in Lincs, where, c1993 a small population was unofficially introduced to a woodland clearing in Chambers Farm Woods, just east of Lincoln). Declining in most European countries due to habitat loss. The 1995/1999 Millennium Atlas survey established that there were 228 colonies left in England, 111 in Wales, 58 in N Ireland and 35 in Scotland. This is a very variable species in which many racial groups are recognised including *anglicana* Fruhstorfer, in England and Wales, *scotica* Robson, in Scotland, and *hibernica* Birchall, in Ireland.

ID NOTES: A distinctively marked fritillary with a stained-glass window pattern in orange, brown, black and pale yellow. Very variable, with over 50 varieties described, some bearing little resemblance to typical specimens. Tends to fly slowly and close to the ground. Females larger than males.

YORKSHIRE STATUS 1995/2003:

Extinct former resident. There are no known dated records of this species in Yorkshire, but using the dates of publications, and birth and death dates of observers as a guide, it seems probable that it became extinct in the 1870s or very soon after.

Marsh Fritillary (Skelton, Cumbria 18/06/1988).

Mike Barnham

CONSERVATION ISSUES: In Yorkshire these would now be only relevant in terms of a carefully planned re-introduction project. The growth of nature reserves and conservation minded farming probably mean that the right conditions already exist, particularly in the Lower Derwent Valley National Nature Reserve (SE73/74/75 approx) where the foodplant appears to be fairly widespread (see Crackles 1990). The biggest issue would be space for a functioning metapopulation with numerous habitat patches and light grazing levels. A 'landscape level' approach to management would be needed, something which might be more practical to facilitate in the LDV NNR than in many other places, due to the management overview already in place through English Nature. Butterfly Conservation has a Species Action Plan for the Marsh Fritillary (Barnett & Warren 1995).

LIFE STORY

HABITAT: Mainly a species of damp, tussocky grasslands with Devil's-bit Scabious *Succisa pratensis*, required as the caterpillar foodplant. Also uses heath and mire habitats where the foodplant is present. More rarely it may use calcareous grasslands where it has occasionally been noted on Field Scabious *Knautia arvensis* and Small Scabious *Scabiosa columbaria*. A wider range of plants is used in continental Europe, including Honeysuckle *Lonicera periclymenum*. Colonies can also survive temporarily in large woodland clearings and on other types of grassland.

Eggs laid in batches from a few tens to around 600 at a time, on the undersides of Devil's-bit Scabious leaves. Larvae hatch after 4-5 weeks. Initially, a group of larvae fold over a leaf, tie it down with silk and feed inside its protection. In the 2nd and 3rd instars, increasingly conspicuous silken webs are spun on successive plants chosen for eating. If threatened, the larvae are able to work as a team, scraping their heads in unison on any dead leaves to make a threatening noise! The 4th instar is usually reached in Aug/Sept after which, larvae spin a silken ball at or near ground level and hibernate inside its protective warmth. The silken structure retains air inside it and can be safely submerged in winter floods for several weeks. Activity may be resumed on the first sunny days of Feb, but larvae can return to sleep if winter dictates. At this time they need to attain a body heat of 35°/37°C in order to be able to digest their food. Larvae are black in colour to encourage heat absorption, and they often gather together, forming a black patch in a sunny but sheltered area in order to communally concentrate the sun's direct warmth.

The 5th instar typically begins in early April and the final moult usually takes place at the end of that month. In the 6th instar, larvae separate and feed alone. Then they pupate by hanging from a silken pad on a leaf or stalk. Pupae hatch after 2 to 4 weeks, followed by emergence in late May/early June. In W Scotland the Marsh Fritillary usually appears in the first week of June irrespective of weather conditions (Thomson 1980). Most of any given brood are very sedentary, rarely moving more than 50m-100m from their emergence points. Freshly mated females are often so heavy with eggs that they cannot fly and end up crawling to their first egg-laying site! However, after depositing the first batch, a few females may then wander further afield to colonise new habitats up to 15km from their birth sites.

It is thought that the long-term survival of any given breeding site may depend on it being part of a metapopulation. Periodically, populations may explode to almost pest proportions. This produces many more wanderers which then link up to other sites in the metapopulation structure. In turn these populations explosions appear to be linked to cycles of attack by parasitic wasps: *Aphanteles bignelli* in the south, and *A. melitaearum* in the north. In explosion years the species may spread to marginal sites, which may then die out after a year or two.

Marsh Fritillary: May 2000 Lincolnshire.

Marsh Fritillary: May 2000 Lincolnshire.

HISTORICAL REVIEW:

Marsh Fritillary
Formerly: *Melitaea artemis* Fab.
(in Porritt 1883)

First described by Ray in 1710, but not given a name. That fell to Petiver in 1717 who appears to have been so confused by the butterfly's variability that he distinguished two species: **Dandridge's Midling Black Fritillary** and **the Small Black Fritillary**. However, by the 1750s it was generally recognised as one species although Harris (1766) published two names which were presumably already in use at that time, namely **the Dishclout** and the **Greasey Fritillary**. Lewin (1795) introduced **Marsh Fritillary**, but Greasey (or Greasy) Fritillary remained the more popular name until South used **Marsh Fritillary** in 1906. The name Greasey Fritillary described *'the glistening appearance of the wings, especially the underside, which look as if they had been rubbed over with grease'* (Duncan 1844). In the Latin *Euphydryas* refers to a shapely wood-nymph whilst the species name *aurinia* is the name of a prophetess mentioned in Tacitus.

orritt (1907) noted that the Marsh ritillary *'was evidently not uncommon ormerly, but is now rare'*. In the 19th entury it was found on various sites cross S Yorkshire and was almost ertainly much more widespread than the nown records indicate. It was reported rom a number of York area sites. The city as pretty well surrounded by damp neadows and marshes in the past so it is robable that there was a fairly extensive netapopulation in the 1700s and first half f the 1800s. William Prest (b1824/d1884) ecorded the Marsh Fritillary at Askham Bog, so the last record from that site could ave pre-dated his death in 1884 by some ears. The date of the Rawdon Common ecord is less clear. It wasn't mentioned in orritt (1883) but was included in his 1904 upplement. So perhaps the observation as made between these two years. lowever, G Jackson is quoted as saying,

*'Larvae **formerly** common on Rawdon Common'*, so this may still have been quite a long time earlier.

The Selby area record (in damp meadows along the River Ouse?) suggests the possibility that populations once existed across large parts of the Vale of York. In like manner the Leeds records may indicate a wider patchwork of colonies linking the Aire and Ouse Valleys. Thomas Stather's specimens and annotated records also hint at a wider presence in the valley of the River Hull, around the same Cottingham and Beverley Marshes, which once hosted the Swallowtail and Large Heath. It is generally thought that we lost the Marsh Fritillary in Yorkshire in the 1870s/1880s. Land enclosures, changing approaches to farming and widespread drainage projects in the 1700s and early 1800s steadily reduced suitable habitat. This would have broken up metapopulations and isolated colonies to such an extent that they would have begun to wither away. The likely timing of the extinction suggests that the exceptionally cold years from 1876 to 1892 may also have been a factor, especially under the combined gloom of volcanic dust from Krakatoa (1883) and growing smoke pollution from industry. Larvae may have had increasing problems if they couldn't attain the high body heat they needed for digestion. They appear to be able to survive quite cold conditions, but increasingly weakened sunshine may have been the last straw.

HISTORICAL RECORDS: All known records are listed below.

VC61: Stainforth (1919) notes that both *'larvae and imagines'* (adults) were found at **Cottingham** (TA03) (Beverley Marshes?) in the lifetime of Thomas Stather (b1812/d1878). It would seem likely, therefore, that before the drainage of the River Hull marshlands in the 1700s, the species was probably found more widely in Holderness. Crackles (1990) indicates that the main foodplant is still found in a few places along the Hull Valley. Morris (1853) gives **Langwith (SE of York at SE64)**, which was probably on the site of today's Elvington Airfield.

VC62: Morris (1853) gives **Stockton Common** (SE65) and **Buttercrambe Moor** (SE75), both E of York. Porritt (1904) adds, *'Larvae formerly common on Rawdon Common, Towthorpe, near York'* (G Jackson). Porritt notes that this came from, *'the late'* G Jackson, so it does not appear to have been a recent record. **Towthorpe** (SE6258k) lies to the NE of York near Strensall Common.

VC63: Porritt (1883) includes a reference to a report in the Aug 1842 edition of the *Entomologist* magazine by John Heppenstall who had recorded the species on Lord Scarborough's estate at **Sandbeck Park** (SK59). Rimington (1992) mentions a site not far away indicated by Hawley (1866), at **Maltby Wood** (SK59) (or more likely the adjacent Maltby Low Common). Porritt also gives **Sheffield** (SK38) (A Doncaster) and **Hunslet nr Leeds** (SE22/32) where J Pickles saw one in Middleton Wood (now Middleton Park).

VC64: Porritt (1883) lists a **Selby** (SE63) site reported by R Hebson and Thomas Foster, and also a **Leeds** (SE23/33) site recorded by Edwin Birchall who appears to have been particularly active in the 1860s/1870s. Porritt (1883) also mentions **Askham Bog** (just W of York SE54) in the name of William Prest (b1824/d1884).

Howard M Frost

[1612 GLANVILLE FRITILLARY] Melitaea cinxia (Linnaeus 1758)
Family: Nymphalidae, sub-group Argynninae ('the Fritillaries').

UK BAP Status: *Species of Conservation Concern.*
BC Priority: *Medium.*
European Status: *Not threatened.*

WORLD STATUS: Mobile resident, 1-2 broods (Apr/Aug), 0-2600m. Range: N Spain to C Norway and eastward across Asia. Also in N Africa. In Britain, restricted mainly to Isle of Wight and Channel Isles, with small, probably introduced presence on Hampshire coast and a private introduction in Somerset which has existed since 1983. In Europe has declined in northern half of range.

ID NOTES: At a glance might be confused with Marsh Fritillary (which can be picked out by the lighter markings on the upperwings and the chequerboard appearance), or Heath Fritillary (which lacks the Glanville's row of black dots on the lower upperwings, and the delicate black marks in the lighter bands of the underwings). However, all three species have distinctive elements, which become easier to distinguish with practice. The Heath Fritillary has never been recorded in or even near Yorkshire; the Marsh Fritillary has, although now extinct. Aberrations are not uncommon in all three species, which could produce occasional ID problems.

CONSERVATION ISSUES: No clear reasons for the decline of this species are evident, especially as continental populations have survived as far north as Norway. Emmet & Heath (1989) suggest the butterfly's ability to produce large numbers of offspring on very small sites means that on occasion the larvae eat all available foodplants before they mature, and the whole colony becomes extinct through starvation. When a breeding site is large enough to support its colony, the production of large numbers of butterflies means plenty of females are also produced, and they can wander away to find new sites and form new colonies. Given favourable conditions (perhaps promoted by global warming) it is just possible that this species could expand northwards again under its own volition. However, the failure of most of the reintroduction attempts made so far, seems to indicate something still lacking in climate or habitat.

YORKSHIRE STATUS 1995/2003:

Possibly a long extinct former resident in S Yorkshire, which disappeared in the late 1700s/early 1800s. There are references in literature to a past Yorkshire presence, and although some commentators dismiss the reports on which they are based, it is relevant to examine the evidence available.

LIFE STORY: Eggs laid in batches of up to 200 on the undersides of foodplant leaves. Bristly black larvae with reddish heads, feed gregariously inside tents and hibernate together in similar structures. They awake in Mar/Apr and feed until the 7th instar in May. Pupation takes place low in vegetation, protected by a web. In the Isle of Wight the adult flies May/Jun usually in one brood, with a partial 2nd possible in good years.

Glanville Fritillary: two views taken Compton Bay Isle of Wight, 26/05/1999.

HABITAT: Lays eggs on Ribwort Plantain *Plantago lanceolata*, a common and widely distributed plant. May sometimes use other plantain species, and very occasionally, quite different species. In the past it was found, *'mainly on sheltered sites in and around open woodland'*. (Emmet & Heath 1989). Today, it is largely restricted to eroding cliffs on the Isle of Wight where periodic collapses provide ideal conditions for plantain colonisation. The butterfly appears to be dependent on sites where plantains grow strongly as the dominant coloniser, a temporary situation in which other plants eventually take over. It also appears to require sites which are undisturbed by grazing or cultivation. (In France, it is particularly associated with uncultivated land and rural tracks in traditionally farmed areas.)

Around 1702 Eleanor Glanville sent a number of specimens to James Petiver including a previously unrecorded fritillary obtained from a site near Lincoln where it had been noted since the 1690s. Petiver illustrated this butterfly in his *Gazophylacii naturae & artis* of 1703 and christened it the **Lincolnshire Fritillary**, but later changed it to the **White Dullidge Fritillary** after the species had been found in Dulwich Wood, Surrey. Then J Dutfield (1748) renamed it the **Glanville Fritillary** after the lady entomologist who discovered it. Around the same time Benjamin Wilkes (1747) introduced **Plantain Fritillary** and over the next century both names were in circulation, with Glanville finally winning the day. In the Latin the derivation of *Melitaea* is uncertain, but could be associated with honey and therefore nectar. The species name *cinxia* refers to being girdled and appears to link the butterfly to Lucina, the goddess of childbirth.

Emmet & Heath (1989) note that the species was formerly widespread in SE England as far north as Lincolnshire, *'and possibly even to Yorkshire'*, a comment based on a reference in Stephens (1828): *This is a very local species and is found in meadows by the sides of woods: in Wilke's time* [born before 1690/d1749] *it was not uncommon in Tottenham-wood: recently, the places where it has been chiefly observed have been near Ryde and the Sandrock hotel, Isle of Wight; in the latter place in plenty: also at Birch-wood, and near Dartford and Dover, and in a wood near Bedford. I believe it has been found in Yorkshire; and from Ray p121* [b1627/d1705] *it would appear to have been abundant in Lincolnshire in his time.'* Garland (1981) (under the heading of 'Improbable or impossible records') draws attention to 4 specimens of the Glanville Fritillary in the William Sheldon Collection in Sheffield City Museum

labelled 'Norton'. The collection dates from the mid-19th century, but it is unclear as to whether this Norton is the Sheffield one (just south of the city VC63/SK38), or any one of about 30 others scattered around the British Isles (including one on the Isle of Wight). However, logic would suggest that in a local collection 'Norton' would mean the local one, unless otherwise designated. A further possibility relates to Eleanor Glanville's original site, which is recorded as 'near Lincoln'. Could there be a connection with Norton Disney, just to the south of Lincoln?

Morris (1853) notes: *'it is also said to have occurred in Yorkshire and Lincolnshire.'* Coleman (1860) mentions Yorkshire, Lincolnshire and Peterborough, as well as a Scottish record. Unfortunately, there is potential for confusion between Glanville Fritillary and Marsh Fritillary. Thomson (1980) views Scottish Glanville records with some scepticism as likely misidentifications of Marsh Fritillaries. The reference used by Coleman as his source for a Scottish record was an article in the *Scottish Naturalist* (1851 Vol **1**: 83). A later edition of the same journal (presumably unnoticed by Coleman) corrected the Glanville Fritillary entry to Marsh Fritillary, which illustrates the fact that literature references cannot always be taken at face value!

Referring to Glanville Fritillary, A Maitland Emmet (Emmet & Heath 1989) commented: *'Authors are apt to dismiss the earliest records as misidentifications of Eurodryas aurinia [Marsh Fritillary] or Mellicta athalia [Heath Fritillary], but such suspicions are completely without foundation'*. Salmon (2000) casts doubt on any Yorkshire presence because the record mentioned by Stephens (1828) *'has been rejected by all subsequent authors on Yorkshire Lepidoptera'*. This rather sweeping statement is of questionable accuracy. The only literature evidence we can find to support it is in Garland (1981) and that refers solely to the Sheldon Collection specimens. The fact that Porritt and others didn't include this species does not necessarily imply rejection. It is equally possible (and probably more likely) that they were either unaware of such records, or the records were from so far back in time they were no longer relevant. It is easy to forget that today we often have a wider range of information relating to past recording than did our predecessors in the 19th century.

In the late 1600s we know the species could be found as far north as the Lincoln area where it was first discovered. That area is in the same latitude as the South Yorkshire border region and only 30 miles from it. Therefore, the reference to a Yorkshire presence in Stephens is far from being a geographical impossibility. The species appears to have begun to decline in the second half of the 18th century, and by the 1850s it had retracted to the Isle of Wight and the Kent coast near Folkstone. In Kent it was last recorded around 1863. Bearing all these in mind a past Yorkshire presence of the Glanville Fritillary certainly cannot be ruled out.

Howard M Frost

UK BAP Status: *Not listed.*
BC Priority: *Low.*
European status: *Near threatened.*

WORLD STATUS: Very sedentary resident, 1 brood (late Jul/early Sept) usually found in higher areas 200m/1800m. Range: from the Cevennes in S France to E Belgium and eastward across Asia to W Siberia. Also in Scotland and NW England well to the north of its continental range. England has just 2 colonies, both on SSSIs in Cumbria: at Arnside Knott (National Trust) and Smardale nr Kirkby Stephen (Cumbrian Wildlife Trust). Has declined in a number of continental countries [eg Latvia, Luxembourg (**endangered**), Belgium (**vulnerable**), France, Germany etc].

View east from Malham Moor, with Grass Wood (mainly hidden in the valley) and Bastow Wood (Upper Wharfedale VC64), spread across the middle distance (July 2003).

ID NOTES: A member of the 'brown' family which looks similar to Meadow Brown, but darker (almost black when fresh) with more spots on the upper wings and a figure of eight eyespot on the forewing in closed wing view. Males are blacker, females browner. The number of eyespots on the upperwings is variable but usually less in male (typically 3) and more in female (typically 4). Tends to fly only when the sun is shining, but can be active as soon as the sun rises in the early morning. On warmer days males may sometimes fly in duller conditions. The English population belongs to the subspecies *aethiops* Esper, the Scottish population to subspecies *caledonia* Verity 1911. Scottish specimens are noticeably smaller. It is quite a variable species with over 30 varieties described. Yorkshire's Grass Wood population was considered a **distinctive local race**. EB Ford (1975) wrote: '*Specimens from that district cannot be confused with any others occurring in these islands, for the orange markings on the uppersides of the males are nearly obsolete and in the females they are scarcely more developed than in an ordinary male. It seems to have arisen in isolation as an independent subspecies*'.

YORKSHIRE STATUS 1995/2003:

Extinct former resident originally found in Upper Wharfedale and adjacent or nearby dales. Particularly well known in Grass Wood (VC64/SD96) where WG Clutten found it *'not uncommon'* in 1923. It was last seen in 1927, and by 1934 it was apparently no longer present. There were no further records until two were seen in 1955. As this was a one-off sighting with no others seen in the years immediately before or after it seems likely that the observation resulted from a private attempt at re-introduction. The little evidence we have suggests that the species became extinct in Yorkshire in the late 1920s/early 1930s. Later sightings made between 1982 and 1984 are thought to have resulted from further private introductions, but wanderers from a remnant population on an overlooked site cannot be ruled out.

CONSERVATION ISSUES: Re-introducing this species to Yorkshire would in local terms be akin to re-introducing the Large Blue to England. It should be possible and certainly worthwhile, but complicated and time consuming. It could only be done with permission from landowners and from all interested parties. The English sites are protected by byelaws and collecting is not allowed. Grass Wood was purchased by the YWT in 1972 and 1983 and is now a Nature Reserve. The Trust has a long-term objective of removing the conifers and replacing them with native broadleaved species. Some parts are being coppiced, but although the wood is slowly being opened up, large parts still appear much too dense for this species, with recent planting likely to decrease open spaces in a few years time. It would need a lot more work to return the site to what it was. The adjacent Bastow Wood is more open and perhaps more like the Grass Wood of the past but it may also be too exposed for more than marginal occupation by this butterfly. Butterfly Conservation has produced a management leaflet for Scottish landowners which provides a useful summary, underlining the facts that the butterfly thrives in woodlands with **large** glades and **wide** sunny rides, as well as **sheltered** grassland areas which are ungrazed or only very lightly grazed.

LIFE STORY

This is a species which needs further study as many details of its life story have yet to be fully observed and described. Eggs are laid singly on blades of grass, which are either part of the foodplant or near it. Purple Moor-grass *Molinia caerulea* appears to be the main foodplant in Scotland, whilst in England, Blue Moor-grass *Sesleria caerulea* is used. However, on the continent, quite a wide range of grasses is used, and the range in

Britain may be broader than is currently apparent. Couch Grass *Agropyron repens* has been recorded at Smardale in Cumbria and other grass species have been noted in Scotland. Greenish-yellow larvae hatch after 2-3 weeks by chewing out a lid on the top of their egg, leaving just enough to act as a hinge so they can push it up and crawl out.

Young larvae feed by day and night and rest at the base of grass clumps when not active. They hibernate in a similar location (usually in the second instar, around Oct). Emmet & Heath (1989) suggest that less than 40% survive winter, and that a mould is probably responsible for most of these deaths. After awakening in March larvae appear to feed only at night. Pupation takes place after the 4th instar, at ground level or just below, and involves the construction of a loose cocoon. Adults fly from late July with the population usually peaking in mid-Aug. Thomson (1980) gives the extremes of the flight season in Scotland as 07/07 to 15/09. The adult is usually very sedentary; studies on the remaining English colonies indicate that 100m is about the limit of any movement. Ford (1975 p104) states that, in common with some other upland or high latitude species, the Scotch Argus takes two years to develop. Other writers do not mention this, but it may be a possibility in a proportion of the population when poor weather dictates. More study is needed to clarify the issue.

HISTORICAL REVIEW:
Scotch Argus
Formerly: *Erebia blandina* (in Porritt 1883)

The species was first recognised by Dr John Walker, Professor of Natural History at Edinburgh University in the 1760s. He caught a number of specimens on the Isle of Bute between 1760 and 1769 and called the new species *Papilio amaryllis*. He showed specimens to Fabricius who wrote it up as *Papilio blandina* in 1787. However, German entomologist EJC Esper had already written up the species on the continent as *Papilio aethiops* in 1777, so his name eventually took precedence. '*Aethiops*' means 'the Ethiopian', so called because this is such a dark-coloured butterfly. The family name *Erebia* also reflects the dark wing characteristic of this group, being derived from Erebus, a dusky region between Earth and the underworld, Hades. In 1807, Donovan introduced **Scotch Argus** as the English name and this has been generally accepted since then.

Female Scotch Argus. Specimen obtained from, '*Grassington 1915*'. Private collection.

Male Scotch Argus. Specimen obtained from, *Grassington Aug 1903*'. Private collection.

The earliest known Yorkshire record appears to be that quoted in Porritt (1883): '*Mr Henry Denny also reports it from Whernside in Craven (VC64/SD78) (Mag. of Zoology and Botany 1837 i. 491), but there are no recent records of its occurrence there, possibly, however, because it has not been looked for.*' Shaw (1978) quotes further from the same magazine: '*Five specimens were captured about the 21st August 1836, at the foot of Whernside in Craven, Yorkshire, by Abraham Clapham Esq*'. Three other areas/sites once held natural populations of this species: Arncliffe (in Littondale) and Buckden (both in VC64/SD97), and Grass Wood (VC64/SD96). The Arncliffe record appears in both *The Naturalist* (1894 **19:** 232) and *The Entomologist* (Vol 25 Oct 1892 p244). In the latter H Wilde notes: '*On August 20th 1892 I found Erebia aethiops fairly abundant in an opening in a wood at Arncliffe, Yorkshire, at a height of about 1000ft. Most of them were in bad condition*'. The Rev Trevor Basil Woodd of Oughtershaw Hall reported catching specimens '*at Buckden*' (*Naturalist*

1883 p53). He also sent examples to Porritt and received confirmation that they were *'well marked specimens of the ordinary types'*. James Dickinson has drawn our attention to a specimen in a private collection labelled: *'Settle Yorks 08/1902'*, which may indicate an observer's starting point for a fairly long journey to Grassington, or even an overlooked colony!

Most people wanting to see and catch this species went to Grass Wood (near Grassington in Upper Wharfedale), which many observers in the 1880s thought was the only site in Yorkshire. Morris (1853) refers to its presence *'near Grassington'*. The earliest YNU reference is to a society meeting at Grass Wood on 07/08/1882. HT Soppitt reported: *'A great number of Erebia blandina were taken in Upper Grass Wood, which is the only Yorkshire locality for this species'*, (*Naturalist* 1882-3, **8**: 30). Porritt (1883) noted the same visit: *'This northern species has long been known to occur in plenty at Grassington, in Upper Wharfedale, and on the occasion of the Yorkshire Naturalists' Union visit there on August 7th 1882, was found to be as abundant as ever on the grassy slopes in the Grass High Wood; I took a beautiful series in splendid condition as also did everyone else who wanted it.'* Porritt (1904) notes: *'Still abundant at Grassington in 1903'*. So at least we know that the species survived the cold years of the latter part of the 19th century. Shaw (1978) states that it was periodically reported until 1923 when WG Clutten of Burnley noted it *'common'*. But by 1927 Clutten found it scarce, and in spite of some searches there were no further records until 1955 when W Reid reported seeing two around Dib Scar in August 1955. Dib Scar is an area of stony slopes just beyond the northern edge of Grass Wood, almost opposite Kilnsey Crag. The record was not confirmed by any additional sightings and although a remnant population can't be ruled out, it seems much more likely that this sighting may have resulted from private introductions.

Many of the Grass Wood records refer to 'High Grass Wood' or 'Upper Grass

Two views of Scotch Argus from Smardale, Cumbria (05/08/1997).

Wood' which highlights a possibility of confusion with Bastow Wood. Today we have three woods that appear as one, although under different ownerships. Low Grass Wood lies between the river and the minor road out of Grassington; Grass Wood lies on the upperside of the road and continues to a point about two-thirds up the valley side, whilst Bastow Wood separated only by a wall and a track, lies above that, being situated on the crest of the valley side and extending into the open pasture above. It is suspected that some past references to High Grass Wood could have referred to Bastow Wood or counted the two as one. In the past, Grass Wood was reportedly a more open woodland than we see today, with grassy slopes, but this is also how Bastow Wood appears today. JW Carter (*Naturalist* Sept 1884, **10**: 57), wrote: *'On the 10th of August of the present year I had the pleasure, in the company of my friend Mr Soppitt, of making acquaintance with E. blandina, in its well-known Yorkshire habitat a Grassington, in Upper Wharfedale. Several examples were noted in Grass Low Wood, close to the river; but in the High Wood they were to be seen sporting themselves in the sun, in open places, in countless numbers'*.

At some point later, the High Wood was replanted, with many conifers included. Disturbance and subsequent shading are thought to have been key factors leading to the extinction, although the excessive attention of collectors can't have helped either. They came from all over the country to add this distinctive Grass Wood variety to their collections. It was generally felt that such collecting had no effect on the population. However, this mus be open to question. It is probable that the Scotch Argus has to maintain high numbers in order to compensate for the big larval losses during hibernation. The regular capture of hundreds of specimens could easily have put the population under stress and more prone to succumbing to other difficulties. For instance, the species can be badly affected by rain falling at the time of emergence, which can cripple large numbers of butterflies and prevent them from flying. If that happened in a year when a lot of collecting also took place the overall effect could have been more serious.

In 1952 and 1953 NW Harwood introduced the species into VC62/NZ51 at Eston Nab on the southern edge of Middlesbrough. In Aug 1954, 18 males, 2 females and 2 pairings were noted, but then the colony failed. In 1976 NW Harwood and PJ Stead released 69 fertile females taken from Smardale/Kirkby

Stephen (VC69/NY70) at a point north of Grass Wood. They returned the following year, but found nothing. However, between 1982 and 1984, several Scotch Argus specimens were recorded by members of Wharfedale Naturalists at Round Hill near Skirethornes, on the opposite side of the valley to Grass Wood (pers comm. David Howson). Further private releases are suspected but no details have ever been reported.

This is a species, which although mainly associated with open woodland, can also establish colonies in sheltered corners of open moorland, and these might be quite difficult to find. Although it seems unlikely that any Yorkshire colonies still survive, either as remnants of the original Grass Wood race or of the introduced specimens, this cannot be ruled out. Setting up a series of methodical searches in the upland terrain centred on Grass Wood would not be easy. However, the fact that the species was discovered in no fewer than 130 new 10km squares in Scotland during the 1995/1999 National Butterfly Survey is an indication that this approach can be very successful! There appear to be quite a number of open woodlands not far from Grass Wood, which look potentially suitable, but which may never have been checked out at suitable times. In addition, the Cumbrian colony at Smardale near Kirkby Stephen is not far from the Yorkshire border and the possibility of occasional wanderers from that area reaching the county cannot be ruled out.

Howard M Frost

1630 MONARCH *Danaus plexippus* (Linnaeus 1758)
Family: Nymphalidae, sub-group Danainae. Also known as the Milkweed.

WORLD STATUS: Common resident in N & S America. Wide-ranging migrant, and rare but regular migrant from N America to Europe. In 1956 listed as a pest in N America for no clear reason other than for its ability to produce huge concentrations of butterflies, (Brewer 1971). Basically a tropical butterfly with continuously generated resident populations in tropical areas, which is also able to migrate northward in spring and through one or more generations *en route* (April/June), reach as far north as southern Canada (July/Aug). In Sept/Oct offspring set off south, gathering in ever-greater numbers on the way, and heading for wintering sites in Mexico and southern California. From time to time, storms along the eastern coast of N America may blow large numbers of butterflies off course, some of which successfully cross the Atlantic and reach Europe, Africa or the Atlantic Islands, a journey estimated to take about 4 days. As a result populations have become established in the Canary Islands (from 1860), the Azores (from 1864), S Portugal and S Spain (from 1980), Madeira (from 1981) and more recently still, in Gibraltar. Butterflies travelling down the western coast of N America are likewise sometimes blown across the Pacific and as a result have established populations in New Zealand (from 1840), Australia (from 1870), in India, some of the islands of the East Indies, and in Mauritius. In addition wanderers are regularly seen on western coasts of the British Isles and Europe. In fact sightings in Britain have increased dramatically in recent years and the species is being increasingly noted around the Mediterranean, eg in S France, Corsica and even in Morocco. Nearly all the winter roosting sites in Mexico and California face threatening development, but local and international efforts are underway to protect them (Pyle 1981). The species is also under threat in S Spain where colonies are isolated and suitable habitats often destroyed by chemical weed clearance.

YORKSHIRE STATUS 1995/2003:

Potentially a very rare vagrant. Probably from N America, possibly from S Europe. Most arrivals of this species in Britain are on the west side of the country, and particularly in the south-west. The most recent Yorkshire records were in 1990 at Easington (Holderness VC61/TA31), and 1997 at Hornsea (Holderness VC61/TA24) (further details below), both of which seem likely to have been escapees from butterfly houses but could just possibly have been immigrants from populations in southern Europe.

LIFE STORY

HABITAT: A butterfly of open areas like meadows, pastures and wastelands which contain Milkweeds (Asclepiadaceae) or Dogbanes (Apocynaceae). None of these are native to the British Isles, but some may be found in Britain as garden plants. Polunin (1969) gives a number of these species which may be found in southern Europe including: Stranglewort *Cynanchum acutum*; Silk-vine *Periploca graeca*; Common Vincetoxicum *Vincetoxicum hirundinaria*; Dark Vincetoxicum *V. nigrum*; Silkweed *Asclepias syriaca* (a N American native naturalised in Central and S Europe); and Bristly-fruited Silkweed *Gomphocarpus fruticosus*. The latter and *Asclepias curassavica* are used by Monarchs in the Canaries. The Dogbane family includes several species of Periwinkle *Vinca* spp and the Oleander bush *Nerium oleander*. It is not known with any certainty if all of these plants are, or could be, used by Monarchs in Europe but the list does at least indicate quite a few possibilities. Key to the potential use of these plants is the fact that they are poisonous (as some of the names indicate!) and the Monarch larvae are able to absorb and retain some of the poison to make themselves and the butterflies distasteful to birds. Autumn arrivals in Britain tend to stay near coastlines and often visit gardens or parks in search of nectar plants. They have been observed roosting in trees.

Monarch: posed picture on an indoor plant. This specimen, caught in the playground of Easington C/E Primary School was on its last legs by the time it was delivered to local recorders Howard & Christine Frost (Easington nr Spurn VC61 23/03/1990).

This is a tropical butterfly which cannot survive winters in northern N America or in N Europe. Eggs, which are laid on Milkweeds or Dogbanes are shaped like a lemon with a flat base. Larvae are barred in strong warning colours, black, white and yellow, with a pair of black filaments (like antennae) at front and rear. Rather dumpy pupae are a pale jade green marked with gold spots towards the bottom. They hang from stems and leaves attached by silk pads. Life cycle may take as little as one month to complete. N American butterflies which head south in late summer/autumn spend winter resting in fir forests or groves of pine, cypress or eucalyptus in Mexico or California. At this time they become sluggish and do not reproduce although they may continue to nectar on suitably warm days.

ID NOTES: Extremely large butterfly with a wingspan up to and even exceeding 10cm (4 inches), making it the largest, naturally occurring butterfly in the British Isles. Bright orange-brown, with veins thickened in black, and wing edges banded in black and sprinkled with white spots. Males and females are very similar, but the male has a small oval sex-brand on each of the upper hindwings. There are around 300 related species worldwide, many of which look similar. One such is the **Plain Tiger** *Danaus chrysippus*, which is found around the Mediterranean, but has never been recorded wild in Britain. It appears to be a migrant from N Africa, and reaches the N Mediterranean coast in varying numbers each year, with offspring returning south in autumn. The Monarch, the Plain Tiger and other related species are often found in Butterfly Houses and may occasionally escape.

CONSERVATION ISSUES: Unfortunately, even if we do see more Monarchs, they will be unlikely to breed because N Europe lacks the suitable foodplants. Some enthusiasts would like to see gardeners encouraged to plant Milkweeds and Dogbanes more widely! There was an intriguing case in 1981 when several escapees from a Butterfly House were seen to lay eggs on *Asclepias incarnata*, *A. syriaca* and *A. speciosa* in Kew gardens. The eggs were collected and successfully reared in captivity. So there must be at least an outside chance that in the coming years we might see a first natural breeding record in Britain in some park or garden containing one of the foodplants. If populations around the Mediterranean grow we might even see the Monarch as a more regular visitor to the county. However, the main conservation issues currently remain in America where there are continued threats to the hibernation areas, and the introduction of genetically modified (GM) maize crops designed to kill one of the main pests of maize was shown to be also capable of killing Monarch larvae feeding on field edge stands of Milkweed onto which GM maize pollen had blown. The pollen grains appear to be as poisonous to insects as the GM maize crop itself!

HISTORICAL REVIEW:

Monarch

Not recorded in Porritt.

Originally called **the Archippus** by Brown (1832) and Coleman (1897). Kirby (1901) used **the Monarch** whilst South (1906) introduced **the Milkweed** and both names have continued in use since then. Newman & Leeds (1913) called it the **Black-veined Brown**, a name favoured by Frohawk and used as recently as 1973 by Howarth. In the Latin, both names recall people in Greek mythology, Danaus being king of Argos and Plexippus (=braided horse-hair) took part in a wild boar hunt in Calydon in which he and many others lost their lives.

YORKSHIRE RECORDS:

1917: One at Kirkheaton Tip, **Huddersfield** (VC63/SE11) on 17/09/1917 (not 1927 as given in some YNU sources) reported in Morley (1928).

1934: One at Storiths, **Bolton Abbey** (VC64/SE05) on 02/10/1934, quoted in YNU (1970).

1986: Sutton & Beaumont (1989) include an unconfirmed **Harrogate** area sighting of a large fritillary-like butterfly seen in late 1986, which was twice the size of a Peacock (*per* Mike Barnham).

????: Emmet & Heath (1989) map an unknown VC61 record, the origins of which we have not been able to ascertain.

1990: One caught in **Easington** C/E Primary School playground (VC61/TA31) by Kelly Whitehead, Verity Sizer and Jane Douglas on 23/03/1990 and presented to the writer for confirmation (courtesy Larry Malkin, Headteacher Easington C/E School). (See adjoining photos of specimen and discussion below.)

1997: One found in a **Hornsea** garden (VC61/TA24) by Pat Browning on 29/05/1997 and confirmed by Gordon Hylands (Butterfly Recorder for the Hornsea and N Holderness Countryside Society). This observation was made close to the Hornsea Pottery Butterfly House and in a year when a number of other exotic species escaped through a cracked pane of glass.

First recorded in Britain in 1876 when 4 were caught in S Wales, Sussex and Dorset. Odd ones have been seen somewhere in the British Isles in most or many years since then. The first really notable year came in **1933** when **40** sightings were recorded, leading to a change in the general idea that previous sightings had been stowaways on ships. Exceptional years have been becoming more common over the last 40yrs with **63** records in **1968**, **135** in **1981**, **150-200** in **1995**, and **300** or more in **1999**. Bearing in mind that between 1876 and 1940 (64yrs) there were 148 reported sightings, and between 1940 and 1988 (48yrs) there were a further 300 reports, taking the total to 448, the number then doubled in just 5 years!

Emmet & Heath (1989) map the 1876/1988 records, which show a strong bias towards the S and SW (Cornwall to the Isle of Wight). This indicates that the majority of Monarchs sweep in from the SW on a track leading along the south coast and English Channel with the biggest number of sightings in the Scillies and Cornwall. They often arrive in conjunction with American bird species. There has also been a scatter of records along the western side of N England and the odd ones on western Scottish islands. One even reached Shetland, but hardly any have been seen on the eastern side of England north of Essex. Little is known about what happens when Monarchs arrive, other than the fact that they often hang around gardens nectaring, eg on Buddleia. We don't know how long they live after arrival or whether or not they continue migrating further south.

Today there is little doubt that Monarchs fly across the Atlantic albeit wind assisted. They have the ability to rest for short periods on water, and there have been reports of Monarchs seen floating on the sea and taking off again. It is probable that the occasional specimen does hitch a lift. There are reports of quite large numbers sometimes setting down on boats. Butterfly Houses (the first of which opened in Guernsey 1977) often stock Monarchs and a few escapees are probably inevitable. Privately reared captive specimens may also be released on occasion.

Yorkshire's two early records in 1917 and 1934 were notably towards the western side of the county, which would be in line with specimens flying in from the west. The Easington record on 23/03/1990 is interesting in drawing attention to a new and growing possibility. Now that there are resident populations in the south of Spain and Portugal and in Gibraltar (albeit very small populations), there must also be the possibility that some individuals will fly northward just as they would have done in N America. That could well bring Monarchs to Yorkshire's east coast. Easington is at the south-eastern extremity of the county, near Spurn and the Humber Estuary. As the land sticks out into the sea, it is often a first landing area for migrant butterflies flying up the east coast or crossing the N Sea. The Easington record seems very early. The vast majority of British sightings are between Aug and Nov, when southward journeys along the east coast of N America are underway. However, in the days preceding this sighting, the weather had been exceptionally spring-like with southerly winds blowing straight up from Spain. Couple this with increasing evidence to suggest that we are indeed beginning to get a small trickle of spring records thought to come from S Europe or the Atlantic Islands, and the possibility of a genuine record grows (see Emmet & Heath 1989 p284/285 for further discussion on these issues.) Unfortunately, at the time of the Easington sighting, just a dozen miles across the Humber, Monarchs were flying inside the butterfly house at Jungle World in Cleethorpes (VC54/TA30). However, the manager was adamant that none had escaped and explained that his stock was from Belize in S America and might be of a recognisably different race to those from N America. However, in spite of worldwide searches on the internet we have not been able to trace any diagnostic characteristic that could clarify this issue.

With two east coast records close to Butterfly Houses it is easy to jump to the obvious conclusion, yet both could be immigrants from S Europe! So, clearly, it is important to keep an open mind on such records, and for observers to send in all reports of this species however suspect they may be. No-one knows why the number of Monarchs crossing the Atlantic appears to be rising. It may be an effect of global warming and that we are seeing more hurricanes occurring during the N American autumn migration, which end up blowing the butterflies eastward across the Atlantic. If south European populations continue to increase as a result, Yorkshire sightings could become more likely.

Howard M Frost

Osiphanes **sp. Courtesy Philip Winter collection, (caught 03/05/1984, Bridlington).**

YORKSHIRE ADVENTIVES

This grouping involves the accidental introduction of foreign butterflies, which could not have made their own way to the British Isles. Arrivals invariably occur by way of trade, especially via the import of fruit and vegetables. Adventives are mainly of passing interest, but are nonetheless considered worthy of note. Just occasionally, such a visitor may have the ability to establish itself, at least temporarily, as did the Geranium Bronze *Cacyreus marshalli*, a South African species, which spread into Europe via the garden centre trade. It was first recorded in Britain in 1978 and again in 1997 and is a potential pest of *Pelargonium* species.

***Opsiphanes* sp**: Philip Winter reported this tropical butterfly (Winter 1985) which was found among bananas in a Bridlington (VC61) warehouse. It originated from the West Indies (Windward Islands or Trinidad & Tobago). The particular cargo was delivered to the warehouse on 03/05/1984, and the butterfly was spotted and caught two days later. It is a member of the Brassolidae family, also referred to as 'Owls' because of their often large wing pattern eyes and crepuscular habits.

Broad-winged Skipper *Poanes viator*: Keith Barrow found this butterfly as a stowaway in a parcel sent from Washington, USA in 2001. It was alive but on its last legs when it reached his home in Bridlington (VC61). It is similar in colour and size to a large Skipper, although the upperwing pattern is distinctively different. It has been identified with the help of Terry Whitaker and with reference to the 'Atlas of North Dakota Butterflies' on the US Government Service website.

Broad-winged Skipper: specimen photographed courtesy Keith Barrow & Tony Ezard (caught 2001, Bridlington). Left: upperside. Right: underside.

This large Nymphalid butterfly was found nectaring on hedgerow plants at the west end of Hornsea Mere on 06/08/1997 together with Peacocks and Meadow Browns. It is thought to be a Malaysian species, probably *Parthenos sylvia*.

It is illegal to release any butterflies into the wild which are not on the British List. This doesn't stop some specimens accidentally escaping, especially from Butterfly Houses with their free-flying collections. Such escapees will usually come to grief fairly quickly due to our fickle climate and the way their bright colours may no longer protect them from predators across our open countryside. Although it is unlikely an alien species could breed outside the protection of its hothouse habitat, the possibility can never be absolutely ruled out. (After all, 50yrs ago, who would have thought Parakeets would become a breeding species across southern England?) Therefore it is considered important to keep a watching brief on the situation by encouraging the reporting and collating of any exotic species seen in the wild. Unfortunately, the precise identification of such species is not always easy as few recorders hold a library of ID books covering species from around the world. However, photographs or actual specimens can often enable an identification to family or genus, as well as country or region of origin. The butterflies illustrated were amongst several that appeared to have escaped through a cracked pane of glass in a Butterfly House at Hornsea Freeport (VC61) in 1997.

An unidentified bright red butterfly seen along the Hornsea Rail Trail on 10/08/1997 on a N Holderness Countryside Society field trip.

INTERESTED IN BUTTERFLIES?
Then why not look at moths?

Anyone becoming interested in butterflies can hardly overlook the moths, as many fly by day, and some may even look like butterflies. True, there are rather a lot of them and many are rather drab in appearance. But many more are highly coloured with some rivalling the best of the butterflies. Most moths can be distinguished by their lack of a 'club' shape at the end of their antennae.

Butterflies and moths belong to the same scientific order, known as the Lepidoptera. For the purpose of moth recording in Yorkshire the moths are divided into macro-moths (the larger species) and micro-moths (the smallest, mainly made up of the Pyralidae family) each group having its own 'Recorder', or co-ordinator of records. In addition there are Co-ordinators for each of the five Yorkshire Vice-Counties (VCs) who help to collect together the huge number of moth records generated within Yorkshire each year. Yorkshire moth recording is organised by the YNU Lepidoptera Group, working closely with Butterfly Conservation.

For anyone wanting to find out more about moths, a good starting point is the Reader's Digest *Field Guide to the Butterflies and other Insects of Britain* (1984). This book provides a colourful introduction to

Elephant Hawk-moth

our butterflies, together with a useful selection of our commoner moths, as well as other groups of insects such as the dragonflies. A more comprehensive book, aimed at both beginner and expert is the *Field Guide to the Moths of Great Britain and Ireland* by Paul Waring, Martin Townsend & Richard Lewington (British Wildlife Publishing 2003). This is an essential reference work for anyone who wants to identify the macro-moths on a regular basis. Both these books illustrate the moths in natural positions.

Howard M Frost

Garden Tiger Moth

Humming-bird Hawk-moth

Death's Head Hawk-moth with Small Tortoiseshell for comparison.

AND DON'T FORGET THE MICROS!

While in the field, recording butterflies, the observant naturalist cannot help noticing some of the moths of the family Pyralidae. During the summer months members of the Crambidae family are frequently disturbed, taking flight briefly, and seeming to disappear just as suddenly, as they resume their resting attitude on grass stems, with their wings tightly wrapped around themselves. There are just over 200 Pyralid species, many of which are very attractive. Some are day-flying and many more are readily disturbed from their resting places among vegetation or on tree trunks or rocks. Others are strictly nocturnal. Pyralid moths are unlikely to be mistaken for butterflies, although some larger species such as Mother of Pearl *Pleuroptya ruralis,* Small Magpie *Eurrhypara hortulata* and females of the Brown China-mark *Elophila nymphaeata* can approach or even exceed the size of the smaller butterflies.

Pyralid larvae utilise a wide range of foods, many feeding in a variety of ways on the roots, in the stems, and on or under the leaves or seeds of herbaceous and woody plants. Other species have adapted to feed on the artificial abundance of human stored food produce. As a result the Indian Meal moth *Plodia interpunctella* is widely distributed in both dwellings and foodstores where it will devour cereal products, nuts and dried fruit. The Bee moth *Aphomia sociella* inhabits the nests of bumble bees, whilst the Wax moth *Galleria mellonella* and the Lesser Wax moth *Achroia grisella* live in the hives of honey bees. The larvae of some species feed on or inside various fungi and those of the family *Nymphulinae* live an aquatic life feeding on waterweeds. With such diverse lifestyles, there are few habitats in which Pyralids are not found.

Most species can be named fairly readily using the excellent *British Pyralid Moths, A Guide to their Identification* by Barry Goater (Harley Books 1986). For many years this group of moths has suffered from neglect but now we have a National Pyralid and Plume Recording Scheme, which distributes newsletters, species keys and distributional information to participants and has given a real impetus to encouraging further study. There is much to learn, for the distribution patterns of many species within Yorkshire are imperfectly known. Further species are still regularly added to the County list, and several which have arrived in recent years, are showing a dynamic expansion of range. The biology of a number of, sometimes common species is yet to be worked out, so there is plenty for the enthusiastic lepidopterist to discover.

Gold Triangle

Harry E Beaumont
(YNU Micro-lepidoptera Recorder)

COLLECTIONS
Information collated by James Dickinson

Yorkshire museums hold some excellent butterfly collections which can usually be examined by prior arrangement. These can provide a valuable tool for research. The following information was correct at the time of preparation but as a number of museums are undergoing major refurbishments lasting several years the contact information and availability of collections may change. The information below indicates name of original collector, notes on the nature of the collection, geographical scope of collection and approximate number of specimens.

Doncaster Museum and Art Gallery
Chequer Rd
DONCASTER DN1 2AE
Tel: 01302 734 293

Hyde GE	Butterflies/Moths 1930s-1970s	Some S Yorks	c12,000
Jackson SM (1914-95)	Butterflies/Moths Post War	Some Yorks	Several 100
Smith E	Butterflies/Moths Post War	Mostly S Yorks	4000+
Waddington LGF	Butterflies/Moths 1870s-1970s	50% Yorks	7,000

Tolson Memorial Museum
Ravensknowle Park
Wakefield Rd
HUDDERSFIELD HD5 8DJ
Tel: 01484 223 830

Morley B (1872-1932)	Butterflies/Moths 19th/20th century	Mostly Yorks	c5,750
Porritt GT (1848-1927)	Butterflies 1860-1920	Some Yorks	23,000
Tolson Collection	Includes micros	Some local	9,000

Kingston-upon-Hull City Museums
Monument Buildings
Ferens Art Gallery
Queen Victoria Square
HULL HU1 3RA
Tel: 01482 610 610

Barraclough W	Butterflies/Moths early 20th century	Some Yorks?	42 drawers
Holt CM	Butterflies/Moths 1900-1934	Some Yorks?	3,500
Taylor F	Butterflies/Moths 1910-1960	Some Yorks	4,000

Cliffe Castle Museum
Spring Gardens Lane
KEIGHLEY B20 6LH
Tel: 01535 618 230

Briggs J (1904-1991)	Butterflies/Moths	50% Yorks	8,000
Carter JW (1852-1920)	Butterflies/Moths	Some Yorks	3,000+
Crooks S	Butterflies/Moths	Yorks	1,000
Haxby CR	Butterflies/Moths 1946-1978	Some Yorks	10,000
Museum Collection		Mostly Yorks	2,300

Leeds Resource Centre
Moorfield Rd
Yeadon
LEEDS LS19 7BN

Armitage J (1900-1996)	Butterflies/Moths	Some Yorks	6,000
Enson-Jowett FR	Palearctic early 20th century		2,500
Thornton JN (1892-1956)	Butterflies/Moths	EUR. UK, Yorks	7,500
Wigan JL	Butterflies/Moths pre-1930s	Some Yorks	4,000
Wilding R	Collection 1870-1925	Some Yorks	2,500

Rotherham Museum & Art Gallery
Clifton Park
ROTHERHAM S65 2AA
Tel: 01709 382 121

Barringer WL	Butterflies/Moths 20th century	Mostly S Yorks	2,600
Young JN & ME	Collection 1870-1925	Some Yorks	7,500

Woodend Museum of Natural History
The Crescent
SCARBOROUGH YO11 2PW
Tel: 01723 367 326

Walsh GB (1880-1957)	Butterflies/Moths	Some Yorks	7,700

Sheffield City Museum Weston Park **SHEFFIELD** S10 2TP			
Buckley W	Butterflies/Moths early/mid 20th century	Some S Yorks	7,500
Fearnehough DT	Butterflies mid-late 20th century	Inc aberrations	1,350
Price EA	Butterflies early/mid 20th century		1,100
Sheldon W	Butterflies/Moths late 19th century	Some Yorks	3,800
Whitaker A	Butterflies/Moths 1880-1920	Some Yorks	6,200

The Yorkshire Museum Museum Gardens **YORK** YO1 2DR			
Allis TH	Macro & Micro mid 19th century		29,000
Bielby-Cook R	1920s		
Heron AMR	Late 20th century.	Some Yorks	4,500
St Quintin WH (1851-1933)	Palearctic late 19th century		15,000

WHO ARE WE?

A brief 'whose who' of the writers and illustrators.

Howard M Frost, editor: Retired teacher and lifelong naturalist. Born Leeds. Worked in Stroud, Paris, Mons (Belgium) and East Yorkshire. Singer and guitarist with the Barn Folk in Belgium. Rail enthusiast and collector of old irons. Has written a history of Spurn and its Military Railway (2000). Editor of *Argus* magazine for Butterfly Conservation Yorkshire.

Nick Lawman, artist: Freelance video producer based near York, creating a wide range of video and interactive programmes, mainly for the corporate and public sectors. Has been interested in painting and natural history since childhood, especially birds and butterflies. Painted the front cover for the Spring 1994 issue of Butterfly Conservation News.

Jim Asher, mapmaker: Physicist. Senior manager with AEA Technology. National Recorder for Butterfly Conservation. Author of *The Butterflies of Berkshire, Buckinghamshire and Oxfordshire* (1994), a region for which he is County Recorder. Key member of the team which produced the *Millennium Atlas of Butterflies in Britain and Ireland* (2001). Would like to thank a patient and long-suffering wife (Denise), a thought echoed by all of us in respect of our husbands, wives and partners!

Mike Barnham: Consultant medical microbiologist in Harrogate. Brought up in Epsom, lived in Knaresborough since 1978 and co-authored *Butterflies of the Harrogate District* (1987). Now working on a 3-decade summary of butterfly changes around Harrogate. Jazz guitarist, long-distance walker and fly fisherman.

Harry E Beaumont: Retired S Yorkshire funeral director. Joint editor: *Butterflies & Moths of Yorkshire* (YNU 1989) and editor: *Butterflies & Moths of Yorkshire a Millennium Review* (YNU 2002). Committed francophile. Past president of YNU. Chairman YNU Entomological Section. YNU Microlepidoptera Recorder.

Roy Bedford: Retired office supervisor from the Wakefield area. Fascinated by meteorology. Walker, mountaineer, author and artist. Has written *My Mountains* and *Mountain High* illustrated with his own landscape watercolours. VC63 co-ordinator of butterfly records for Butterfly Conservation.

David S Blakeley: MSc Administrator, Zoology Dept, Leeds University. Interested in fly-fishing and insect photography. Has co-authored various scientific papers on butterflies.

Sean A Clough: Trainee primary school teacher in Hull area. Plays and coaches roller hockey. Plays drum kit. Has written a paper on the Small Pearl-bordered Fritillary for the N York Moors National Park (2003). VC61 co-ordinator of records for Butterfly Conservation.

Peter A Crowther: University cataloguer, Birmingham and Hull. Now retired to Kilnsea near Spurn. A moth enthusiast. Helps produce the annual *Spurn Wildlife* report. Has written articles and reports for Tophill Low, *Argus* magazine, *Amateur Entomologist* etc.

James Dickinson: Museum natural history conservator, currently working with the Lancashire County Museum Service. Interested in birdwatching and natural history. Thanks Brooke Bond tea cards for starting a life-long passion for butterflies!

Sam Ellis: Further and higher education teacher and ecological consultant, now Butterfly Conservation's Senior Regional Officer (North of England) based in Co Durham. Has written many scientific papers (see bibliography for selection). A cricket enthusiast.

Bill Ely: Former biology teacher, now Biological Records Officer for Rotherham Metropolitan Borough Council. Interested in military history.

Geoffrey Fryer: Biologist who worked for 28yrs with the Freshwater Biological Association. Hon Professor, University of Lancaster since 1988. Spent 7yrs in Africa. Author of *The Freshwater Crustacea of Yorkshire* (YNU). Co-authored a study of Huddersfield area butterflies with Jill Lucas (Fryer & Lucas 2000).

Marie-Christine Frost: Half French and married to the editor. Primary school teacher (Special Needs). Formerly taught in Belgium and also played guitar and sang with the Barn Folk. Keen swimmer, lace-maker, gardener and iron collector. Has written various butterfly reports and articles for *Holderness Countryside* and *Argus*.

Adrian F Johnson: Worked in engineering and served with the forces in Africa and Middle East. Before retiring worked in the N Sea oil and gas industry (enabling him to record birds and butterflies on platforms off the Yorkshire coast). A keen birdwatcher and general naturalist.

Jeff Lunn: Works in the environmental sector, currently with English Nature at Wakefield. Has written many papers on environmental topics and is especially interested in the natural history of brownfield sites.

Derek Parkinson: A general practitioner in Shipley, especially interested in medical information technology. Longstanding member of Butterfly Conservation Yorkshire and former Treasurer. Runs the yorkshiremoths.org.uk website.

Robert Parks: A social services manager in Cumbria. He became interested in the Duke of Burgundy when living in North Yorkshire (1990/1993) and has written many privately published papers in connection with his survey and conservation work undertaken in relation to this species.

Ted Rimington: Retired microbiologist formerly at Doncaster Royal Infirmary. Has written various papers on butterflies (see selection in bibliography). Author of *Butterflies of the Doncaster District* (Sorby Record Special Series No9, 1992).

Peter C Robinson: Teacher. Botanical consultant to English Nature (South-west Team) and geological consultant to the NE Yorkshire Geology Trust. Leader of the N York Moors Forest District Butterfly Recording Group 1993-2003.

Arnold J Robson: Retired secondary school teacher, although initially trained in agriculture. Born in Co Durham, but based in Richmond since 1971. A keen birdwatcher and gardener.

Bill Smyllie: Retired metallurgist. Former technical director to the Sheffield Smelting Co Ltd and later a metallurgical consultant. Has written 14 papers mainly on aspects of the Argus group of butterflies (see bibliography for selection). Lepidoptera Recorder for the Sorby Natural History Society (Sheffield) 1963-1977.

Peter Waterton: Retired research chemist (ICI) living in Great Ayton. Former VC62 co-ordinator of butterfly recording. Interested in birdwatching, botany and photography.

David & Stuart Wise: Twins, living in London. Former university lecturers on the avant-garde who retrained as builders and specialise in work for English Heritage. Authors of various books on general social theory in relation to culture, science, urbanism and politics, mainly published in the USA. Also authors of a number of privately produced booklets on butterflies in South and West Yorkshire.

Terry Whitaker: Born Leeds, grew up in West Wales. Armed with a zoology degree he did work experience under CB Williams at the Rothamsted Experimental Station. Later worked for 11yrs with the British Antarctic Survey. Returned to the Yorkshire Dales earning a living as a builder and a biological consultant. Besides being VC64 co-ordinator of butterfly records for Butterfly Conservation he is currently working on a pictorial guide to the pyralid and thyridid moths of Borneo.

SPECIAL NOTE:

SPECIAL NOTE: The **YNU** *Naturalist*: The first nine volumes each ran from Aug to Jul, starting in 1875/6. The 10th volume ran from Aug 1884 to Dec 1885. From 1886 (Vol: **11**) until the present, volumes have been counted annually, but were not indicated on the journals until 1976 (Vol: **101**). Since then it has become customary to extrapolate backwards and to indicate annual volume numbers in references, even though the journals do not carry such numbers. Therefore the 1900 volume is indicated as *Naturalist* **25** and the 1950 volume *Naturalist* **75.** Many of our writers have used this form of reference, some have preferred to give the dated form.

Bibliography
for Butterflies of Yorkshire

Aagaard K., Hindar K., Pullin A.S., James C.H., Hammarsted O., Balstad T, & Hanssen O. (2002) Phylogenetic relationships in brown argus butterflies (Lepidoptera: Lycaenidae: *Aricia*) from north-western Europe. *Biol. J. Linn. Soc.* **75**: 27-37.

Allan P.B.M. (1958) A note on *Papilio machaon* L. *Entomologist's Rec J. Var* **70**: 87-88.

Allan P.B.M. (1980) *Leaves from a Moth-Hunter's Notebook.* Faringdon.

Albin E. (1720) *The natural history of English insects.* London.

Allison K.J. (1976) *The East Riding of Yorkshire Landscape.* Hodder and Stoughton Ltd, London.

Anon (1832) Lepidoptera in the immediate vicinity of Wath-on-Dearne, Lepidoptera Diurna. *The Village Magazine, or Wath Repository.* **2**: 121-123.

Archer-Lock A. (1989) Butterflies in Winter. *Entomologist's Record* Vol 101.

Arnold S. (1986) *Wild Flowers of the North York Moors National Park.* Hutton Press Ltd, Cherry Burton.

Asher J. *et al* (2001) *The Millennium Atlas of Butterflies in Britain and Ireland* Oxford University Press.

Austin G (1856) Communications. *Entomologist's Weekly Intelligencer* **1**: 140.

Baker R.R. (1969) The evolution of the migratory habit in butterflies. *Journal of Animal Ecology* **38**: 703-746.

Barnett L.K. & Warren M.S. (1995) *Species Action Plan: Marsh Fritillary Eurodryas (Euphydryas) aurinia,* Butterfly Conservation, Wareham.

Barnham M. & Foggitt G.T. (1987) *Butterflies in the Harrogate District.* Published by the authors.

Barnham M. & Foggitt G.T. (1991) *Harrogate Lepidoptera: A summary of records for the district.* Published by the authors.

Barnham M., Foggitt G.T. & Ratliffe L. (1993) Recent changes in butterfly distribution in the Harrogate district. *Naturalist* **118**: 47-53.

Barrett C.G. (1893) *The Lepidoptera of the British Islands. Vol 1: Rhopalocera.* Reeve, London.

Batty J. (1858) Captures near Sheffield. *Entomologist's Weekly Intelligencer* **4**: 85.

Bayford E.G. (1940) The Predecessors of *the Naturalist*: A Critical Survey, *Naturalist* **65**: 228-232.

Beaumont H.E. (Ed.) (2002) *Butterflies and Moths of Yorkshire. A Millennium Review.* Yorkshire Naturalists' Union.

Bedford R. (2002) *Krakatoa and the Weather 1878-1895.* Research Report published privately.

Belcher H. (1836) *The Scenery of the Whitby and Pickering Railway* Longman, Rees, Orme, Brown, Green and Longman, London. (1976 reprint by EP Publishing Ltd, East Ardsley, Wakefield.)

Berkenhout J. (1769) *Outlines of the natural history of Great Britain & Ireland.* London.

Birdsall J. (1988) *The Boys and the Butterflies, a wartime rural childhood.* Pavilion Books Ltd.

Blakeley D. (1997) Small Heath report in *Argus* No: **33** (Ed. Frost & Winter 1997).

Blakeley D. (1998) Small Heath report in *Argus* No: **35** (Ed. Frost & Winter (1998).

Blakeley D. (1999) Small Heath report in *Argus* No: **37** (Ed. Frost & Winter (1999).

Bolton (1796) *Harmonia ruralis; or, An Essay towards a Natural History of British Songbirds.* **Vol 2.** Vol 1 published in 1794.

Boult J.W. (1899) List of the Macro-Lepidoptera collected within eight miles of Hull. *Transactions of the Hull Scientific and Field Naturalists' Club for 1899.* **Vol 1:** 54-65.

Bourn N.A.D. & Warren M.S. (1995) Species Action Plan PEARL-BORDERED FRITILLARY *Boloria euphrosyne.* Butterfly Conservation.

Bourn N.A.D. & Warren M.S. (1997) Species Action Plan LARGE HEATH *Coenonympha tullia.* Butterfly Conservation.

Brady W.E. (1884) A List of the Macrolepidoptera of Barnsley - Diurni. *Quarterly Transactions of the Barnsley Naturalists' Society* **4**: 48-50.

Bradley J.D. (2000) *Checklist of Lepidoptera recorded from the British Isles.* Published by D.J. & M.J. Bradley.

Brakefield P.M. (1979a) An experimental study of the maintenance of variation in the spot pattern in *Maniola Jurtina.* PhD Thesis, University of Liverpool.

Brakefield P.M. (1979b) Spot number in *Maniola Jurtina.* Variation between generations and selection in marginal populations. *Heredity* **42**:259-266.

Brakefield P.M. (1982a & b) Ecological Studies on the butterfly *Maniola Jurtina* in Britain: 1. Adult behaviour, micro-distribution and dispersal. 2. Population dynamics: the present situation. *J. Anim. Ecol.* **51**: 713-738.

Brakefield P.M. (1984) The ecological genetics of quantitative characters of *Maniola Jurtina* and other butterflies, pp167-190. *In* Vane-Wright R.I. & Ackery P.R. (Eds), *The biology of* *utterflies.* London.

Brakefield P.M. (1987) Geographical variability in, and temperature effects on, the phenology of *Maniola Jurtina* and *Pyronia tithonus* (Lepidoptera: Satyrinae) in England and Wales. *Ecological Entomology:* **12**: 139-138.

Brakefield P.M. & van Noordwijk A.J. (1985) The genetics of spot pattern characters in the meadow brown butterfly *Maniola Jurtina* (Lepidoptera: Satyrinae) *Heredity* **54**: 275-284.

Bretherton R.F. (1951) The Early History of the Swallow-tail Butterfly (*Papilio machaon* L.) in England. *Entomologist's Rec.J.Var.* **63**: 206-211.

Brewer J. (1971) *Wings in the Meadow* Country Book Club edition, London. (Life story of the Monarch butterfly.)

Brimblecombe P. (2000) Acid Drops. *Inside Science 150, New Scientist 2343* 18/05/2002.

Brindle A. (1939) The Lepidoptera of the Pendle Hill area. *North Western Naturalist* Sept-Dec 1939: 1-34.

Brindle A. (1963) Lepidoptera by H.N. Michaelis in Insects of Malham Tarn Area – Yorkshire Naturalists' Union. *Proceedings of the Leeds Philosophical and Literary Society Scientific Section* Vol **IX** Pt II, March 1963.

Brooks M. & Knight C. (1982) *A Complete Guide to British Butterflies.* Jonathan Cape Ltd, London.

Brown P.R. (1998) *Journal of Meteorology* **23**: 233.

Brown T. (1832) *The book of butterflies, sphinxes and moths.* Edinburgh.

Burton W. (1997) *The Malton and Driffield Junction Railway* Martin Bairstow, Halifax.

Butterfield R. (1906) Vanishing local plants and animals. *Bradford Scientific Journal.* **1**: 111-114.

Butterfield E.P. (1911) The butterflies of the Bradford district. *Bradford Scientific Journal.* **3**: 111-114.

Butterfield E.P. (1925) Immigration of White Butterflies in the Wilsden District. *Naturalist* **50**: 346

Butterfield *et al* (1930) *Silva Gars (Grass Wood) and Guide to Grassington and Upper Wharfedale.* Published by John Crowther.

Cain B.D. & Baggaley W. (1997) Lepidoptera Report 1995. *Nat. Hist. Calderdale* **7**: 13-22.

Cain B.D. & Baggaley W. (1998) Lepidoptera Report 1996. *Nat. Hist. Calderdale* **8**: 12-15.

Calder N. (1974) *The Weather Machine and the Threat of Ice.* BBC London.

Carter D.J. & Hargreaves B. (1986) *A Field Guide to Caterpillars of Butterflies and Moths in Britain and Europe.* William Collins & Sons & Co Ltd. London.

Carter D. (1992) *Butterflies & Moths*, Eyewitness Handbooks, Dorling Kindersley, London.

Cawdell P. (2002) Crowle Waste LWT Reserve. Butterfly Conservation *Lincolnshire Branch Newsletter* **49**: 4-5.

Clark S. (1858) Grapta c-album. *Entomologist's Weekly Intelligencer* **4**: 52.

Clough S.A. (2003) *The distribution of the Small Pearl-bordered Fritillary butterfly, Boloria selene, in the North Yorkshire Moors National Park.* Contract report for English Nature, North Yorkshire Moors National Park Authority & Forestry Commission.

Cohen J.B. & Ruston A.J. (1912, 1925) *Smoke: a Study of Town Air.* Arnold, London.

Coleman W.S. (1860) (1897 3rd edn) *British Butterflies.* George Routledge & Sons, London.

Collinson W.E. (1969). *The Butterflies and Moths of Halifax and*

district. Halifax Scientific Society, 72pp.

Corbett H.H. (1901) *Argynnis adippe* and *Dryas paphia* near Doncaster. *Naturalist* **26**: 288.

Corbett H.H. (1918) Doncaster Natural History Notes for 1917. *Naturalist* **43**: 262-263.

Cordeaux J. (1866) Lincolnshire. *Naturalist* **11**: 1-15.

Corke D. (1997) *The Butterflies of Essex* Lopinga Books, Wimbish, Essex.

Crackles F. E. (1990) *Flora of the East Riding of Yorkshire,* Hull University Press/Humberside County Council.

Crolla J., Tunmore M. & Bowles N. (2002) Identification of American Painted Lady *Vanessa virginiensis* (Drury) and Historical Status in the British Isles. *Atropos* No **16**: 3-18

Crossland C. (1910) *An Eighteenth Century Naturalist: James Bolton, Halifax.* Privately printed, Halifax.

Crowther J. (1930) See Butterfield *et al* (1930).

Curtis J. (1824-1839) *British Entomology* Vols 1-16. London.

Dal B. (1982) (Ed Morris M.) *The Butterflies of Northern Europe.* Croom Helm

Dale C. W. (1890) *The History of our British Butterflies.* London.

Dale J.C. (1833) Observations on the influence of Locality, Time of Appearance Etc on Species and Varieties of Butterflies. *Ent. Mag.* **1**: 357.

Dale J. C. (1838) Entomological Notes. *Naturalist* [Neville Wood] **3**: 213-214.

Davey P. (2002) The Potential Sources of American Painted Lady *Vanessa virginiensisi* (Drury) in the British Isles. *Atropos* No **16**: 18-24.

Donovan E. (1792-1813) (In Emmet & Heath 1989) *Natural history of British insects,* **1-16**. London.

Dowdeswell (1981) *The life of the meadow brown.*165pp London.

Duddington J. & Johnson R (1983) *The Butterflies and Larger Moths of Lincolnshire and South Humberside.* Lincolnshire Naturalists' Union

Duncan J. (1844) *The Naturalist's Library Vol XXXIX Entomology British Butterflies.* (Series Editor: Jardine W.) W.H. Lizars, Edinburgh.

Dunn T.C. & Parrack J.D. (1986) *The Moths and Butterflies of Northumberland and Durham Part One: Macrolepidoptera.* The Vasculum-Supplement No.2. The Northern Naturalists' Union.

Dutfield J. (1748-1749) *A new and complete natural history of English moths and butterflies.*London. M Payne.

Easterbrook M. (1987) *Butterflies: The Nymphalidae* Shire Publications, Princes Risborough.

Eden P. (1995) *Weatherwise.*

Ellis S. (1997) The northern brown argus in north-east England. *British Wildlife,* **9**: 22-27.

Ellis S. (2000a) *Butterfly Conservation Regional Action Plan North East England.* Butterfly Conservation.

Ellis S. (2000b) *The Small Pearl-bordered Fritillary Boloria selene in County Durham.* Contract report to English Nature, Durham County Council and Northumbrian Water.

Ellis S. (2001) *The Conservation of the Pearl-bordered Fritillary Boloria euphrosyne on the North Yorkshire Moors.* Butterfly Conservation.

Ellis S. (2002a) *The Conservation of the Pearl-bordered Fritillary, Boloria euphrosyne, on the North York Moors.* (updated edition) Butterfly Conservation.

Ellis S. (2002b) *The conservation of the Duke of Burgundy,*

Hamearis lucina, on the North York Moors. Butterfly Conservation.

Ellis S. (2003) *A Survey of the Northern Brown Argus Butterfly Aricia artaxerxes in the Yorkshire Dales.* Contract Report to English Nature.

Emmet A.M. & Heath J. (1989) *The Moths and Butterflies of Great Britain and Ireland Vol, 7 Part 1.* Harley Books, Great Horkesley, Colchester.

Emmet A.M. (1991) *The Scientific Names of the British Lepidoptera their History and Meaning.* Harley Books, Colchester.

Fagan B. (2000) *The Little Ice Age. How Climate Made History 1300-1850.* Basic Books. New York.

Feltwell J. et al (1984) *Field Guide to the Butterflies and other Insects of Britain.* Reader's Digest Association Ltd, London.

Filler A. & Smith C. (Eds) (1979). *A Wood in Ascam: a study in wetland conservation.* Sessions, York.

Findlay R., Young M.R., & Findlay J.A. (1983) Orientation behaviour of the Grayling butterfly: thermoregulation or crypsis? *Ecological Entomology* **8**: 145-153.

Fitter A. (1987) *Wild Flowers of Britain and Northern Europe.* Collins New Generation Guides, William Collins & Sons Ltd, Glasgow.

Foggitt B & Markham L. (1993) *The Yorkshire Weather Book.*

Ford E. B. (1975) *Butterflies.* Collins New Naturalist series. (Revised edition by Fontana of original 1945 publication).

Forsythe C.H. (1905) *Entomologist* **38**: 86-90.

Frohawk F.W. (1934) *British Butterflies.* London.

Frost C. (1996) Playing Dead. *Argus No* **28**: 27.

Frost H.M. (1995) A Yorkshire White Admiral *Ladoga camilla* First this century? *Argus No:* **25**: 12-14 Spring 1995.

Frost H. M. & Frost C. (1991) The Holly Blue Invasion 1991. *Holderness Countryside* No.35: 74-75

Frost H.M. & Frost C. (1995) South Holderness Butterflies 1982/1994. Combined volume of annual reports originally published in *Holderness Countryside* the magazine of the South Holderness Countryside Society.

Frost H.M. & Frost C. (2003) But too hot for Purples! *Argus No* **44**: 14-16.

Frost H.M. & Winter P.Q. (1997) Yorkshire Lepidoptera Report 1996. *Argus No:* **31**. 52pp Butterfly Conservation Yorkshire.

Frost H.M. & Winter P.Q. (1998) Yorkshire Lepidoptera Report 1997. *Argus No:* **33**. 52pp Butterfly Conservation Yorkshire.

Frost H.M. & Winter P.Q. (1999) Yorkshire Lepidoptera Report 1998. *Argus No:* **35**. 60pp Butterfly Conservation Yorkshire.

Frost H.M. & Winter P.Q. (2000) Yorkshire Lepidoptera Report 1999. *Argus No:* **37**. 60pp Butterfly Conservation Yorkshire.

Frost H.M. & Winter P.Q. (2001) Yorkshire Lepidoptera Report 2000. *Argus No:* **39**. 64pp Butterfly Conservation Yorkshire.

Frost H.M. (2002) Yorkshire Lepidoptera Report 2001. *Argus* **41**. 64pp Butterfly Conservation Yorkshire.

Frost H.M. (2003) Yorkshire Lepidoptera Report 2002. *Argus* **43**. 68pp Butterfly Conservation Yorkshire.

Frost H.M. (2004) Yorkshire Lepidoptera Report 2003 *Argus* **45**. 64pp Butterfly Conservation Yorkshire.

Fryer G. (2000) James Bolton's 18th century paintings of Lepidoptera. *Naturalist* **125**: 113-120.

Fryer G. & Lucas M.J. (2001) A Century and a Half of Change in the Butterfly Fauna of the Huddersfield Area of Yorkshire. *Naturalist* **126**: 49-112.

Furneaux W. (1897) *Butterflies and Moths.* Longman, Green & Co. London.

Garland S.P. (1981) *Butterflies of the Sheffield Area.* Sorby Record Special Series No.5. Sorby Natural History Society, Sheffield.

Garland S.P. & Garland B.M. Clouded Yellow Invasion of the Sheffield Area 1983, *Sorby Record,* **21**: 82-84.

Goss H. (1885) Lepidopterous fauna of Lancashire and Cheshire. *Naturalist* **10**: 206.

Goulson D., Ollerton J., & Sluman C. (1997) Foraging strategies in the small skipper butterfly, *Thymelicus flavus*: when to switch? *Animal Behaviour.* **53**: 1009-1016.

Gregson C.S. (1859) Thoughts on Geographical Distribution. *Entomologist's Weekly Intelligencer* **7**: 54-56

Gregson C.S. (1862) Emigration of Insects. *Weekly Entomologist* **1**: 91-93.

Hanski I. (1991) Single-species metapopulation dynamics: concepts, models and observations. *Biol. J. Linn. Soc.,* **42**: 17-38.

Hardy P.B. (1998) *Butterflies of Greater Manchester* PGL Enterprises, Sale, Cheshire.

Harris A. (1961) *The Rural Landscape of the East Riding of Yorkshire 1700-1850.* University of Hull/OUP.

Harris M. (1766) *The Aurelian or natural history of English insects; namely, moths and butterflies. Together with the plants on which they feed.* London.

Harris M. (1775) *The English Lepidoptera: or, the Aurelian's pocket companion.* London.

Harrison F. & Sterling M.J. (1985) *Butterflies and moths of Derbyshire (Part 1).* Derbyshire Entomological Society.

Harmer A.S. (2000) *Variation in British Butterflies.* Paphia Publishing, Lymington , Hants.

Hawley J. (1866) Report in the *Doncaster, Nottingham, & Lincoln Gazette* 20/04/1866 – Extracts from 'The Reminiscences of an Entomologist' – lecture delivered to Doncaster Philosophical Society by J Hawley on 16/04/1866.

Haworth A.H. (1803) *Lepidoptera Britannica.* London.

Heath J., Pollard E. & Thomas J.A. (1984) *Atlas of Butterflies in Britain and Ireland.* Viking (Penguin Books) Harmondsworth.

Heppenstall (1842a) Art. XCI – Varieties. 195, *Entomologist* **1**: 356.

Heppenstall (1842b) Art. CVII – Varieties. 224. Note on Hipparchiae. *Entomologist* **1**: 407-408.

Heslop I.R.P. (1959) Revised indexed check-list of the British Lepidoptera 1, *Entomologists' Gazette* **9**: 44.

Hewett W. (1907) Notes on Yorkshire Lepidoptera in 1906. *Naturalist* **32**: 144-146.

Hewson F. (1952) Lepidoptera, in YNU 90th Annual Report. *Naturalist* **77**: 21-22.

Hewson F. (1958) Lepidoptera, in The Yorkshire Naturalists' Union Ninety-seventh Annual Report. *Naturalist* **83**: 21-22

Hewson F. (1961) Lepidoptera Report 1960. *Naturalist* **86**: 17

Hill J.K., Thomas C.D. & Blakeley D.S. (1999) Evolution of flight morphology in a butterfly (*Pararge aegeria*) that has recently expanded its geographic range. *Oecologia* **121**: 165-170

Hill J.K., Thomas C.D., Fox R., Telfer M.G., Willis S.J., Asher J, & Huntley B. (2002) Responses of butterflies to twentieth century climate warming: implications for future ranges. *Proc. Roy. Soc. Lond.*

Hobkirk C.P. (1859) (2nd edt 1868) *Huddersfield: its History and Natural History.* Tindall, Huddersfield.

Hodgkinson J.B. (1885) Lysandra coridon in the North of England. *Naturalist* **10**: 246.

Hodgkinson J.B. (1888) *Entomologist* **21**: 54.

olford I (1977) *The Guiness Book of Weather Facts and Feats.*

oole K. (1976) *Railways in Yorkshire 2- The East Riding.* alesman Books, Clapham.

owarth T.G. (1973) *Colour Identification Guide to Butterflies the British Isles.* Frederick Warne 1973. Revised edition iking/Penguin Books 1984.

owarth T.G. (1973b) *South's British Butterflies* London.

udson P & Rust B (2003) *Weather or Not!* Great Northern ooks.

udson S. (1860) Correspondence (Mazarine Blue). *ntomologist's Weekly Intelligencer* 8: 139

udson S. (1864) Correspondence (Mazarine Blue). *ologist* 22: 8985.

umphreys H.N. & Westwood J.O. (1841) *British butterflies d their transformations.* London

unter M. & Norman R. (2003) *Butterfly Summary 2003* utterfly Conservation, North East England Branch.

unter M. & Norman R. (2004) *Butterfly Summary 2004* utterfly Conservation, North East England Branch.

ackson S.M. (1968) Lepidoptera (*in* YNU Annual Report for 967): 17-19.

ackson S,M. (1969) Lepidoptera (*in* YNU Annual Report for 968): 18-20.

ackson S.M. (1970) Lepidoptera (*in* YNU Annual Report for 969): 25-28.

ackson S.M. (1971) Lepidoptera (*in* YNU Annual Report for 970): 15-18.

ackson S.M. (1972) Lepidoptera (*in* YNU Annual Report for 971): 33-35.

ackson S.M. (1973) Lepidoptera (*in* YNU Annual Report for 972): 21-24.

ackson S.M. (1976) Lepidoptera (*in* Entomological Reports for 974) *Naturalist* 101: 28-30.

ackson S.M. (1980) Changes since 1900 in the distribution of utterflies in Yorkshire and elsewhere in the north of England. *ntom. Rec. J. Var.* 92: 139-142.

ackson S.M. (1983) Lepidoptera Report 1975-1980 *Naturalist* 08: 28-30.

arvis F.V.L. (1966) The genus *Aricia* (Lep. Rhopalocera) in ritain. *Pro. & Trans. S. London Ent. & Nat. Hist. Soc.* 1966: p37-60.

arvis F.V.L. (1969) A biological study of *Aricia agestis* ssp *almacis* (Stephens). *Pro. Br. Ent. Nat. Hist. Soc.* 1969: 107-117.

enkins A.C. (1978) *The Naturalists* Hamish Hamilton, London.

ermyn L. (1824) *The butterfly collector's vade mecum.* Ipswich nd London.

oy J. (1996a) How common is hilltopping in the Painted Lady *ynthia cardui*? *Butterfly Conservation News* No 63: p17.

oy J. (1996b) The larval habits of the Grayling butterfly *ipparchia Semele* (Linnaeus) (Lepidoptera: Satyridae at inland ead mine sites in Shropshire *Entomologist's Gazette* 47: 139-42.

oy J. & Pullin A.S. (1997) The effects of flooding on the urvival and behaviour of overwintering Large Heath butterfly *oenonympha tullia* larvae. *Biological Conservation* 82: 61-66.

ious & Tilling (1996) *This Dynamic Earth: The Story of Plate ectonics.* US Government Service.

irby W.F. (1896) *A hand-book to the order lepidoptera 1-3: utterflies.* London, Lloyds Natural History.

irkland P. (1995) A review of the distribution, ecology and ehaviour of the scotch argus. *Bulletin of the British Ecological ociety,* 26:2, 95-102.

Kudrna O. (2002) *The Distribution Atlas of European Butterflies.* Oedippus 20: 1-342 Naturschutzbund Deutschland e.V. & Gesellschaft für Schmetterlingsschutz e.V. in co-operation with Apollo Books, Denmark.

Lafranchis T. (2000) *Les Papillons de jour de France, Belgique et Luxembourg et leurs chenilles.* Collection Parthénope, Mèze, France.

Lafranchis T. (2004) Butterflies of Europe. Diatheo, 35 rue Broca F-75005 Paris (France). ISBN 2-9521620-0-X

Lankester E. (1842) *An Account of Askern.* London.

Law E.J. (2001) *Huddersfield & District History: Storthes Hall,Thurstonland.*http://homepage.eircom.net/~lawedd/STORTH ESHALL.htm

Lees F.A. (1888) The Flora of West Yorkshire. *Bot. Ser. Trans. Yorks. Nat. Un. Vol 2.*

Lees E. (1962) Factors determining the distribution of the speckled wood butterfly (*Pararge aegeria* L.) in Great Britain. *Entomologist's Gazette* 13: 101-113.

Lewin W. (1795) *The Papilios of Great Britain.* London.

Lewington R. (2003) *Pocket Guide to the Butterflies of Great Britain and Ireland.* British Wildlife Publishing.

Limbert M. (1975) The Gatekeeper Butterfly in Yorkshire. *Naturalist* 100: 111-114.

Limbert M. & Eversham B.C. (Eds) (1997) *Thorne & Hatfield Moors Papers Vol:4.* Thorne & Hatfield Moors Conservation Forum.

Linnaeus C. (1758) *Systema Naturae* (Edn 10). Stockholm.

Lofthouse T.A. (1899) A Few Notes on Lepidoptera That Have Been Recorded for the Cleveland District During Past Years. *Cleveland Naturalists' Field Club Record of Proceedings 1899* p123.

Lockwood M. (2002) *Butterfly Introductions.* Private publication.

Lunn J. (2000) Ecological and nature conservation aspects of mining in the Yorkshire Coalfield. Unpublished M Phil thesis, Sheffield Hallam University.

Lunn J. (2001) Wildlife and mining in the Yorkshire Coalfield. *British Wildlife* 12: 318-326

Mason A. (1857) Communications [Lepidoptera]. *Entomologist's Weekly Intelligencer* 2: 147

Mason P.G. (1990) *The Lost Railways of East Yorkshire.* Mason Publications, Driffield.

McAndrew D. (2002) *Habitat Fragmentation and the Survival of the Duke of Burgundy Butterfly around Helmsley in North Yorkshire.* MSc field project 2000.

Merret C. (1666) *Pinax rerum Naturalium Britannicarum, continens Vegetabilia, Animalia et Fossilia, in hac Insula reperta Inchoatus.* London.

Michaelis H. N. (1951) Lepidoptera (*in* 'The Entomology of Spurn Peninsula') *Naturalist* 76: 183-190.

Michaelis H.N. (1963) Lepidoptera *in* 'The Insects of the Malham Tarn Area' (YNU Entomological Section 1954/1958 Survey). *Proc. Leeds Phil. & Lit. Soc.* Vol: IX, Part II.

Morland B. & Morland S. (2000) *River Ure Study: Bellflask Butterflies 2000.* Bellflask Ecological Survey Team.

Morland B. & Morland S. (2001) *River Ure Study: Bellflask Moths and Butterflies 2001.* Bellflask Ecological Survey Team.

Morley B. (1902) Notes on the Lepidoptera of Skelmanthorpe during 1901. *Naturalist* 27: 141-144.

Morley B. (1928) Monarch butterfly at Huddersfield. *Naturalist* 53: 47.

Morris F.O. (1853) (and subsequent editions to 1890) *A history of British butterflies.* London Groombridge.
Morris R.B. (1975) Iridescence from diffraction structures in the wing scales of *Callophrys rubi*, the Green Hairstreak. *Journal of Entomology* **A49:** 149-159.
Mosley S.L. (1883) A catalogue of the Lepidoptera found in the Huddersfield district. Macro-Lepidoptera. *Trans. Huddersfield Nat Soc 1883:* 1-30.
Moss C.E. (1901) Changes in the Halifax flora during the last century and a quarter. II *Naturalist* **26: 99-107.**
Mouffet T. (1634) *Insectorum sive minimorum animalium Theatrum.* London.
Murray J.B., & Souter R. (1998) *Hertfordshire and Middlesex Butterfly and Moth Report for 1998.* Butterfly Conservation, Hertfordshire and Middlesex Branch.
Murton J. (1861) Exchange. *Entomologist's Weekly Intelligencer* **10:** 165.

Newman E. (1860) *A natural history of all the British butterflies.* Judd & Glass, London.
Newman E. (1870/71) *The illustrated natural history of British butterflies.*
Newman L.H. (1955) *Nymphalis antiopa*: migrant or stowaway? *Entomologist* **88:** 25-27
Newman L.W. & Leeds H.A. (1913) *Textbook of British butterflies and moths.* St Albans, Gibbs & Bamforth.
Newton A. (1883) Correspondence. *Naturalist* 1883/4 p102.
Nijhout H.F. (1991) *The Development and Evolution of Butterfly Wing Patterns.* Smithsonian Institution Press (USA).
Nowell J (1866) Notes on some rare mosses at Todmorden. *Naturalist* (Old Series) **3:** 1-3.

Oates M., Taverner J., Green D. *et al* (2000) *The Butterflies of Hampshire.* Pisces Publications.
Oates M. (2000) The Duke of Burgundy - conserving the intractable. *British Wildlife* **11:** 250-257.
Oates M. (2004) The ecology of the Pearl-bordered Fritillary in woodland. *British Wildlife* **15:** 229-236
Opler P.A. (1992) *A Field Guide to Eastern Butterflies* Houghton Mifflin Co., Boston.
Opler P.A. & Krizek G.O. (1984) *Butterflies East of the Great Plains.* John Hopkins University Press, Baltimore.

Parks R. & Kirtley S. (1994) *The Historical Distribution and Current Status of the Duke of Burgundy Butterfly.* Private publication.
Parkinson D. (1994) The Current Status of Butterflies in Yorkshire. Butterfly Conservation *Yorkshire Branch Newsletter.* Spring 1994.
Parmesan C. *et al* (1999) Poleward shifts in geographical ranges of butterfly species associated with regional warming. *Nature Lond.* **399:** 579-583.
Payne J. (1985) The Clouded Yellow in Yorkshire in 1983. *YNU Bulletin* **4:** 8-11.
Perring F.H. & Walters S.M. (1962) *Atlas of the British Flora.* London.
Perring F.H. & Walters S.M. (1990) *Atlas of the British Flora.* Botanical Society of the British Isles.
Petiver J. (1695-1703a) *Musei Petiveriana centuria prima-decima.* London.
Petiver J. (1702-1706b) *Gazophyllacii naturae & artis*: decas prima-decas decima. London.
Petiver J. (1717) *Papilionum Britanniae icons.* London.

Philp E.G. (1993) *The Butterflies of Kent an atlas of their distribution.* Transactions of the Kent Field Club Vol 12
Pickard H.T. (1860) Singular, considering the Season! *Entomologist's Weekly Intelligencer* **8:** 171-172.
Pickett A. (1999) *The Distribution of the Large Heath Butterfly, Coenonympha tullia (Muller) on Crowle Moors 1999.* English Nature/University of Lincolnshire and Humberside.
Pilleau N.C. (1952) (In Rimington 1992) Three forms of *Aphantopus hyperantus* and one of *Coenonympha tullia* which may be new to the British List. *Entomologist's Rec. J. Var.* **64:** 6
Plant C.W. (1995) *A Survey of the Large Heath Butterfly at Thorne, Crowle, Goole and Hatfield Moors in 1995.* English Nature, Humber to Pennines Team.
Pollard E. (1979) Population ecology and change in range of the white admiral butterfly *Ladoga Camilla* (L) in England. *Ecol. Ent.* **4:** 61-74.
Pollard R.S. (1956) *Naturalist* **81:** 22.
Polunin O. (1969) *Flowers of Europe, A Field Guide* OUP.
Porter A.H. & Geiger H (1995) Limitations to the inference of gene flow at regional geographic scales – an example from the *Pieris napi* group (Lepidoptera: Pieridae) in Europe. *Biol. J. Linn. Soc.* **54:** 329-348.
Porter J. (1997) *The Colour Identification Guide to Caterpillars of the British Isles.* Viking, London (Penguin Group).
Porritt G.T. (1883) *Entomological Transactions of the Yorkshire Naturalists' Union Vol. 2. List of Yorkshire Lepidoptera.* Yorkshire Naturalists' Union, Leeds.
Porritt G.T. (1904) *EntomologicaL Transactions of the Yorkshire Naturalists' Union Vol.2. List of Yorkshire Lepidoptera Second Edition* (Updated) A. Brown & Sons Ltd, London.
Porritt G.T. (1907) Lepidoptera. *Victoria County History of Yorkshire* **1:** 245-276.
Porritt G.T. (1918) [Footnote to note by EP Butterfield] *Naturalist* **43:** 335.
Porritt G.T. (1922) The Lepidoptera of Hull pp421-430, *Handbook to Hull & the East Riding of Yorkshire*, British Association for the Advancement of Science, Ed: T Sheppard, A Brown & Sons Ltd, London & Hull.
Potts T. (1873) *Vanessa polychloros* at Doncaster. *Entomologist* **6:** 387.
Pyle R.M. (1981) *The Audubon Society Field Guide to North American Butterflies.* Alfred A. Knopf, Inc, New York.

Rafe R.W. & Jefferson R.G. (1983) The Status of *Melanargia galathea* (Lepidoptera: Satyridae) on the Yorkshire Wolds. *Naturalist* **108:** 3-7.
Ravenscroft N.O.M. & Warren M.S. (1996) *Species Action Plan: northern brown argus, Aricia artaxerxes.* Butterfly Conservation.
Ray J. (1710) *Historia Insectorum,* London.
Reid W. (1955) Collecting notes 1955. *Entom. Rec. J. Var.* **67:** 281-282.
Rennie J. (1832) *A conspectus of the butterflies and moths found in Britain.* London.
Revels R. (1994) The rise and fall of the Holly Blue butterfly. *British Wildlife* **5:** 236-9.
Rimington W.E. (1987) Historical Records of the Swallowtail Butterfly (*Papilio machaon L*) in Yorkshire. *Naturalist* **112:** 81-84.
Rimington W.E. (1988) Lysandra coridon in the North: the Bermuda Triangle? *Ent. Rec.J.Var.* **100:** 49-53.
Rimington E. (=W.E.) (1992) *Butterflies of the Doncaster District.* Sorby Record Special Series No.9, Sorby Natural History Society, Sheffield.

Rimington W.E. (1994) Re-introduction of the Marbled White *Melanargia galathea* L to Doncaster. *The Bulletin of the Amateur Entomologists' Society* **53**: 194-200.

Rimington W.E. & Beaumont H.E. (1996) Joseph William Dunning (1833-1897) informal annotations in a copy of Rennie 1832) by a forgotten Yorkshire Naturalist together with biographical notes. *Naturalist* **122**: 145-155.

Roberts T.J. (2001) *The Butterflies of Pakistan.* OUP.

Robson J.E. (1902) *A Catalogue of the Lepidoptera of Northumberland, Durham, and Newcastle-upon-Tyne, Vol I Macro-Lepidoptera.*

Rockett C.E. (1888) Black-veined White butterfly. *Hardwicke's Scientific Gossip* 28:21

Roine A. (2000) Butterflies of Europe. CD Rom. Winlab Oy.

Russwurm A.D.A. (1978) *Aberrations of British Butterflies.* EW Classey Ltd, Faringdon, Oxon.

Rutherford C.I. (1971) Lepidoptera of Yorkshire: A Commentary. *Naturalist* **96**: 93-104.

Rylands P. (1839) Statement of the claims of *Papilio podalirius* to rank as a British Insect. *Naturalist* (Neville Wood) **4**: 227-229.

Salmon M.A. (2000) *The Aurelian Legacy British Butterflies and their Collectors.* Harley Books, Great Horkesley, Essex.

Samouelle G. (1819) (In Emmet & Heath 1989). *The entomologist's useful compendium.* London.

Sanders E. (1939) *A butterfly book for the pocket.* Oxford University Press.

Saville R. (1996) Butterfly Biodiversity. *Scottish Wildlife* Winter 996. Scottish Wildlife Trust.

Scott J.A. (1986) *The Butterflies of North America.* Stanford University Press, California.

Seaward M.R.D. (1975) Lichen flora of the West Yorkshire conurbation. *Proc. Leeds Phil. Lit. Soc.* Sci. Sect. **10**: 141-208.

Shaw G.A. (1978) *Erebia aethiops* Esp (Scotch Argus) the Yorkshire localities (*in* Field Notes) *Naturalist*, **103**: 26-28.

Sheppard T. (1900) Bye-gone Hull Naturalists 1-George Norman (1823-1882), *Transactions of the Hull Scientific and Field Naturalists' Club for 1900.* **Vol I**: 104-112.

Sheppard J.A. (1957) The Medieval Meres of Holderness. *Inst.Brit. Geog. Trans. & papers.* **23**: 75-85.

Sheppard J.A. (1958) The Draining of the Hull Valley. *East Yorks. Local Hist.* Ser. 8: 1-24.

Shepperson C. (1998) *Hertfordshire Grizzled Skipper survey report.* Hertfordshire Biological Records Centre.

Shreeve T.G. (1984) Habitat selection, mate location and microclimate constraints on the activity of the speckled wood butterfly *Pararge aegeria. Oikos* **4**: 371-377.

Shreeve T.G. (1986) Egg-laying by the speckled wood butterfly, *Pararge aegeria*), the role of female behaviour, host plant abundance and temperature. *Ecological Entomology* **11**: 229-236.

Shreeve T.G. (1987) The mate location behaviour of the male speckled wood butterfly, *Pararge aegeria*, and the effect of phenotype differences in hindwing spotting. *Animal Behaviour* **35**: 682-690.

Skelton M. (2000) UK over-wintering of Clouded Yellow. *Butterfly Conservation News* **73**: 26.

Skidmore P., Limbert M., Eversham B.C. (1985) *The Insects of Thorne Moors.* Sorby Record No.23 (Supplement), Sorby Natural History Society.

Smith J.K. (1966) Insects in *The Natural History of Teesmouth* Ed Bell D.G.) Cleveland Naturalists' Field Club & Teesmouth Bird Club: 21.

Smith W.H. (1858) Entomological Excursions to Roche Abbey. *Entomologist's Weekly Intelligencer* **4**: 85

Smyllie W.J. (1992a) The Brown Argus Butterfly in Britain – a range of *Aricia* hybrids. *Entomologist* **111**: 27-37.

Smyllie W. J. (1992b) The Brown Argus butterfly in Britain with particular reference to the Peak District. *Sorby Record* No. 29: 2-17, pls.

Smyllie W.J. (1995) The Brown Argus Butterfly in N.W. Europe. *Entomol. Rec. J. Var.* **107**: 15-23.

Smyllie W. J. (1997) Similarities between the Xerces blue, *Glaucopsyche lygdamus xerces*, northern brown argus *Aricia ataxerxes artaxerxesi* and common blue *Polyommatus icarus* (Lepidoptera: Lycaenidae) with further comments on genus *Aricia. Entomologist* **116** (3): 245-253.

Smyllie W.J. (1998) Similarities between British and north-west European *Aricia* 'subspecies' (Lepidoptera: Lycaenidae). *Nach. Entomol. Ver. Apollo, N.F.* **19** (1): 69-88.

Smyllie W. J. (2001) Lunulation similarities in the genus *Aricia* Reich. (Lepidoptera: Lycaenidae) in Britain, Spain and Switzerland. *Entomol. Rec. J. Var.* **113**: 209-226.

Smyllie W. J. (2004) Lunulation and Genetic Analysis in *Aricia*. Butterflies. *Entomologists' Rec. J. Var.* **116**: 161-172.

South R. (1906) *The Butterflies of the British Isles.* Warne, London & New York.

Spence B.R. (1991) *The Moths and Butterflies of Spurn.* Spurn Bird Observatory.

Stainforth T. (1919) The Thomas Stather Collection of Lepidoptera. *Transactions of the Hull Scientific and Field Naturalists' Club for the Years 1907-1918.* **Vol IV**: 281-298.

Stainton H.T. (1857/1859) *A manual of British butterflies and moths* (2 vols), London, Van Voorst.

Stainton H.T. (1861) Lepidoptera: rare British species captured in 1860. *Entomologist's Annual* **1861**: 93.

Stephens J.F. (1828) *Illustrations of British Entomology* Haustellata Vol: 1. London.

Stephens J.F. (1856) *List of specimens of British animals in the collection of the British Museum* **5**: Lepidoptera.

Sterland W.J. (1875) The Zoology of Sherwood Forest *in: Worksop, the Dukery and Sherwood Forest* 255-282. Simkin, Marshall & Co, London.

Stewart R. (1996) A Swallowtail Surprise. Butterfly Conservation *Norfolk Branch Newsletter.* **49**: 9-10.

Stewart R., (2001) *The Millennium Atlas of Suffolk Butterflies.* Suffolk Naturalists' Society.

Sutton S.L. & Beaumont H.E. (1989) *Butterflies and Moths of Yorkshire Distribution and Conservation.* Yorkshire Naturalists' Union.

Swaay C. & Warren M.S. (1999) *Red data book of European Butterflies (Rhopalocera)*, Nature & Environment No 99. Council of Europe, Strasbourg.

Teesdale R. (1800) A Supplement to the Plantae Eboracenses. *Trans. Linn. Soc.* **5**: 36-93.

Tetley A.S. (1915) (In Stainforth 1919) Lepidoptera round about Scarborough. *Ent. Rec.* April 1915.

Theakston (1871) 10th edition. *Theakston's Guide to Scarborough.* Contained a Lepidoptera list compiled by Peter Inchbald, partly based on specimens collected by Thomas Wilkinson.

Thomas J. & Lewington R. (1991) *The Butterflies of Britain & Ireland.* Dorling Kindersley/National Trust.

Tetley A.S. (1915) Lepidoptera round about Scarborough. *The Entomologist's Record.* April 15th 1915

Thomas J, & Lewington R. (1991) *The Butterflies of Britain and Ireland.* Dorling Kindersley Ltd, London.
Thomson G. (1980) *The Butterflies of Scotland A Natural History.* Croom Helm, London.
Tolman T. & Lewington R. (1997) *Butterflies of Britain & Europe* Collins Field Guide series. HarperCollins.
Tomlinson D. & Still R. (2002) *Britain's Butterflies.* WILDGuides Ltd., Old Basing, Hants. ISBN 1-903657-03-2
Tucker M. (1991) *The Red Admiral (Vanessa atalanta Linn) Problems posed by the hibernation and Migration Habits of the Species.* Butterfly Conservation.
Tucker M. (1997) *The Red Admiral Butterfly.* Butterfly Conservation.
Tutt J.W. (1908) *A natural history of the British butterflies.* London.
Tutt J.W. (1910) *Natural History of British Butterflies IV* London.
Tyszka M. (1994) *Lincolnshire Branch Report '94.* Butterfly Conservation Lincolnshire Branch.

UK Biodiversity Group (1998,1999) *Tranche 2 Action Plans Vols I to VI.* English Nature.
Utley J.P. (1941) *Naturalist 66:* 282.

Viner D. & Jones P. (2000) 13- Volcanoes and their effect on climate. Climatic Research Unit.

Wacher J. (1998/9) Successful UK Overwintering of Painted Lady. *Butterfly Conservation News.* 70: Winter 1998/9.
Wacher J., Worth J., & Spalding A. (2003) *A Cornwall Butterfly Atlas* Pisces Publications.
Wainwright D. (2002) *The Distribution of the Grayling Butterfly (Hipparchia Semele) on Teeside.* Contract Report to Northumbria Water.
Wallis J. (1769) *Natural History and Antiquities of Northumberland and North Durham* (as quoted in Robson 1902).
Walsh G.B. (1952) The Present Status of the Butterfly Population of the Scarborough District. *Entomologist's Monthly Magazine Vol: lxxxviii (26/08/1952).*
Walsh G.B. & Rimington F.C. (1953) *The Natural History of the Scarborough District Vol 1: Geology and Botany.* Scarborough Field Naturalists' Society.
Walsh G.B. (1956) Order Lepidoptera Moths and Butterflies in
Walsh G.B. & Rimington F.C. (1956) *The Natural History of the Scarborough District Vol:2 - Zoology.* Scarborough Field Naturalists' Society.
Warren B.C.S. (1951) Biological Notes on the subspecies *alpica* and *bigenerata* of *Papilio machaon. Entomologist* 84: 11-16.
Warren M.S. *et al* (2001) Rapid responses of British butterflies to opposing forces of climate and habitat change. *Nature* 414: 65-68.
Warren M.S., Barnett L.K., Gibbons D.W., & Avery M.I. (1997) Assessing national conservation priorities: an improved red list of British butterflies. *Biological Conservation* 82: 317-328
Weir J.J. (1888). Notes on the comparative rarity of Lepidoptera-Rhopalocera, once common in the neighbourhood of Lewes. *Proc. Trans. S. Lond. Ent. Nat. Hist. Soc.* 1887: 31-36.
Whalley P.E.S. (1971) William Arderon, F.R.S., of Norwich, an 18th century diarist and letter writer. *J.Soc. Biblphy Nat Hist.* 6: 30-49.
Whalley P.E.S. (1980) *Butterfly Watching.* Severn House Publishers Ltd.

Whitaker T.M. (2001) Small Heath report in Argus No: 41 (Ed. Frost & Winter 2001).
Whitaker T.M. (2002) The Status of the Small Pearl-bordered Fritillary *Boloria selene,* in Western Yorkshire. *Naturalist* 127: 3-17.
Whitaker T.M. (2003) The distribution of the Small Pearl-bordered butterfly, *Boloria selene*, in Yorkshire VC65, *Naturalist* 128: 59-65.
Whiteley D. (Ed) (1992) *Sorby Record No.29 Butterfly Atlas Edition.* Sorby Natural History Society, Sheffield.
Wickman P-O. (1985a) The influence of temperature on the territorial and mate locating behaviour of the small heath butterfly, *Coenonympha pamphilus* (L.) (Lepidoptera: Satyridae) Behav. Ecol. Sociobiol. 16: 233-238.
Wickman P-O. (1985b) Territorial defence and mating success in males of the small heath butterfly, *Coenonympha pamphilus* (L.) (Lepidoptera: Satyridae). *Anim. Behav.* 33: 1162-1168.
Wickman P-O. (1986) Courtship solicitation by females of the small heath butterfly *Coenonympha pamphilus* (L.) (Lepidoptera Satyridae) and their behaviour in relation to male territories before and after copulation. *Anim. Behav.* 34: 153-157
Wilkes B. (1741-42) *The British Aurelian. Twelve new designs of English butterflies.* London.
Wilkes B. (1747/1749) *The English moths and butterflies.* London. (Published by the author).
Williams C.B. (1958) *Insect Migration.* No 26 in Collins New Naturalist series (reprinted 1971). Collins, London.
Williams H. (1961) *Great Biologists.* G Bell & Sons Ltd, London.
Willmott K.J. (1999) *The Holly Blue butterfly.* Butterfly Conservation, Colchester.
Winter P.Q. (1985) Notes in: Foreign Macrolepidoptera, 1984 Annual Exhibition. *Proc. Trans. Br. Ent. Nat. Hist. Soc.* 18: 14.
Wise D. & Wise S. (2000) *Varieties, adaptations and aberrations among the butterflies of W Yorkshire.* Published by the authors.
Wise D & Wise S. (2001) *The Green Hairstreak Colonises the Bradford Metropolitan District.* Published by the authors.
Wise D. & Wise S. (2002) *The Purple Hairstreak moves en masse into the Bradford Metropolitan District of the West Yorkshire Pennines.* Published by the authors.
Wise D. & Wise S. (2003) *A brief survey of Dingy Skipper colonies on old colliery spoil heaps in Yorkshire.* Published by the authors.
Wright A.E. (1940) Lysandra coridon: Its reputed Occurrence in Lancashire and Westmoreland. *Entomologist* 73: 217-221.

YNU (Yorkshire Naturalists' Union) (1967/70) *The Lepidoptera of Yorkshire (Macro-Lepidoptera).* Bound re-print of 50 pages from a series of reports first published in *The Naturalist* 1967-70 in the name of the YNU Lepidoptera Committee.

aberration: a specimen which looks different to the normal form as a result of genetic variation.
aestivate: to become dormant for a period in summer.
bivoltine: producing two broods or generations.
diapause: a period of suspended growth.
fulvous: brownish-yellow.
hibernaculum: structure in which larvae spend winter.
instar: referring to larval development – the period or stage between moults. Butterfly larvae have between 4 and 7 moults.
larva: = caterpillar (plural – larvae, adj – larval)
melanin: dark pigment which produced the black and brown colours.
moult: period of change as larvae (caterpillars) move from one growth period (instar) to another.
polyvoltine: having many broods annually.
pupa: = chrysalis (plural – pupae, adj – pupal)
trivoltine: 3 broods annually.
univoltine: 1 brood annually
voltinism: refers to brood frequency and variation in breeding sequences.

ABBREVIATIONS

b in front of a date eg b1849 = born.
BC = Butterfly Conservation.
c = circa or about (approximately).
d in front of a date eg d1849 = died.
fl in front of a date eg fl1849 = flourished (used where the year of birth is unknown).
k after an Ordnance Survey map reference = kilometre square (to distinguish it from a tetrad which might have the same reference).
NR = Nature Reserve.
NNR = National Nature Reserve.
SSSI = Site of Scientific Interest.
after an Ordnance Survey map reference = tetrad. This is a 2x2km square made up of 4x1km squares using even-numbered reference points on the Ordnance Survey map grid.
YNU = Yorkshire Naturalists' Union.
YWT = Yorkshire Wildlife Trust.
VC = Vice- County as defined on p5 and illustrated on p54.

WEBSITES

Butterfly and moth websites can be valuable sources of information. Those listed below are of particular relevance and useful points of contact for further details.

www.butterfly-conservation.org All kinds of news and information about British butterflies.

www.europeanbutterflies.org A forum for discussing many aspects of European butterflies and where to send records made in European countries.
www.mothrecording.org.uk About the national macro-moth recording scheme.
www.nhm.ac.uk/entomology Site of the London Natural History Museum.
www.ynu.org.uk Details about the activities of the Yorkshire Naturalists' Union which is the county's main recording body for most branches of wildlife.
www.yorkshirebutterflies.org.uk This is the website of Butterfly Conservation in Yorkshire, the publishers of this book.
www.yorkshiremoths.org.uk Information about moths and moth recording in Yorkshire.
www.yorkshire-wildlife-trust.org.uk The Yorkshire Wildlife Trust manages a large number of nature reserves (including Spurn National Nature Reserve) and is the county's main organisation involved in practical conservation work.

BUTTERFLY CONSERVATION YORKSHIRE MEMBERSHIP

Membership of Butterfly Conservation Yorkshire is only possible through membership of the national organisation. Details are available from the relevant websites above, or by contacting Butterfly Conservation's national headquarters: Butterfly Conservation, Manor Yard, East Lulworth, Wareham, Dorset BH20 5QP, Tel: 0870 774 4309 or email: info@butterfly-conservation.org Members receive national and local magazines and have the opportunity of joining field trips and other activities.

Help us record!

Butterflies need our help, but we can only take the right actions if we know what is happening on the ground. Continual monitoring is of vital importance. You don't have to be a member to help our work by sending in butterfly records. You will see from our distribution maps that there are many places without records and we would like to fill up all of these spaces in the coming years. If you can't get out and about very much don't forget that collecting regular garden records can be of immense importance. Contact national headquarters for details of recording forms and where to send records. Thanks!!

NOTE:

rynnis tages (Dingy Skipper)

ssex Skipper (*Thymelicus lineola*) 10, 24, 40, 46, 59, 4, **66, 233-235**

uphydryas aurinia (Marsh Fritillary)

abricius, Johann Christian **12**

awcett, Benjamin **13**

ord, Edmund Brisco **13**

rankland, Thomas **14**

rowhawk, Frederick William **13**

arden Tiger Moth 14

Gatekeeper or **Hedge Brown** (*Pyronia tithonus*) 9, 21, 3, 24, 33, 35, 36, 40, 44, 45, 114, **208-212**, 214

lanville, Eleanor **11**

Glanville Fritillary (*Melitaea cinxia*) 51, **286-287**

Grayling (*Hipparchia semele*) 7, 10, 20, 36, 40, 44, **203-**07, 214

reen-veined White (*Pieris napi*) 7, 24, 40, **84, 93-97**

Green Hairstreak (*Callophrys rubi*) 7, 9, 10, 20, 31, 33, 0, 42, 44, 46, **48-50, 103-107**

Grizzled Skipper (*Pyrgus malvae*) 9, 20, 42, 43, 44, 37-240

onepteryx Cleopatra (Cleopatra)

onepteryx rhamni (Brimstone)

Harris, Moses 12

Hawley, John Riley 15

Haworth, Adrian Hardy 12, 14

Hamearis lucina (Duke of Burgundy)

Heath, John **14**

Heath Fritillary 51

Hedge Brown (*Pyronia tithonus*) See Gatekeeper.

Hesperia comma (Silver-spotted Skipper)

Hewson, Frank **16**

High Brown Fritillary (*Argynnis*

dippe) 23, 51, 184, **277-279**

Hipparchia semele (Grayling)

Hobkirk, Charles P **15**

Holly Blue (*Celastrina argiolus*) 9, 20, 21, 23, 24, 31, 40, 4, 46, 110, 134, **138-142**

Hyde, George **16**

Immaculate Green Hairstreak (USA) (*Callophrys affinis*) 48

nachis io (Peacock)

nchbald, Peter **15**

phiclides podalirius (Scarce Swallowtail)

ssoria lathonia (Queen of Spain Fritillary)

Kirby, William **12**

Lankester, Dr Edwin **15**

Large Blue 51

Large Copper 51

Large Heath (*Coenonympha tullia*) 9, 20, 38, 40, 42, 44, 219, **223-227**

Large Skipper (*Ochlodes faunus*) 33, 35, 40, 44, 58, 59, 61, **63-67**

Large Tortoiseshell (*Nymphalis polychloros*) 14, 23, 33, 51, **269-271**

Large White (*Pieris brassicae*) 24, 40, 44, 45, 79, **83-87**

Lasiommata megera (Wall or Wall Brown)

Lawson, Isaac **12**

Leptidea reali (Réal's Wood White)

Leptidea sinapis (Wood White)

Limenitis camilla (White Admiral)

Linnaean Society of London **12**

Linnaeus, Carl **12**

Little Blue = Small Blue

Lofthouse, Thomas Ashton **16**

Lulworth Skipper 51

Lycaena phlaeas (Small Copper)

Lysandra bellargus (Adonis Blue)

Lysandra coridon (Chalk Hill Blue)

Maniola jurtina (Meadow Brown)

Marbled White (*Melanargia galathea*) 7, 10, 20, 23, 39, 40, 44, **198-202**

Marsh Fritillary (*Euphydryas aurinia*) 23, 51, **283-285**

Mazarine Blue (*Cyaniris semiargus*) 23, **261-262**

Meadow Brown (*Maniola jurtina*) 22, 31, 33, 35, 36, 40, 44, 114, 189, 204, 209, **213-217**

Melanargia galathea (Marbled White)

Micros (ie micro-moths) **296**

Milkweed = Monarch

Monarch or **Milkweed** (*Danaus plexippus*) 33, **291-294**

Morris, Rev Francis Orpen **13** (portrait),

Mosely, SL **16**

Moths **295**

Mouffet, Thomas **11**

Neozephyrus quercus (Purple Hairstreak)

Newman, Edward **13**

Northern Brown Argus (*Aricia artaxerxes*) 7, 39, 40, 42, 44, 51, **123-132**

Northern Grizzled Skipper (*Pyrgus centaureae*) 239

Nymphalis antiopa (Camberwell Beauty)

Nymphalis polychloros (Large Tortoiseshell)